A Revised Handbook
to the
FLORA OF CEYLON

VOLUME II

APOSTASIACEAE
ORCHIDACEAE
BIGNONIACEAE
LEMNACEAE
MYRTACEAE

PITTOSPORACEAE
PRIMULACEAE
PROTEACEAE
RHIZOPHORACEAE
THYMELAEACEAE

TT 78–52029/02

A Revised Handbook
to the
FLORA OF CEYLON

VOLUME II

Sponsored jointly by the
University of Peradeniya,
Department of Agriculture, Peradeniya, Sri Lanka,
and the Smithsonian Institution,
Washington, D.C., U.S.A.

General Editor

M.D. DASSANAYAKE

Editorial Board

M.D. DASSANAYAKE and F.R. FOSBERG

Published for the Smithsonian Institution, and the
National Science Foundation, Washington, D.C.,
by Amerind Publishing Co. Pvt. Ltd., New Delhi
1981

January 1981

Published for the Smithsonian Institution, pursuant to
an agreement with the National Science Foundation,
Washington, D.C., by Amerind Publishing Co. Pvt. Ltd.,
66 Janpath, New Delhi 110001

Available from the U.S. Department of Commerce,
National Technical Information Service,
Springfield, Virginia 22161

Printed at Oxonian Press Pvt. Ltd., Faridabad, India

FOREWORD

The Handbook to the Flora of Ceylon, by Henry Trimen, published in 1893–1900, was in its time, one of the most comprehensive and outstanding floras available for any comparable tropical area. In 1931 A.H.G. Alston added a volume of additions, updating, and corrections to the original five volumes. These six volumes for many years served their purpose very well.

However, the original Handbook was published in a very small edition, and the paper on which it was printed, as was usually the case at the time, was very poor and has deteriorated very badly. Hence the Handbook has for years been absolutely unobtainable, and there are very few copies available even in libraries in Ceylon. Furthermore, botanical science has made substantial progress since the Handbook appeared, and many of Trimen's taxonomic and nomenclatural conclusions are now outdated. Also, with more thorough botanical exploration, new plants have been found to be members of the Ceylon flora. Hence, a new edition of this magnificent work was long overdue.

For quite a number of years Professor B.A. Abeywickrama had in mind a revision of Trimen's Handbook. But heavier and heavier administrative duties consumed his time and there was little opportunity for work on the Ceylon flora, though he did produce, in 1959, an updated Checklist of the Ceylon Flora, which has been most useful to botanists.

Fortuitously, in 1967, the Smithsonian Institution initiated a number of research projects in Ceylon, in cooperation with Ceylonese institutions and scientists. These included an investigation of several problems in plant ecology, with which Prof. Abeywickrama was associated as Co-Principal Investigator. These projects were financed by the Smithsonian using U.S. excess foreign currency under the provisions of Public Law 480.

While we were discussing the ecological investigations, Prof. Abeywickrama wondered if it might not be possible to initiate, using PL-480 support, a project for the revision of Trimen's Handbook to the Flora of Ceylon. I offered to work up a cooperative proposal and submit it to the Smithsonian Special Foreign Currency Program.

This was duly done, approved, and a year's tentative budget authorized. The project was started under the joint auspices of the Smithsonian Institution, the Ceylon Department of Agriculture and the University of Ceylon. I was appointed Principal Investigator. Co-Principal Investigators are Prof. B.A. Abeywickrama, Dr. J.W.L. Peiris, Mr. D.M.A. Jayaweera, Prof. M.D. Dassanayake and Mr. K.L.D. Amaratunga. The plan was to enlist the cooperation of botanists, from wherever available, who were preferably experts in particular families represented in the Ceylon flora. These monographers would be given a period of field work in Ceylon, an opportunity to study the specimens in the Ceylon National Herbarium, in the Royal Botanic Gardens, Peradeniya, with expenses met by the Smithsonian Institution. In return, they would provide updated manuscripts of their families for the revised Handbook, which would then be published by the University of Ceylon, with Smithsonian financing.

This enterprise was initiated in February, 1968, and has been continued without interruption since that date. Quarters for the work, herbarium and library, and other facilities have been furnished by the Division of Systematic Botany of the Department of Agriculture, Peradeniya and by the Botany Department, Faculty of Science, University of Ceylon, Peradeniya. We have enjoyed the cooperation of the U.S. Embassy, Colombo, various Ceylon government departments and agencies, especially the Wildlife Department and the Forest Department, and of many plantations and individuals in all parts of Ceylon, too numerous to enumerate.

Special thanks must be offered to Professor Dieter Mueller-Dombois, of the Botany Department, University of Hawaii, who was for two years Principal Field Investigator for the plant ecology project, and who, on top of his duties in that capacity, supervised the activities of the flora project staff, facilitated the work of the visiting botanists, and acted as finance officer of the project. Without his help, the flora project could not have got started.

Special thanks are also offered to Dr. Marie-Hélène Sachet, Research Botanist, Smithsonian Institution, who, though in no official capacity in the Project, has carried much of the administrative burden, at a sacrifice of her own work. The members of the Flora Project staff at Peradeniya directed by Mr. F.H. Popham, Smithsonian Representative in Ceylon, also deserve great credit for their willing and enthusiastic assistance to the visitors, handling and processing of specimens, typing of labels and manuscripts, and keeping the Project's work going.

The materials on which the flora revisions are based are the visiting botanists' own collections, the herbarium at Peradeniya, personal collections of Mr. K.L.D. Amaratunga and the late Mr. Thomas B. Worthington of Kandy, and materials housed in various foreign herbaria, especially those of Kew, British Museum, and the Indian National Herbarium, Calcutta for the use of which we are grateful to those in charge. A large amount of valuable material was amassed as vouchers for the ecological observations mentioned above and has been utilised by the flora project botanists. Sets of the specimens collected under the auspices of the Smithsonian projects are deposited and permanently available in the U.S. National Herbarium and the Ceylon National Herbarium, Peradeniya. Partial sets are also being deposited in several other Ceylon institutions and in a number of herbaria with tropical interests in other parts of the world.

The resulting revised treatments of the families are to be published, as material accumulates, in volumes of convenient size, without regard to the order of families. Those families, previously published in fascicles 1 and 2, are to be republished, in revised form, in the new format, as manuscripts are received from the authors. An editorial format has been suggested by us, but the content of each revision and the taxonomic conclusions are those of the various authors. An attempt has been made to have the nomenclature in accord with International Code of Botanical Nomenclature, but the application of the Code is, again, the final responsibility of the authors.

A comprehensive index to these volumes will be prepared and published as a separate volume.

It is hoped that, after the Handbook treatments are published, simplified versions can be prepared, suitable for lower school use and for the use of non-botanists.

We also have the hope that the new Handbook will stimulate active interest in the plant resources of Ceylon. Above all, it is hoped that this interest will bring about the establishment of more national parks and nature reserves in all parts of Ceylon, in order that the remarkable Ceylon flora may still have a suitable range of habitats in which to live. By this means, only, the species will be able to survive for the use and pleasure of many future generations of Ceylonese and of visitors from other parts of the world. Without a great increase in such reserves, at the present rate of deforestation and bringing land under agriculture, very many species will surely become extinct in the near future, as some probably already have.

F.R. FOSBERG,
Botanist, Emeritus,
Smithsonian Institution,
Washington, D.C., U.S.A.

CONTENTS

A Revised Handbook
to the
FLORA OF CEYLON

VOLUME II

APOSTASIACEAE

(by D.M.A. Jayaweera*)

Terrestrial, rhizomatous, erect herbs with leafy stems bearing terminal spikes racemes or panicles of medium or small white or yellow flowers. Perianth superior of 3 sepals and 3 petals, lanceolate, cuspidate. Stamens 3, or one aborted, filaments connate at base with the cylindric style, anthers dorsifixed. Ovary inferior, triquetrous, 3-locular with numerous anatropous ovules on axile placentas. Fruits capsular, rarely baccate, seeds minute.

Three genera, *Apostasia* Blume, *Adactylus* Rolfe and *Neuwiedia* Blume.

APOSTASIA

Blume, Bijdr. 423, t. 5. 1825.

Terrestrial, perennial leafy herbs with a short rootstock and thick fibrous roots. Leaves narrow, linear, acuminate, strongly veined, sheathing the stem. Flowers small in terminal, nodding, panicled spikes or racemes. Sepals, petals and lip all equal and similar, free, spreading or recurved. Stamens 2, the third reduced to a staminode or absent, filaments fused to the side of the column opposite the petals; anther cells 2, parallel, opening inwards; pollen grains free, dry, ellipsoid. Ovary inferior, very slender, 3-locular; ovules many in axile placentas; style slender; stigmas simple, terminal. Fruits narrow, linear, trigonous; seeds minute, ellipsoid; testa black and reticulate.

About 10 species distributed in India, China, Malaya and Australia.

Apostasia wallichii R. Br. in Wall., Pl. As. Rar. 1: 76. pl. 84. 1830.—**Fig. 1.**

Apostasia odorata Blume, Bijdr. 423. 1825.

Stem 30–60 cm tall, stout and leafy throughout; leaves 10–20 cm long, linear-lanceolate, finely acuminate, spreading and recurved, coriaceous, strongly 5–7 nerved, base sheathing. Flowers yellow, about 0.6 cm broad, in terminal, spicate decurved panicles 10–25 cm long; spikes 5–7.5 cm long; bracts lanceolate, acuminate; sepals, petals and lip linear lanceolate, cuspidate, tips spreading; filaments adnate to the style along with staminode; anther oblong, bases of cells unequal. Ovary trigonous, with anatropous ovules on axile placentas; capsule 1.2–1.8 cm long, hispidulous.

*Royal Botanic Gardens, Peradeniya, Ceylon.

Fig. 1. *Apostasia wallichii.* A, upper portion of stem with inflorescence. B, flower from side. C, perianth from front showing column and stamens. D, dissection of flower showing sepals, petals, lip, ovary and column with adnate stamens. E, column with adnate stamens and staminode. F, stamen from front and side. G, transverse section of ovary. H, anatropous ovule. B–H, all enlarged.

D i s t r. This species occurs in the forests of Nepal, Assam, Malay Peninsula, Java, Sumatra and New Guinea. In Ceylon, rare, found in Sinharaja Forest and Dolosbage.

I l l u s t r. Wall., Pl. As. Rar. 1: pl. 84. 1830; PDA, drawing.

S p e c i m e n s   E x a m i n e d. CEYLON: LOCALITY UNKNOWN: on banks of streams, *s. coll. C.P. 2744* (K, PDA, AMES). INDIA: Sikkim Himalaya, Valley of Teesta, *Pantling 414* (PDA).

ORCHIDACEAE

(by D.M.A. Jayaweera*)

Perennial herbs or rarely shrubs or vine-like climbing plants, terrestrial and often tuberous-rooted or epiphytic or saprophytic but never parasitic, occasionally lithophytic; roots subterranean or aerial, solitary, fascicled or rarely adventitious, fibrous, fleshy, tuberous or corm-like; stems terete, flattened or angular, more or less elongated but often much abbreviated and swollen into pseudobulbs; pseudobulbs slender and stem-like to globose, fusiform or pyriform, naked, bracteate or leafy, bearing one or more leaves, subtended by cataphylls or sheaths; leaves solitary or many, quite entire, sometimes evanescent or rarely wanting, radical or cauline, alternate or occasionally whorled, simple, papyraceous, coriaceous or fleshy, flat or plicate, parallel-veined. Inflorescence terminal or lateral, short- or long-pedunculate, one- to many-flowered, spicate, racemose or paniculate. Flowers minute and inconspicuous or large and showy, gynandrous, usually hermaphroditic, sometimes cleistogamous. Perianth superior, of 6 segments, free or variously united: an outer whorl of 3 sepals and an inner whorl of 2 petals and one lip or labellum. Sepals similar or the dorsal smaller, laterals more or less adnate to the inferior ovary or the column-foot. Petals rather similar to sepals, lip dissimilar and variously modified, slightly or very much, into a saccate pouch or basally elongated spur. Stamen and style confluent in a column opposite the lip; anther one, sessile on the column, attached onto or near the apex or laterally. Pollen powdery or waxy, compressed into 2 to 8 distinct masses or pollinia. Fruit a dry loculicidal capsule or sausage-shaped berry; seeds numerous, minute, without endosperm.

A very large family of flowering plants comprising over 30,000 species distributed in every part of the globe except the polar regions, with the greatest concentration of species in the mountainous regions of the tropics both in the Old and New Worlds.

Authentic fossil records of orchids are lacking as they probably did not grow in conditions favourable for fossilization. Nothing is known of the early history of the family and according to Schultes (1960) it is "a vast and highly specialized family" of recent origin "in an extremely active period of evolution."

*Royal Botanic Gardens, Peradeniya, Ceylon.

The family is of very little economic importance. A few species such as *Ephemerantha macraei* Hunt & Summerhayes, *Vanda tessellata* (Roxb.) Loddiges ex G. Don, *Anoectochilus setaceus* Blume and *Zeuxine regia* Trimen, are used medicinally in Ceylon while the cured capsules of some species of the genus *Vanilla* yield the widely used flavouring agent as the only commercial product. Horticulturally some attractive species occupy an enviable position owing to the beautiful variations in the colour of their flowers and the ease with which they hybridize.

Orchids are never wind-pollinated. External agents such as ants, bees, wasps, flies and butterflies are responsible for the transfer of pollinia on to the stigmas in their search for nectar. Cleistogamy is not uncommon in the family. Seeds of orchids are very minute and dust-like and they are dispersed by the wind. A single capsule may produce well over a million seeds, depending on its size. Orchid seed is exalbuminous and the family is characterized by the absence of a root in the embryo. Hence it is dependent on a symbiotic relationship with certain mycorrhizal fungi for its early supply of food during germination.

In nature the environment plays an important part in the struggle for existence of the family. Some epiphytic members are selective in the species of trees on which they grow and saprophytic ones thrive only under certain conditions of soil, moisture and shade. A few terrestrial ones prefer the acid "patana" soils.

Acknowledgements. I wish to express my sincere gratitude and thanks to all my colleagues in the Royal Botanic Gardens, Peradeniya, Mr. K.L.D. Amaratunga, and Dr. M.F. Chandraratne for all the assistance given and facilities provided during the course of this study. Also I wish to express my deep gratitude to Dr. Leslie A. Garay, Curator, Oakes Ames Orchid Herbarium and Mr. Peter Taylor of the Orchid Herbarium, Kew, for their invaluable assistance in all matters; I have drawn freely from their vast knowledge of the family. In particular I wish to thank the Director, Royal Botanic Gardens, Kew, the Curator, Oakes Ames Orchid Herbarium of the Harvard University, and the Systematic Botanist, Department of Agriculture, Peradeniya for permission to examine the collections in their charge. The contents of Lindley Herbarium, Kew, were carefully examined for comparison. I owe a deep debt of gratitude to Dr. Richard A. Howard, Professor of Dendrology, Harvard University and Director of the Arnold Arboretum for encouragement given at all times and I wish to thank him most sincerely for it. Further I wish to thank Prof. M.D. Dassanayake of the University of Peradeniya for his valuable suggestions.

KEY TO THE GENERA

1 Pollinia waxy
  2 Pollinia free or adhering in pairs or fours by a viscus
   3 Pollinia 4 or 2

4 Pollinia 4
  5 Lip deflexed or decurved from base; sepals and petals widely spreading
    6 Lip superior; flowers resupinate; column very short
      7 Leaves fleshy, laterally compressed, equitant.......................**1. Oberonia**
      7 Leaves membranous, plicate, not equitant..........................**2. Malaxis**
    6 Lip inferior; sepals and petals often deflexed under lip.................**3. Liparis**
  5 Lip erect from base; sepals and petals approximate
    8 Column prolonged into a foot
      9 Lip not articulate on foot
        10 Pseudobulbs on branches consisting of a single internode below a leaf......
        ....**4. Ephemerantha**
        10 Pseudobulbous stems consisting of several nodes and internodes.............
        ....**5. Dendrobium**
      9 Lip articulate on foot......................................**6. Bulbophyllum**
    8 Column not prolonged into a foot
      11 Bracts large; pollinia cohering in pairs by a viscus
        12 Lip embracing the column..................................**7. Coelogyne**
        12 Lip not embracing the column..............................**8. Pholidota**
      11 Bracts minute; pollinia not cohering in pairs but free.............**9. Adrorhizon**
4 Pollinia 2..**10. Chrysoglossum**
3 Pollinia 8
  13 Epiphytes
    14 Inflorescence a lateral or terminal spike or raceme.....................**11. Eria**
    14 Inflorescence a sessile, terminal head.......................**12. Agrostophyllum**
  13 Terrestrials
    15 Stems pseudobulbous
      16 Lip sessile at base of column or hinged to the end of the column-foot
        17 Sepals connate into a fleshy inflated tube with a saccate mentum..............
        ....**13. Acanthephippium**
        17 Sepals free
          18 Lip hinged to the column-foot.................................**14. Tainia**
          18 Lip adnate to the base of the column
            19 Lip not spurred...**15. Ipsea**
            19 Lip spurred embracing the column............................**16. Phaius**
      16 Lip adnate to the top of the column, spurred.....................**17. Calanthe**
    15 Stems non-pseudobulbous.....................................**18. Arundina**
2 Pollinia attached singly or in pairs by straps or caudicles to a distinct viscid gland
  20 Pollinia 2 (or 4 unequal halves)
    21 Plants terrestrial with pseudobulbous or tuberous stems
      22 Lip inferior, side lobes embracing column, disc crested or echinate; pollinia atta-
        ched by a short broad strap to a distinct gland....................**19. Eulophia**
      22 Lip superior; flowers resupinate; pollinia subsessile on a broad gland...........
      ....**20. Geodorum**
    21 Plants epiphytic
      23 Stems pseudobulbous.......................................**21. Cymbidium**
      23 Stems non-pseudobulbous
        24 Column prolonged into distinct foot
          25 Leaves absent at time of flowering........................**22. Chiloschista**
          25 Leaves present at time of flowering
            26 Spur or sac with no calli within............................**23. Pteroceras**
            26 Spur or sac pubescent or puberulous or with calli within....**24. Thrixspermum**

27 Lateral sepals adnate to a short foot of the column with which the lips are continuous
28 Flowers in densely crowded, short-peduncled drooping racemes............
....**25. Rhynchostylis**
28 Flowers in 1-few-flowered erect racemes
29 Leaves terete, lateral lobes of lip either parallel with or enfolding the column, rostellum elongate.....................................**26. Papilionanthe**
29 Leaves lorate, lateral lobes of lip small, rostellum porrect........**27. Aerides**
27 Lateral sepals adnate to base of lip forming a spur-like mentum from which the lobes of the lip are borne directly...........................**28. Kingidium**
24 Column usually not prolonged into a foot or if prolonged, foot indistinct or short or absent
30 Leaves not articulated or jointed on sheaths
31 Leaf apex not bilobed..**29. Luisia**
31 Leaf apex bilobed
32 Side lobes of lip large..**30. Vanda**
32 Side lobes of lip small or absent
33 Spurs 2, collateral.....................................**31. Diplocentrum**
33 Spur or sac single
34 Lips of flowers at top or pointing to apex of inflorescence
35 Spur naked without any callosities inside....................**32. Acampe**
35 Spur with fleshy thickening in front wall and an erect tongue at the back wall reaching the mouth of the spur.......................**33. Potamocalpa**
34 Lips of flowers not pointing to apex of inflorescence; calli on the dorsal wall of the spur completely closing the entrance to the nectariferous cavity
....**34. Trichoglottis**
30 Leaves articulated or jointed on sheaths
36 Lip produced into a sac or spur
37 Pollinia on two separate stipes or viscidia, base of lip enveloping the column
....**35. Angraecum**
37 Pollinia on single stipe
38 Inflorescences often 2 at a node, lip basin-shaped, sides firmly adnate to column..**36. Gastrochilus**
38 Inflorescence one at a node, lip cylindric or ellipsoid
39 Spur with callosities inside, rostellum long-bifid
40 Anther beak abruptly up-curved.......................**37. Schoenorchis**
40 Anther beak cuspidate in front..........................**38. Robiquetia**
39 Spur without callosities inside............................**39. Aerangis**
36 Lip not produced into a sac or spur
41 Lip subpanduriform with villous margins.....................**40. Cottonia**
41 Lip cymbiform, sigmoidly curved into a 2-caudate tip.........**41. Diploprora**
20 Pollinia 4 or 8
42 Pollinia 4
43 Leaves present on the stem
44 Anther terminal on the column or facing the lip
45 Stem pseudobulbous; inflorescence paniculately branched, lip not spurred
46 Lip inferior, disc with a transverse membrane between the side lobes and the midlobe...**42. Sirhookera**
46 Lip superior, disc pubescent...............................**43. Polystachya**
45 Stem not pseudobulbous; inflorescence racemose; lip spurred......**44. Sarcanthus**
44 Anther posticous on the column facing the dorsal sepal...........**45. Podochilus**

43 Leaves absent..**46. Taeniophyllum**
42 Pollinia 8
47 Lip inserted on column-foot, very small; inflorescence terminal; anther terminal....
....**47. Phreatia**
47 Lip sessile on the base of the column, column-foot absent; inflorescence axillary;
anther dorsal..**48. Octarrhena**
1 Pollinia granular, powdery or lamellate
48 Anther operculate
49 Anther dorsal on the column, facing the dorsal sepal
50 Leaves not plicate
51 Lip superior
52 Pollinia 4; lip not lobed, inserted at the base of the column and embracing it..
....**49. Cryptostylis**
52 Pollinia 2; lip saccate, containing papillae and glands............**50. Hetaeria**
51 Lip inferior
53 Sepals joined and swollen to form a tube.....................**51. Cheirostylis**
53 Sepals free
54 Spur or sac of the lip projecting between lateral sepals
55 Claw of lip entire, spur or sac with 4 or more mamillate calli on the wall near
the base...**52. Erythrodes**
55 Claw of lip pectinate; spur or sac with 2 large unstalked glands.............
....**53. Anoectochilus**
54 Spur or sac of lip concealed by lateral sepals
56 Flower spikes twisted or flowers spirally arranged on the spike
57 Lip entire, cymbiform...................................**54. Goodyera**
57 Lip crenate-toothed, saccate.............................**55. Spiranthes**
56 Flower spike not twisted spirally...........................**56. Zeuxine**
50 Leaves plicate
58 Flowers in axillary panicles; column long...................**57. Corymborkis**
58 Flowers in unbranched terminal spikes or paniculate racemes; column short......
....**58. Tropidia**
49 Anther terminal on the column or facing the lip
59 Climbing plants...**59. Vanilla**
59 Terrestrial herbs
60 Leafless saprophytes
61 Sepals and petals connate to form a 5-lobed perianth-tube........**60. Gastrodia**
61 Sepals and petals free
62 Lip spurred...**61. Epipogium**
62 Lip not spurred
63 Disc of lip bearded; column winged.........................**62. Galeola**
63 Disc of lip not bearded; column not winged................**63. Aphyllorchis**
60 Leaves produced after flowering..............................**64. Nervilia**
48 Anther not operculate but confluent with the column
64 Lip inferior
65 Lip spurred
66 Stigma bilobed, more or less extended with clavate or papillose processes; anther-
tubes prominent..**65. Habenaria**
66 Stigma sessile, united to base of lip and auricles of the column; anther-tubes
absent or very short.......................................**66. Peristylus**
65 Lip not spurred...**67. Disperis**
64 Lip superior...**68. Satyrium**

1. OBERONIA

Lindl., Gen. Sp. Orch. Pl. 15. 1830.

Tufted epiphytes; stems close together; leaves distichous, equitant, much laterally compressed, fleshy, ensiform, oblong or linear; inflorescence terminal, short or long, usually curved, densely covered with very small flowers, sometimes in regular whorls; sepals nearly equal, often reflexed; petals usually narrower than sepals, sometimes toothed: lip superior, sessile on the base of the column, usually 3-lobed, spreading, concave at the base, often with the basal lobes embracing the column; column very short; anther terminal, incumbent; pollinia 4, in two pairs, without caudicles.

About 160 species distributed from East Africa through India, Ceylon, Burma, Malaya, China, etc. to Samoa.

KEY TO THE SPECIES

1 Lateral lobes of lip at the same level as or below the column; sepals subequal, ovate or oblong-ovate
  2 Lip not distinctly lobed or obscurely trifid or 5-fid at apex, pollinia attached to a gland
    3 Margin of lip entire, bracts broadly subulate, irregularly serrate at apex............
    ....**1. O. zeylanica**
    3 Margin of lip irregularly crenate or dentate; bracts ovate and erose at the margin
      4 Petals linear, 1 mm long; lip fleshy, lateral lobes rounded, midlobe trifid, lateral lobules longer than the midlobule.................................**2. O. forcipata**
      4 Petals linear-oblong, 0.86–1 mm long; lip quadrate, concave......**3. O. quadrilatera**
  2 Lip 3-lobed, pollinia not attached to a gland
    5 Lip shorter than sepals, subreniform, 3-veined, lateral lobes slightly dentate........
    ....**4. O. truncata**
    5 Lip equal to or longer than sepals, lateral lobes distinct from the midlobe
      6 Bracts longer than the flower...............................**5. O. longibracteata**
      6 Bracts shorter than the flower
        7 Petals linear, 1.2 mm long.......................................**6. O. wightiana**
        7 Petals ovate or ovate-oblong
          8 Flowers conspicuously whorled; bracts ovate-lanceolate, pilose, margin irregular; lip obcuneately obcordate, lateral lobes reduced to rounded knobs, midlobe bifid, margins distantly crenate.......................................**7. O. thwaitesii**
          8 Flowers not conspicuously whorled; bracts lanceolate, acuminate; lip twice as long as sepals, conspicuously and irregularly crenate, lateral lobes orbicular, midlobe 2-lobulate...**8. O. recurva**
1 Lateral lobes of lip rising above the column, erect and parallel or arching; lateral sepals orbicular
  9 Petals ciliate, lip 3-lobed
    10 Petals oblong-lanceolate; plant small............................**9. O. dolabrata**
    10 Petals lanceolate or linear-lanceolate
      11 Midlobe of lip ciliate entirely along the margin or at the tips of the lobules only
        12 Lateral lobes of lip subulate, erect, parallel, midlobe semilunate; dorsal sepal lanceolate, straight and parallel to the petals, apex ciliate.............**10. O. scyllae**

12 Lateral lobes of lip clavate, arched, and overlapping behind the column, midlobe trifid, ciliate at the tips, lateral lobules subulate, diverging; lateral sepals orbicular, rounded; petals lanceolate, shaggy..............................**11. O. claviloba**
11 Midlobe of lip not ciliate
   13 Dorsal sepals and petals ciliate................................**12. O. fornicata**
   13 Dorsal sepal not ciliate, only petals ciliate
      14 Petals lanceolate; lateral sepals broadly orbicular-ovate, obtuse; lateral lobes of lip arched, midlobe bifid, concave, lobules bluntly subulate and diverging..........
      ....**13. O. wallie-silvae**
      14 Petals linear-lanceolate; dorsal sepal ovate, acuminate; lateral lobes of lip parallel; semilanceolate, midlobe trifid, lateral lobules finely subulate, diverging, midlobule short, triangular and blunt........................**14. O. weragamaensis**
9 Petals not ciliate, lateral lobes of lip forming an arc round the column, midlobe with a long neck, trifid and hatchet-shaped................................**15. O. tenuis**

1. Oberonia zeylanica Hook. f., Hook. Ic. Pl. 18, pl. 1782. 1888; Trimen, Handb. Fl. Ceylon 4: 138. 1898.—**Fig. 1.**

Oberonia browneana Thw. ex Hook. f., Fl. Br. Ind. 5: 680. 1888.

Tufted epiphyte with compressed, non-pseudobulbous stems. Leaves distichous, equitant, laterally compressed, linear-ensiform, 4–6 to a single stem, 7.5–16 × 1.2–2.2 cm acuminate and slightly bent towards the apex. Flowers reddish-brown in very stout spiciform racemes curved upwards; peduncle flat, green, together with the rachis 18 cm with a small, adnate leaf reaching to about half its length. Flowers open from apex downwards, 3.6 × 2 mm, floral bracts 2.1 × 1.1 mm, broadly subulate, acute, margin irregularly serrate towards the upper half; sepals and petals reflexed with their backs to the ovary; dorsal sepal 1.5–1.7 × 0.9 mm, ovate -obtuse; lateral sepals 1.7 mm long, 0.96 mm broad, ovate, subacute; petals 1.6 × 0.36 mm, linear, obtuse or rounded at the apex, sharply reflexed and curved; lip the most conspicuous portion of the flower, 1.9 × 2.1 mm, quadrate, concave, with a triangular waxy, shining area at the centre; margin entire, slightly 5-lobed at the apex with the centre lobe smaller and shorter; rostrum bluntly conical with a broad neck, 0.7 mm high and 0.5 mm broad. Anther terminal, 0.54 × 0.48 mm, incumbent, 2-loculed; pollinia 4, in two pairs; each pollinium club-shaped 0.46 × 0.1 mm. Ovary with pedicel 1.8 mm. Fruit an oblong capsule, 5.6 × 2.4 mm, stalked and straight-ribbed.

D i s t r. Submontane or mid-country tropical wet evergreen forests extending to subtropical montane forests in Ceylon between 1,220 and 1,829 m alt. Rare, usually found growing on tops of tall trees, especially *Ficus* sp. at Hakgala, Adam's Peak, Hunnasgiriya, Hewaheta, Matale East and Hantane. Also in South India.

E c o l. Flowers October–November, December, January.

I l l u s t r. PDA, drawing from *C.P. 3869.*

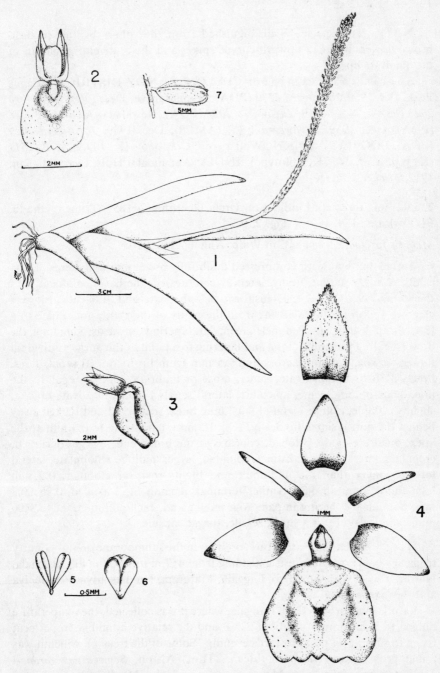

Fig. 1. *Oberonia zeylanica* Hook. f. 1, plant with inflorescences. 2, flower from front. 3, flower from side, three quarters view. 4, bract, sepals, petals and lip spread out from front, column from inside. 5, pollinia. 6, operculum from inside. 7, fruit.

N o t e. This species is distinguished from the others by the reddish-brown flowers borne in upward-curved spikes and the quite entire margin of the quadrate lip.

S p e c i m e n s E x a m i n e d. CEYLON, KANDY DISTRICT: Adam's Peak, Oct. 1959, *Jayaweera 2189* (PDA); Hunnasgiriya, Dec. 1960, *Jayaweera 2026* (PDA), Nov. 1959, *Jayaweera 2027* (PDA); Hewaheta, *Jayaweera 2028* (PDA), Dec. 1959, *Jayaweera 1 (5)* (AMES), Dec. 1959, *Jayaweera 2029* (PDA). LOCALITY UNKNOWN: *s. coll. C.P. 3869* (K, PDA); *C.P. 2511* (K) p.p.; *C.P. 543* (K, holotype). INDIA: Annaimalai Hills, Lyarpadi, Jan. 1912, *Fischer 3263* (K).

2. Oberonia forcipata Lindl., Fol. Orch. Oberonia 2. 1859; Trimen, Handb. Fl. Ceylon 4: 139. 1898.—**Fig. 2.**

Malaxis forcipata Reichb. f. in Walp. Ann. 6: 209. 1861.

Tufted epiphyte with compressed doubtfully pseudobulbous stems. Leaves distichous, equitant, fleshy, laterally compressed, the bases confluent with the stem, 7–9 × 1.3–1.7 cm, ensiform or subfalcate and subacute. Flowers greenish-yellow in spikes arising from the centre of the plant, not adnate to a leaf, central leaf linear. Peduncle green, flat, tapering outwards, 5 cm long, the flower-bearing portion as long and tapering to a point at the apex. Individual flowers sessile, 1.4 mm across and 2.5 mm from lip to dorsal sepal; floral bracts 1.36 × 1.1 mm, ovate, acute, erose or fimbriate; dorsal sepal 1 × 0.6 mm, ovate-oblong, acute, apiculate; lateral sepals 1 × 0.7 mm, ovate-oblong, slightly oblique, obtuse; petals 1 × 0.3 mm, linear, decurved and tucked away behind the dorsal sepal; lip fleshy, 1.7 × 1.5 mm, narrowing to 0.9 mm at the apex, quadrate-ovate, 3-lobed, concave at the broad end, margin decurved, crenulate; lateral lobes indistinct, rounded, large; midlobe trilobulate, lateral lobules longer than the midlobule and blunt; rostrum globular, 0.3 mm high and 0.36 mm broad. Anther terminal, incumbent, 2-loculed, 0.36 × 0.3 mm; pollinia 4, cohering in pairs to a small gland, each pollinium 0.24 × 0.06 mm, cylindrical. Fruit a short, sessile, turgid capsule.

D i s t r. Endemic. Rather rare, on trees in the submontane or mid-country tropical wet evergreen forests extending from 457 m to 1,829 m alt. Rangala, Nuwara Eliya (Westward-Ho), Laggala, Maturata, Hunnasgiriya, Peradeniya and Hewaheta.

E c o l. At Corbet's Gap, Rangala, where it was collected, the temperature ranged to a maximum of about 71° F and the relative humidity 76 per cent rising to saturation point towards evening. Some of the trees on which it was found growing are *Neolitsea fuscata* (Thw.) Alston, *Semecarpus gardneri* Thw., *Canthium dicoccum* Merr., *Ostodes zeylanica* Muell., *Litsea gardneri* (Thw.) Hook. f., *Walsura gardneri* Thw., *Acronychia pedunculata* Miq., *Ficus retusa* L., *Nothopegia* sp. and *Scolopia* sp. Other plants growing in association

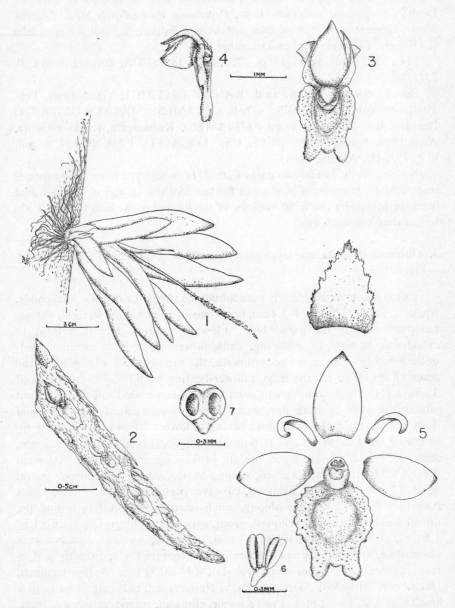

Fig. 2. *Oberonia forcipata* Lindl. 1, plant with an inflorescence. 2, apical portion of inflorescence. 3, flower from front. 4, flower from side. 5, bract, sepals, petals and lip spread out from front, enlarged. 6, pollinia with gland. 7, operculum from inside.

with this species were the following, besides mosses and lichens: *Eria bicolor* Lindl., *Lycopodium setaceum* Ham., *Peperomia dindigulensis* Miq., *Lycopodium phlegmaria* L., *Lycopodium squarrosum* Forst., *Nephrolepis cordifolia* (L) Pr., etc. Flowers October–December.

I l l u s t r. Hook. Ic. Pl. 18: pl. 1782, fig B. 1888; PDA, drawing from *C.P. 2511.*

S p e c i m e n s E x a m i n e d. KANDY DISTRICT: Gannoruwa, Feb. 1904, *Schlechter s.n.* (AMES), *s. coll. s.n.* (AMES). MATALE DISTRICT: Laggala, Jan. 1960, *Jayaweera 1 (7)* (AMES); Kabaragala, Raxawa Estate, Aug. 1969, *Wheeler 12249* (PDA, US). LOCALITY UNKNOWN: *s. coll. C.P. 2511* (K, AMES, PDA).

N o t e. Herb. Lindley contains *C.P. 2511* in the type cover. This species resembles *O. brunoniana* Wight but for the toothed lip and is distinguished from the others by the trifid midlobe of the lip where the lateral lobules are longer than the midlobule.

3. Oberonia quadrilatera Jayaweera, Bot. Mus. Leafl. 20 (4): 93–96. 1963. —**Fig. 3.**

Tufted epiphyte with faintly pseudobulbous stems. Leaves few, distichous, equitant, fleshy, 4.5–17 × 1–1.4 cm, linear-ensiform or almost straight, obtuse, bases ensheathing the pseudobulb. Flowers minute, greenish yellow, in cylindrical, straight or drooping, dense-flowered spiciform racemes. Peduncle 8–9.5 cm, flat, green or yellowish, the topmost leaf adnate to it and reaching up 1/3 to 1/2 the length, flower-bearing portion 6–7.5 cm long and 3 mm diam. The first flowers to open located in the middle of the spike and subsequent ones opening progressively and simultaneously upwards and downwards, terminal flowers not opening. Flowers 2 mm long from the tip of dorsal sepal to the lip and 1.16 mm broad; floral bracts 2 × 1.16–1.2 mm, recurved, ovate, pilose, acute, margin broken up irregularly; dorsal sepal 0.9–1.1 × 0.68–0.8 mm, recurved, oblong-ovate, obtuse or rounded; lateral sepals 1.1 × 0.56–0.9 mm, recurved, concave, triangular-ovate, obtuse; petals 0.86–1 × 0.3–0.4 mm, linear-oblong, much recurved and curling behind the dorsal sepal; lip green or yellowish-green, superior, sessile, thick, 1–1.6 × 1.5–1.6 mm, at the base, tapering to 0.9 mm, quadrate, 3-veined, concave; base subcordate, apex bluntly and obscurely trifid, margin thick, distantly and irregularly dentate; column short, globular, 0.44 × 0.34 mm. Anther terminal, incumbent, 2-loculed; pollinia 4, waxy, club-shaped, cohering in pairs to a small gland, 0.24 × 0.1 mm. Fruit a sessile, ellipsoid, ridged capsule 4 × 2 mm.

D i s t r. Endemic. Very rare, on trees in the submontane or mid-country tropical wet evergreen forests from 713 to 1268 m alt. Rangala (Corbet's Gap), Hunnasgiriya.

E c o l. Flowers August–October.

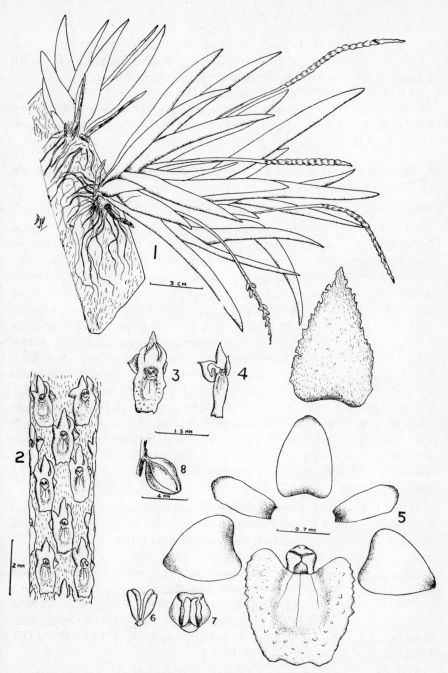

Fig. 3. *Oberonia quadrilatera* Jayaweera. 1, plants with inflorescences. 2, part of inflorescence showing arrangement of flowers on the rachis. 3, flower from front. 4, flower from side, three quarters view. 5, bract, sepals, lip and column spread out from front. 6, pollinia with gland. 7, operculum from front. 8, fruit.

I l l u s t r. Bot. Muś. Leafl. 20 (4): pl. 11. 1963.

N o t e. This species is allied to *Oberonia zeylanica* Hook. f., from which it differs in the linear-oblong petals and irregularly dentate lip.

S p e c i m e n s E x a m i n e d. KANDY DISTRICT: Corbet's Gap, *Jayaweera 2001* (PDA, holotype); Hunnasgiriya, *Jayaweera 2191* (PDA). KURUNEGALA DISTRICT: Doluwakande, Jan. 1972, *Jayasuriya & Balakrishnan 584* (PDA, US).

4. Oberonia truncata Lindl., Fol. Orch. Oberonia 3. 1859; Trimen, Handb. Fl. Ceylon 4: 136. 1898.—**Fig. 4.**

Malaxis truncata Reichb. f. in Walp. Ann. 6: 210. 1861.

Tufted epiphyte with very short, non-pseudobulbous stems. Leaves fleshy, distichous, equitant, laterally compressed, 5–13 × 1–1.4 cm, ensiform straight or subfalcate and acute at the apex, bases confluent with the stem. Flowers greenish-yellow in spiciform racemes opening all together; peduncles adnate to the uppermost leaf and flattened; flower-bearing portion of the raceme 4 cm long, stout, straight and curved. Individual flowers in obscurely whorled fascicles along the inflorescence, 1.1 mm across; floral bracts 3.2–3.6 × 1.2–1.4 mm, as long as or longer than the flower, lanceolate, acuminate, apiculate and somewhat serrulate at the margin; dorsal sepal 0.9 × 0.6 mm, ovate, subacute, serrulate just below the apex only; lateral sepals 1 × 0.6 mm, ovate, acute and also serrulate below the apex; petals 0.8 × 0.3 mm, linear-oblong, obtuse and entire; lip superior, 0.94 × 1.6 mm, subreniform with large, orbicular side-lobes folding inwards in the flower, 3-veined and margin entire or slightly dentate at the lateral lobes; rostrum globular, 0.3 mm high and as broad. Anther terminal, incumbent, 0.28 × 0.36 mm, 2-loculed; pollinia 4, cohering in pairs, each pollinium 0.22 × 0.1 mm. Ovary with pedicel 1.3 mm long.

D i s t r. Endemic. Rare, on trees in the submontane or mid-country tropical wet evergreen forests between 915 and 1,220 m alt. Hatton (Duke's Nose), Adam's Peak, Wariagala, Hantane and near Bibile.

E c o l. Flowers October–December.

N o t e. This species is distinguished by the small straw-yellow flower spikes turned upwards, 3-lobed lip and the pollinia not attached to a gland.

S p e c i m e n s E x a m i n e d. KANDY DISTRICT: Adam's peak, Nov. 1959, *Jayaweera 2018* (PDA); Hantane, *Champion s.n.* (K, holotype). MONERAGALA DISTRICT: Bibile, June 1901, *s. coll. s.n.* (PDA). LOCALITY UNKNOWN: *s. coll. C.P. 3913* (PDA).

5. Oberonia longibracteata Lindl., Gen. et Sp. Orch. 15. 1830; Trimen, Handb. Fl. Ceylon 4: 138. 1898.—**Fig. 5.**

Malaxis longibracteata Reichb. f. in Walp. Ann. 6: 209. 1861.

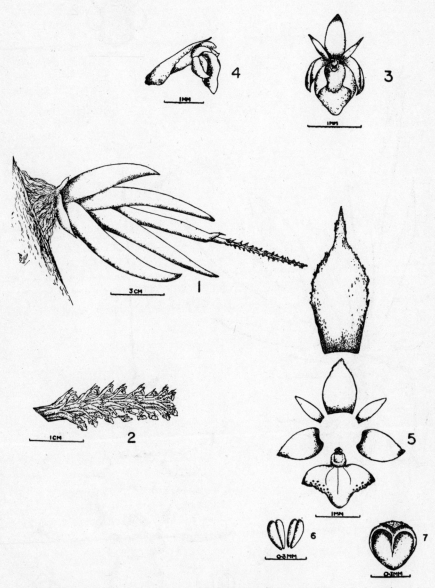

Fig. 4. *Oberonia truncata* Lindl. 1, plant with inflorescence. 2, apical portion of inflorescence, magnified. 3, flower from front. 4, flower from side. 5, bract, sepals, petals and lip spread out from front, column from inside. 6, pollinia. 7, operculum from inside.

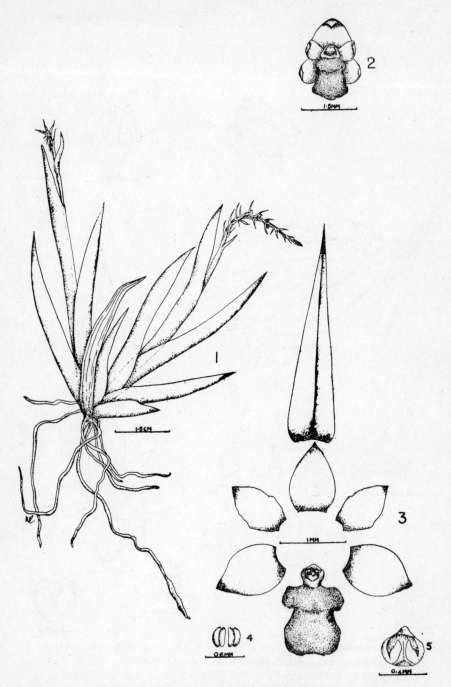

Fig. 5. *Oberonia longibracteata* Lindl. 1, plant with inflorescences. 2, flower from front. 3, bract, sepals, petals and lip spread out from front, column from inside. 4, pollinia. 5, operculum from inside.

Tufted epiphyte with compressed, non-pseudobulbous, flexuous stems. Leaves fleshy, equitant, laterally compressed, 3.7–5.5 × 0.3–0.5 cm, linear-oblong or linear, acute at the apex, veins obscure, bases confluent with the stem. Flowers yellowish-brown in long bracteated, sharply decurved, spiciform racemes; first flowers opening at end of raceme and then progressively downwards; terminal flowers not opening; peduncle 3 cm long and the flower-bearing portion 1–2.7 cm; pedicel 0.16 mm; floral bracts linear-subulate, 4.6 × 1.2 mm, entire, acuminate, 1-veined and much longer than the flower; dorsal sepal 1 × 0.66 mm, broadly ovate, subacute or obtuse; lateral sepals as long as the dorsal sepal, 0.76 mm broad, broadly ovate, obtuse; petals 0.84 × 0.56 mm, oblong, subacute, with an irregularly undulating margin; lip fleshy, 3-lobed, 1 mm long; side lobes small, orbicular, truncate; midlobe broadly orbicular, obscurely bilobed, 0.9 mm broad; rostrum globular, 0.34 × 0.46 mm. Anther terminal, 2-loculed, incumbent, 0.3 × 0.35 mm; pollinia 4, sausage-shaped in two pairs, each pollinium 0.24 × 0.1 mm. Ovary 0.74 mm long. Fruit a small, subsessile capsule.

D i s t r. Endemic. Rather rare, on trees in the submontane or mid-country tropical wet evergreen forests at about 1981 m alt. Adam's Peak, Hantane, Hewaheta, Maturata and Hakgala.

E c o l. Flowers September, October–March. *Palaquium rubiginosum* (Thw.) Engl. is one of the host plants on which it thrives.

I l l u s t r. PDA, drawing from *C.P. 542*.

N o t e. This species is intermediate in habit between caulescent and stemless species, much similar to *Lam 28083* from Hainan but for the midlobe of the lip.

S p e c i m e n s E x a m i n e d. KANDY DISTRICT: Kandy, *Walker s.n.* (K); Hunnasgiriya, Oct. 1960, *Jayaweera 2021* (PDA); Madulkele Estate, Nov. 1975, *Sohmer & Jayasuriya 10633* (PDA, US); Maturata, High Forest, May 1906, *A.M. Silva s.n.* (PDA); Adam's Peak, Nov. 1959, *Jayaweera 1 (4)* (AMES). NUWARA ELIYA DISTRICT: Hakgala, Oct. 1906, *A.M. Silva s.n.* (PDA). LOCALITY UNKNOWN: *s. coll. C.P. 543* (AMES), *Gardner 842* (K), *Macrae 25* (K, holotype).

6. Oberonia wightiana Lindl., Bot. Reg. 25: 14, Misc. 9. 1839; Trimen, Handb. Fl. Ceylon 4: 138. 1898.—Fig. 6.

Oberonia stachyoides A. Rich., Ann. Sc. Nat. Bot. 11. 15: 15, pl. 1. 1841.
Oberonia arnottiana Wight, Ic. Pl. Ind. Or. 5: pl. 1628 & pl. 1627. 1852.
Malaxis wightiana Reichb. f. in Walp. Ann. 6: 212. 1861.

Small tufted epiphyte with compressed, non-pseudobulbous stems. Leaves 3 or 4, distichous, equitant, laterally compressed, fleshy, 1.2–3.5 × 0.4–0.8 cm, ensiform, acute, confluent with the stem, veins obscure. Flowers greenish

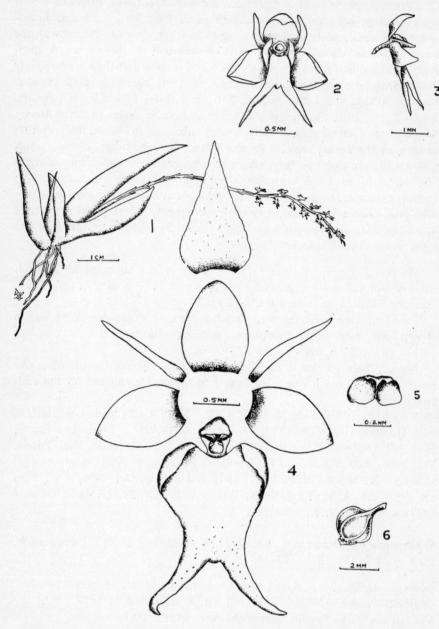

Fig. 6. *Oberonia wightiana* Lindl. 1, plant with inflorescence. 2, flower from front. 3, flower from side. 4, bract, sepals, petals and lip spread out from front, column from inside. 5, operculum from inside. 6, fruit.

yellow, distantly placed on slender, decurved, lax-flowered racemes which measure 6–10 cm in length; peduncle short, terete, with a few sterile bracts. Individual flowers 3×1.1 mm; floral bracts 1.4×0.8 mm, ovate, acuminate, acute; dorsal sepal 1.1×0.8 mm, oblong-ovate, obtuse; lateral sepals 1×0.74 mm, of the same shape as the dorsal sepal; petals 1.2×0.24 mm, linear, obtuse, standing out of the flower; lip 1.6 mm long, 1.3 mm broad at the base, 3-lobed; latera llobes orbicular; midlobe bifurcated into two linear, diverging lobules; rostrum globular, 0.4 mm high and 0.36 mm broad. Anther terminal, incumbent, 0.16×0.3 mm, 2-loculed; pollinia 4, very small, cohering in two pairs. Ovary with pedicel 1.3 mm long. Fruit a globular, rigid capsule, 1.8×2 mm.

D i s t r. Common on trees in the submontane or midcountry tropical wet evergreen forests from 548 to 2134 m alt. Rangala, Ambagamuwa, Hakgala, Hatton (Duke's Nose, abundant), Hantane, Ramboda, Nuwara Eliya, Horton Plains, Namunukula and Pidurutalagala. Also in India, Khasia, Nilgiri and Pulney Hills.

E c o l. Flowers October–November. Some of its host plants are *Apodytes benthamiana* Wight, *Antidesma* sp., *Eurya japonica* Thunb.

I l l u s t r. Hook. Ic. Pl. 18: pl. 1784, fig. B. 1888; PDA, 3 drawings from *C.P. 2506.*

N o t e. Lindley has described the species from a specimen collected from Madras and from four other collections mounted on the same type cover at Kew. From these *Wight 181* is selected as the lectotype. This species resembles *Oberonia verticillata* Wight and *O. arnottiana* Wight but differs from the latter in the shape of the bract, which is not serrated in the Ceylon species.

S p e c i m e n s E x a m i n e d. CEYLON, BADULLA DISTRICT: Namunukula, Mar.–Apr. 1907, *J.M. Silva s.n.* (PDA). NUWARA ELIYA DISTRICT: Hakgala, Oct. 1960, *Jayaweera 2022* (PDA); Sita Eliya, on road to Blackpool, Apr. 1932, *Simpson 9612* (PDA); Nuwara Eliya, Westward-Ho, Nov. 1963, *Jayaweera 2364* (PDA); Pidurutalagala, Oct. 1973, *Sohmer, Jayasuriya & Eliezer 8409* (PDA, US), Oct. 1974, *Davidse & Sumithraarachchi 8019* (PDA, US), Sept. 1969, *C.F. & R.J. van Beusekom 1390* (PDA, US). KANDY DISTRICT: Adam's Peak, Nov. 1927, *F.W. de Silva 40* (PDA), Nov. 1974, *Davidse & Sumithraarachchi 8637* (PDA, US), Dec. 1975, *Bernardi 15813, 15936* (PDA, US), Nov. 1959, *Jayaweera 1024* (PDA); Hatton, *Jayaweera 2023* (PDA), Nov. 1959, *Jayaweera 1 (8)* (AMES); Ambagamuwa, *s. coll. C.P. 592* (PDA). LOCALITY UNKNOWN: *s. coll. C.P. 2506* (K, AMES, PDA), *Gardner 843* (K). INDIA: Khasia Hills, *Lobb* (K), Madras, Nilgiris, *Perrottet 1093* (AMES), *Hohenecker 961* (K), *Herb. Wight 2061, 2062* (K), *Lobb s.n.* (K), *Gamble 21399* (K), *Herb. Wight 2942* (K); Pulney Hills, Jun. 1879, *Bourne 531* (K); Ind. Orient, *Herb. Wight 2942* (AMES), *Wight 181* (K, lectotype).

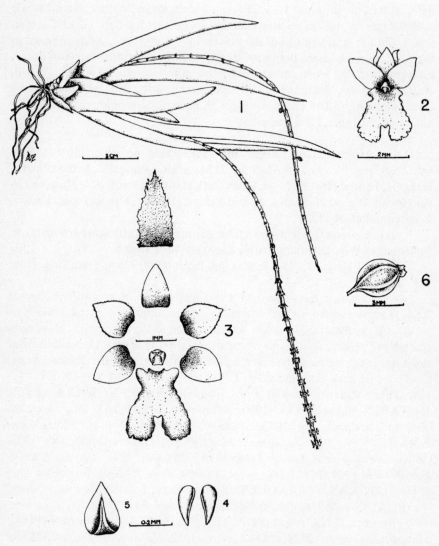

Fig. 7. *Oberonia thwaitesii* Hook. f. 1, plant with inflorescences. 2, flower from front. 3, bract, sepals, petals and lip spread out from front, column from inside separated from the lip. 4, pollinia. 5, operculum from inside. 6, fruit.

7. Oberonia thwaitesii Hook. f., Fl. Br. Ind. 5: 678. 1888; Trimen, Handb. Fl. Ceylon 4: 137. 1898.—**Fig. 7.**

Oberonia verticillata var. *pubescens* Lindl., Fol. Orch. Oberonia 3. 1859.
Malaxis verticillata var. *pubescens* Reichb. f. in Walp. Ann. 6: 210. 1861.

Tufted epiphyte with very short, non-pseudobulbous, compressed stems. Leaves laterally compressed, distichous, equitant, fleshy, linear, ensiform, slightly curved, 6.9–20.5 × 0.7–1.2 cm, veins obscure. Flowers pale orange-yellow in terminal, densely flowered, spiciform racemes which measure 12.5–23.5 cm in length; peduncle 2.3 cm long, adnate to the base of the uppermost leaf, 8-ribbed, ridges continued in the rachis. Individual flowers small, 2.8 mm from lip to dorsal sepal, in regular whorls, 7 or 8 flowers to each whorl, whorls 0.5 cm apart; floral bracts ovate-lanceolate, 1.6 × 0.6 mm, margin irregular and pilose outside; sepals broadly ovate, recurved, 1 × 0.8 mm, acute and pilose outside; petals broadly oblong-ovate, erose, subacute, of the same size as sepals; lip longer than sepals and petals, 1.8 × 1.3 mm, obcuneately obcordate, side lobes reduced to curved knobs at the base, terminal lobe 2-lobulate, lobules rounded with a broad obtuse sinus, margin distantly denticulate-crenate; rostrum globular, 0.36 mm high and 0.4 mm broad. Anther terminal, superior, incumbent, 0.26 mm long, pollinia 4, waxy, cohering in pairs, each pollinium 0.18 × 0.08 mm. Fruit very small, 2.8 × 2.2 mm, subglobose, sessile; seeds extremely small, testa provided with diagonal ridges.

D i s t r. Endemic. Rare, on trees in the tropical semi-evergreen forests or "Intermediate" evergreen forests of the dry low-country. Kurunegala, Mirigama, Puttalam and Bibile.

E c o l. Flowers July–August. In Doluwakanda jungle, Kurunegala, it grows epiphytic on *Vitex leucoxylon* L. and *Nothopegia beddomei* Gamble; on *Ficus* sp. and *Artocarpus heterophyllus* Lam. by roadside towards Kurunegala along Kurunegala-Dambulla road; on *Samanea saman* (Jacq.) Merr. at Bibile and Wariapola along the Kurunegala-Puttalam road. In these areas the climate is hot and dry, temperatures average about 80° F, humidity 56–74 per cent going down to 38 per cent in dry weather and rainfall 1672–1697 mm a year. The months of July and October are wet. The flowering habit of this species is curious. The first flowers open about 2/3 to 3/4 way up the spike and the later ones on either side progressively and simultaneously, those towards the apex opening a little earlier than towards the base.

I l l u s t r. PDA, drawing from *C.P. 2572.*

N o t e. Trimen says that *C.P. 2516,* cited by Hooker in Flora of British India and represented in Herb. Kew and Herb. Lindley, was of the old numbering and was cancelled subsequently. Hence *C.P. 2572* is selected as lectotype.

Specimens Examined. MONERAGALA DISTRICT: Bibile, *Armstrong s.n.* (PDA), *Jayaweera 2019* (PDA). PUTTALAM DISTRICT: Puttalam, Aug. 1883, *s. coll. s.n.* (PDA). KURUNEGALA DISTRICT: Doluwakanda, Aug. 1959, *Jayaweera 2020* (PDA), Aug. 1959, *Jayaweera 2185* (PDA), Sept. 1960, *Jayaweera 1 (3)* (AMES). COLOMBO DISTRICT: Mirigama, July 1904, *Tomlin s.n.* (PDA). LOCALITY UNKNOWN: *s. coll.* *C.P. 2516* (K); *C.P. 2572* (AMES, PDA, lectotype); *s. coll. s.n.* (AMES).

8. Oberonia recurva Lindl., Bot. Reg. 25: 14, Misc. 8. 1839; Trimen, Handb. Fl. Ceylon 4: 137. 1898.—**Fig. 8.**

Oberonia setifera Lindl., Fol. Orch. Oberonia 3. 1859.
Oberonia gardneriana Thw., Enum. Pl. Zeyl. 296. 1861.
Malaxis setifera Reichb. f. in Walp. Ann. 6: 210. 1861.
Malaxis recurva Reichb. f. in Walp. Ann. 6: 212. 1861.

Tufted epiphyte with very short, non-pseudobulbous, compressed stems. Leaves laterally compressed, ensiform, equitant, distichous, 1.8–6 × 0.5–0.9 cm, nearly straight, fleshy, acute, veins obscure, bases confluent with the stem. Flowers reddish-brown, 1.4 mm broad, in obscurely whorled fascicles along slender, decurved, dense-flowered, spiciform racemes which measure 1.5–6.5 cm in length; peduncle short, terete, adnate to a small upper leaf, clothed in ovate, acuminate, appressed bracts; floral bracts 1.3 × 0.4 mm, lanceolate, acuminate and subcrenulate; dorsal sepal 0.6 × 0.44 mm, broadly ovate and obtuse; lateral sepals 0.8 × 0.54 mm, also broadly ovate, subacute or obtuse and reflexed; petals 0.46–0.6 × 0.26–0.28 mm, obovate-oblong, obtuse, reflexed and irregularly crenate; lip superior, 0.84–1 × 0.9 mm, 3-lobed, margin irregularly crenate, lateral lobes orbicular, midlobe 2-lobulate and broadly obcordate; column 0.42 mm high, 0.36 mm broad at the top, tapering to a narrow neck at the base. Anther terminal, 2-loculed, incumbent, 0.2 × 0.28 mm; pollinia 4, waxy, obovoid, cohering in two pairs, one of each pair slightly smaller; larger pollinia 0.22 × 0.14 mm and the smaller ones 0.2 × 0.12 mm. Ovary with pedicel 0.9 mm long.

D i s t r. Very rare, on trees in the tropical wet evergreen forests extending to subtropical montane forests from 548 to 1829 m alt. Ambagamuwa, Laggala, Maturata, Hakgala, etc. At Ambagamuwa it was found growing on *Turpinia malabarica* Gamble and at Laggala on *Canthium dicoccum* Merr. Also in India from Bombay to Kerala.

E c o l. Flowers January, February and August.

I l l u s t r. Hook., Ic. Pl. 18: pl. 1784, fig. A. 1888; PDA, drawing from *C.P. 593.*

N o t e. Herb. Lindley contains Dalzel's collection from S. Konkan. This species is distinguished by the recurved spiciform racemes and 3-lobed irregularly crenate lip.

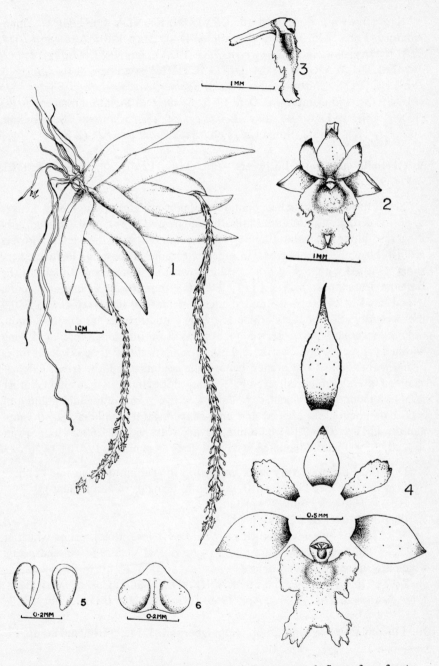

Fig. 8. *Oberonia recurva* Lindl. 1, plant with inflorescences. 2, flower from front. 3, lip and column from side. 4, bract, sepals, petals and lip spread out from front, column from inside. 5, pollinia. 6, operculum from inside.

Specimens Examined. CEYLON, KANDY DISTRICT: Ambagamuwa, Feb. 1846, *s. coll. C.P. 593* (PDA), May 1961, *Jayaweera 2034, 2178* (PDA), Jan. 1960, *Jayaweera 2033* (PDA), Jan. 1960, *Jayaweera 1 (2)* (AMES). NUWARA ELIYA DISTRICT: Hakgala, Apr. 1914, *Bryce & Petch s.n.* (PDA); Pattipola, Nov. 1973, *Sohmer, Jayasuriya and Eliezer 8546* (PDA, US); Pidurutalagala, Oct. 1975, *Sohmer & Sumithraarachchi 10193* (PDA, US). INDIA: Bombay, *Loddiges s.n.* (K, holotype); S. Konkan, *Dalzel 38* (K); Kerala, Bonuckad, Feb. 1913, *Rama Rao 826* (K).

9. Oberonia dolabrata Jayaweera, Bot. Mus. Leafl. 20 (4): 96–97. 1963. —Fig. 9.

Small tufted epiphyte with compressed, non-pseudobulbous stems. Leaves 3, fleshy, distichous, equitant, laterally compressed, 1.3–1.7 × 0.3–0.5 cm, oblong or oblong-lanceolate, acute, bases confluent with the stem. Flowers reddish-brown, 1.3 mm across, in suberect racemes 4 cm long. Peduncle very short, covered with sterile bracts right down to the base and adnate to the topmost leaf; floral bracts 1.8–2.3 × 0.7–0.8 mm, ovate acuminate, acute; dorsal sepal 1–1.4 × 0.56–0.8 mm, ovate, acute; lateral sepals 0.6–0.8 × 0.7–0.9 mm, broadly and obliquely orbicular-ovate, obtuse; petals 1.2 × 0.36–0.4 mm, oblong-lanceolate, subacute, ciliate, appressed on the dorsal sepal and lying within it; lip superior, sessile, 0.6 × 0.72 mm, fleshy, 3-lobed; lateral lobes cylindrical-subulate and arched behind the column; midlobe trifid, hatchet-shaped, lateral lobules diverging; column globular, 0.2 × 0.26 mm. Anther terminal, incumbent, 2-loculed; pollinia 4, in two pairs, individual pollinia of each pair unequal, appressed and club-shaped, larger pollinia 0.2 × 0.1 mm and the smaller ones 0.14 × 0.06 mm. Ovary with pedicel 1.6 mm long. Fruit stalked, 2.3 × 0.9 mm diameter.

Distr. Endemic. Very rare, on trees in the submontane or mid-country tropical wet evergreen forests at 1,288 m alt. Rangala (Corbet's Gap).

Ecol. Flowers January–April.

Ill. Bot. Mus. Leafl. 20 (4): pl. 12. 1963.

Note. This species is allied to *Oberonia tenuis* Lindl. from which it differs in the small size of the plant, ovate dorsal sepal and ciliated petals which are subacute at their apices.

Specimens Examined. KANDY DISTRICT: Corbet's Gap, Mar. 1960, *Jayaweera 2142* (PDA), Apr. 1960, *Jayaweera 2160* (PDA, holotype).

10. Oberonia scyllae Lindl., Fol. Orch. Oberonia 5. 1859; Trimen, Handb. Fl. Ceylon 4: 139. 1898.—Fig. 10.

Malaxis scyllae Reichb. f. in Walp. Ann. 6: 213. 1861.

Tufted epiphyte with very short, compressed, non-pseudobulbous stems.

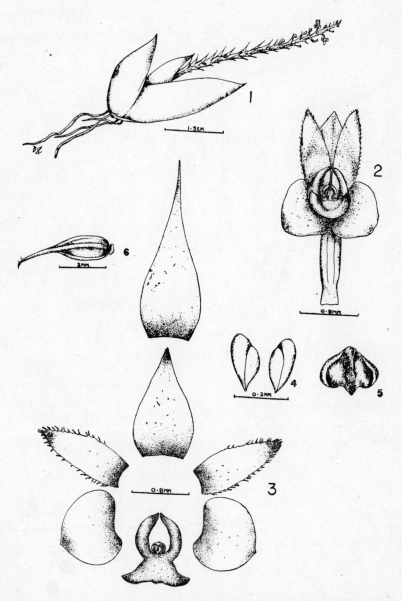

Fig. 9. *Oberonia dolabrata* Jayaweera. 1, plant with inflorescence. 2, flower from front. 3, bract, sepals, petals, lip and column spread out from front. 4, pollinia. 5, operculum from inside, magnified. 6, fruit.

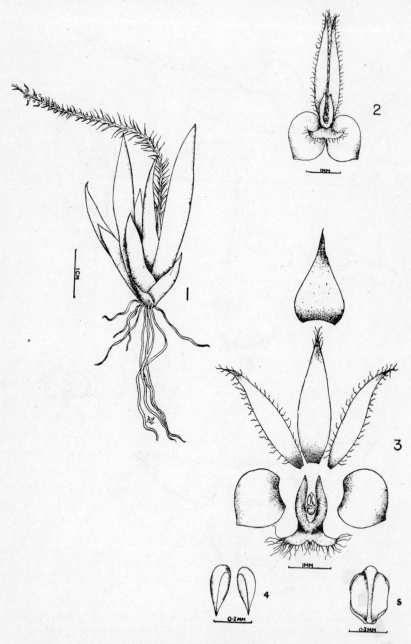

Fig. 10. *Oberonia scyllae* Lindl. 1, plant with inflorescence. 2, flower from front. 3, bract, sepals, petals and lip spread out from front, column from inside. 4, pollinia. 5, operculum from inside.

Leaves few, distichous, equitant, fleshy, laterally compressed, 2.2–3.5 cm ×
3.7–5.5 mm, acute, base confluent with the stem, veins obscure. Flowers reddish-brown, 1.8 mm across in obscurely whorled, spiciform racemes, conspicuous by the claw-like dorsal sepal and petals; floral bracts broadly ovate,
acuminate-acute, 1.9–2 × 0.9–1 mm; dorsal sepal 2.9–3.3 × 0.74 mm, lanceolate, acuminate, acute, ciliate at the apex; lateral sepals 1.1–1.4 × 1.3–1.4 mm,
orbicular and obtuse; petals 2.8–3.1 × 0.5–0.56 mm, lanceolate, acuminate,
acute, ciliate; lip 1.4–1.7 mm, lateral lobes erect, parallel, rising above the
rostrum, fleshy, more or less cylindrical, subulate, surrounding the column
except at the top, the midlobe also fleshy, lunate, trifid, the lateral lobules
larger and diverging from each other, ciliate; rostrum very small, at the
base of the lateral lobes of the lip. Anther terminal, incumbent, 2-loculed,
0.3 × 0.22 mm; pollinia 4 in two pyriform pairs, 0.26 × 0.12 mm; smaller pollinium of each pair strongly appressed to the larger one. Ovary with pedicel
0.64 mm long.

D i s t r. Endemic. Very rare, on trees in the submontane or mid-country
tropical wet evergreen forests extending to the subtropical montane forests.
Rangala, Maturata, Elephant Plains, East Matale and Hunnasgiriya.

E c o l. Flowers January–May. At Rangala (Corbet's Gap) it was epiphytic on *Kendrickia walkeri* (Wight) Hook. f. ex Trimen.

I l l u s t r. Hook., Ic. Pl. 18: pl. 1781. 1888; PDA, drawing from *C.P.
3124.*

N o t e. This is a very singular plant. The dorsal sepal and the two petals
being equal and similar, curve upwards and inwards like the beak of a bird
whilst the orbicular hyaline lateral sepals resemble a globose pouch at the base
of the flower. The minute lip is very much like that of *Oberonia tenuis*, the
lateral lobes resembling a pair of horns.

S p e c i m e n s E x a m i n e d. KANDY DISTRICT: Maturata, Apr.
1804, *s. coll. C.P. 3124* (K); Rangala, Feb. 1960, 1288 m alt., *Jayaweera 1 (9)*
(AMES).

11. Oberonia claviloba Jayaweera, Bot. Mus. Leafl. 20 (4): 98–101. 1963.
—Fig. 11.

Tufted epiphyte with very short, compressed, non-pseudobulbous stems.
Leaves 4 or 5, distichous, equitant, laterally compressed, not fleshy, 4–6.5 ×
0.3–0.6 cm, straight or subfalcate, acute, veins obscure, bases confluent with
the stem. Flowers brown in obscurely whorled, spiciform, erect racemes, 6.8
cm long, apical flowers opening first, followed by the lower flowers progressively downwards, buds at the very top not opening. Peduncle 2 cm long, adnate to the uppermost linear, acuminate, arched leaf; lower bracts sterile.
Flowers 1.1 mm across; floral bracts 1.2–1.6 × 0.4–0.5 mm, ovate, acuminate,
acute, margin slightly and distantly serrate; dorsal sepal 1 × 0.46–0.54 mm,

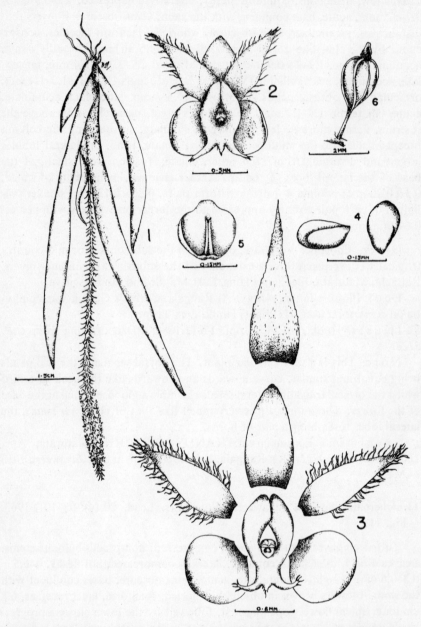

Fig. 11. *Oberonia claviloba* Jayaweera. 1, plant with inflorescence. 2, flower from front. 3, bract, sepals, petals and lip spread out from front. 4, pollinia from inside and back. 5, operculum from inside. 6, fruit.

oblong-ovate or oblong-lanceolate, obtuse; lateral sepals 0.6×0.76 mm, orbicular, rounded; petals 1.1–1.2 mm long, 0.36 mm broad, lanceolate, spreading, acute, ciliate, almost shaggy; lip 1.2 mm, fleshy; lateral lobes 0.8 mm, clavate, overlapping each other behind the rostrum, midlobe trifid, and ciliated at their apices, lateral lobules 0.3 mm, curving outwards, acuminate, midlobule 0.1 mm long, triangular, acute; column very small, 0.2×0.16 mm. Anther terminal, incumbent, 0.16×0.24 mm, 2-loculed; pollinia 4, cohering in two pyriform pairs, each pair 0.14×0.08 mm, consisting of a larger polli-nium and a smaller one, appressed, fused laterally. Ovary with pedicel 0.6 mm long. Fruit a minute globular or obovate, stalked capsule, 1.6×1.2 mm.

D i s t r. Endemic. Very rare, on trees in the transitional jungle between the tropical wet evergreen forests and the submontane or mid-country tropi-cal wet evergreen forests at 579 m alt. Ambagamuwa.

E c o l. Flowers December.

I l l. Bot. Mus. Leafl. 20 (4): pl. 13. 1963.

N o t e. This species differs from the others in the thin subfalcate leaves, ciliated petals, club-shaped arching lateral lobes of the lip and the ciliated apices of the trifid midlobe.

S p e c i m e n s   E x a m i n e d. KANDY DISTRICT: Ambagamuwa, Dec. 1969, *Jayaweera 2144* (PDA, holotype).

12. Oberonia fornicata Jayaweera, Bot. Mus. Leafl. 20 (4): 106–108. 1963. —Fig. 12.

Tufted epiphyte with compressed, non-pseudobulbous stems. Whole plant 3–3.5 cm high. Leaves few, reddish-green, fleshy, distichous, equitant, later-ally compressed, short, oblong-ensiform, 1.5–2.5×0.5–0.7 cm, acute, bases confluent with the stem. Flowers greenish-brown with a very pale coral lip, in long drooping racemes, 14 cm long, the basal bracts sterile. Peduncle 1.5 cm long, bracteate almost to the base. Flowers in distant, whorled fascicles on a very slender rachis; floral bracts ovate, 1.2–1.26×0.56–0.7 mm, obtuse and entire; dorsal sepal 1.4×0.8 mm, ovate, acute, margin ciliate; lateral sepals 1×0.9 mm, orbicular-oblong, margih entire or slightly denticulate; petals lanceolate, 1.4×0.54 mm, acuminate, acute, ciliate; lip shorter than sepals or about the same length as lateral sepals, 3-lobed; lateral lobes linear, falcate, ascending, forming an arc round the column; midlobe trifid, the two lateral lobules subulate, diverging, midlobule short and blunt; column glo-bular, 0.36 mm high, 0.3 mm broad. Anther terminal, incumbent, 0.24×0.3 mm, 2-loculed; pollinia 4 in two pairs, one in each pair larger than the other; larger pollinia 0.24×0.14 mm, one face flattened and fitting in the smaller one; smaller pollinia 0.2×0.8 mm and disc-shaped. Ovary with pedicel 1.7 mm long.

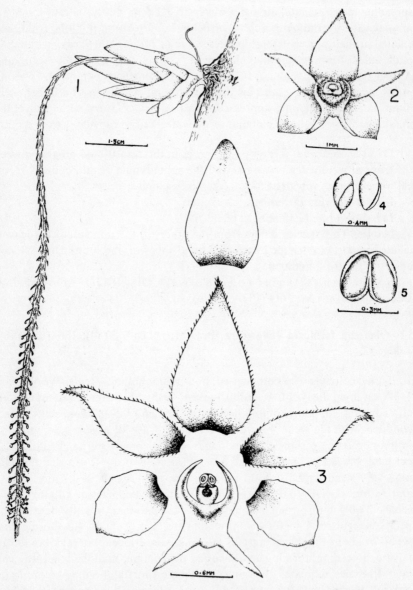

Fig. 12. *Oberonia fornicata* Jayaweera. 1, plant with inflorescence. 2, flower from front. 3, bract, sepals, petals, lip and column with operculum flapped over from front. 4, pollinia. 5, operculum from inside.

D i s t r. Endemic. Very rare, on trees in the submontane or mid-country tropical wet evergreen forests at 1288 m alt. Rangala (Corbet's Gap).

E c o l. Flowers October.

I l l. Bot. Mus. Leafl. 20 (4): pl. 16. 1963.

N o t e. This species does not appear to have any close allies. It is distinguished by the ciliated dorsal sepal and petals and the lip partly resembling *Oberonia wallie-silvae* and partly *Oberonia weragamaensis*.

S p e c i m e n s E x a m i n e d. KANDY DISTRICT: Rangala, *Jayaweera 2025* (PDA, holotype).

13. Oberonia wallie-silvae Jayaweera, Bot. Mus. Leafl. 20 (4): 101–103. 1963. —Fig. 13.

Tufted epiphyte with compressed non-pseudobulbous stems. Leaves distichous, fleshy, equitant, laterally compressed, 2–5.2 × 0.4–0.7 cm, ensiform, decurved, acuminate, acute, bases confluent with the stem, veins obscure. Flowers very small, reddish-brown, 1.2 mm across in spiciform racemes measuring about 10 cm in length. Peduncle closely covered with sterile bracts right down to the base; floral bracts 2 × 0.9 mm, ovate, acuminate, acute; dorsal sepal 1.2 × 0.74 mm, ovate, acute; lateral sepals 0.8 × 1 mm, obliquely suborbicular, obtuse; petals lanceolate, 1 × 0.36 mm, acute, ciliate; lip 1 mm long, thick; lateral lobes linear, falcate, horseshoe shaped round the column; midlobe thick, 1 mm broad, bifid, sometimes trifid, lateral lobules bluntly subulate and diverging; column very small, globular, at the base of the lateral lobes. Anther terminal, incumbent, 2-loculed; 0.24 × 0.3 mm; pollinia 4, waxy, in two pairs, individuals of each pair unequal; each pair of pollinia 0.24 × 0.1 mm, pyriform. Ovary with pedicel 1.4 mm long.

D i s t r. Endemic. Very rare, on trees in the submontane or mid-country tropical wet evergreen forests at 1288 m alt. Rangala.

E c o l. Flowers Februray–March.

I l l. Bot. Mus. Leafl. 20 (4): pl. 14. 1963.

N o t e. This species does not appear to have and close allies. It is distinguished from others by its ensiform, decurved, acuminate leaves, lanceolate and ciliated petals, linear falcate lateral lobes and the bifurcated diverging midlobe of the lip.

S p e c i m e n s E x a m i n e d. KANDY DISTRICT: Rangala, Mar. 1960, *Jayaweera 2143* (PDA, holotype).

14. Oberonia weragamaensis Jayaweera, Bot. Mus. Leafl. 20 (4): 103–106. 1063.—Fig. 14.

Tufted epiphyte with very short, compressed non-pseudobulbous stems. Leaves 4 or 5, distichous, laterally compressed, equitant, fleshy, 2–8 × 0.3–0.6

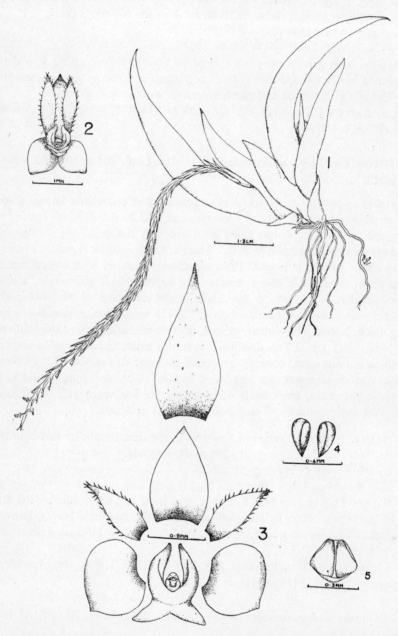

Fig. 13. *Oberonia wallie-silvae* Jayaweera. 1, plant with inflorescence. 2, flower from front. 3, bract, sepals, petals, lip and column spread out from front. 4, pollinia. 5, operculum from inside.

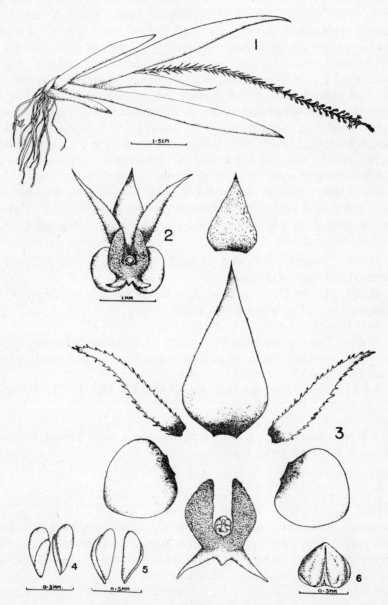

Fig. 14. *Oberonia weragamaensis* Jayaweera. 1, plant with inflorescence. 2, flower from front. 3, bract, sepals, petals, lip and column spread out from front, magnified. 4, young pollinia. 5, older pollinia. 6, operculum from inside.

cm, lanceolate or ensiform, acute, bases confluent with the stem and veins obscure. Flowers reddish-brown, in whorled racemes 5.6 cm long, first flowers to open located a little way below the terminal end and then flowers opening progressively downwards, terminal flowers not opening. Flowers 2 mm long, from the tip of the dorsal sepal to the apex of the lip and 1.2 mm across; floral bracts 1×0.52 mm, ovate, acute, margin slightly irregular; dorsal sepal 1.2×0.52 mm broad, ovate, acuminate, acute; lateral sepals 0.6×0.74 mm, suborbicular, rounded; petals longer than sepals, 1.4×0.28 mm, linear-lanceolate; acuminate, ciliate or denticulate; lip 1.2×0.8 mm; lateral lobes 0.7 mm long, subtriangular, erect, fleshy, parallel, papillate, blunt at the apex, broadening towards the middle; midlobe trifid, the lateral lobules subulate, acuminate, diverging and looped back posteriorly in the open flower, the midlobule triangular and much shorter; column short, 0.4 mm high, 0.36 mm broad. Anther terminal, incumbent, 0.24×0.32 mm, 2-loculed; pollinia 4, waxy, cohering in two pyriform pairs; larger pollinia 0.3×0.12 mm, oblong, smaller ones 0.24×0.08 mm and disc-shaped. Ovary with pedicel 0.8 mm long, 0.3 mm diameter.

D i s t r. Endemic. Very rare, on small trees in the tropical wet evergreen forests at 210 m alt. Ratnapura.

E c o l. Flowers October–November. It was found epiphytic on *Wormia triquetra* Rottb., *Celtis wightii* Planch., etc.

I l l. Bot. Mus. Leafl. 20 (4): pl. 16. 1963.

N o t e. This species differs from others in the linear-lanceolate, denticulate petals, subtriangular, erect, parallel lateral lobes of the lip and diverging, subulate, lateral lobules of the midlobe.

S p e c i m e n s E x a m i n e d. RATNAPURA DISTRICT: Weragama, *Jayaweera 2037* (PDA, holotype).

15. Oberonia tenuis Lindley, Fol. Orch. Oberonia 3. 1859; Trimen, Handb. Fl. Ceylon 4: 138. 1898.—**Fig. 15.**

Malaxis tenuis Reichb. f. in Walp. Ann. 6: 211. 1861.

Tufted epiphyte with short, compressed, non-pseudobulbous stems. Leaves distichous equitant, laterally compressed, $4–9 \times 0.5–1.2$ cm, ensiform-lanceolate, thin, acuminate-acute, bases confluent with the stem. Flowers light reddish-brown with a conspicuous, dark chocolate-brown lip, 1.6 mm broad, in long, curved racemes 10 cm long; peduncle inconspicuous; floral bracts 3×0.8 mm, ovate, acuminate, acute and long-drawn-out; dorsal sepal ovate-oblong, 1.4×0.8 mm, acute, reflexed; lateral sepals 0.9×0.8 mm, orbicular, obtuse; petals lanceolate, 1.2×0.34 mm, acute or subacute, reflexed; lip 1.6×1 mm; the lateral lobes linear, ascending, forming an arc round the column but not overlapping or meeting; midlobe trifid, neck long, the lateral lobules acuminate and diverging, midlobule triangular, blunt and obtuse;

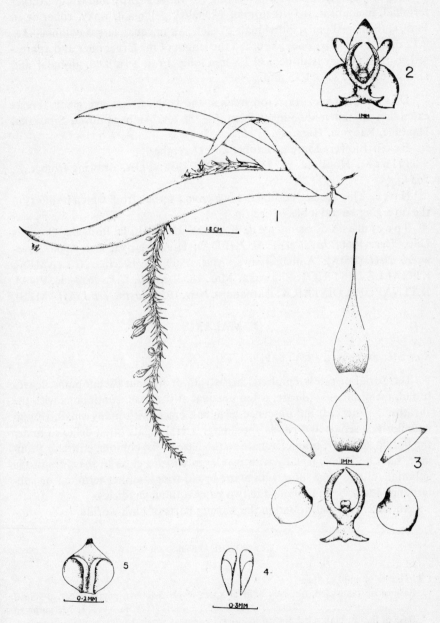

Fig. 15. *Oberonia tenuis* Lindl. 1, plant with inflorescence and fruits. 2, flower from front. 3, bract, sepals, petals and lip spread out from front. 4, pollinia. 5, operculum from inside.

column very short, rostellum projecting forwards slightly and trifid. Ahther terminal, incumbent, 0.3×0.26 mm, 2-loculed; pollinia 4, waxy, cohering in long, club-shaped pairs, individuals of each pair unequal, larger pollinia 0.3×0.12 mm, the smaller ones about 2/3 the length of the larger ones and appressed to them; ovary with pedicel 1.8 mm long. Fruit a stalked, globular and shining capsule, 2.5×1.75 mm.

D i s t r. Endemic. Rare, on trees in the tropical wet evergreen forests extending to the mid-country from 548 m alt. Ambagamuwa, Sitawaka, Hantane, Rangala, Hunnasgiriya etc.

E c o l. Flowers March, October and December.

I l l u s t r. Hook. Ic. Pl. 18: pl. 1779B. 1888; PDA, drawing from *C.P. 2654*.

N o t e. This species is similar to *Oberonia scyllae* from which it differs in the diverging lateral lobes of the lip.

S p e c i m e n s E x a m i n e d. KANDY DISTRICT: Rangala, Corbet's Gap, Dec. 1960, *Jayaweera 2032* (PDA); Hunnasgiriya, Oct. 1960, *Jayaweera 2031* (PDA); Ambagamuwa, Mar. 1960, *Jayaweera 1 (6)* (AMES). KEGALLE DISTRICT: Sitawaka, Mar. 1853, *s. coll. C.P. 2654* (K, PDA). RATNAPURA DISTRICT: Ratnapura, Nov. 1959, *Jayaweera 1 (6)* (AMES).

2. MALAXIS

Solander ex Swartz, Prod. 8: 119. 1788.

Terrestrial or rarely epiphytic herbs with or without pseudobulbs; leaves broad, membranous, plicate, often unequal at the base, continuous with the sheaths, 5–7-nerved; inflorescence terminal, erect, with many small, resupinate flowers; sepals and petals spreading, lateral sepals often deflexed under the lip; lip superior, sessile, adnate to the base of the column, entire or pectinate, base hollowed, usually with two large auricles close to the sides of the column; column very short with short broad wings; anther terminal or subterminal, incumbent; pollinia 4 in two pairs without caudicles.

About 275 species, found in the warmer parts of both worlds.

KEY TO THE SPECIES

1 Lip entire or bifid at apex
  2 Base of lip biauricled, obtusely bifid at apex; sepals 5-veined; petals linear, 3-veined
    ....**1. M. purpurea**
  2 Base of lip not biauricled, lip subreniform, 5-veined; sepals 3-veined; petals lanceolate, 1-veined...**2. M. discolor**
1 Lip pectinate
  3 Lip 3-toothed or 3-lobed...**3. M. latifolia**
  3 Lip more than 3-toothed

4 Leaves ovate, stem elongate
  5 Arms of the column short or absent; leaves 7-veined; petals lanceolate, 1-veined; lip
    subquadrate, 9–13-toothed......................................**4. M. versicolor**
  5 Arms of the column spreading; leaves 5-veined; petals linear, obtuse; lip subquadrate-
    subreniform..**5. M. densiflora**
4 Leaves lanceolate, undulate, 3-veined..............................**6. M. lancifolia**

1. Malaxis purpurea (Lindl.) Kuntze, Rev. Gen. Bot. 2: 673. 1891.—Fig. 16.

Microstylis purpurea Lindl., Gen. et Sp. Orch. 20. 1830;
    Trimen, Handb. Fl. Ceylon 4: 140. 1898.

Terrestrial herb with somewhat fleshy fibrous roots; stem 7.5–10 cm tall, stout, base slightly pseudobulbous. Leaves 4–6, petioled, 7.5–12.5 × 3.5–5.5 cm, oval to suborbicular, acute or acuminate, 5- or 6-veined, base unequal. Flowers dark purple, 6–10 mm long from the dorsal sepal to the tip of the lip, in many-flowered, terminal racemes; peduncle 9–25 cm long, quadrangular, with many reflexed sterile bracts; rachis over 4 cm long; floral bracts 6–6.7 × 2 mm, lanceolate, acuminate, reflexed, 1-veined; dorsal sepal 5–5.5 × 2.5–2.8 mm, oblong-ovate, obtuse, 5-veined, margins reflexed; lateral sepals 4–4.5 × 2.5–2.8 mm, oblong, obtuse or rounded, 5-veined; petals 4.5–4.9 × 1 mm, linear, truncate, 3-veined, margins reflexed; lip superior, fleshy, 7–7.5 × 5–5.4 mm, concave, tip narrowed, obtusely bifid, basal auricles narrowing upwards, obtuse, sides dilated; column very short, adnate to the base of the lip, arms obscure. Anther terminal, incumbent, 0.36 × 0.4 mm, 2-loculed; pollinia 4, unequal, 0.3 mm long, ovoid, in two pairs, one of each pair smaller. Fruit 1 cm long, clavate, shortly pedicelled.

D i s t r. Very rare, usually growing by streams under the shade of trees in the tropical wet evergreen forests in the low country up to 457 m alt. Pasdun Korale and Mapalagama near Galle. One specimen however was collected at Udawattekelle, Kandy, in the mid-country. Also in Java and Philippine Islands.

E c o l. Flowers June–August.

I l l u s t r. PDA, drawing.

S p e c i m e n s E x a m i n e d. CEYLON, KANDY DISTRICT: Udawattekelle, Kandy, Aug. 1960, *Jayaweera 2 (1)* (AMES). KALUTARA DISTRICT: Weligala, Jun. 1973, *Waas 1307* (PDA). GALLE DISTRICT: Godakande, Jul. 1975, *Wheeler & Balakrishnan 12621* (PDA, US); Pasdun Korale, near Hiniduma falls, Aug. 1865, *s. coll. C.P. 3786* (K, PDA). JAVA: *Zollinger 2536* (AMES). PHILIPPINE ISLANDS: Sept. 1907, *Kranzlin s.n.* (AMES).

N o t e. Macrae's collection at Oakes Ames Orchid Herbarium contains an inflorescence only without any part of the plant.

2. Malaxis discolor (Lindl.) Kuntze, Rev. Gen. Bot. 2: 673. 1891.—Fig. 17.

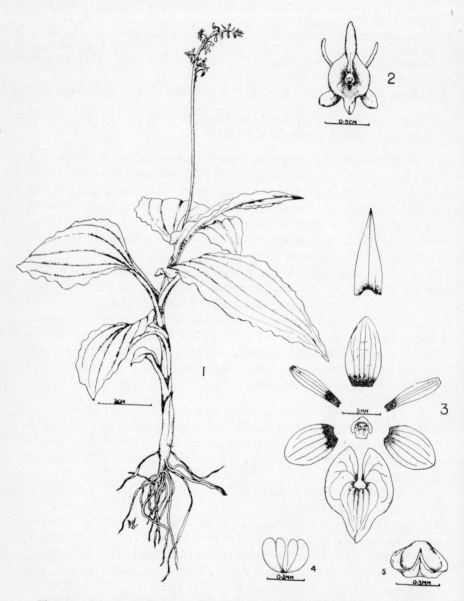

Fig. 16. *Malaxis purpurea* (Lindl.) Kuntze. 1, plant with inflorescence. 2, flower from front. 3, bract, sepals, petals and lip spread out from front, top of the column from inside. 4, pollinia. 5, operculum from inside.

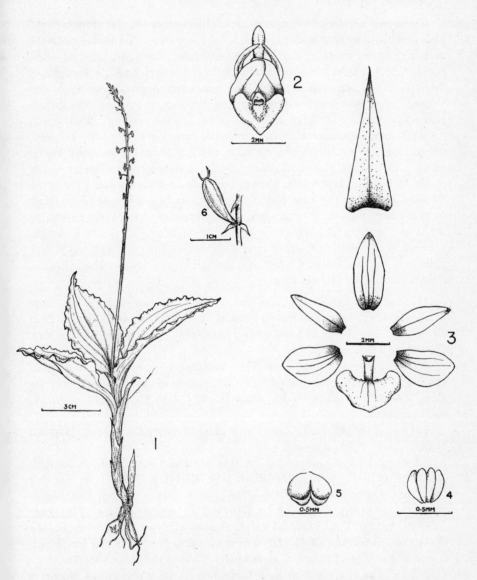

Fig. 17. *Malaxis discolor* (Lindl.) Kuntze. 1, plant with inflorescence. 2, flower from front. 3, bract, sepals, and petals spread out from front, lip and rostrum natural position from front. 4, pollinia. 5, operculum from inside. 6, fruit.

Microstylis discolor Lindl., Gen. et Sp. Orch. 20. 1830; Trimen, Handb. Fl. Ceylon 4: 141. 1898.

Terrestrial herb with stout, non-pscudobulbous stems and filiform roots. Leaves with sheathing bases; lamina 5.5–7.5 × 3–4 cm, continuous with the sheathing bases, ovate or oval, plicate, acuminate, undulate, unequal-sided, purplish, 5–7-veined, veins prominent below. Flowers small, resupinate, 4 mm long, 3 mm across in terminal, long peduncled racemes, younger flowers yellow, fading into purplish-red; peduncle purplish, 6 cm long, the flower-bearing portion 3.3 cm long and light green; bracts persistent; floral bracts 3.5 × 1.2 mm, subulate, reflexed, acuminate, tapering to a point, 1-veined; dorsal sepal 3.6 × 1.5 mm, oblong-ovate, obtuse, decurved, 3-veined; lateral sepals 2.6 × 1.5 mm, obliquely oblong, obtuse, 3-veined, reflexed under the lip; petals 3 × 0.8 mm, lanceolate, obtuse, 1-veined; lip subreniform, 1.6 × 3 mm, 5-veined adnate to the base of the column, apex blunt, obtuse or rounded, margin entire; column 1.3 mm high, slightly broader at the apex, narrowing below and bending forward a little with long obtuse projecting arms. Anther terminal, incumbent, 0.32 × 0.46 mm, 2-loculed; pollinia 4, ovoid, waxy, each pollinium 0.3 × 0.08 mm. Ovary with pedicel 3 mm long, ribbed. Fruit a clavate capsule, 0.7–1.1 cm long.

D i s t r. Endemic. Rather common, along with other herbs under shade of trees in moist, warm and humid tropical wet evergreen forests up to 1829 m alt. in the Central and Sabaragamuwa provinces. It was introduced to Kew Gardens in 1862.

E c o l. Flowers July–August. The amount of sunlight it receives is about 57 per cent of the normal light. Other ground orchids found growing along with it were *Eulophia sanguinea* Hook. f. and *Malaxis densiflora* (A. Rich.) Kuntze.

I l l u s t r. Wight, Ic. Pl. Ind. Or. 5: pl. 1631. 1851; Curtis, Bot. Mag. 89: pl. 5403. 1863; PDA, drawing.

S p e c i m e n s E x a m i n e d. ANURADHAPURA DISTRICT: Ritigala, Dec. 1975, *Bernardi 16114* (PDA, US). KANDY DISTRICT: Corbet's Gap, Aug. 1960, *Jayaweera 2016* (PDA); Ambagamuwa, Aug. 1960, *Jayaweera 2 (2)* (AMES). KALUTARA DISTRICT: Denihena, Aug. 1976, *Waas 1888* (PDA, US). GALLE DISTRICT: Hiniduma, Nov. 1969, *Cramer 1764* (PDA, US). LOCALITY UNKNOWN: in 1829, *Macrae 3* (K, lectotype); *s. coll. C.P. 2375* (K), *s. coll. C.P. 3698* (K, PDA), *s. coll. s.n.* (AMES).

N o t e. The type sheet at Kew herbarium contains collections *Macrae 3* and *C.P. 2375*. Macrae's collection is selected as the lectotype. This species is allied to *Microstylis plantaginea* Steud. except for the edenticulate lip.

3. **Malaxis latifolia** Smith in Rees, Cyclop. 22: n3. 1813.—**Fig. 18.**

Dienia congesta Lindl., Bot. Reg. 10: sub. t. 825. 1824 in textu.

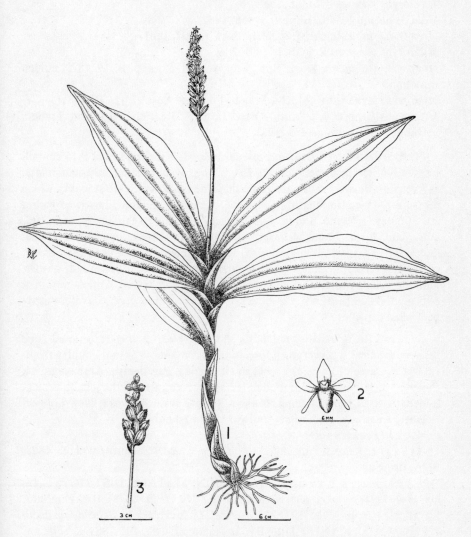

Fig. 18. *Malaxis latifolia* Smith, redrawn from a drawing in PDA. 1, plant with inflorescence. 2, flower from front. 3, fruits.

44 ORCHIDACEAE

Gastroglottis montana Blume, Bijdr. 397. 1825.
Crepidium flavescens Blume, ibid. 388.
Dienia fusca Lindl., Gen. et Sp. Orch. 22. 1830.
Microstylis flavescens Lindl., ibid. 20.
Malaxis plicata Roxb., Fl. Ind. 3: 456. 1832.
Microstylis fusca Reichb. f. in Walp. Ann. 6: 207. 1861.
Microstylis congesta Reichb. f., ibid. 206.
Microstylis trilobulata Kurz, Rep. Veg. Andam. 51, app. B. 19. 1870, nomen
    nudum.
Microstylis bernaysii F. Muell., Fragm. Phytogr. Austral. 11: 21. 1881.
Microstylis latifolia J.J. Smith, Orch. Java 6: 248. 1905; Alston in Trimen,
    Handb. Fl. Ceylon 6: 272. 1931.

Terrestrial herb with a stout, pseudobulbous base and stems 5–15 cm tall.
Leaves 3–6, sessile or petioled, 10–25 cm long, ovate or lanceolate-acuminate,
5–7 veined. Flowers dull purple, small, in dense-flowered stout spikes which
measure 8–15 cm in length; peduncle 15–25 cm long, stout, furrowed with a
few subulate reflexed bracts; floral bracts as long as the ovary, subulate-
lanceolate, lower bracts deflexed; dorsal sepal oblong, margins recurved;
lateral sepals larger, oblong, obtuse, deflexed; petals linear; lip ovate-oblong,
concave, with a fold under the column, 3-lobed; lateral lobes broad, obtuse;
midlobe small, ovate, obtuse; columnar arms short, erect. Anther terminal,
2-loculed, incumbent; pollinla 4, waxy. Fruits crowded, erect, clavate, shortly
pedicelled capsules.

D i s t r. Rare, usually under the shade of trees in the transitional zone
between tropical wet evergreen forests and submontane or mid-country tropical wet evergreen forests up to 915 m alt. Kandy, Peradeniya, Ambagamuwa,
Pussellawa, Hiniduma, Ramboda. It has become rarer in the localities mentioned. Also in India, Burma, Malaya, China, Java, Sumatra, New Guinea,
Celebes, Australia, Philippines and Andaman Islands.

E c o l. Flowers July.

I l l u s t r. King & Pantling, Ann. R. Bot. Gard. (Calcutta) 8: pl. 23. 1898;
PDA, drawing.

S p e c i m e n s E x a m i n e d. CEYLON, MATALE DISTRICT: Lagg-
ala, Dec. 1971, *Balakrishnan & Dassanayake 1143* (PDA, US); Illukkumbura,
Karakolagastenna, Dec. 1971, *Jayasuriya, Dassanayake & Balasubramaniam
429* (PDA, US). KANDY DISTRICT: Ambagamuwa, Jul. 1884, *s. coll. s.n.*
(PDA). HAMBANTOTA DISTRICT: Ruhuna National Park, Oct. 1968,
Mueller-Dombois 68102012 (PDA, US). INDIA: Khasia Hills, July 1850,
Hooker & Thomson 1872 (K). CHINA: Kwangtung, Naam Kevan Shan, Jan.
1935, *Tsang 2569* (AMES); Hong Kong, Tung Chung & vicinity, Jun. 1941,
Taam 2119 (AMES). HAINAN: Ta Hien, Jun. 1935, *Gressitt 91* (AMES).
JAVA: in Dec. 1936, *Brinkman 818* (AMES). BORNEO: N. Borneo, Kinabalu,

Aug. 1916, *Haslam* (AMES); Dallas, at 3300 ft. May 1933, *Carr 27366* (AMES). KAISER WILHELM ISLAND: Nov. 1908, *Schlechter 18855* (AMES). PHILIPPINE ISLANDS: Luzon. Bontoc Prov., May-July 1913, *Vanoverbergh 3678* (AMES); Laguna Prov., Aug. 1910, *Ramos 12085* (AMES), in July 1917, *Elmer 18013* (AMES); Sorsogon Prov., Sept. 1916, *Elmer 17233* (AMES); Palawan, Aug. 1947, *Ebalo & Conklin 1321* (AMES); Mindanao, Surigao, Sept. 1916, *Wenzel 1099* (AMES).

4. Malaxis versicolor (Lindl.) Abeywick., Ceylon J. Sci. Biol. Sci. 2 (a): 147. 1959.—Fig. 19.

Crepidium rheedii Blume, Bijdr. 387. 1825.
Malaxis rheedii Heyne ex Wall., Cat. sub. n. 1939. 1829.
Microstylis versicolor Lindl., Gen. et Sp. Orch. 21. 1830, non Wight.
Liparis intermedia A. Rich., Ann. Sc. Nat. Bot. 11. 15: 17. 1841.
Liparis priochilus Lodd., Bot. Cab. 18: pl. 1751. 1831.
Microstylis rheedii Wight, Ic. Pl. Ind. Or. 3 (2): 9 pl. 902. 1844–1845; Trimen, Handb. Fl. Ceylon 4: 141. 1898.

Terrestrial herb, stems 8–21 cm long, 1.5–2 cm diameter, pseudobulbous at length, annulate. Leaves 2 or 3, sessile, 6–10 × 3–5.5 cm, ovate or lanceolate, membranous, plicate, 7-veined, acute or acuminate, bases continued into purple-tinged sheaths about 6 cm long but not articulating with them, margins wavy. Flowers small, greenish-yellow to orange-yellow or purplish, 3.4 mm across, in terminal racemes; peduncle 4.5–7 cm long, 6-ribbed, purplish with a single leafy bract; flower-bearing portion 4–8 cm long, the length of the rachis between the peduncle and the oldest flower increasing with age but with persistent, deflexed bracts; floral bracts 3.6–5.6 × 1.4–2.1 mm, ovate-lanceolate or ovate-subulate, acuminate, acute, deflexed, 1-veined; dorsal sepal 3.3–4.6 × 1.2–1.3 mm, linear-oblong, obtuse, 3-veined; lateral sepals deflexed, 2.2–3 × 1.4–1.7 mm, obliquely oblong, obtuse, 3-veined; petals 2.8–3.8 × 0.94–1.06 mm, lanceolate, obliquely truncate, 1-veined; lip 1.6–1.9 × 2.5–3.2 mm, subquadrate, pectinate, 9–13-toothed, mid-tooth short, blunt and trifid at the apex; column 1.2 mm high, 0.8 mm broad at the top, with 2 suberect horns at the apex, narrowing towards the middle and again broadening towards the base. Anther terminal, 0.34 × 0.56 mm, 2-loculed; pollinia 4, cohering in two pairs, pyriform or obovoid, 0.3 × 0.1 mm, one of each pair slightly larger than the other. Fruit a pyriform or oblong-obovate capsule 0.7 × 0.4 cm.

Distr. Rather common, in shady places in the submontane or mid-country tropical wet evergreen forests extending to the subtropical montane forests between 396 and 1829 m alt. Ramboda, Nuwara Eliya, Muruthalawa, Dolosbage, Ambagamuwa, Kalutara etc. Also in South India.

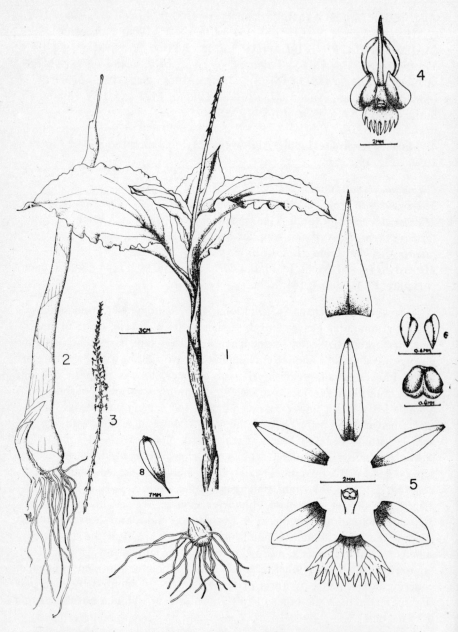

Fig. 19. *Malaxis versicolor* (Lindl.) Abeywick. 1, plant with the flowerless lower part of inflorescence, basal portion with roots separated. 2, old pseudobulb with new lateral shoot. 3, top of inflorescence. 4, flower from front. 5, bract, sepals, petals and lip spread out from front, tip of column from inside. 6, pollinia. 7, operculum from inside. 8, fruit.

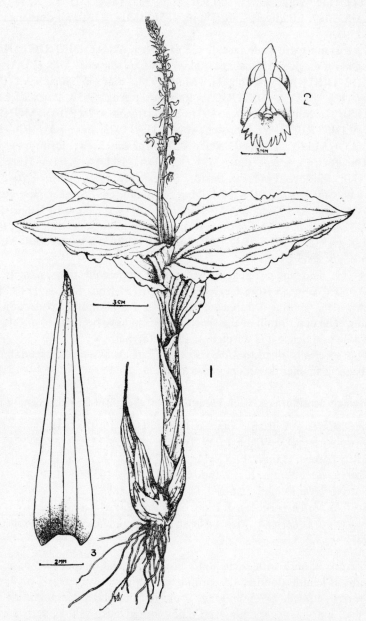

Fig. 20. *Malaxis versicolor* (Lindl.) Abeywick. 1, plant with inflorescence. 2, flower from front. 3, bract spread out from front.

E c o l. Flowers May–July.

I l l u s t r. Wight, Ic. Pl. Ind. Or. 3: pl. 902. 1844–5; Hook. f., Ic. Pl. 19: Pl. 1832. 1889; Loddiges, Cab. 18: pl. 1751. 1831; PDA, two drawings from *C.P. 2395.*

S p e c i m e n s E x a m i n e d. CEYLON, KANDY DISTRICT: Kandy, *Champion s.n.* (K); Dolosbage, May 1960, *Jayaweera 2015* (PDA). KE-GALLE DISTRICT: Kitulgala, May 1928, *J.M. de Silva s.n.* (PDA). NUWARA ELIYA DISTRICT: Ramboda, Aug. 1959, *Jayaweera 2 (5)* (AMES); Horton Plains, Dec. 1971, *Balakrishnan 412* (PDA). MONERA-GALA DISTRICT: Westminster Abbey, Dec. 1973, *Bernardi 16036* (PDA, US). LOCALITY UNKNOWN: 1829, *Macrae 2* (K, lectotype); 1847, *Gardner 844* (K), *s. coll. C.P. 2375* (K, PDA). INDIA: Khasia Hills; *Lobb 124* (K); Madhya Pradesh: Bastar State, July 1939, *Mooney 1042* (K); Bombay: *Gibson s.n.* (PDA); Malabar, Konkan, etc., *Stocks, Law* etc. *s.n.* (PDA); Karnataka: Canara & Mysore, *Law s.n.* (K); Coonoor: Nilgiris, June 1883, *Gamble 12001* (K), *Lobb s.n.* (K); Kodaikanal region: Sept. 1905, *Barber 7570* (K), 1832, *Wallich 1939* (K); Pulneys, 1897, *Bourne 371* (K); Madras, *Herb Wight 2063* (K).

N o t e. The type cover at Kew contains three collections, namely *Macrae 2* and *Champion* from Ceylon and *Lobb 124* from Khasia Hills. Herb. Lindley also contains a duplicate of *Macrae 2* and another collection from Ceylon. The description of the species seems to have been based on Macrae's collection and hence it is selected as the lectotype.

This species is allied to *Malaxis rheedii* but always small, pseudobulbous and bearing smaller flowers in dense spike.

5. Malaxis densiflora (A. Rich.) Kuntze, Rev. Gen. Bot. 2: 673. 1891.—Fig. 21.

Liparis densiflora A. Rich., Ann. Sc. Nat. Bot. 11. 15: 18. 1841.

Microstylis versicolor Wight, Ic. Pl. Ind. Or. 3 (2): 9, pl. 901. 1844–1845 (non-Lidl.); Trimen, Handb. Fl. Ceylon 4: 141. 1898.

Microstylis lutea Wight, Ic. Pl. Ind. Or. 5(1): 4, pl. 1632. 1851.

Microstylis bella Reichb. f., Gard. Chron. 25: 9. 1886.

Microstylis pratensis Ridley, J. Linn. Soc. Bot. 24: 344. 1888.

Microstylis densiflora (A. Rich.) Alston in Trimen, Handb. Fl. Ceylon 6: 272. 1931.

Terrestrial herb with stems 8–15 cm long, pseudobulbous at base; pseudobulbs at length globose, 1.5 cm diameter, annulate. Leaves 2 or 3, sessile or shortly petioled, 5–7.5 cm long, ovate to lanceolate, acuminate or acute, 5-veined, margins wavy. Flowers yellow or greenish-yellow, very small, in dense-flowered racemes which measure 5–10 cm in length; peduncle 2.5–7.5 cm long with a few deflexed, empty bracts; floral bracts about as long as the flower, lanceolate, deflexed; sepals linear-oblong, laterals deflexed, dorsal

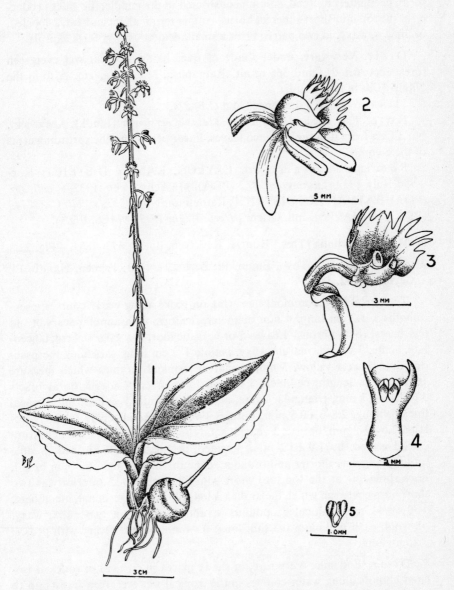

Fig. 21. *Malaxis densiflora* (A. Rich.). Kuntze, redrawn from a drawing of *C.P. 2743* in PDA. 1, plant with inflorescence and an old pseudobulb. 2, flower from the side. 3, flower from side with sepals and petals removed and showing inside of the lip and bract. 4, column from inside. 5, pollinia.

narrowest; petals linear, obtuse; lip subquadrate, short, cuneate or subreniform, pectinately toothed; column constricted in the middle, the sides produced at the top into short suberect horns. Anther terminal, incumbent, 2-loculed; pollinia 4, waxy, in two pairs. Fruit a small, pedicelled, pyriform capsule.

D i s t r. Very rare, under shade of trees in the tropical wet evergreen forests between 213 and 366 m alt. Ratnapura, Maskeliya, etc. Also in the Nilgiri Hills in South India.

I l l u s t r. PDA, 3 drawings from *C.P. 2743*.

N o t e. This species is allied to *Malaxis versicolor* (Lindl.) Abeywick., but differs from it in the 5-veined leaves, linear petals and the spreading arms of the column.

S p e c i m e n s E x a m i n e d. CEYLON, KANDY DISTRICT: Norwood, July 1932, *Lushington 9872* (PDA); Maskeliya, Feb. 1932, *s. coll. s.n.* (PDA). RATNAPURA DISTRICT: Ratnapura, Nov. 1853, *s. coll. C.P. 2743* (PDA). INDIA: Pen. Ind. Orient., *Herb. Wight 2943* (AMES, PDA).

6. Malaxis lancifolia (Thw.) Kuntze, Rev. Gen. Bot. 2: 673. 1891.—**Fig. 22.**

Microstylis lancifolia Thw., Enum. Pl. Zeyl. 297. 1861; Trimen, Handb. Fl. Ceylon 4: 142. 1898.

Terrestrial herb commonly growing on rocks along water courses; pseudobulbs 1–1.2 cm long, 4 mm diameter, fusiform with annular scars of old leaf bases; roots fibrous. Leaves 5 or 6, distichous, 4–8 × 0.6–0.9 cm, lanceolate, acute, 3-veined, margin waxy, petiole 1–2 cm long, sheathing the pseudobulb. Flowers yellow, 3 mm broad, in terminal racemes which measure 16–17 cm in length; peduncle 3.5–5 cm long, green, 4-edged; floral bracts 3.6–4.1 × 1.7 mm, triangular-ovate, acuminate, acute, 1-veined; dorsal sepal linear-oblong, 2.8–3 × 0.8 mm, obtuse, 1-veined; lateral sepals falcately oblong, 2.6 × 1.2 mm, obtuse, 3-veined; petals linear-oblong, 2.8 × 0.7 mm, truncate, 1-veined; lip 1.9 × 3.2 mm, 3-veined, pectinately 7–9 toothed: middle tooth triangular, shorter and broader; column 1.2 mm high, 0.5 mm broad, sides spreading at the top into short wings and projected anteriorly as two short horns between which the anther is lodged. Anther terminal, incumbent, 0.36 × 0.44 mm, 2-loculed; pollinia 4, almost equal, in two pairs, waxy, obovoid; each pollinium 0.3 mm long, 0.14 mm broad. Ovary with pedicel 3.2 mm long.

D i s t r. Endemic. Very rare, in shady places in crevices of rocks as isolated clumps along water-courses in the tropical wet evergreen forests up to 610 m alt. Kuruwita and Karawita Kande in Ratnapura, Rasagala, Balangoda, Sinharaja Forest, Kitulgala.

E c o l. Flowers March, September.

N o t e. The undulate lanceolate leaves, yellow flowers with the triangular-ovate, suberect bracts distinguish this species from the others.

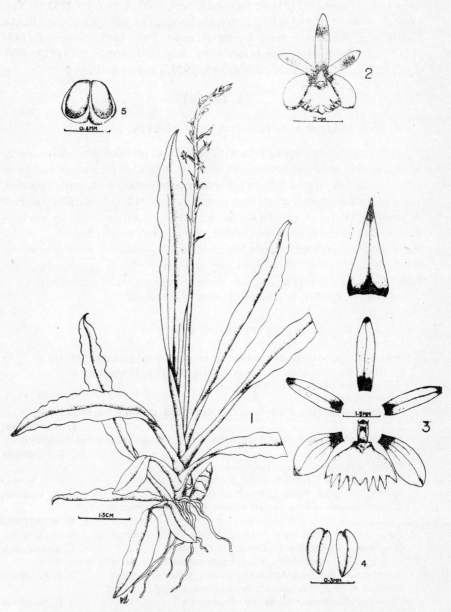

Fig. 22. *Malaxis lancifolia* (Thw.) Kuntze. 1, plant with inflorescence. 2, flower from front. 3, bract, sepals, petals and lip spread out from front, column from inside. 4, pollinia. 5, operculum from inside.

52 ORCHIDACEAE

Specimens Examined. RATNAPURA DISTRICT: Beraliya, May 1926, *Alston 2362* (PDA); Rasagala, Sept. 1895, *s. coll. s.n.* (PDA), Apr. 1960, *Jayaweera 2 (6)* (AMES); Sinharaja Forest, Jan. 1892, *s. coll. s.n.* (PDA); Hettikanda, Bambarabotuwa Forest Reserve, Feb. 1969, *Hoogland 11434* (PDA, US); Dotaluoya, Bambarabotuwa, July 1971, *Meijer 868* (PDA, US). KEGALLE DISTRICT: Kitulgala, Feb. 1924, *Livera s.n.* (PDA).

3. LIPARIS

A. Rich. in Mem. Mus. Hist. Nat. 4: 43, 52. 1818.

Terrestrial or epiphytic herbs with or without pseudobulbs; leaves one or more, membranous and continuous with the sheath, or coriaceous and jointed on the sheath or pseudobulb; inflorescence terminal, erect, many-flowered, small or medium-sized; sepals and petals erect or reflexed, margins recurved or revolute, lateral sepals and sometimes petals placed under the lip; lip inferior, adnate to the base of the column, not 3-lobed, usually bent at or below the middle, often cleft at apex; column slender, incurved, often winged towards the top; anther terminal, its apex pointing forwards and downwards in front of the column; pollinia 4, free or cohering by a viscid appendage.

About 268 species, in almost all parts of the world.

KEY TO THE SPECIES

1 Plants terrestrial; stem swollen at base; leaves plaited, not jointed on the sheath
  2 Sepals oblong, oblong-ovate or lanceolate or obliquely oblong or ovate
    3 Lip orbicular or cuneately obovate
      4 Petals linear
        5 Lip usually purple, 9 mm long, 11.5 mm broad, disc with two minute calli.......
        ....**1. L. wightiana**
        5 Lip usually green, 7.5 mm long, 8 mm broad, base 2-auricular and 2-tubercled....
        ....**2. L. barbata**
      4 Petals linear-lanceolate or spathulate
        6 Sepals 5-veined, petals 3-veined, lip cuneately obovate..............**3. L. nervosa**
        6 Sepals 3-veined, petals 1-veined, lip orbicular...................**4. L. walkeriae**
    3 Lip transversely oblong, cordate at base with a short emarginate callus............
    ....**5. L. brachyglottis**
  2 Sepals linear, dorsal sepal 3-veined, lateral sepals 5-veined; lip orbicular-obovate, fleshy with 2 long confluent tubercles at the base...............**6. L. atropurpurea**
1 Plants epiphytic; pseudobulbs ovoid; leaves subcoriaceous, jointed on the sheath
  7 Racemes with distichous bracts and flowers; sepals 3-veined...........**7. L. gibbosa**
  7 Racemes without distichous bracts and flowers; sepals 1-veined
    8 Racemes shorter than leaves; lip subquadrate...................**8. L. caespitosa**
    8 Racemes longer than leaves; calli absent in the lip................**9. L. viridiflora**

1. Liparis wightiana Thw., Enum. Pl. Zeyl. 295. 1861; Trimen, Handb. Fl. Ceylon 4: 144. 1898.—**Fig. 23.**

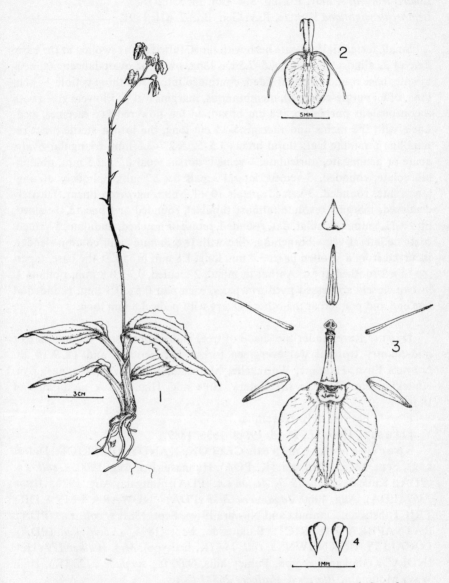

Fig. 23. *Liparis wightiana* Thwaites. 1, plant with inflorescence. 2, flower from front. 3, bract, sepals, petals and lip spread out from front, column from inside, all magnified. 4, pollinia.

Liparis atropurpurea Wight, Ic. Pl. Ind. Or. 3 (2): 9, pl. 904. 1845, non Lindl.
Liparis trimenii Ridley, J. Linn. Soc. Bot. 24: 350. 1888.
Leptorchis wightiana Kuntze, Rev. Gen. Bot. 2: 671. 1891.

Small, terrestrial, delicate herb with short, tufted stems swollen at the base. Leaves 2, almost opposite, 4.5–7.5 cm long, ovate or ovate-lanceolate, acuminate, base rounded, equal sided, continued into a sheathing petiole 1–3 cm long, often purple-coloured, membranous, margins wavy. Flowers green with a conspicuous purple lip, 0.8 cm broad, in few-flowered lax racemes; peduncle with the rachis and raceme 5–15 cm long, the lowest sterile bract resembling a minute leaf; floral bracts 3.5–5.5 × 2.7–3.5 mm, triangular-ovate, acute or acuminate, auriculate, 1-veined; dorsal sepal 8.7 × 2.5 mm, oblong-lanceolate, rounded, 3-veined; lateral sepals 8 × 2.7 mm, obliquely oblong-lanceolate, rounded, 3-veined; petals 10 × 1.2 mm, narrowly linear, falcately decurved, margins revolute (almost tubular), rounded or truncate, 1-veined; lip 9 × 11.5 mm, orbicular, flat, rounded, retuse or notched, undulate, 5-veined, extreme lateral veins branching, disc with two minute calli; column slender, incurved from a swollen base, 3.7 mm long, 1.8 mm broad at the base, tapering to a 2-toothed apex. Anther terminal, 2-loculed, 0.7 × 0.8 mm, pollinia 4, in two closely appressed pyriform pairs, each pair 0.5 × 0.3 mm, rounded at one end and pointed at the other. Ovary with pedicel 8 mm long.

D i s t r. Rare, under the shade of trees and shrubs in the submontane or mid-country tropical wet evergreen forests between 915 and 1829 m alt. Nuwara Eliya, Hantane, Wattekelle, Maturata, Madulkelle, Hunnasgiriya, Knuckles, etc. Also in the Pulney Hills and High Wavy mountains of India.

E c o l. Flowers July–November.
I l l u s t r. Hook. f., Ic. Pl. 19: pl. 1836. 1889.
S p e c i m e n s E x a m i n e d. CEYLON, KANDY DISTRICT: Dolosbage, Sept. 1885, *s. coll. s.n.* (K, PDA); Hunnasgiriya, Aug. 1900, *s. coll. s.n.* (PDA); Knuckles, July 1927, *Alston s.n.* (PDA); Rangala, Aug. 1926, *Alston 1369* (PDA), Aug. 1960, *Jayaweera 2013* (PDA). NUWARA ELIYA DISTRICT: between Dimbula and Nuwara Eliya, Sept. 1881, *s. coll. s.n.* (PDA). RATNAPURA DISTRICT: Balangoda, Sept. 1895, *s. coll. s.n.* (PDA). LOCALITY UNKNOWN: *s. coll. 187* (K, neotype), *Mrs. Walker 1794* (K). INDIA: Kodaikanal region, Pulney hills, 6000 ft., *Anglade 2123* (K); High Wavy Mountain, *Blatter & Hallberg 26547* (K).
N o t e. A form where the flowers are smaller with a smaller lip occurs at Rangala. Also the lip is greenish-yellow as compared to the purplish lip of the typical species. *C.P. 3179* originally cited in Thwaites Enum. has been transferred as a type under *Liparis thwaitesii* Hook. f. which is a synonym of *Liparis barbata* Lindl.

2. Liparis barbata Lindl., Gen. et Sp. Orch. 27. 1830; Trimen, Handb. Fl. Ceylon 4: 145. 1898.—**Fig. 24.**

Liparis thwaitesii Hook. f., Fl. Br. Ind. 5: 692. 1890.

Terrestrial herb sometimes epiphytic along with mosses on trunks of trees or rocks; stem 3 cm long, swollen at the base, covered over by five leaf sheaths, outer two papery, others light green, older pseudobulbs attached; roots tufted. Leaves 2, opposite or 3, subsessile, the first the largest, lamina 4.5–6.5 × 2–3.5 cm, ovate, membranous, plicate, purplish or purplish-green, unequal at the base continued into sheaths 1.5 cm long covering the stem, acute, 5-veined, undulate, veins prominent beneath. Flowers green, in lax, terminal, few-flowered racemes; peduncle 13.5 cm long, 5-ribbed, ribs purplish, with two sterile bracts; the flower-bearing portion of the raceme 6.5 cm long; floral bracts ovate, 4 × 2.3 mm, acuminate, acute, 1-veined; dorsal sepal 6.7 × 2 mm, lanceolate-ovate, acuminate, acute, 3-veined; lateral sepals obliquely ovate, of the same length as the dorsal but 2.5 mm broad, pressing on the back of the lip and folded like the two wings of a bird on its tail; petals linear, 8 × 0.6 mm, recurved, 1-veined; lip 7.5 × 8 mm, orbicular, mucronate, entire, 2-auricled, 2-tubercled, at the base, 5-veined, the two outermost veins giving off several branches to the margin; column conical, 4 mm high, 1 mm broad at the base, tapering to 0.3 mm at the apex, incurved, 2-toothed, adnate to the base of the lip. Anther terminal, 2-loculed, 0.56 × 0.66 mm; pollinia 4 in two pairs, 0.54 × 0.28 mm, obovate resembling a top. Ovary with pedicel 0.8 cm long and ribbed. Fruit a capsule, 0.8–1 cm long.

D i s t r. Endemic. Very rare, under the shade of trees on the floor of the jungle by streams in the subtropical montane forests between 915 and 1829 m alt. Nuwara Eliya, Rangala, Horagala, Dolosbage, between Dimbula and Nuwara Eliya, Pasdun Korale, etc.

E c o l. Flowers July–August.

I l l u s t r. Hook. f., Ic. Pl. 21: pl. 2006. 1890.

N o t e. Hooker's observation of the absence of hairs in the lip contrary to that described by Lindley and Ridley is confirmed.

S p e c i m e n s E x a m i n e d. KANDY DISTRICT: Rangala, Aug. 1926, on wet rocks, *Alston 1370* (PDA); Maskeliya, Moray Estate, June 1971, *Balakrishnan 581* (PDA, US). NUWARA ELIYA DISTRICT: Westward-Ho, on Pundaluoya Road, Aug. 1959, *Jayaweera 2012* (PDA), *Jayaweera 3 (4)* (AMES).

3. Liparis nervosa (Thunb.) Lindl., Gen. et Sp. Orch. Pl. 26. 1830; Trimen, Handb. Fl. Ceylon 4: 145. 1898.—**Fig. 25.**

Liparis odorata (Willd.) Lindl., Gen. et Sp. Orch. 26. 1830; Alston in Trimen, Handb. Fl. Ceylon 6: 272. 1931.

Malaxis odorata Willd., Sp. Pl. 4: 19. 1805.

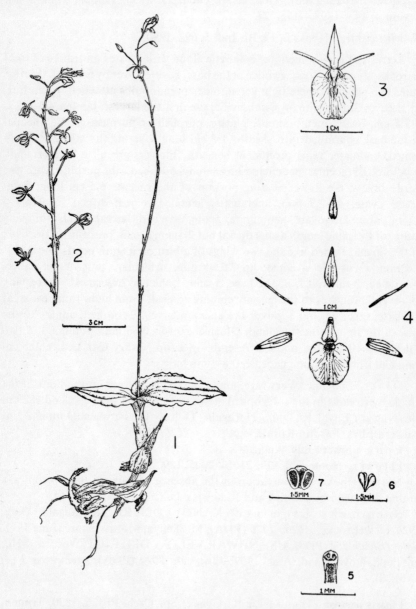

Fig. 24. *Liparis barbata* Lindl. 1, plant with inflorescence. 2, inflorescence. 3, flower from front. 4, bract, sepals, petals and lip spread out from front, column from inside. 5, top of the column from inside. 6, pollinia. 7, operculum from inside.

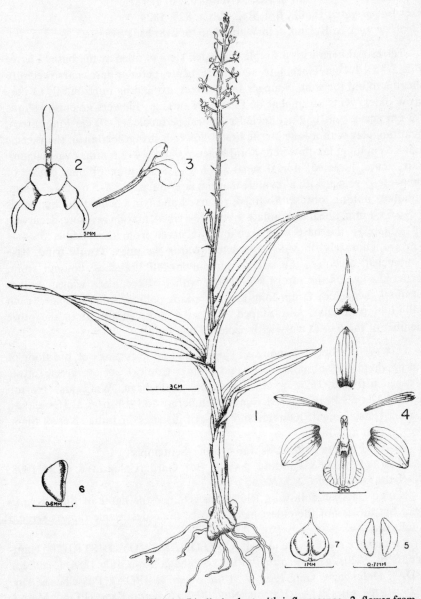

Fig. 25. *Liparis nervosa* (Thunb.) Lindl. 1, plant with inflorescence. 2, flower from front. 3, ovary, lip and column, side view. 4, bract, sepals, petals, lip and column spread out from front. 5, pollinia. 6, a pair of pollinia, lateral view. 7, operculum from inside.

Malaxis lancifolia Smith in Rees, Cyclop. 22: n. 7. 1813.
Empusa paradoxa Lindl., Bot. Reg. sub. t. 825. 1824.
Liparis paradoxa Reichb. f. in Walp. Ann. 6: 218. 1861.

Terrestrial herb with a simple elongated stem swollen at the base. Leaves 1–5, 5–15 × 1.4 cm, lanceolate, acuminate, acute, petiolar bases narrowed into sheaths round the stem, younger leaves erect, expanding horizontally as they grow older, veins prominent on the under surface. Flowers greenish-yellow, 1.2 cm across, in long-peduncled racemes; peduncle 11–10 cm long, green, quadrangular with a long sterile bract; flower-bearing portinn of the raceme 4.5–8.5 cm long, lax-flowered; floral bracts 5.9–6.8 × 2–2.6 mm, ovate, acuminate, acute, 1-veined; dorsal sepal 5.6–6.8 × 1.8–2.4 mm, oblong, obtuse or subacute, 5-veined with a revolute margin; lateral sepals 4.8–5.6 × 2.8–3.4 mm, obliquely oblong, obtuse, 5-veined, recurved and lying behind the lip; petals 5.8–6.6 × 1 mm, linear-spathulate, obtuse, 3-veined, margin revolute, decurved; lip adnate to the base of the column, recurved from the middle, 5 × 4.4–4.8 mm, cuneately obovate, crenulate towards the apex, faintly trifid, base 2-tubercled, 5-veined, the lateral veins giving off branches; column stout, incurved towards the top, 4.8 × 1.7 mm with two crenulate wings. Anther terminal, 2-loculed, 1 mm long and as broad; pollinia 4 in two pairs, each pollinium triangular, disc-shaped, 0.58 × 0.4 mm, appressed to the other member of the pair. Ovary with pedicel 9 mm long.

D i s t r. Rather common, on slopes along hill cuttings or the floor of the jungle in the submontane or mid-country tropical wet evergreen forests between 610 and 1524 m alt. Ramboda, Dolosbage, Watawala, Norton Bridge, Adam's Peak, etc. Also in the temperate and subtropical Himalayas, Khasia Hills, Bengal, Konkan and Mysore districts in India, Nepal, Siam, Java, China and Japan.

E c o l. Flowers February–March, June–September.

I l l u s t r. King & Pantling, Ann. R. Bot. Gard. (Calcutta) 8: pl. 34. 1898; PDA, drawing from *C.P. 3180*.

N o t e. Hooker following Ridley has retained the name of *Liparis paradoxa* but this is not the oldest name. Hence the oldest name *Liparis nervosa* is adopted.

S p e c i m e n s E x a m i n e d. CEYLON, KANDY DISTRICT: Hantane, Sept. 1960, *Jayaweera 2010* (PDA); Ambagamuwa, July 1884, *s. coll. s.n.* (PDA); Dolosbage, Oct. 1925, *J.M. de Silva s.n.* (PDA); Pussellawa, Aug. 1926, *Alston s.n.* (PDA); Hatton, Nov. 1949, *Senaratne s.n.* (PDA); Madulkele, July 1927, *Alston s.n.* (PDA). NUWARA ELIYA DISTRICT: Watawala, *Jayaweera 2011* (PDA), 1959, *Jayaweera 3 (5)* (AMES); Talawakelle—Kotmale, June 1972, *Hepper, Maxwell & Jayasuriya 4486* (PDA). RATNAPURA DISTRICT: Rakwana, Bulutota, *Simpson 9974* (PDA). INDIA: Simla, Aug. 1878, 8000 ft., *Gamble 6437A* (K); W. Sikkkim July 1896, *Pantling*

228 (K); Khasia Hills, 5000 ft., *J.D. Hooker & Thomson s.n.* (K, PDA); Assam, Naga Hills, 1886, *Prain 41* (K); Bengal, July 1872, *Clarke 17244A* (K); Mysore, *Law 11* (K). CHINA: Yunnan, Meng-tsze, *Henry 11105A* (K, AMES); Szemoa, *Henry 12300* (AMES); S.E. China, Liung Chon San, July 1936, *Gressitt 1667* (AMES). FORMOSA: *Henry 896* (K). JAPAN: Yokohama, 1862, *Maximowicz s.n.* (K); Kumokiri-so, May 1890, *Watanabe s.n.* (AMES). LOO CHOO ISLANDS: 1853–1856, *Wright 342* (K, AMES).

4. Liparis walkeriae R. Grah., Edinburgh New Philos. J. 20: 194. 1836; Trimen, Handb. Fl. Ceylon 4: 146. 1898.—**Fig. 26.**

Terrestrial herb with a swollen or pseudobulbous base. Leaves 2–4, lamina 3.5–8.5 × 2.5–4.5 cm, ovate, acute, membranous, base unequal-sided, one-half more or less folding over the other half; petiolar sheaths purplish, sheathing the stem. Flowers purple, 1.1 cm across, in many flowered, terminal racemes; peduncle 7 cm long, tinged purple, quadrangular, carrying 1–3 sterile bracts; rachis straight, green, about 6 cm long, curving downwards at the apex; floral bracts 8–10.6 × 2.4–3 mm, subulate, acute, 3-veined; dorsal sepal 6.2–6.6 × 2 mm, linear-oblong, obtuse, 3-veined; lateral sepals 5–5.2 × 2.1–2.3 mm, falcate-oblong, obtuse, 3-veined and pressing on the back of the lip; petals 5.8–6 × 0.6–0.8 mm, linear or linear-lanceolate, obtuse, 1-veined, margin revolute and faintly dentate; lip 4.4 mm long and as broad, fleshy, orbicular, wrinkled and recurved from the middle, crenulate, 5-veined, lateral veins giving off branches to the outer margin, two confluent tubercles at the base; column 2.8 mm high, 1.6 mm broad at the base, tapering towards the summit and incurved, columnar wing uncinate. Anther terminal, 2-loculed, 0.7 × 0.64 mm, pollinia 4 in two pairs, members of each pair unequal, disc-shaped and triangular, larger pollinia 0.4 × 0.24 mm and the smaller ones 0.34 × 0.24 mm. Ovary with pedicel 7.4 mm long.

D i s t r. Rare, under the shade of trees in the subtropical montane forests up to 1829 m alt. Ramboda, Nuwara Eliya, Adam's Peak, Pidurutalagala, Hakgala etc. Also in the Deccan Peninsula from the Nilgiri Hills to Kerala in India.

E c o l. Flowers June, October, December.

I l l u s t r. Graham in Bot. Mag. 66: pl. 3770. 1840, Herb. Peradeniya, 2 drawings.

N o t e. This plant was sent to Edinburgh by Mrs. Walker in 1834. The species is allied to *Liparis atropurpurea* but is distinguished from it by the acute-angled and almost winged stem.

S p e c i m e n s E x a m i n e d. CEYLON, KANDY DISTRICT: Peradeniya, Botanic Gardens, cultd. July 1960, *Jayaweera 2008* (PDA). NUWARA ELIYA DISTRICT: Westward-Ho, Jun. 1960, *Jayaweera 2007* (PDA), *Jayaweera 3 (6)* (AMES), Dec. 1925, *Alston 1370* (PDA), Mar. 1906,

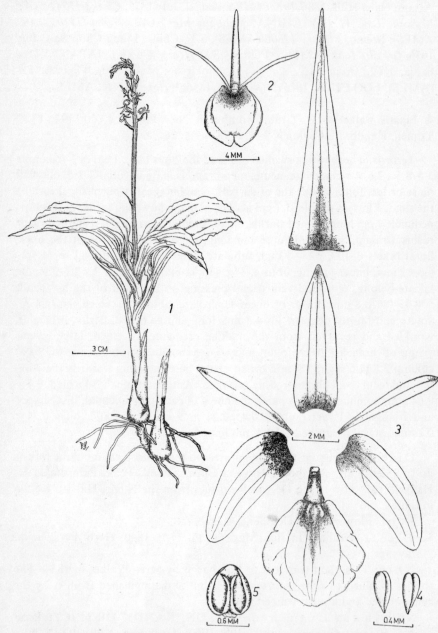

Fig. 26. *Liparis walkeriae* R. Grah. 1, plant with inflorescence. 2, flower from front. 3, bract sepals, petals and lip spread out from front, column from inside. 4, pollinia. 5, operculum from inside.

A.M. Silva s.n. (PDA); Hakgala, Sept. 1960, *Jayaweera 2009* (PDA), Oct. 1914, *Petch s.n.* (PDA), Sept. 1914, *s. coll. s.n.* (PDA), Sept. 1969, *Read 2260* (PDA), May 1971, *Jayasuriya 171* (PDA, US). LOCALITY UNKNOWN: *s. coll. C.P. 2376* (PDA); *Maxwell s.n.* (PDA). INDIA: Coonoor, Nilgiri Hills, 7000 ft, *Gamble 18075* (K); Kodaikanal region, 6000 ft, *Souliere 143* (R); Kerala, 1867, *Johnson s.n.* (K); Pen. Ind. Or., Herb. *Wight 2946* (K, AMES).

5. Liparis brachyglottis Reichb. f. ex Trimen, Cat. 87. 1885; Trimen, Handb. Fl. Ceylon 4: 146. 1898.—**Fig. 27.**

Slender herb with stem swollen at the base. Leaves 1 or 2, alternate, sessile or the lower petioled, 3.8–6.4 cm long, cordate, acuminate, membranous, 5-veined, base equal-sided, margin crisped. Flowers small, purple, in lax-flowered, short-peduncled, slender racemes; peduncle together with the rachis 5–7.5 cm long; floral bracts ovate, acute, concave, persistent, not reflexed but spreading; dorsal sepal oblong-lanceolate, obtuse, 3-veined, margins recurved; lateral sepals broadly ovate-oblong, obtuse, 3-veined margins recurved and placed under the lip; petals linear, spreading, margins recurved; lip short, transversely oblong, obtuse or retuse or emarginate, base cordate with obscure basal thickenings; column short, stout, truncate. Anther terminal, 2-loculed; pollinia 4 in two pairs.

D i s t r. Endemic. Very rare, under shade of trees in the submontane or mid-country tropical wet evergreen forests between 1220 and 1829 m alt. Knuckles, Wattekelle, Horton Plains, etc.

E c o l. Flowers September, January.

I l l u s t r. PDA, drawing from *C.P. 4002.*

N o t e. This is a small terrestrial species with small purple flowers where the bracts are concave and not reflexed and lateral sepals 3-veined.

S p e c i m e n s E x a m i n e d. MATALE DISTRICT: Madulkele, Wattakele Hill, Sept. 1868, *s. coll. C.P. 4002* (K, Holotype, PDA). NUWARA ELIYA DISTRICT: between Horton Plains and Belihul Oya, Jan. 1910, *Rothart s.n.* (PDA).

6. Liparis atropurpurea Lindl., Gen. et Sp. Orch. 28. 1830; Trimen, Handb. Fl. Ceylon 4: 146. 1898.—**Fig. 28.**

Liparis olivacea Wight, Ic. Pl. Ind. Or. 3 (2): 9, pl. 903. 1844–1845.
Liparis walkeriae Wight, ibid. pl. 905, non Graham.

Terrestrial leafy herb with stout, hardly swollen stems 15–20 cm long. Leaves 3 or 4 petioled, 7.5–10 cm long, ovate or orbicular, membranous, 5-veined, base very unequal-sided, one side acute and the other rounded or auricled, somewhat cordate, margins smooth or crisped; petiole 2–2.5 cm long. Flowers dull vinous purple, large, about 2.5 cm across in slender lax-flowered,

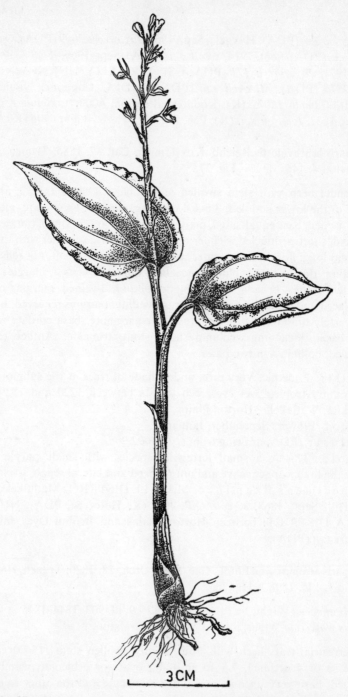

3CM

Fig. 27. *Liparis brachyglottis* Reichb. f. ex Trimen. Plant with inflorescence
redrawn from a drawing of *C.P. 4002.*

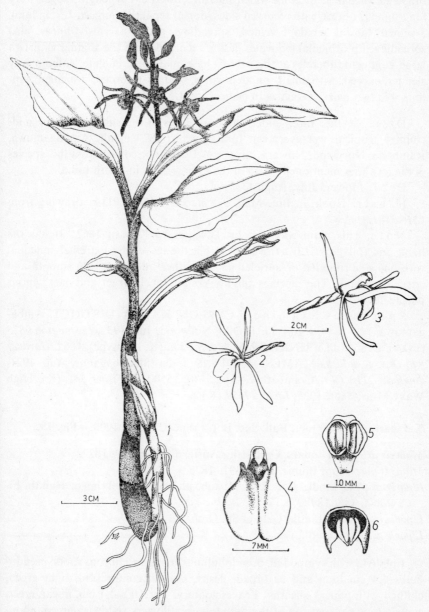

Fig. 28. *Liparis atropurpurea* Lindl. Redrawn from a drawing of *C.P. 3181* in PDA.
1, plant with inflorescence. 2, flower from above. 3, flower from side. 4, lip and
column from front. 5, rostrum from inside showing the pollinia. 6, pollinia with a
portion of the column surrounding them.

bracteate or naked racemes which measure 10–20 cm in length; sepals very long, linear, obtuse with recurved sides, dorsal sepal the longest, 1.5 cm long, 3-veined; lateral sepals 5-veined, spreading; petals narrowly linear, also spreading; lip orbicular-obovate, fleshy, recurved from the middle with two large confluent tubercles at the narrow base, margins crenulate, column very slender, curved, with small rounded wings. Anther terminal, 2-loculed; pollinia 4 in two pairs. Ovary with pedicel 1.2–1.5 cm long.

D i s t r. Rather rare, under shade of trees in the submontane or mid-country tropical wet evergreen forests up to 1829 m alt. Ambagamuwa, Ramboda, Norwood, Nuwara Eliya, etc. I have not come across this species in the localities mentioned. Also in the Pulney Hills in South India.

E c o l. Flowers July, August.

I l l u s t r. Hook. in Bot. Mag. 91: pl. 5529. 1865; PDA, drawing from *C.P. 3181.*

N o t e. This plant was sent by Thwaites to Kew in 1862. It has the habit and foliage of *Liparis walkeriae* but the leaves are extremely unequal with one side rounded or auricled and the other side acute with smooth and crisped margins. The racemes and flowers are much larger and dark vinous purple in colour.

S p e c i m e n s E x a m i n e d. CEYLON, KANDY DISTRICT: Ambagamuwa, July 1884, *s. coll. s.n.* (PDA); Norwood, July 1932, *Lushington 9873* (PDA). LOCALITY UNKNOWN: *Macrae s.n.* (K, holotype), 1862, *Gardner 846* (K), *s. coll. s.n.* (AMES). INDIA: S. India, Shambaganur, Aug. 1921, *Anglade 2110* (K); Coimbatore, Aug. 1905, 5500 ft, *Fisher 342* (K); High Wavy Mtns, Sept. 1925, *Jacob 17621* (K).

7. **Liparis gibbosa** Finet, Bull. Soc. Bot. France 55: 342. 1908.—Fig. 29.

Malaxis disticha Thouars, Orch. Isles Austr. d'Afr. pl. 89. 1822.
Malaxis mucronata Blume, Bijdr. 391. 1825.
Liparis disticha Lindl., Bot. Reg. 11: sub. pl. 882. 1825; Trimen, Handb. Fl.
    Ceylon 4: 148. 1898.
Liparis mucronata Lindl., Gen. et Sp. Orch. 32. 1830.
Liparis gregaria Lindl., ibid. 33.

Epiphyte with sympodial, pseudobulbous stems and fibrous roots; pseudobulbs 1.4 cm long and as broad, fleshy, slightly compressed, light green, clothed with papery sheaths. Leaves solitary, 7–9 × 0.8–1.1 cm, linear, erect, acute, coriaceous, at top of the pseudobulb. Flowers yellowish-green, about 4–5 mm across in terminal racemes which arise from the axils of the leaves, one to each pseudobulb; racemes 2.5 cm long, compressed, winged at the top of a stout peduncle measuring 6.5 cm in length, rachis flattened; floral bracts 4.8 × 2.5 mm, ovate, acuminate, keeled, 1-veined, coriaceous, distichous,

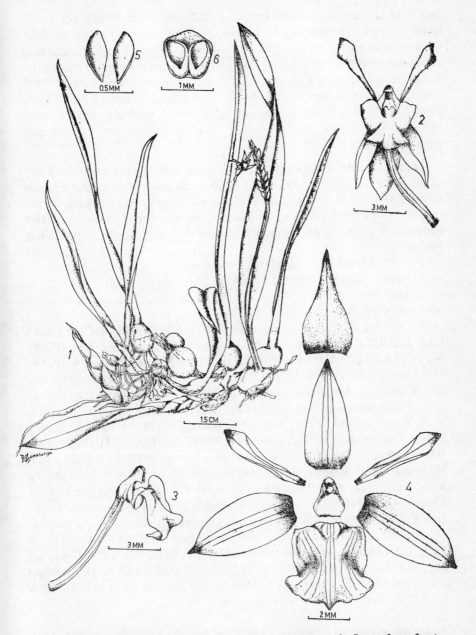

Fig. 29. *Liparis gibbosa* Finet. 1, plants with inflorescence. 2, flower from front. 3, column and lip from side, three quarters view. 4, bract, sepals, petals and lip spread out from front, column from inside. 5, pollinia from side. 6, operculum from inside.

imbricate and equitant; dorsal sepal 5.2 × 2.2 mm, ovate-oblong, acute, reflexed, 3-veined; lateral sepals 5 × 2.7 mm, ovate-oblong or broadly lanceolate-oblong, mucronate, acute, reflexed, 3-veined; petals 4.4 × 1 mm, lateral margins incurved giving a linear-spathulate appearance, obtuse, 1-veined; lip fleshy, recurving twice with two thickened prominences at each bend, 3.6 × about 5 mm, quadrate, mucronate, acute, 9-veined; column 2.2 mm high, 2 mm broad, erect, triangular-conical, sides winged, uncinate. Anther terminal, 2-loculed; 0.9 × 1 mm, pollinia 4 in two pairs, members of each pair equal, appressed, 0.52 × 0.3 mm.

D i s t r. Rather common, on trees in the submontane or mid-country tropical wet evergreen forests extending up to the subtropical montane forests from 1220 to 1829 m alt. Rangala, Maturata, Hantane, Hakgala, Haputale, Horton Plains, etc. Also in Malaya, Burma, Timor, Mauritius, Java, Sumatra, Borneo, the Philippine Islands and Bourbon but not in the Indian Peninsula.

E c o l. Flowers January, March–November.

I l l u s t r. Thouars, Orch. Ins. Afr. pl. 89; PDA, drawing.

N o t e. This species is distinguished by the distichous equitant bracts with only a few flowers opening at a time.

S p e c i m e n s E x a m i n e d. CEYLON, KANDY DISTRICT: Corbet's Gap, Jan. 1954, *Jayaweera 992* (PDA), June 1960, *Jayaweera 2174* (PDA). NUWARA ELIYA DISTRICT: Hakgala, Apr. 1906, *A.M. Silva s.n.* (PDA), Oct. 1906, *s. coll. s.n.* (PDA), Jun 1907, *Nock s.n.* (AMES), Sept. 1969, *Grupe 262* (PDA, US); Maturata, Kabaragala, Nov. 1959, *Jayaweera 2005* (PDA), Nov. 1959, *Jayaweera 3 (12)* (AMES). RATNAPURA DISTRICT: Balangoda, Gawaranhena Forest, Aug. 1976, *Waas 1805* (PDA); Bambarabotuwa Forest Reserve, July 1971, *Jayasuriya & Meijer 253* (PDA, US); Dotalu Oya, Bambarabotuwa Oya, July 1971, *Meijer 871* (PDA). BADULLA DISTRICT: Haputale Forest Reserve, July 1969, *Wheeler 12143* (PDA, US); Namunukula, Apr. 1974, *Sumithraarachchi & Waas 274* (PDA, US), Sept. 1976, *Cramer 4724* (PDA, US); between Haputale & Ohiya, Sept. 1890, *s. coll. s.n.* (PDA); between Hakgala & Fort Macdonald, May 1906, *Willis s.n.* (PDA). MADAGASCAR: July 1863, *Blackburn* (AMES). MAURITIUS: *Lang 168* (AMES). MALAY PENINSULA: Pahang, Oct. 1927, *Henderson 19456* (AMES). SINGAPORE, 1890, *Ridley* (AMES). JAVA: Hort. Bogor *s. coll. s.n.* (AMES). SUMATRA: Mar. 1901, *Schlechter s.n.* (AMES). NEW CALEDONIA: Oct. 1902, *Schlechter 14858* (AMES).

8. Liparis caespitosa (Thouars) Lindl. in Bot. Reg. 11: sub. t. 882. 1825. —Fig. 30.

Liparis obscura Hook. f., Hook., Ic. Pl. 19: pl. 1886. 1889.
Malaxis caespitosa Thouars, Orch. Isles Austr. d'Afr. pl. 90. 1822.

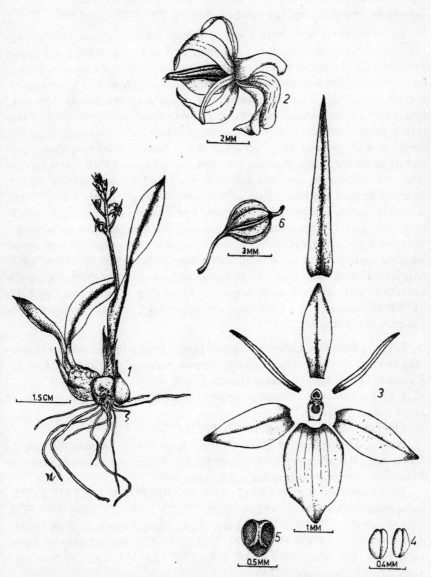

Fig. 30. *Liparis caespitosa* (Thou.) Lindl. 1, plant with inflorescence. 2, flower from side, obliquely three quarters view. 3, bract, sepals, petals and l.p. spread out from front, top of the column from inside, dorsal view. 4, pollinia. 5, operculum from inside. 6, fruit, lateral view.

Malaxis angustifolia Blume, Bijdr. 393. 1825.
Liparis angustifolia Thw., Enum. Pl. Zeyl. 296. 1861, non Lindl.
Liparis caespitosa Ridley, J. Linn. Soc. Bot. 22: 290. 1887, non Lindl.

Tufted epiphyte with short, ovoid, flattened, pseudobulbous stems crowding together; pseudobulbs 0.5–1 cm long and as broad, 0.6 cm thick and smooth; young flowering pseudobulb enclosed in four scaly sheaths, foliage leaves borne at the summit and articulating with it. Leaves 1 or 2, coriaceous, costate, 1–5 × 0.7–1.3 cm, oblanceolate or ovate, acute mucronate, base contiguous with a short sheathing petiole. Flowers small, greenish-yellow, 5 mm across, in pedunculate, terminal racemes; peduncle 1–2.5 cm long, flat, green; flower bearing portion 1–2.3 cm long; floral bracts 7 × 1.2 mm linear, acuminate or aristate, stiff, straight, 1-veined; dorsal sepal 2.4 × 0.8 mm, lanceolate, recurved, obtuse, 1-veined; lateral sepals 2.4 × 1.1 mm, obliquely oblong, recurved behind the lip, obtuse or rounded, 1-veined; petals 2.2 × 0.3 mm, narrowly linear, deflexed and recurved, 1-veined; lip oblong ovate or subquadrate, 2.2 × 1.7 mm, recurved from about the middle, acute or subacute, base slightly auriculate but lobes obscure; column 1.3 m high, 0.4 mm broad, bending slightly about the middle with a deep hollow stigma. Anther terminal, 2-loculed, 0.4 mm long and as broad; pollinia 4 in two pairs, each pollinium 0.3 × 0.18 mm. Ovary with pedicel 3 mm long. Fruit a small globular or oblong capsule, 3 mm long and as broad, ridged, with the remains of the rostrum at the summit.

D i s t r. Probably endemic. Rather rare, on trees of the submontane or mid-country tropical wet evergreen forests between 610 and 1524 m alt. Rangala, Dolosbage, Hantane, Hunnasgiriya, etc.

E c o l. Flowers September, January, March. At Rangala it was found epiphytic on *Litsea* sp.

I l l u s t r. PDA, drawing from *C.P. 2351.*

N o t e. This species is allied to the Javan *Liparis angustifolia* but the flower and fruit are much smaller and the lip shorter and quadrate while the Mauritius *Liparis caespitosa* has a lanceolate lip.

S p e c i m e n s E x a m i n e d. ANURADHAPURA DISTRICT: Ritigala, Mar. 1905, *Willis s.n.* (PDA); Sept. 1972, *Wheeler & Cramer 896* (PDA, US). KANDY DISTRICT: Rangala, Sept. 1959, *Jayaweera 2006* (PDA), *Jayaweera 3 (9)* (AMES). RATNAPURA DISTRICT: Warukandeniya, Sinharaja, Feb. 1977, *Waas 1980* (PDA, US). LOCALITY UNKNOWN: *s. coll. C.P. 2351* (K, lectotype, PDA).

9. Liparis viridiflora Lindl., Gen. et Sp. Orch. 31. 1830; Trimen, Handb. Fl. Ceylon 4: 148. 1898.—**Fig. 31.**

Liparis longipes Lindl. in Wall., Pl. As. Rar. 1: 31, pl. 35. 1830.
Malaxis viridiflora Blume, Bijdr. 392, pl. 54. 1825.

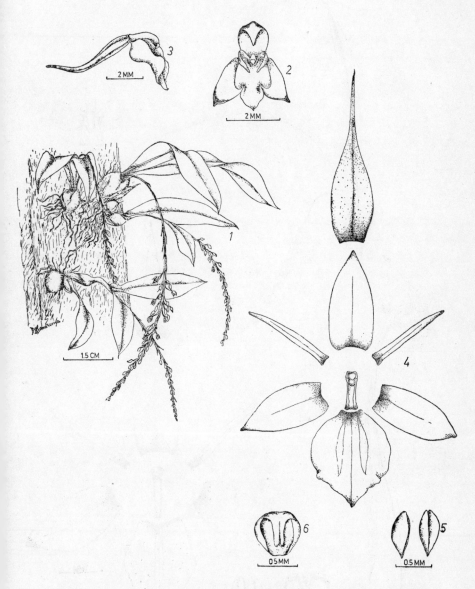

Fig. 31. *Liparis viridiflora* Lindl. 1, plants with inflorescences. 2, flower from front. 3, flower with the sepals and petals removed showing lateral view of column and lip. 4, bract, sepals, petals and lip spread out from front, column from inside, enlarged. 5, pollinia from side. 6, operculum from inside.

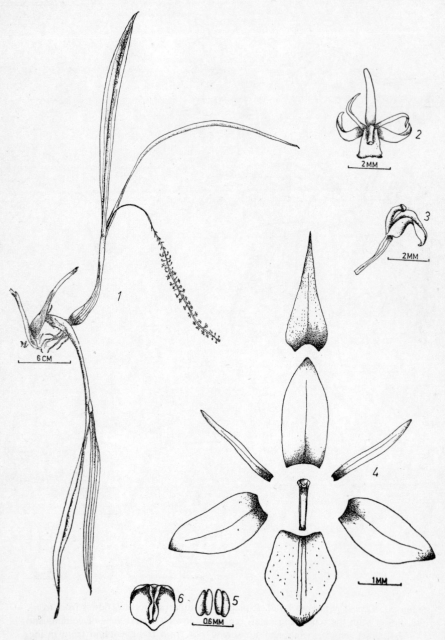

Fig. 32. *Liparis viridiflora* Lindl., another form. 1, plants with inflorescence. 2, flower from front. 3, column and lip from side. 4, bract, sepals, petals and lip spread out from front, column from inside. 5, pollinia. 6, operculum from inside, magnified.

Liparis elliptica Wight, Ic. Pl. Ind. Or. 5 (1): 17, pl. 1735. 1851.
Liparis wightii Reichb. f. in Walp. Ann. 6: 218. 1861.
Liparis hookeri Ridley, J. Linn. Soc. Bot. 22: 288. 1836.
Liparis pendula Lindl., Bot. Reg. 24: 94, Misc. 180. 1838.
Liparis spathulata Lindl., Bot. Reg. 26: 81, Misc. 189. 1840.
Liparis boothii Regel, Ind. Sem. Hort. Petrop. Suppl. 14. 1864.
Liparis nesophila Reichb. f., Otia Bot. Hamb. 1: 56. 1878.
Liparis elegans Lindl. in Wall., Cat. n. 1943. 1829.

Tufted epiphyte with ovoid or slender and conical pseudobulbs 1–9 × 0.8–2 cm clothed in papery sheaths; leaves 2 or 3, coriaceous, jointed on and continuing with pseudobulb, sessile, 3–24.5 × 1–2.5 cm, erect or drooping, oblanceolate or linear-lanceolate, broader towards the apex of the upper half, narrowing to the base, slightly reflexed, 5–7-veined; flowers green, 2.8–3.5 mm across in long, pendulous, terminal, many-flowered racemes which measure 17–18 cm in length; peduncle 5–8 cm long, green, terete, with sterile bracts towards the end; flower-bearing portion of the raceme 5–8 cm long, green, pedicel bending sharply at the commencement of the ovary; floral bracts 2.6–5.2 × 0.9–1.3 mm, lanceolate, acuminate, acute, 1-veined; dorsal sepal 2.4–4 × 0.9–1.8 mm, oblong, acute, 1-veined; lateral sepals 2.2–3.8 × 1–1.9 mm, oblong or oblanceolate, 1-veined, obtuse or mucronate, revolute, recurved and reflexed; petals 2.2–4 × 0.34–0.6 mm, linear, margin revolute, 1-veined; lip 2–3.2 × 1.5–2.9 mm, orbicular-ovate, obscurely 3-lobed, concave or recurved about the middle, fleshy, thickened, callus absent, 5-veined; column 1.8–2 mm high, 0.5–0.7 mm broad, arched. Anther terminal, 2-loculed, 0.6 × 0.56 mm; pollinia 4, waxy in two pairs, each pollinium 0.36–0.6 × 0.14–0.16 mm, spindle-shaped and closely appressed. Ovary with pedicel 5.2 mm long.

D i s t r. Rather common, on trees in the submontane or mid-country tropical wet evergreen forests between 915 and 1829 m alt. Rangala, Adam's Peak, Ambagamuwa, Ramboda, Hantane, etc. Also in Sikkim Himalaya, Upper Assam, Khasia and the Nilgiri Hills in India, Burma, Malaya, China, Java, Sumatra, Borneo, the Philippines and Fiji Islands.

E c o l. Flowers October, November, December.

I l l u s t r. King & Pantling, Ann. R. Bot. Gard. (Calcutta) 8: pl. 47. 1898; PDA, drawing from *C.P. 3177* and 3 drawings from *C.P. 3178*.

N o t e. Collections of Macrae and Champion from Ceylon are in the same type cover at Kew. Of these *Macrae 11* is selected as the lectotype. Herb. Lindley contains four collections, two of which are Hooker's from Sikkim and Wight's from Madras. The original description of the plant was from a specimen of Macrae from Ceylon. This species is distinguished by the 2 linear-lanceolate-leaved pseudobulb, long dense-flowered raceme and 1-nerved sepals in the flower, and the subsecund flowers ascending from the at length decurved pedicels.

Specimens Examined. CEYLON, KANDY DISTRICT: Panwila, Oct. 1887, *s. coll. s.n.* (PDA); Peradeniya, Dec. 1959, *Jayaweera s.n.* (AMES); Hantane, *Champion s.n.* (K); Peradeniya Botanic Gardens, cultd. Jan. 1954, *Jayaweera 984* (PDA); Corbet's Gap, Mar. 1959, *Jayaweera 2305* (PDA), Oct. 1959, *Jayaweera 3 (11)* (AMES). RATNAPURA DISTRICT: Rassagala, Sept. 1895, *s. coll. s.n.* (PDA). LOCALITY UNKNOWN: *Macrae 20* (K, holotype), *s. coll. C.P. 3177* (PDA), *Gardner 848* (K), Oct. 1845, *Thomson s.n.* (K). INDIA: Khasia Hills, *J.D. Hooker & T. Thomson s.n.* (AMES); Khasia Hills and Upper Assam, Herb. *Griffith 5076* (K), *Wallich s.n.* (PDA); Sikkim, Sikkim Himalaya, Oct.-Dec. 1892, 2000–4000 ft, *Pantling 59* (K, AMES); Darjeeling, Oct. 1870, *Clarke 13245A* (K), *J.D. Hooker s.n.* (PDA), *J.D. Hooker 108* (K); Assam, Lacham, Nov. 1935, *Bor 6735* (K); Manipur state, Dec. 1945, *Bullock 828* (K, AMES); Madras, *Wight 920* (K); Herb. *Wight 2944* (K), *Loddiges s.n.* (K); N.W. India Dehra Dun, Sept. 1899, *Mackinnon 24184* (AMES); Khasia Hills, 4000 ft, *J.D. Hooker & T. Thomson 109* (K); Kodaikanal Region, Pulney Hills, Peruya Shola, Oct. 1899, *Bourne 1203* (K); Assam, *Griffith s.n.* (K); Jan. 1928, *s.coll. 535* (K). ANDAMAN ISLANDS, Domel Island, 1839, Herb. *Helfer 5057* (K).—BURMA: *Griffith 772* (K); Tavoy, Moulmein, 1859, *Parish 180* (K). THAILAND: Doi Chindao, Dec. 1951, *Garrett 1373* (AMES). CHINA: Kwangtung, Tsing Wan Shan, Sept. 1933, fairly common, *Lau 2449* (AMES); Yunnan Prov., *Forrest s.n.* (AMES); Kwangtung Prov., Lin Fa Shan, Sept. 1935, *Tsang 25765* (AMES); HONGKONG, Sept. 1940, *Taam 1790* (AMES). HAINAN: Oct. 1936, *Law 28048* (AMES); Pak Shik Ling & vicinity, abundant, Oct. 1932, *Lei 185* (AMES). SUMATRA: Jun. 1936, *Lutjeharms 4511A* (AMES). BORNEO: North Borneo, Mt. Kinabalu, May 1921, *Clemens 90* (AMES). PHILIPPINE ISLANDS: Luzon, Rizal Prov., Sept. 1909, *Loher 14656* (AMES); Laguna Prov., Feb. 1910, *Robinson 9679* (AMES); Mindoro, Mt. Haleon, Mar. 1922, *Ramos & Edano s.n.* (AMES); Mindanao, Jan. 1908, *Whitford & Hutchinson 9218* (AMES). FIJI ISLANDS: Viti Levu, May 1946, *Greenwood 1150* (AMES).

4. EPHEMERANTHA

Hunt and Summerhayes, Taxon 10 (4): 101. 1961.

Epiphytes with pendulous branched stems, and the terminal internode of each branch developed into an oblong, flattened pseudobulb with one coriaceous leaf, new branches usually arising at the base of a pseudobulb; peduncle short, enveloped by papery scale leaves with 1–3 flowers on top of the pseudobulb from a tuft of bracts below the leaf; sepals and petals lanceolate; lateral sepals adnate to the foot of the column; mentum short; conical; lip 3-lobed, midlobe long, dilated, recurved, crenulate, subquadrate, crisped with two fleshy crests; column short, toothed at apex; foot short and broad with a well-developed mentum; anther terminal, 2-chambered; pollinia 4 in two pairs without caudicles.

About 68 species, distributed from India and Ceylon through Malaysia, Java, Sumatra, Borneo, Celebes, New Guinea as far as the Philippine Islands.

Ephemerantha macraei (Lindl.) P.F. Hunt & Summerhayes, Taxon 10 (4): 101. 1961.—Fig. 33.

Dendrobium macraei Lindl., Gen. et Sp. Orch. Pl. 75. 1830; Trimen, Handb. Fl. Ceylon 4: 150. 1898.
Callista macraei (Lindl.) Kuntze, Rev. Gen. Bot. 6: 55. 1891.
Desmotrichum fimbriatum Blume, Bijdr. 329. 1825.

Tufted epiphyte with a creeping, annular rootstock and pendulous, sympodially branching stems, 20–40 cm or more long; each branch terminating in a fusiform pseudobulb; pseudobulbs 2.5–5 × 0.7–1.9 cm, rather flat, green, shining, grooved longitudinally, covered with papery scale leaves when young; internodes 0.5–3 cm long, terete, smooth. Leaves one to each pseudobulb, terminal, 4.5–14 × 1.2–4.2 cm, sessile, linear-oblong or lanceolate, obtuse, dark green and shining above, paler beneath, many-veined. Flowers white with a pale yellow lip, 1.7 cm across, 1–3 arising from the top of the pseudobulb at the base of the leaf; peduncles 5.4 mm long, enveloped by a number of small, greyish-white, papery, acuminate, scaly leaves; floral bracts 1.8 × 2.5 mm, broadly ovate, acuminate, acute, annular, fleshy, 3-veined; dorsal sepal 10.5–11 × 3.5–3.8 mm, oblong-lanceolate, acute, 5- or 7-veined; lateral sepals 10–11 × 4–4.5 mm, obliquely oblong, lanceolate, acute or acuminate, 7-veined, adnate to the foot of the column; petals 9.5–10 × 2.4–2.9 mm, lanceolate acute 3-veined; lip 1.2 × 0.6 cm, 3-veined; lateral lobes oblong, supplied by branches from the lateral veins of the lip, obtuse; midlobe recurved, crenulate, crisped, terminating in a subquadrate, 2-lobed limb with two fleshy crests; column 3.2 mm high, 3 mm broad, oblong or oval, toothed, at the apex; foot short but broad, margin curved in with a well-developed mentum. Anther terminal, 2-loculed; pollinia 4 in two pairs, oblong, 1.06 mm long, the outer pollinia 0.3 mm broad, the inner 0.2 mm broad and as long. Ovary with pedicel 4.4 mm long.

D i s t r. Rare, on branches or on rocks in the submontane or mid-country tropical wet evergreen forests up to 762 m alt. Hunnasgiriya, Hantane, Ritigala, Peradeniya, etc. Also in the Sikkim Himalaya, Khasia Hills, Nilgiri Hills and Konkan Ghats in India and in Java.

E c o l. Flowers March, August.
U s e s. Used in local medicine.

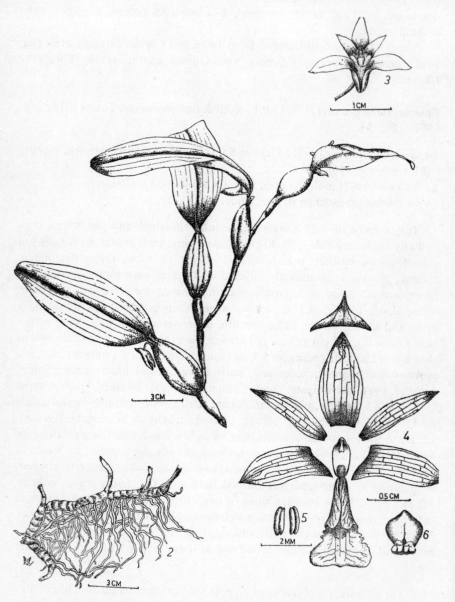

Fig. 33. *Ephemerantha macraei* (Lindl.) P.F. Hunt & Summerhayes. 1, branch with partially opened flowers. 2, stem with roots. 3, flower from front. 4, bract, sepals and petals spread out from front, lip from front not spread out, column from front. 5, pollinia. 6, operculum from front, magnified.

V e r n. Jata-Makuta.

I l l u s t r. King and Pantling, Ann. R. Bot. Gard. (Calcutta) 8: pl. 86. 1898; PDA, drawing.

N o t e. Lindley's original description of the species is based on drawings supplied by Macrae probably from his collection No. 21. This species is distinguished by the pendulous branching stems, each branch terminating in a 1-leaved fusiform internodal pseudobulb and 1-3 white flowers borne on short peduncles below the leaves.

S p e c i m e n s   E x a m i n e d. CEYLON: ANURADHAPURA DISTRICT: Ritigala, Mar. 1905, *Willis s.n.* (PDA), Feb. 1973, *Jayasuriya & Burtt 1156* (PDA, US), Sept. 1972, *Jayasuriya 917* (PDA, US), May 1924, *Jayasuriya 1718* (PDA, US). KANDY DISTRICT: Hunnasgiriya, *Jayaweera 1983* (PDA), Jun. 1960, *Jayaweera 4 (1)* (AMES); Peradeniya Bot. Gard, cultd., Oct. 1883, *s. coll. s.n.* (PDA). BADULLA DISTRICT: Haputale, Thotulagalla Estate, July 1969, *Wheeler 12169* (PDA, US). LOCALITY UNKNOWN: *Macrae 21* (K, lectotype). INDIA: Sikkim, May 1893, *Pantling 266* (AMES); Khasia Hills, 4000 ft, *Hooker 26* (K); Bengal, *Biswas 1938* (AMES); Coonoor, Nilgiri Hills, *J.D. Hooker 27* (K), *Thomson s.n.* (AMES); Assam, *Rita s.n.* (AMES).

5. DENDROBIUM

Swartz, Nova Acta Regiae Soc. Sci. Upsal. 6: 82. 1799.

Epiphytes; stems pseudobulbous or elongate and slender; leaves sessile, coriaceous or membranous but never plaited, distichous or not; flowers solitary or few-flowered, racemes leaf-opposed or terminal on pseudobulbs; sepals subequal, lateral sepals obliquely adnate by their bases to the column-foot, forming a mentum; petals smaller or larger than sepals; lip 3-lobed or entire, adnate to and incumbent on the foot of the column, concave or saccate, side lobes embracing the column; disc ridged or lamellate; column very short with a distinct foot which is often long; anther attached at its apex by a filament; pollinia 4 in two pairs without caudicles, free or pairs slightly adhering by a viscus.

Over 1000 species distributed from India and Ceylon to China and Japan and southwards through Malaysia to Australia and New Zealand.

KEY TO THE SPECIES

1 Stems very small
2 Lateral sepals 5-veined, lip panduriform, mentum long............**1. D. panduratum**
2 Lateral sepals 3-veined, lip rhomboidly cuneate, mentum short, column expanded into
   2 lateral processes at the top......................................**2. D. diodon**
1 Stems large, enlongate, erect or pendulous

3 Flowers in 1- or 2-flowered clusters on nodes along whip-like terminal ends of pseudobulbs...**3. D. crumenatum**
3 Flowers in 2–4-flowered clusters on nodes of leafy stems or thick pseudobulbs with or
without leaves
  4 Flowering pseudobulbs erect
    5 Sepals 5-veined, petals 3-veined, lip obovate-lanceolate................**4. D. nutans**
    5 Sepals 7-veined, petals 5-veined, lip ovate, pubescent............**5. D. heterocarpum**
  4 Flowering pseudobulbs or stems pendulous
    6 Flowers borne in leafy stems
      7 Flowers in terminal racemes, large...........................**6. D. maccarthiae**
      7 Flowers in leaf-opposed tubercles bursting through leaf sheaths below the mouth
      ....**7. D. bambusaefolium**
    6 Flowers borne in leafless pseudobulbs, lip ciliate.............**8. D. macrostachyum**

1. **Dendrobium panduratum** Lindl., J. Linn. Soc. Bot. 3: 19. 1859; Trimen, Handb. Fl. Ceylon 4: 150. 1897.—Fig. 34.

Dwarf epiphyte with tufted, pseudobulbous stems 5–10 cm long; pseudo-bulb ovoid or subglobose, about 1 cm long, superposed. Leaves distichous from the upper nodes, sessile, 2.5–3.8 cm long, linear-oblong or lanceolate, acuminate or acute, thinly coriaceous and spreading. Flowers about 1.2 cm long, narrow white, tinged with pink in terminal, erect, laxly 2–6-flowered racemes which measure 2.5–7.5 cm in length; floral bracts minute, ovate; dorsal sepal oblong-lanceolate, acuminate, 3-veined; lateral sepals falcately ovate, lanceolate, acuminate, 5-veined; petals oblanceolate, acute, 3-veined; lip panduriform, lateral lobes small, acute, midlobe broadly ovate or orbicular, crenulate, 3-veined, disc 5-veined, the outer veins branching; mentum stout, spur-like, straight or slightly incurved and 2-lobed at the tip, column very short, produced into a foot. Anther terminal, 2-loculed; pollinia 4, waxy, collateral in pairs. Ovary with pedicel 2.5–3 mm long.

D i s t r. Endemic. Rather rare, on branches of trees in the submontane or mid-country tropical wet evergreen forests extending on to the subtropical montane forests up to 1829 m alt. Ambagamuwa, Galboda, Hantane, Ramboda, Nuwara Eliya, Hakgala, Balangoda, etc.

E c o l. Flowers July–October.

I l l u s t r. PDA, drawing from *C.P. 2353*.

N o t e. This species is distinguished by the very small 2–3-leaved pseudobulb, 2–6 erect white-flowered racemes and the panduriform lip. This is allied to *Dendrobium diodon* Reichb. f. but differs from it in the 5-veined lateral sepals and the panduriform lip. Collections of Thwaites and Hooker are both in the same type cover in Herb. Lindley. *C.P. 2353* is selected as the lectotype.

S p e c i m e n s E x a m i n e d. KANDY DISTRICT: Hantane, Oct. 1881, *s. coll. s.n.* (PDA). EXACT LOCALITY UNKNOWN: Central Province, *s. coll. C.P. 2353* (K, lectotype, AMES, PDA), *Hooker 147* (K).

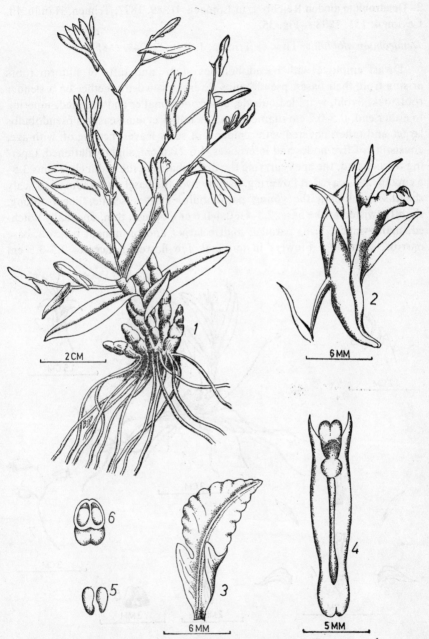

Fig. 34. *Dendrobium panduratum* Lindl. redrawn from a drawing of *C.P. 2353* in PDA. 1, a clump with pseudobulbs, leaves and flowers. 2, flower from the side. 3, lip, three quarters view from front. 4, rostrum from front. 5, pollinia, magnified. 6, operculum from inside, magnified.

2. Dendrobium diodon Reichb. f. in Linnaea 41: 89. 1877; Trimen, Handb. Fl. Ceylon 4: 151. 1898.—**Fig. 35.**

Dendrobium albidulum Thw. ex Trimen, J. Bot. 23: 243. 1885.

Dwarf epiphyte with pseudobulbous stems and tufts of filiform roots arising from their bases; pseudobulbs several, crowded together on a slender rootstock, ovoid, wrinkled outside, older ones smaller and rounded, tapering to either end, 0.5–0.7 cm diameter and as tall; previous season's pseudobulbs larger and taller, covered with remnants of scaly leaves, peeling off with age, consisting of five nodes and internodes, 1.6 × 0.6 cm, slightly flattened, tapering to each end, the apex carrying the dry remains of the peduncle; stems 3.5–5 cm tall, 2–4-leaved at flowering, usually two, the basal ones reduced to scaly sheaths enveloping the young pseudobulb. Leaves sessile, linear-oblong, slightly twisted at the base, 2.8–4 × 0.4–0.6 cm, obtuse, thin, unequally notched, many-veined, veins parallel, midrib larger and prominent beneath, base narrow, sheathing. Flowers in terminal, few-flowered racemes 2.5–3.5 cm

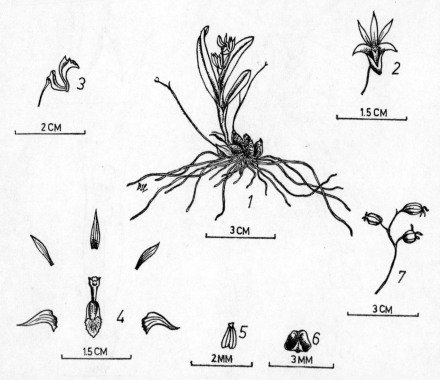

Fig. 35. *Dendrobium diodon* Reichb. f. 1, plant with inflorescence. 2, flower from front. 3, lip and column from side. 4, sepals and petals spread out from front, lip from front not spread out, column with a portion of the foot from front. 5, pollinia with gland. 6, operculum from inside. 7, fruits.

long; peduncle short; floral bracts 2.5–3 × 1.5 mm, ovate, acuminate, acute; dorsal sepal 6.5 × 2 mm, oblong-ovate, acuminate, acute, 3-veined, midrib more prominent; lateral sepals falcately ovate-oblong, 6 × 5 mm at the base, acuminate, acute, bases fusing along their inner edges to the back of the foot and projecting forwards, 3-veined with a strong midvein; petals 6.5 × 1.3 mm, lanceolate, acute, 3-veined; lip 6.8 × 6 mm, rhomboidly cuneate, curved; lateral lobes small, folded inwards, acute; midlobe slightly longer than the lateral lobes, orbicular, irregularly toothed, 3-veined; disc ridged as far as the base of the midlobe, terminating in a 3-toothed callus; column 1.5 mm high, sides expanded into two processes and bending inwards at the top, base continuing into a foot 4 × 1.5 mm, inner edges of the lateral sepals fusing with it. Anther terminal, 2-loculed, 1 × 0.8 mm, pollinia 4, waxy, cohering in two pairs to a small gland; each pollinium oblong or club-shaped, 0.7 × 0.16 mm. Ovary with pedicel 7.5 mm long. Fruit a globular capsule, 0.8 × 0.5 cm broad.

D i s t r. Endemic. Rather rare.

E c o l. Flowers July–October. Grows on trees in the subtropical montane forests where the climate is wet throughout the larger part of the year and windy from August to October. This area has an average annual rainfall of 3175 mm distributed over 217 days. Months of May to December are wet, cloudy and misty with occasional spells of sunshine. The temperature averages from a minimum of 30°F to a maximum of 79°F with humidity 71–88 per cent. Adam's Peak on *Eurya* sp., Hakgala, Hantane, Dumbagala, Rangala, etc.

I l l u s t r. PDA, drawing from *C.P. 3926*.

N o t e. Collections of Thwaites and Nock both from Hakgala are in same type cover at Herb. Kew. *C.P. 3926* is selected as the lectotype. The species is very similar to *Dendrobium panduratum* Lindl. but differs in the much smaller flowers, broader sepals, irregularly toothed midlobe of the lip and 3-toothed callus on the disc.

S p e c i m e n s E x a m i n e d. KANDY DISTRICT: Rangala, Sept. 1888, *s. coll. s.n.* (PDA); Hunnasgiriya, Nugagalla, Oct. 1972, *Jayasuriya 952* (PDA, US); Kabaragala, Raxawa Estate, Aug. 1969, *Wheeler 12253* (PDA, US). NUWARA ELIYA DISTRICT: Hakgala, 1867, *s. coll. C.P. 3926* (K, lectotype, PDA), 1900, *W. Nock s.n.* (K), Oct. 1882, *W. Nock s.n.* (PDA).

3. Dendrobium crumenatum Swartz, J. Bot. (Schrad.) 2: 237. 1700; Trimen, Handb. Fl. Ceylon 4: 151. 1898.—**Fig. 36.**

Onychium crumenatum Blume, Bijdr. 328. 1825.

Tufted epiphytic plant with pseudobulbous stems and fibrous roots; pseudobulbs 5–7 × 1–1.6 cm, spindle-shaped, ridged, located a node or two above

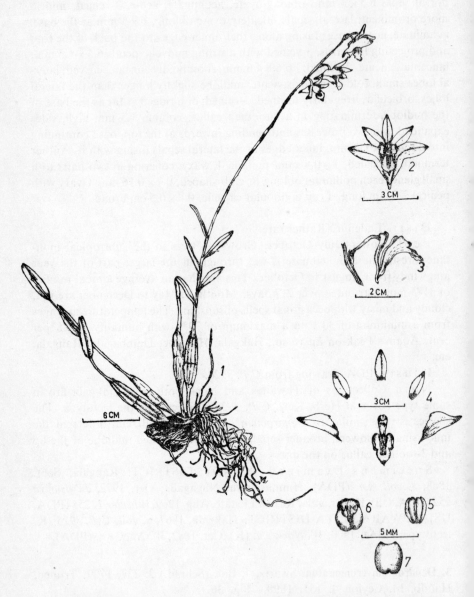

Fig. 36. *Dendrobium crumenatum* Swartz. 1, plant with inflorescence. 2, flower from front. 3, lip, foot and column from side. 4, sepals, petals, lip and column spread out from front. 5, pollinia. 6, operculum from inside. 7, operculum from behind.

the base of the stem. Leaves 3.4–4.4 × 0.6–1.2 cm, oblong or oblong-lanceolate, coriaceous, unequally notched at the apex, base sheathing the internode above, midrib prominent below. Flowers white, fragrant, 3.5–4.2 cm broad, in 1- or 2-flowered, short-peduncled clusters along the terminal, slender, naked end of the stem beyond the pseudobulb; floral bracts 5 × 3 mm, oblong, sheathing the pedicel, more or less annular, many-veined; dorsal sepal 2.2–2.5 cm × 7–8 mm, ovate-lanceolate, subacute, 7-veined, lateral veins branching at base giving a 9-veined appearance; lateral sepals 2.4–2.5 cm × 9–10 mm, obliquely ovate-lanceolate, hooded at acute apex, base broad, adnate obliquely along the entire length of the foot of the column, 7-veined; petals 2.1–2.2 cm × 6.5–7 mm, acute, 3-veined, lateral veins branching at base giving a 5-veined appearance; lip 3.3 × 1.4 cm, articulating with the foot of the column by a short mentum, lateral lobes orbicular, truncate, midlobe broadly ovate, acuminate, fimbriate, 5-veined, the extreme lateral veins much branched and supplying the lateral lobes, disc with 3 crenulate parallel ridges extending along the 3 centre veins as far as the middle of the midlobe; column 4 mm high, 3 mm broad, apex grooved to accommodate the anther, sides extending as two teeth, base produced into a foot 1.7 cm long. Anther terminal, 2-loculed, 2.5 × 2.3 mm, mitre-shaped; pollinia 4, collateral in pairs, 2.2 × 0.5 mm, sausage-shaped, placed horizontally at the base of the operculum. Ovary with pedicel 1.4 cm long.

D i s t r. Common, cultivated in the wet zone of the low-country where it thrives on the following host plants: *Cocos nucifera* L., *Area catechu* L., *Artocarpus heterophyllus* Lam., *Plumeria* spp., etc. Not found growing in the jungles and probably introduced originally from Malaya. It also occurs in Burma, Siam, China, Borneo, Sumatra, Java and Andaman Islands.

E c o l. Flowers March, December.

V e r n. Sudu-pareyi-mal (S); White dove orchid (E).

I l l u s t r. Hooker in Bot. Mag. 69: pl. 4013. 1843; Lindley, Bot. Reg. 25: pl. 22. 1839; Rumphius, Herb. Amb. 6: pl. 47, fig. 2. 1750; Miquel, Choix de Pl. Rar. ou Nov. Jard. Bot. Buit. pl. 22, fig. 1. 1864; Reichenbach, Gard. Chron. 72: 107. 1922; PDA, drawings.

N o t e. In Herb. Lindley thrre are three collections, two of which are Griffith's from Burma and the third is Cumming's collection from the Philippine Islands. This species is distinguished by the white fragrant flowers in 1- or 2-flowered clusters on slender whip-like terminal ends of pseudobulbs, all flowers opening at the same time.

S p e c i m e n s   E x a m i n e d. CEYLON: KANDY DISTRICT: Peradeniya. Bot. Gard., cultd. *s. coll. s.n.* (PDA). INDIA: Madras, 1901, *Bourne 2763* (K). BURMA: 1844, *Griffith s.n.* (K), 1838, *Griffith 14* (K). THAILAND: Dec. 1917, *Haniff 2709* (AMES), Apr. 1923, *Kerr 11* (AMES). MALAYA PENINSULA: May 1913, *C.B. Robinson s.n.* (AMES); SINGAPORE, Jan.

1960, *Bels 216* (AMES). INDO-CHINA: Mar. 1923, *Poilane 5737* (AMES).
SUMATRA: Kisaran, July 1927, *Yates 2584* (AMES), *Lutjeharms 4242*
(AMES), Jun. 1936, *Lutjeharms 5035* (AMES). JAVA: *Drake 1338* (AMES),
Kothals s.n. (AMES). BORNEO: Sarawak, May 1908, *Foxworthy 280*
(AMES); Tawao, Mar. 1923, *Elmer 10605* (AMES). PHILIPPINE ISLANDS:
Cumming s.n. (K).

4. Dendrobium nutans Lindl., Gen. et Sp. Orch. 90. 1830; Trimen, Handb.
Fl. Ceylon 4: 152. 1897.—**Fig. 37.**

Epiphyte with slender, pseudobulbous stems 8–20 cm long and tufted
roots; pseudobulb confined to the upper portion of the stem consisting of
many nodes and internodes; internodes 0.7–2.5 cm long, much swollen towards the middle, slender towards the base, yellowish, 4-grooved, hispidulous. Leaves distichous, distant, one leaf to a node, sessile, lower nodes bare,
2–4.2 × 0.5–0.8 cm, ovate-lanceolate or narrowly lanceolate, stiff, dark green,
shining on the upper surface, obtuse or unequally bifid. Flowers orange, yellow, pink or greenish-white, 2 cm across, in short, leaf-opposed, 2–4-flowered
racemes arising from the nodes of the pseudobulb; peduncle very short; floral bracts 2.2 × 2 mm, triangular-ovate, acute or subacute, 1-veined; dorsal
sepal 13.5 × 4.8 mm, oblong-lanceolate, rounded, 5-veined; lateral sepals obliquely oblong-ovate, 16 × 5 mm, obtuse, 5-veined, adnate to the foot of the
column; petals 14 × 4 mm, oblong-lanceolate, acute, crenulate, 3-veined, the
two lateral veins branching at the base; lip 19 × 6 mm, obovate-lanceolate;
lateral lobes small, obtuse, crenulate; midlobe ovate, undulate, subacute with
three prominent ridges on the disc continuing into the midlobe; mentum 5
mm, long; column 4 mm high, 2 mm broad, truncate, continuing into a foot
5 mm long. Anther terminal, 2-loculed, 1.4 × 1.2 mm; pollinia 4, in two pairs;
each pollinium 1.3 × 0.26 mm, sausage-shaped, appressed to its fellow. Ovary
with pedicel 2.3 cm long. Fruit a fusiform, smooth capsule, 1.1–1.5 cm long,
0.6 cm diameter, decurved at the pedicel.

D i s t r. Rather common, adapted to grow in a variety of climatic conditions ranging from the tropical wet evergreen forests to the subtropical montane forests from 1220 to 1829 m alt. Hantane, Ambagamuwa, Rangala,
Hunnasgiriya, Adam's Peak, Nuwara Eliya, Pidurutalagala, etc. Also in
South India.

E c o l. Flowers April, November–March. Some of its many host plants
are *Apodytes gardneriana* Miers, *Eugenia* sp., *Glochidion* sp., *Adinandra lasiopetala* (Wight) Choisy, *Palaquium rubiginosum* (Thw.) Engl. and *Neolitsea
fuscata* (Thw.) Alston.

I l l u s t r. Hook. f., Ann. R. Bot. Gard. (Calcutta) 5: pl. 18, 1895; PDA,
drawing.

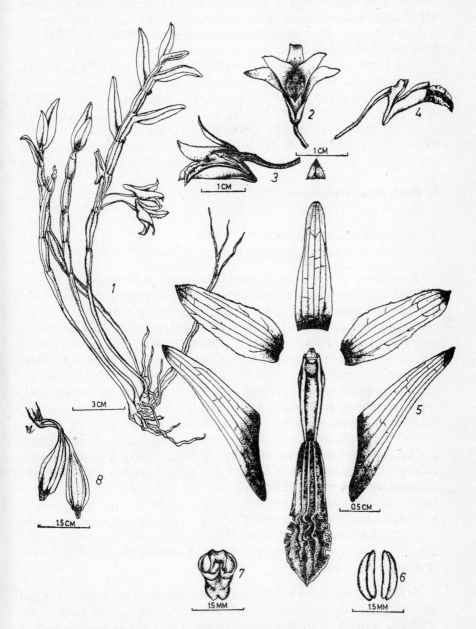

Fig. 37. *Dendrobium nutans* Lindl. 1, plant with flowers. 2, flower from front. 3, longitudinal section of flower. 4, lip, column and foot from side. 5, bract, sepals, petals and lip spread out from front, column from inside. 6, pollinia. 7, operculum from inside. 8, fruits.

N o t e. A varietal form of this species occurs in Ceylon where the leaves are less acute and sometimes almost oblong with a pink lip. The above species is much similar to *Dendrobium jerdonianum* Wight except that the latter is a more robust plant with deeper cleft leaves and much larger flowers.

S p e c i m e n s E x a m i n e d. CEYLON: KANDY DISTRICT: Peradeniya, Bot. Gard., Mar. 1916, *Supdt. s.n.* (PDA); Hunnasgiriya, Apr. 1960, *Jayaweera 4 (5)* (AMES). NUWARA ELIYA DISTRICT: Nuwara Eliya, Apr. 1970, *Cramer 2939* (PDA, US). Ambewela, *A.M. Silva s.n.* (PDA); *s. coll. s.n.* (PDA). LOCALITY UNKNOWN: *s. coll. C.P. 2357* (K, AMES, PDA), *C.P. 156* (K); 1916, *Macmillan s.n.* (PDA). INDIA: Nilgiris, May 1889, *Gamble 20516* (K); Kerala, Mar. 1896, *Bourdillon 802* (K).

5. Dendrobium heterocarpum Wall. ex Lindl., Gen. et Sp. Orch. 78. 1830; Trimen, Handb. Fl. Ceylon 4: 154. 1898.—**Fig. 38.**

Dendrobium aureum Lindl., ibid. 77.
Dendrobium rhombeum Lindl., Bot. Reg. 29: pl. 17. 1843.

Epiphyte with subclavate, yellowish-green, pseudobulbous stems 10–30 cm long, constricted at the nodes, leafless when flowering; internodes 1–2.7 × 0.8–1.5 cm, ribbed. Leaves 7–9.5 × 1.1–2.1 cm, oblong-lanceolate, flat, subcoriaceous, unequally notched at the apex or emarginate, bases sheathing the internodes above. Flowers dull pale yellow, fragrant, lip blotched brown, 4.5–7 cm across, 2 or 3 together arising from several nodes of the pseudobulb on short, stout peduncles; floral bracts 0.6 cm long and as broad, oblong, rounded or emarginate, 5–7 veined; dorsal sepal 2.8 × 0.9 cm, linear-oblong, rounded or truncate, 7-veined; lateral sepals 2.6 × 1.3 cm at the base, obliquely oblong-ovate, rounded, 7-veincd, attached to the foot of the column; petals 2.9 × 1.4 cm, ovate, apiculate or rounded, undulate, 5-veined; lip 2.9 × 2.5 cm, ovate, 3-lobed; lateral lobes vertical, rounded, embracing the column; midlobe recurved, pubescent and ridged; column 5 mm high and as broad, conical, produced into a broad foot which together with the disc forms a shallow mentum; apex of the column 3-toothed. Anther terminal, 2-loculed, 2.4 mm long, and as broad; pollinia 4, collateral in pairs; each pollinium 1.5 × 0.4 mm, inner pollinium of each pair narrower. Ovary with pedicel 2.3–2.9 cm long. Fruit a smoothly ridged, fusiform or conical capsule narrowly tapering to the pedicel.

D i s t r. Common, on trees from the submontane or mid-country tropical wet evergreen forests to subtropical montane forests above 1220 m alt. Rangala, Nuwara Eliya, Mt. Pedro, Hakgala, etc. Also in India at the foot of the Himalayan Range, Khasia and Nilgiri Hills, Burma, Siam, China, Java and the Philippine Islands.

E c o l. Flowers January–April. Epiphytic on a variety of trees some of

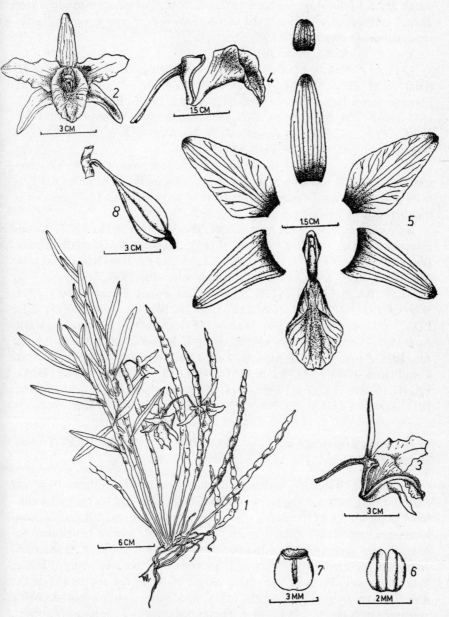

Fig. 38. *Dendrobium heterocarpum* Lindl. 1, plant with flowering pseudobulbs.
2, flower from front. 3, longitudinal section of flower. 4, lip, column and foot from
side. 5, bract, sepals and petals spread out from front, lip not spread out, column
with a portion of foot from front. 6, pollinia. 7, operculum from front. 8, fruit.

which are the following: *Kurrimia ceylanica* Arn., *Calophyllum trapezifolium* Thw., *Neolitsea fuscata* (Thw.) Alston, *Glochidion* sp., *Eurya japonica* Thunb. vars., *Gordonia speciosa* (Gardn.) Choisy, etc.

V e r n. Primrose Orchid (E).

I l l u s t r. Veitch, Manual orch. Pl. 1(3): 20 fig. 1888; Griffith, Ic. Pl. Asiat. 3: pl. 306. 1851; Lemaire, Jard. Fleur. 4: pl. 386. 1854; Vanhoutte, Flore de Serres Jard. l'Europe 8: pl. 842. 1852–3; Lindl., Bot. Reg. 29: pl. 17. 1843; Hook., Bot. Mag. 79: pl. 4708. 1853; Hook., Bot. Mag. pl. 4970. 1857; Gard. Chron., n.s. 23: 472 fig. 84b. 1885; Lindl., Bot. Reg. 25: pl. 20. 1839; Wight, Ic. Pl. Ind. Or. 5: pl. 1646. 1851.

N o t e. This is one of the most widely distributed of the *Dendrobium* species. It is much similar to *Dendrobium cucullatum* Br. from which it differs in its yellow fragrant flowers and the form of the labellum. The fragrance is that between violets and primrose.

S p e c i m e n s E x a m i n e d. CEYLON: KANDY DISTRICT: Kunudiyaparwita, Dec. 1917, *Lewis s.n.* (PDA); Maskeliya, Rajamally Estate, Dec. 1974, *Cramer 4388* (K, PDA). NUWARA ELIYA DISTRICT: Hakgala, Mar. 1906, *A.M. Silva s.n.* (PDA); Kandapola, May 1959, *Jayaweera 4 (9)* (AMES). BADULLA DISTRICT: Haputale Forest Reserve, July 1969, *Wheeler 12144* (PDA). LOCALITY UNKNOWN: *s. coll. C.P. 574* (K, PDA), in 1829, *Macrae 68* (K), *Walker 218* (K). INDIA: Sikkim Himalaya, Apr. 1891, *Pantling 200* (K, AMES); Bengal, *Biswas 2083* (AMES); Assam, Jan. 1928, *Parry 521* (K); Mysore, Feb. 1908, *Meebold 8826* (K); Madras, Coimbatore, *Fischer 988* (K). BURMA: Feb. 1837, *Griffith 5151* (K). THAILAND: North Thailand, Feb. 1914, *Kerr s.n.* (AMES); Doi Sutep, Jan. 1912, *Kerr 69* (AMES). YUNAN: Oct. 1937, *Tsai 56357* (AMES).

6. Dendrobium maccarthiae Thw., Bot. Mag. 11: pl. 4886. 1855; Trimen, Handb. Fl. Ceylon 4: 153. 1898.—**Fig. 39.**

Epiphyte with slender, terete, pendulous, pseudobulbous stems 16–60 cm long and tufted fibrous roots; internodes 1–4 cm long and leaves borne clustered at the apices of the stems, one to each node. Leaves, 4–8 × 0.9–1.3 cm, lanceolate, acuminate, membranous, veins parallel, midrib prominent beneath, bases sheathing the internodes; leaf sheaths 2 cm long, green when young but mottled brown when old, appressed to the internodes. Flowers light violet-pink, lip paler but with a purple blotch in the centre and on the disc, 5.5–6 cm long, 7.5 cm across, in lax, pendulous, 2–4-flowered, drooping racemes which measure 9–11 cm in length; peduncle 2–3 cm long with short, imbricate, basal, sterile bracteolar sheaths; pedicel arched at the point where it meets the ovary; floral bracts 0.6–0.8 × 0.3 cm, lanceolate, subulate, pale brown, papery, 3-veined; dorsal sepal 3.5–4 × 1 cm, lanceolate, acuminate, acute, 7-veined; lateral sepals 4–4.5 × 1.3 cm, subfalcately lanceolate, acumi-

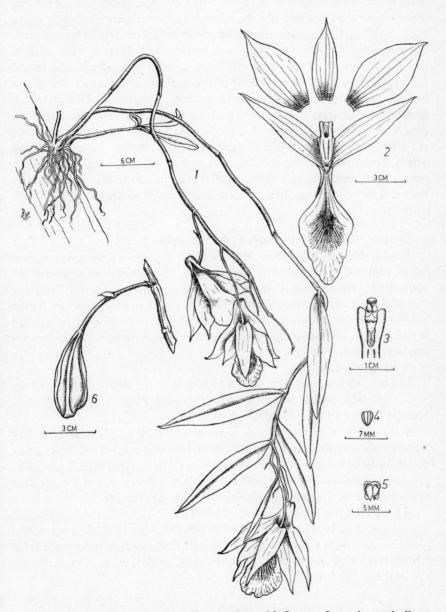

Fig. 39. *Dendrobium maccarthiae* Thw. 1, plant with flowers. 2, sepals, petals, lip and column spread out from front. 3, top of the column from inside. 4, pollinia. 5, operculum from inside. 6, fruit.

nate, acute, bases adnate to the foot of the column; petals 4–4.3 × 1.9 cm, oblong-lanceolate or ovate-oblong, acuminate, acute, margins slightly rolled back, 5-veined; lip 6 × 3 cm, rhomboid or subspathulate; lateral lobes rounded, convolute; midlobe broadly ovate, mucronate; column 0.4 cm high, 3-toothed at the top, the centre tooth short, straight and pointed, the lateral teeth recurving, the two projections of the operculum fitting into the spaces between the teeth; column continued into a foot, 1.6 cm long and 0.6 cm broad; mentum short, straight and conical. Anther terminal, versatile, 2-loculed, 2 × 2.4 mm, helmet-shaped with 2 projections behind to which the pollinia are attached when they are dislodged; pollinia 4, lodged in an operculum which articulates with the column by a narrow neck, oblong, collateral in pairs, slightly adhering to a viscus; each pollinium 2.3 × 0.44 mm. Ovary with pedicel 2.4–3.1 cm long. Fruit a loculicidal, fusiform capsule 3.2 × 1.17 cm diameter.

D i s t r. Endemic. Rare, only in the Ratnapura jungles.

E c o l. Flowers May–July. In tropical wet evergreen forests with a rainfall of over 150 inches, relative humidity 75–85 per cent and temperatures above 80°F. The amount of sunlight that these plants get is about 28–61 per cent of the normal sunlight. Some of the host plants on which it grows are the following: *Hevea brasiliensis* (Kunth) Muell. Arg., *Wendlandia bicuspidata* Wight & Arn., *Wormia triquetra* Rottb., *Elaeocarpus serratus* Linn., *Dipterocarpus zeylanicus* Thw., etc.

V e r n. Wesakmal (S).

I l l u s t r. Thwaites, Bot. Mag. 11: pl. 4886. 1855; Warner. Orch. Album 7: pl. 319. 1888; Bateman, Second Century Orch. Pl. pl. 158. 1867; Veitch, Manual Orch. Pl. 1 (3): 58. 1888.

N o t e. Plants of this species were sent to Kew by Thwaites and they flowered for the first time in 1864. It was named after Mrs. MacCarthy whose husband was the Colonial Secretary of Ceylon at that time. Later other growers too flowered it in England. The plant is distinguished by the large colourful flowers which hang down in 2–4-flowered racemes.

S p e c i m e n s E x a m i n e d. CEYLON: RATNAPURA DISTRICT: Ratnapura, Jun. 1925, *J.M. de Silva s.n.* (PDA), May 1959, *Jayaweera 4(8)* (AMES); Kuruwita Kande, May 1855, *s. coll. C.P. 3462* (K, holotype, PDA). ENGLAND: Cultivated, Nov. 1888, Hort. Kew (K), Aug. 1889, *J. Obrien s.n.* (K), Jan. 1887, *Veitch s.n.* (K).

7. Dendrobium bambusaefolium Par. et Reichb. f. in Trans. Linn. Soc. *D*ondon 30: 149. 1874.—**Fig. 40.**

Dendrobium haemoglossum Thw., Enum. Pl. Zeyl. 429. 1864; Trimen, Handb. Fl. Ceylon 4: 152. 1898.

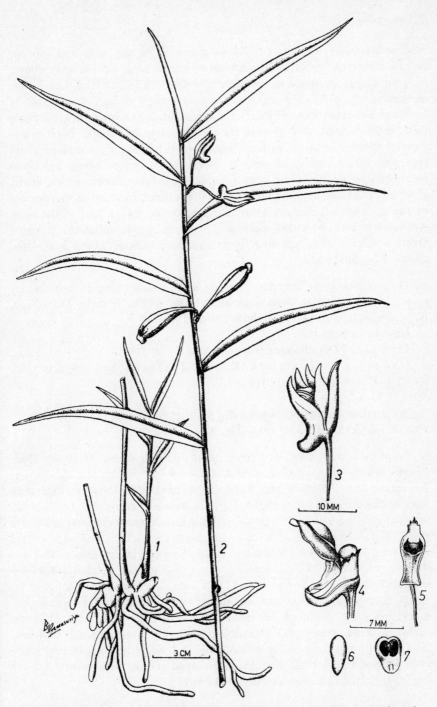

Fig. 40. *Dendrobium bambusaefolium* Par. et Reichb. f. redrawn from a drawing of
C.P. 3842 in PDA. 1, nodose rootstock with vermiform roots. 2, portion of the stem
with flowers and fruits. 3, flower, side view. 4, lip, foot and column, side view.
5, front view of column from inside. 6, pollinium. 7, operculum from inside.

Epiphyte with slender, pendulous stems 30–45 cm long and woody, nodose rootstock; roots long, vermiform; stems hard, naked, leafy above, base sometimes swollen and obpyriform; internodes 2–3 cm long. Leaves distichous, sessile, 8–12 × 0.4 cm, linear, rigidly papery, striate, obtuse, slightly incurved. Flowers yellow with dark red tinged lip, in 2–4-flowered, leaf-opposed tubercles which burst through the sheath below the mouth; floral bracts cupular at the base of the pedicel; sepals about 1.2 cm long, connivent, with recurved tips; dorsal sepal oblong; lateral sepals ovate-oblong, apiculate; petals as long as the sepals, linear-oblong; lip tongue-shaped, entire, acute, glabrous, undulate, adnate to the foot of the column; mentum short, rounded at the tip and incurved; column short, produced into a foot at the base. Anther terminal, 2-loculed; pollinia 4, oblong, waxy, collateral in pairs. Ovary with pedicel 1.2 cm long. Fruit an oblong capsule, about 2 cm long, narrowed at both ends.

D i s t r. Rare, on branches of trees in the submontane or mid-country tropical wet evergreen forests at about 1067 m alt. Matale, Dolosbage, Knuckles Hills, etc. Also in Malabar, South India.

E c o l. Flowers July.

I l l u s t r. PDA, drawing from *C.P. 3842.*

S p e c i m e n E x a m i n e d. KANDY DISTRICT: Dolosbage, in 1865, *s. coll. C.P. 3842* (PDA, holotype).

8. Dendrobium macrostachyum Lindl., Gen. et Sp. Orch. 78. 1830; Trimen, Handb. Fl. Ceylon 4: 152. 1898.—**Fig. 41.**

Epiphyte with slender, drooping, pseudobulbous stems 30–70 cm long. Leaves distichous, spreading, sessile, 4–6 × 0.9–2.3 cm, oblong or oblong-lanceolate, acute, many-veined, basal sheaths enveloping the stem, extending from one node to the other above. Flowers greenish-yellow, 2–2.3 cm across, arising from nodes of leafless pseudobulbs in 2–4-flowered clusters; peduncles short; floral bracts 2.6 × 1.8 mm, oblong-ovate, acute, 3-veined; dorsal sepal 1.3 × 0.4 cm, oblong-lanceolate, acute, 5-veined; lateral sepals 1.4–1.5 × 0.45 cm, obliquely oblong-lanceolate, acute, 5–7-veined; petals 1.3–1.4 × 0.4 cm, lanceolate, acute, 3-veined; lip 1.7 × 1.2 cm, 5-veined; lateral lobes of lip small, rounded and convolute, embracing the column; midlobe quadrately ovate, apiculate, recurved, crenulate, ciliate; column 4 mm high, 2.2 mm broad, a dorsal connective articulating with the anther. Anther terminal, 2-loculed, 1.6 mm long and as broad; pollinia 4, waxy in two collateral pairs; each pollinium 1.14 × 0.25 mm, sausage-shaped. Ovary with pedicel 1.3–1.7 cm long. Fruit a fusiform capsule, 3 × 0.7 cm.

D i s t r. Common and widely distributed from the wet low country and dry zone jungles right up to the subtropical montane forests at 1220 m

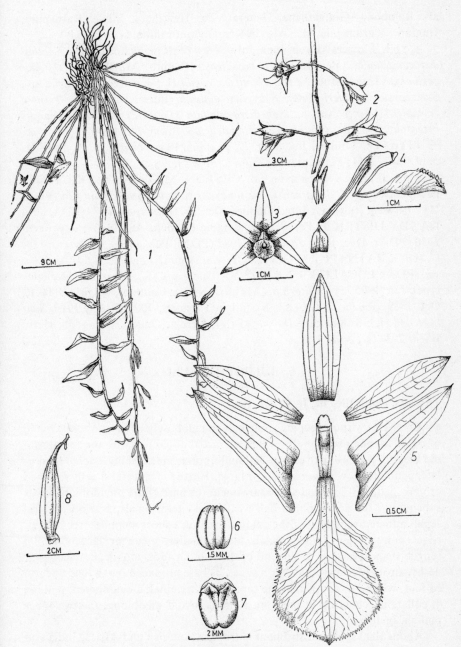

Fig. 41. *Dendrobium macrostachyum* Lindl. 1, plant with young fruits. 2, portion of
a pseudobulb showing flowers. 3, flower from front. 4, lip, column and foot from
side. 5, bract, sepals, petals and lip spread out from front, column from inside.
6, pollinia. 7, operculum from front. 8, fruit.

alt. Ramboda, Ginigathena, Heneratgoda, Hewaheta, Bibile, Ratnapura, Hantane, Kurunegala, etc. Also in Kerala, South India.

E c o l. Flowers March, June, July. A few of its many host plants: *Spathodea campanulata* Beauv. *Hevea brasiliensis* (Kunth) Muell. Arg., *Ostodes zeylanica* (Thw.) Muell. Arg., *Neolitsea cassia* (L.) Kosterm., *Scolopia* sp., *Semecarpus gardneri* Thw., *Syzygium aqueum* (Burm. f.) Alston, *Ouratea zeylanica* (Lam.) Alston., *Schefflera stellata* (Gaertn.) Baill., *Artocarpus heterophyllus* Lam., *Canthium coromandelicum* (Burm. f.) Alston.

I l l u s t r. Lindley, Bot. Reg. 22: pl. 1865. 1836; Wight, Ic. Pl. Ind. Or. 5: pl. 1647. 1851; PDA, drawing from *C.P. 3183*.

S p e c i m e n s E x a m i n e d. CEYLON, MATALE DISTRICT: Dikpatana, Dec. 1971, *Jayasuriya, Dassanayake & Balasubramaniam 436* (PDA, US); between Rattota & Illukkumbura, Oct. 1971, *Jayasuriya 277* (PDA, US). KANDY DISTRICT: Peradeniya, Botanic Garden, Aug. 1955, *Jayaweera 1430* (PDA), Dec. 1959, *Jayaweera 1982* (PDA), Feb. 1960, *Jayaweera 4 (6)* (AMES). RATNAPURA DISTRICT: Ratnapura, June 1925, *J.M. de Silva s.n.* (PDA). LOCALITY UNKNOWN: *Walker s.n.* (K), *Macrae 17* (K, holotype), Jun. 1905, *Schlechter s.n.* (AMES). INDIA: Coonoor, Nilgiris, 6000 ft, Oct. 1889, *Gamble 21415* (K); Kodaikanal Region, 7000 ft, July 1913, *Souliere 848* (K); S. Konkan, *Dalzell 45* (K); Kerala, Quilon, Oct. 1835, Herb. *Wight 2950* (K, AMES).

6. BULBOPHYLLUM

Thouars, Orch. Illes Fr. tt. 92–97. 1882.

Epiphytes with a creeping rootstock and globosely or subglobosely ovoid or ovoid oblong pseudobulbs which are naked or clothed with the remains of old sheaths; leaves one to each pseudobulb, coriaceous, oblong, oval or lanceolate, petiolate; flowers very small or large, 1-many in spicate, shortly racemed or umbelled, 2–8-flowered scapes arising at the base of the pseudobulb; sepals subequal or the dorsal about half as long as lateral sepals, 5-veined, lateral sepals adnate to the foot of the column forming a short mentum, free or their edges more or less joined; petals much smaller, ovate or lanceolate; lip tongue-shaped, hinged to the end of the column foot, mobile, coriaceous or fleshy, strongly recurved; column short, its base produced into a long upcurved foot, winged or toothed at the top; anther terminal, 2-chambered; pollinia 4, collateral, cohering in pairs by a viscus, ovoid or oblong, the two inner pollinia smaller.

About 1000 species distributed in tropical America and Africa, India and New Zealand.

KEY TO THE SPECIES

1 Plants small
  2 Flowers solitary or 2 together, dorsal sepal 5-veined...............**1. B. crassifolium**
  2 Flowers in 2–5-flowered umbels
    3 Dorsal sepal 4-veined......................................**2. B. maskeliyense**
    3 Dorsal sepal 3-veined
      4 Flowers purple..**3. B. purpureum**
      4 Flowers greenish-orange or straw-coloured
        5 Fruit capsules 6–8 mm long
          6 Lip tomentose-papillate, bract very small....................**4. B. tricarinatum**
          6 Lip papillate in the midlobe, bract broadly ovate, 1-veined......**5. B. petiolare**
        5 Fruit capsules 2 cm long, margin of petals irregularly suberose.......**6. B. trimeni**
1 Plants large, lateral sepals of flowers curving inwards
  7 Flowers solitary or 2 together, dull purple; dorsal sepal 9-veined........**7. B. elegans**
  7 Flowers 2–7 in umbels, dorsal sepal 5-veined
    8 Petals ciliate with long hairs..**8. B. wightii**
    8 Petals serrate or entire
      9 Petals serrate...**9. B. elliae**
      9 Petals entire
        10 Lip tongue-shaped, 6 mm long..............................**10. B. macraei**
        10 Lip ovate, 2.6 mm long.....................................**11. B. thwaitesii**

1. **Bulbophyllum crassifolium** Thw. ex Trimen, J. Bot. 23: 244. 1885; Trimen, Handb. Fl. Ceylon 4: 155. 1898.—**Fig. 42.**

Dwarf epiphyte about 2 cm tall with smooth, pisiform pseudobulbs 0.6–2 cm diameter, crowded on a stiff, slender rootstock bearing numerous, flexuous, filiform roots. Leaves solitary, sessile, 1.3–2 × 0.7 cm, oval or suborbicular, thickly coriaceous and channelled along the centre. Flowers solitary, minute, 6.5 mm across, yellowish-green spotted with red and with white or reddish lip, shortly peduncled in the sheath of a short, truncate bract; dorsal sepal broadly ovate, 4 mm long and as broad, arched, erect, 5-veined; lateral sepals of the same size as the dorsal, spreading, 5-veined; petals minute, broad, truncate; lip very small, 3 mm long, tongue-shaped, truncate or obtuse, curved, articulating on the foot of the column; column very short, produced into an upcurved foot at the base. Anther terminal, 2-loculed, 1.6 mm long; pollinia 4, ovoid, collateral in two pairs, the outer pollinia 0.5 × 0.25 mm and the inner ones 0.37 × 0.12 mm. Ovary with pedicel 7 mm long.

D i s t r. Endemic. Very rare, on trees in the tropical wet evergreen forests Kukul Korale, Ritigala etc.

E c o l. Flowers September, March.

I l l u s t r. PDA, drawing from *C.P. 3879.*

N o t e. This is a small inconspicuous species with leaves resembling those of *Hoya* in miniature and very small solitary flowers. It is allied to *Bulbophyllum elegans* Gard. but the plants are smaller.

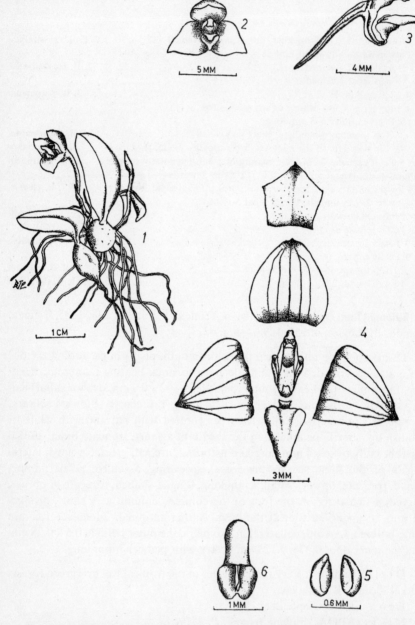

Fig. 42. *Bulbophyllum crassifolium* Thw. ex Trimen. 1, plant with an inflorescence. 2, flower from front. 3, column and lip from side. 4, bract, sepals and lip spread out from front, column from inside with the minute petals attached to the sides of the foot. 5, pollinia. 6, operculum from inside.

Specimens Examined. ANURADHAPURA DISTRICT: Ritigala, Mar. 1905, *Willis s.n.* (PDA). RATNAPURA DISTRICT: Kukul
Korale, Mar. 1905, *s. coll. C.P. 3879* (PDA, holotype).

2. Bulbophyllum maskeliyense Livera, Ann. R. Bot. Gard. (Peradeniya) 10:
142. 1926; Alston in Trimen, Handb. Fl. Ceylon 6: 273. 1931.—**Fig. 43.**

Dwarf epiphyte with small, naked, crowded pseudobulbs 4–7 mm diameter; roots long and fibrous. Leaves sessile, one to each pseudobulb and
from the top of it, 1.2–2.1 × 0.3–0.7 cm, oblong, thickly coriaceous, retuse,
unequal, entire, shining above and dull green below. Flowers small in 2–4-
flowered, erect scapes arising from the base of the pseudobulb. Peduncle
about 1 cm long, jointed, bearing two brown membranous scaly leaves;
floral bracts 2–2.5 × 1–1.2 mm, ovate, acute, 1-veined, membranous; pedicel
very short and swollen; dorsal sepal 5–6 × 1.2–2 mm, linear-lanceolate,
acute, 4- or 5-veined; lateral sepals 5–5.5 × 2–2.5 mm, falcate-ovate, acute, 4-
or 5-veined, adnate to the foot of the column at base; petals 2.5–3 × 1.4 mm
ovate or oblong-ovate, obtuse, 1–3-veined; lip small, thick, 3 × 1.2 mm, tongue-shaped, recurved, articulating with the foot; column short, about 1 mm
tall, toothed, base produced into a foot. Anther terminal, 0.56 mm long and
as broad, 2-locular; pollinia 4 in two pairs, the inner of each pair smaller; larger pollinia 0.47 × 0.3 mm, smaller pollinia 0.34 × 0.2 mm. Ovary 2 mm long.
Fruit a smooth oblong, shining capsule 6 × 4.5 mm.

D i s t r. Endemic. Rare, on the bark of trees and wet rocks in the subtropical montane forests. Maskeliya, Dolosbage, Nuwara Eliya, Rangala, etc.

E c o l. Flowers August, September.

I l l u s t r. PDA, drawing.

N o t e. This species is distinguished by the small, solitary-leaved naked
pseudobulbs, 2–4-flowered scapes and almost equal sepals which are 4- or 5-
veined.

Specimens Examined. KANDY DISTRICT: Maskeliya, Meeri-
cotta Estate, Aug. 1924, *Stedman s.n.* (PDA, holotype); Dolosbage, Raxawa
Estate, Aug. 1969, *Jayaweera 3061* (PDA), Aug. 1969, *Wheeler 12255* (PDA,
US); Rangala, Sept. 1969, *Jayaweera 3067* (PDA); Adam's Peak, Jun. 1972,
Cramer 3797 (PDA, US). NUWARA ELIYA DISTRICT: Nuwara Eliya,
s. coll. C.P. 2740 (PDA), in part.

3. Bulbophyllum purpureum Thw., Enum. Pl. Zeyl. 298. 1861; Trimen, Handb.
Fl. Ceylon 4: 155. 1898.—**Fig. 44.**

Dwarf epiphyte with small, 1-leaved pseudobulbs; pseudobulbs 5 mm long,
4 mm broad, ovoid on a very short slender rootstock with thread-like, branched roots. Leaves 1–2.4 × 0.3–0.7 cm, thick, obovate, reflexed, notched or emarginate, coriaceous, each narrowed at the base into a petiole about 2 mm long.

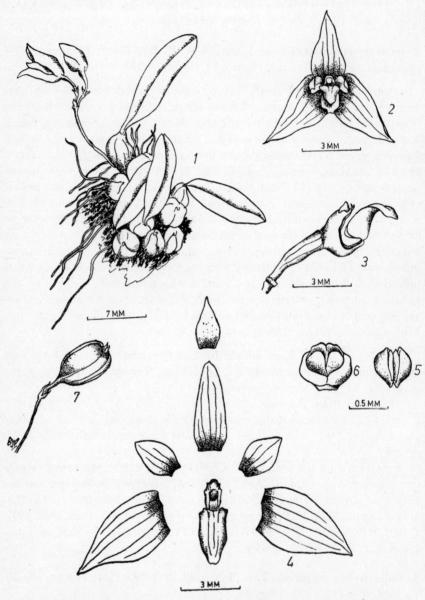

Fig. 43. *Bulbophyllum maskeliyense* Livera. 1, a clump of 1-leaved, naked pseudobulbs and a 2-flowered scape. 2, flower from front. 3, column, foot and lip from
side. 4, bract, sepals, petals, lip and column spread out from front. 5, pollinia.
6, operculum from inside. 7, fruit.

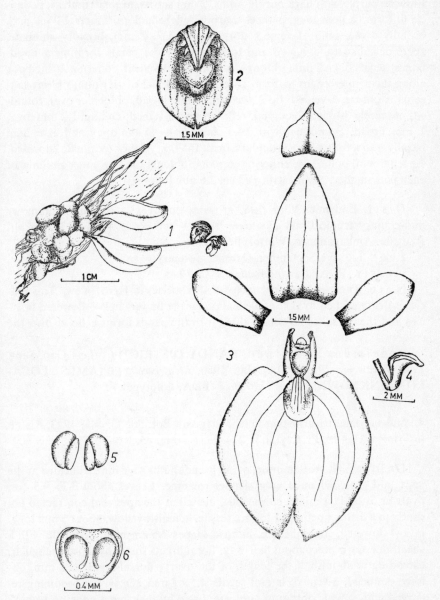

Fig. 44. *Bulbophyllum purpureum* Thw. 1, plant with inflorescence. 2, flower from front. 3, bract, sepals, petals and lip spread out from front, column from inside, lateral sepals and column much enlarged. 4, lip from side. 5, pollinia, magnified. 6, operculum from inside.

Flowers purple with dark purple veins, 2 mm across, in small umbels; peduncle filiform, 2.3 cm long; pedicel sharply deflexed; floral bracts 1.2 × 1 mm,
broadly ovate, acute, 1-veined; dorsal sepal 3.6 × 2 mm, broadly subulate,
acute or subacute, 3-veined and together with the petals forming a hood;
lateral sepals 3.4 × 2 mm, oblong-ovate, acute, 3-veined, cohering at the back
along their inner edges to form a keel; petals 1.8–2 × 1–1.1 mm, oblong-lanceolate, obtuse, 1-veined; lip 2 mm long, 1 mm broad, oblong or oval, rounded, obscurely 3-lobed, recurved, reflexed and 5-veined; column 1.2 mm high,
1 mm broad, cylindrical with two short arms at the apex and extending
basally into a foot which articulates with the lip. Anther terminal, 2-loculed,
1.5 × 0.6 mm, pollinia 4, cohering in pairs, oblong, the two inner pollinia of
each pair smaller. Ovary with pedicel 2.6 mm long.

Distr. Endemic. Very rare, growing on trees in the submontane or
mid-country tropical wet evergreen forests between 571 and 1372 m alt.
Rangala, Ambagamuwa, Wattekelle, Hantane, etc.

Ecol. Flowers September–October, January.

Illustr. PDA, drawing from *C.P. 3679.*

Note. There are no specimens of this species in Herb. Kew. This species is distinguished by the sessile leaves, purple flowers in 2–5-flowered fascicles and the dorsal sepal which along with the petals forms a hood over the
column.

Specimens Examined. KANDY DISTRICT: Corbets Gap, Sept.
1960, *Jayaweera 1973* (PDA), Jan. 1960, *Jayaweera 5 (3)* (AMES). LOCA-
LITY UNKNOWN: *s. coll. C.P. 3677* (PDA, holotype).

4. Bulbophyllum tricarinatum Petch, J. Indian Bot. Soc. 3: 148. 1923; Alston
in Trimen, Handb. Fl. Ceylon 6: 274. 1931.—**Fig. 45.**

Dwarf epiphyte with minute, ovoid pseudobulbs 4 × 3 mm, truncated at the
apex and crowded on a very slender rhizome. Leaves about 3.2 × 0.5 cm,
ovate or ovate-lanceolate, coriaceous, incised at the apex and contracted abruptly to a distinct petiole. Flowers sessile, greenish-yellow, about 5 mm long,
in 2–4-flowered, subumbellate, filiform scapes 2.5 cm high; peduncle with a
sheathing sterile bract about half-way; floral bracts small, hyaline, triangular,
extending to about half the length of the ovary; dorsal sepal 5 × 2 mm, oblong, rounded, 3-veined; lateral sepals 4.5 × 2 mm, semi-ovate becoming recurved and convex, obtuse or truncate, fused by their inner edge up to half-
way or close to the top, adnate to the foot, 3-veined; petals small, 2 × 0.75 mm,
oblong with a triangular tip, 1-veined; lip tongue-shaped, recurved, channelled
in the centre, tomentose-papillate with two small, erect, lateral lobes before
the bend; column short, toothed at the apex. Anther terminal, 2-loculed;
pollinia 4, pear-shaped in two pairs, one of each pair smaller than the other.

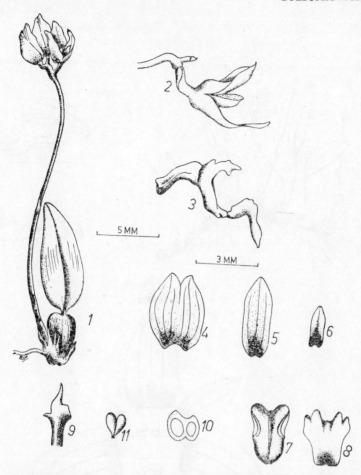

Fig. 45. *Bulbophyllum tricarinatum* Petch, redrawn from the original figure. 1, pseudobulb and inflorescence. 2, flower, side view. 3, column and lip, lateral view. 4, lateral sepals. 5, dorsal sepal. 6, petal. 7, lip from front. 8, lip from behind. 9. lateral process of column. 10, operculum. 11, pollinia from front.

Ovary green, curved, feebly ribbed and about 2 mm long. Fruit a small capsule 6–8 mm in length.

D i s t r. Endemic. Very rare, on trees in the subtropical montane forests up to 1524 m alt. Maturata.

E c o l. Flowers October–November.

I l l u s t r. Petch, J. Indian Bot. Soc. 3: 150 (Fig.) 1923.

N o t e. Very similar to *Bulbophyllum maskeliyense*, named *tricarinatum* because of the three ribs or keels on the dorsal sepal. It seems to be allied to *Bulbophyllum moniliforme* Par. & Reichb. f. from Tenasserim but the latter has the dorsal and lateral sepals 5-nerved.

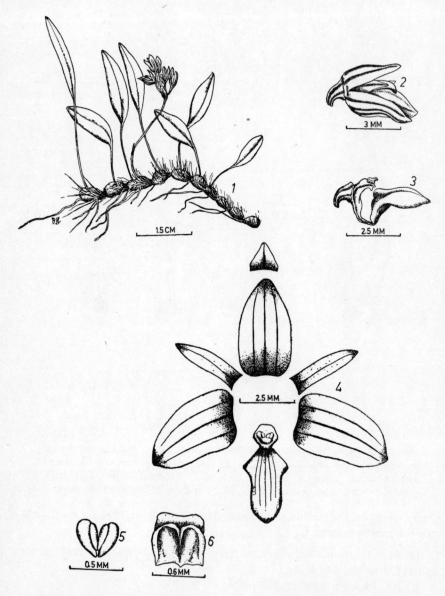

Fig. 46. *Bulbophyllum petiolare* Thw. 1, plant with inflorescence. 2, flower from side. 3, lip and column from side, three quarters view. 4, bract, sepals, petals, lip and column spread out from front; petals enlarged. 5, pollinia. 6, operculum from inside.

S p e c i m e n s E x a m i n e d. NUWARA ELIYA DISTRICT:Maturata, Oct. 1921, *Paine s.n.* (PDA, holotype).

5. Bulbophyllum petiolare. Thw., Enum, Pl. Zeyl. 298. 1861; Trimen, Handb. Fl. Ceylon 4: 155. 1898.—**Fig. 46.**

Epiphyte with a creeping rootstock and long, filiform roots; pseudobulbs pisiform, 4–6 mm diameter, edge-to-edge like a chain. Leaves one to each pseudobulb, petioled, lamina 2–5 cm long, linear-oblong or oblanceolate, thick, coriaceous, subacute, notched or rounded at the apex, base tapering to a slender petiole about 1–2.5 cm long. Flowers greenish-orange with a red lip, in 4- or 5-flowered fascicles at the top of a slender, erect peduncle about 2.5–7.5 cm long with a subulate, sterile bract about half way; pedicel 1.5 mm long; floral bracts 1.5×1.7 mm, broadly ovate, acute, 1-veined; sepals oblong-lanceolate, obtuse, 3-veined, ridged dorsally along the veins; dorsal sepal 4.5×2.2 mm, lateral sepals 5×2 mm, attached to the foot of the column; petals 2.5×0.8 mm, linear-oblong, subacute, 1-veined, ringed along the vein dorsally; lip 3.6×1.5 mm, tongue-shaped, convex, recurved, obscurely 3-lobed, 3-veined, lateral veins branching at base to give a 5-veined appearance; lateral lobes rounded, merging into the midlobe, obscure; midlobe oblong, rounded at apex and papillate; column 0.7 mm tall and as broad, sides expanded, terminating in two lateral, ovate, acute teeth extending beyond. Anther terminal, 2-loculed, 0.5×0.6 mm, quadrate, hinged to the short truncate tooth of the column by a slender stalk; pollinia 4, collateral in two pairs, individuals of each pair unequal, larger pollinia 0.36 mm long and the smaller ones on the inside of larger ones. Ovary 1 mm long and fruit a small capsule, measuring about 8 mm in length.

D i s t r. Endemic. Rare, on trees in the submontane or mid-country tropical wet evergreen forests up to 1372 m alt. Rangala, Ambagamuwa, Sinharaja forest, Maskeliya, etc.

E c o l. Flowers March, August, November, December.

I l l u s t r. PDA drawing from *C.P. 3184.*

N o t e. The only specimen in Herb. Kew is that of Walker from Ceylon. This species is allied to *Bulbophyllum purpureum* Thw. from which it differs in the longer scape, longer petioled leaves and rather larger flower and the purple lip.

S p e c i m e n s E x a m i n e d. KANDY DISTRICT: Maskeliya, Mar. 1891, *s. coll. s.n.* (PDA); Rangala, Mar. 1961, *Jayaweera 5 (2)* (AMES). RATNAPURA DISTRICT: Sinharaja Forest, *s. coll. C.P. 3184* (PDA, lectotype). LOCALITY UNKNOWN: *Walker s.n.* (K).

6. Bulbophyllum trimeni (Hook. f.) J.J. Sm. in Bull. Jard. Bot. Buitenz. 2, s.8: 28. 1912.—**Fig. 47.**

Cirrhopetalum trimeni Hook. f. in Trimen, Handb. Fl. Ceylon 4: 158. 1898.

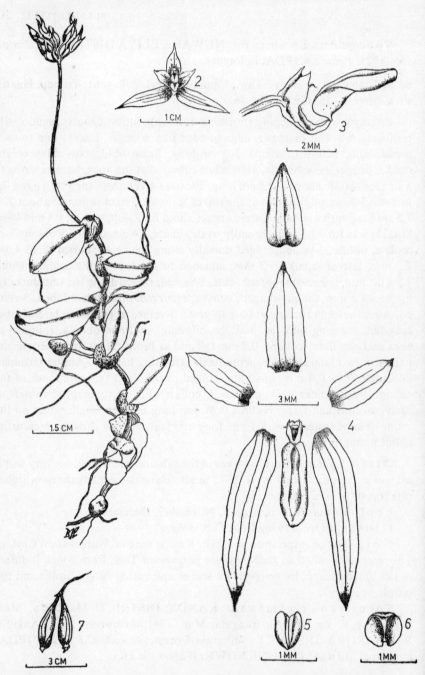

Fig. 47. *Bulbophyllum trimeni* (Hook. f.) J.J. Sm. 1, plant with inflorescence.
2, flower from front, spread out. 3, lip and column from side. 4, bract, sepals,
petals and lip spread out from front, column from inside. 5, pollinia. 6, operculum from frout. 7, fruits.

Epiphyte with pseudobulbous stems on a creeping rootstock; internodes 0.5–2 cm long; pseudobulbs brownish-green, globose-ovoid, duck-like, asymmetrical, 0.5–0.8 × 0.4–0.7 cm, wrinkled or corrugated. Leaves sessile, sharply turned away from the pseudobulb, 1 or 2 to each pseudobulb, 0.7–2.3 × 0.4–1.2 cm, oblong, lanceolate or oblong-ovate, notched or emarginate, thick, coriaceous, stiff, prominently 1-veined. Flowers straw-coloured, less than 1 cm long, 6–8 flowers in long-peduncled umbels arising from the bases of pseudobulbs; peduncle slender, 4.5 cm long with three or more sheathing scaly bracts, speckled reddish-brown; floral bracts 2.6 × 1.1 mm, subulate-ovate, acute, or subacute, 3-veined; dorsal sepal 5.4 × 2.3 mm, oblong-subulate or ovate-oblong, shortly acuminate, acute, margin irregular and hyaline, 3-veined; lateral sepals 8.2–8.6 × 2.1–2.4 mm, lanceolate-ovate, acute, 3-veined; petals 3.2–4.2 × 1.6 mm, oval-oblong, apiculate or obtuse, margin irregularly suberose; lip 3.6 × 1.2 mm, thick, tongue-shaped, obtuse, strongly recurved, connected to the base of the column by a narrow, curved foot; column 1.6 mm high, 1 mm broad, cylindrical, 3-toothed at the top and the base, continuing into the foot. Anther terminal, 2-loculed, 0.53 mm long and as broad; pollinia 4, oblong, collateral in pairs, each pollinium 0.6 × 0.3 mm. Ovary with pedicel 3.2 mm long. Fruit a fusiform capsule, 2 × 0.55 cm.

D i s t r. Endemic. Rare, on trees above 762 m alt. in the subtropical montane and the mid-country tropical wet evergreen forests. Maskeliya, Kandapola, Rangala (Corbet's Gap), Nuwara Eliya, Hakgala, etc.

E c o l. Flowers September. Two of its host plants are *Neolitsea fuscata* (Thw.) Alston and *Eurya japonica* Thunb. vars.

I l l u s t r. PDA, 2 drawings.

N o t e. Hooker's description of the species from Trimen's single collection is not applicable generally. The umbels are 6–8-flowered and the sepals and petals 3-veined. This species is distinguished from the others by the miniature duck-like appearance of the pseudobulb and leaf, and the pale straw-coloured flowers with a dark recurved lip.

S p e c i m e n s E x a m i n e d. KANDY DISTRICT: Maskeliya, Mariacotta Estate, Aug. 1922, *Stedman s.n.* (PDA); Hatton, Nov. 1959, *Jayaweera 6 (3)* (AMES); July 1923, *s. coll. s.n.* (PDA); Gampola, Nuwara Eliya Road, Oct. 1974, *Davidse & Sumithraarachchi 7964* (PDA, US). NUWARA ELIYA DISTRICT: Hakgala, Sept. 1894, *Trimen s.n.* (K, Holotype), Sept. 1960, *Jayaweera 1974* (PDA), Feb. 1924, *Livera s.n.* (PDA), Apr. 1906, *A.M. Silva s.n.* (PDA); Kandapola, Jan. 1923, *Paine s.n.* (PDA).

7. Bulbophyllum elegans Gardner ex Thw., Enum. Pl. Zeyl. 298. 1861; Trimen, Handb. Fl. Ceylon 4: 156. 1898.—**Fig. 48.**

Epiphyte with pseudobulbous stems on a stout, creeping rootstock; pseu-

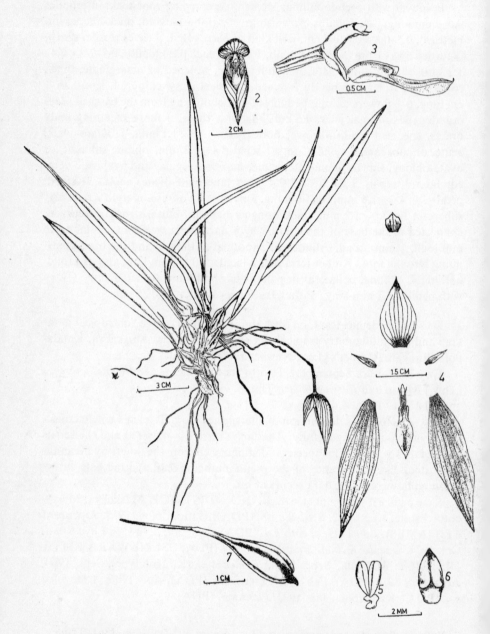

Fig. 48. *Bulbophyllum elegans* Gardner ex Thw. 1, plant with inflorescence. 2, flower from front. 3, column and lip from side. 4, bract, sepals and petals spread out from front, lip from front not spread out, column from inside. 5, pollinia with gland. 6, operculum from inside. 7, fruit.

dobulbs 1.2–1.6 cm long, 0.7–0.9 cm broad, ovoid, slightly bent, tapering to the apex, ridged at length; roots fibrous, branched, spreading out from the base of the pseudobulbs and internodes. Leaves solitary, attached to the apices of pseudobulbs by very short petioles, 5.5–14.2 × 0.8–1.1 cm, linear or linear-lanceolate, coriaceous, acute or subacute; midrib conspicuously grooved. Flowers dull purple with a green lip, 4 cm long, 1 cm across, solitary or two together in slender, decurved, pendulous inflorescences; peduncle 6.5 cm long; floral bracts 5.2 × 4.8 mm, oblong, mucronate, papery, 7–9-veined; dorsal sepal ovate, 2 × 1.1 cm, acuminate, acute, 9-veined and hooded; lateral sepals lanceolate, 3.9 × 1 cm, acuminate, acute, 9-veined, curved inwards, cohering in the midline along their outer edges forming a keel; petals 5.6 × 2.1 mm, lanceolate, acuminate, acute, 3-veined, scantily toothed at the apical portion of the margin; lip 1.4 × 0.35 cm, lanceolate, fleshy, acuminate, acute, 3-lobed; lateral lobes rounded, incurved; midlobe greenish-purple, spotted, grooved in the centre; column 6 mm high, 1.6 mm broad, cylindrical with two long narrow arms projecting beyond the anther. Anther terminal, 2-loculed, 2.4 × 1.5 mm; pollinia 4, collateral in two pairs and attached to a small gland; each pollinium 1.52 × 0.74 mm oblong or subpyriform, closely appressed to its fellow. Ovary with pedicel 1.5–1.7 cm long. Fruit a long peduncled, pyriform capsule, 2.5 × 1 cm.

Distr. Endemic. Rather rare, on trees in the tropical wet evergreen forests and submontane or mid-country tropical wet evergreen forests between 457 and 1829 m alt. Ambagamuwa, Rangala, Adam's Peak, Hantane, Maskeliya, Ritigala, etc.

Ecol. Flowers January, February–May.

Illustr. Trimen, Handb. Fl. Ceyl. pl. 88. 1893; PDA, 2 drawings from *C.P. 2350.*

Note. This species is distinguished from the others by its large leaves, 1- or 2 large -flowered inflorescences and 9-veined sepals in the flower.

Specimens Examined. ANURADHAPURA DISTRICT: Ritigala, May 1905, *Willis s.n.* (PDA), May 1974, *Jayasuriya 1697* (PDA, US). KEGALLE DISTRICT: Kitulgala, May 1928, *J.M. Silva s.n.* (PDA). RATNAPURA DISTRICT: Ratnapura, Jan. 1932, *Foote 9017* (PDA); Gilimale, Feb. 1960, *Jayaweera 1972* (PDA), Jan. 1960, *Jayaweera 5 (4)* (AMES). LOCALITY UNKNOWN: *s. coll. C.P. 2350* (K, holotype, PDA).

8. Bulbophyllum wightii Reichb. f. in Walp. Ann. 6: 262. 1861.—**Fig. 49.**

Cirrhopetalum grandiflorum Wight, Ic. Pl. Ind. Or. 5: 1, 7. 1851; Trimen, Handb. Fl. Ceylon 4: 157. 1898.

Epiphyte with pseudobulbous stems on a creeping rootstock; internodes 5.5–13.5 cm long, ribbed, brown, covered with dark brown leaf sheaths;

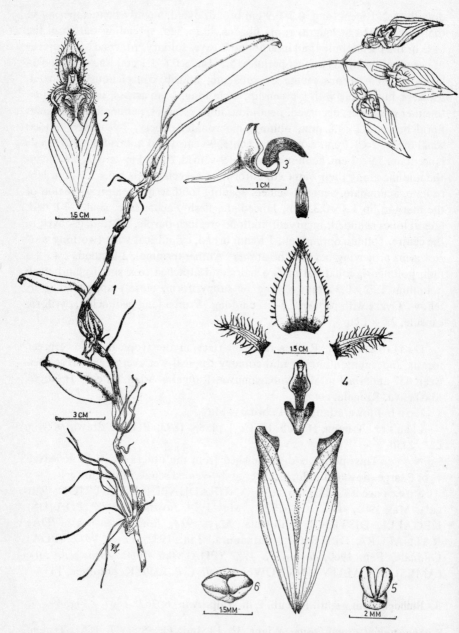

Fig. 49. *Bulbophyllum wightii* Reichb. f. 1, plant with inflorescence. 2, flower from front. 3, lip and column from side, column exaggerated. 4, bract, dorsal sepal, petals, column and lip spread out from front, column with a portion of foot; lateral sepals natural position, fused in front. 5, pollinia with viscus. 6, operculum, oblique view from inside.

vermiform roots arising from bases of scaly leaves and pseudobulbs; pseudobulbs 1.3–3.7 × 1.1–1.4 cm, ovoid, oblong or fusiform, green, clothed in brown, papery sheaths, smooth when young, ribbed when old. Leaves 3.5–17 × 1.2–3.2 cm, linear-oblong, dark green, thick, coriaceous, emarginate, grooved along the midrib, base narrowed into a short petiole. Flowers orange-yellow, streaked and spotted red, with dark purple lip in 2–4-flowered umbels arising from the bases of pseudobulbs; peduncle 13 cm long, streaked red with about 6 dark brown, sterile bracts; flowers 5.5–6 cm long, 1.5 cm broad; floral bracts 0.7–0.8 × 0.35 cm, lanceolate or ovate-lanceolate, acute, 7-veined; dorsal sepal 2.5 × 1.15 cm ovate, acuminate, galeate, distantly ciliate along the margin, 5-veined; lateral sepals 3.8–5.3 × 0.7–0.9 cm, attached to the foot of the column, linear-oblong or broadly lanceolate, parallel, curving inwards so as to bring the outer surfaces to the front and cohering in the midline, apex drawn out, rounded, 5-veined; petals 1–1.2 × 0.4–0.5 cm, also attached to the foot of the column, linear-lanceolate from a broad base, ciliate with long hairs, 3-veined; lip 1.5 × 0.7 cm, tongue-shaped, recurved, obtuse, lateral lobes appearing as raised edges on either side, projecting anteriorly and fading into the midlobe, densely hirsute; column 0.8 cm high, 0.7 cm broad, two-winged, projecting anteriorly to two teeth at the top; base produced into a foot curved upwards, uniting and articulating with the base of the lip. Anther terminal, 2-loculed, 1.8 × 1.6 mm, pollinia 4, collateral in two pairs attached to a viscus, disc-shaped, the outer larger ones 1.3 × 1.2 mm, the inner ones 1.2 × 0.9 mm. Ovary with pedicel 2 cm long.

Distr. Endemic. Rather rare, epiphytic on trunks of trees in the submontane or mid-country tropical wet evergreen forests between 713 and 1829 m alt. Rangala, Nuwara Eliya, Hakgala, Hunnasgiriya, Maturata, Hantane, Dimbula, etc.

Ecol. Flowers February–April. The following are a few of its many host plants: *Kurrimia ceylanica* Arn., *Calophyllum trapezifolium* Thw., *Calophyllum calaba* L., *Neolitsea* sp., *Psychotria* sp., etc.

Illustr. PDA, drawing from *C.P. 3657.*

Note. This is a beautiful species with the long lateral sepals often connected for some distance by their extremities. It is distinguished by its very large flowers and ciliated dorsal sepal and petals.

Specimens Examined. KANDY DISTRICT: Hunnasgiriya, Apr. 1960, *Jayaweera 2193* (PDA); Corbet's Gap, Feb. 1960, *Jayaweera 2177* (PDA), Dec. 1959, *Jayaweera 6 (1)* (AMES); Peradeniya, Bot. Gard. cultd., Jan. 1954, *Jayaweera 983* (PDA). NUWARA ELIYA DISTRICT: Hakgala, Apr. 1906, *A.M. Silva s.n.* (PDA); Maturata, May 1906, *A.M. Silva s.n.* (PDA). BADULLA DISTRICT: Pita Ratmalie Estate, July 1964, *Wheeler 12184* (PDA, US). LOCALITY UNKNOWN: *Walker 168* (K, lectotype), *s. coll. C.P. 3657* (PDA).

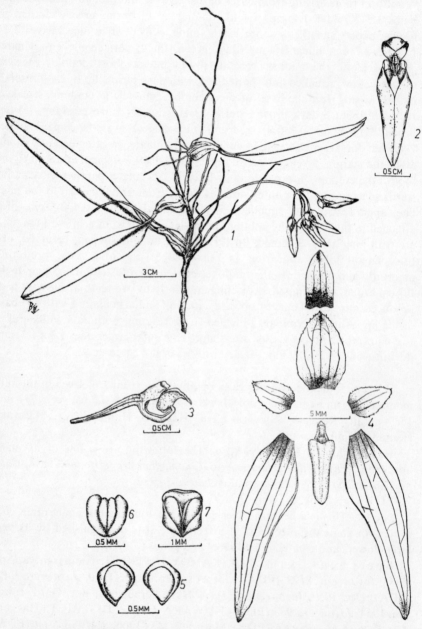

Fig. 50. *Bulbophyllum elliae* Reichb. f. 1, plant with inflorescence. 2, flower from front. 3, lip, column and foot from side, column exaggerated. 4, bract, sepals and petals spread out from front, lip and column natural position. 5, pollinia from side. 6, pollinia from front. 7, operculum from inside.

9. **Bulbophyllum elliae** Reichb. f. in Walp., Ann. 6: 263. 1861; emend. J. Bot. 3: 198. 1874.—**Fig. 50.**

Cirrhopetalum wightii Thw., Enum. Pl. Zeyl. 299. 1861; Tirmen, Handb. Fl. Ceylon 4: 157. 1898.
Cirrhopetalum roseum Jayaweera, Bot. Mus. Leafl. 20 (4): 108–111. 1963.
Cirrhopetalum elliae Trimen, Cat. 88. 1885.
Cirrhopetalum macraei Wight, Ic. Pl. Ind. Or. 5 (1): 7, pl. 1652. 1851, not of Lindl.

Epiphyte with pseudobulbous stems on a creeping rootstock; internodes 1.5–6.5 cm long, covered with dry black leaf scales; roots long flexuous, branched, tufted, arising from bases of pseudobulbs; pseudobulbs ovoid, tapering to the apex, ribbed, green, enveloped in 4 papery scales when young but peeling off and exposing the pseudobulb when old. Leaves solitary, 3.5–14 × 1–2.7 cm, oval, linear-oblong or oblanceolate, shortly petioled, thickly coriaceous, emarginate, veins obscure excepting along the midrib. Flowers small, purplish, 5–7 mm broad in 5–8-flowered umbels arising from bases of pseudobulbs, speckled red with 2 or 3 scaly bracts; pedicels yellowish-green, speckled red; floral bracts 3–4.8 × 1.4–2 mm, subulate, subacute, 1–3-veined; dorsal sepal 5.5–7 × 3–4.2 mm, broadly ovate, obtuse, 5-veined, erose or dentate towards the apex bending over to form a hood over the rostrum and petals; lateral sepals 13–15 × 3.8–5 mm, linear-ovate or linear-oblong, curved inwards and cohering in the midline along their outer edges so as to form a keel, subacute, 5-veined, red-speckled inside; petals 2.9–3.8 × 2–2.4 mm, ovate, acute, serrate, 3-veined; lip 3.9–4.6 × 1.7–1.9 mm, tongue-like, linear-oblong, thick, fleshy, strongly recurved, speckled red, jointed to the foot of the column, versatile and 7-veined; column 1.8 mm high, 1.3–1.7 mm broad, base produced into a foot curving inwards, columnar teeth very short. Anther terminal, 2-loculed, 0.86–1 × 0.76–1.1 mm, pollinia 4, waxy, collateral in 2 pairs, inner ones of each pair smaller, outer pollinia 0.52–0.6 × 0.26–0.46 mm, inner pollinia 0.44–0.46 × 0.36 mm. Ovary with pedicel 7.2–12 mm long. Fruit a short-pedicelled, oblong, cylindrical capsule, 2 × 0.7 cm.

D i s t r. Endemic. Rather common, growing on trees in the subtropical montane forests as well as in the submontane or mid-country tropical wet evergreen forests above 854 m alt. Hakgala, Hantane, Horton Plains, Rangala, Nuwara Eliya, Veddagala etc.

E c o l. Flowers January–May and September. Some of its host plants are: *Kurrimia ceylanica* Arn., *Apodites gardnerana* Miers, *Neolitsea* sp. and *Michelia nilagirica* Zenk.

I l l u s t r. PDA, 2 drawings from *C.P. 3160*; Bot. Mus. Leafl. 20 (4): pl. 17. 1963.

N o t e. This species is distinguished by the ochreous-green, red-speckled flowers in 5–7-flowered umbels, 1–3-veined bracts and glabrous 5-veined sepals of which the lateral ones are parallel.

Specimens Examined. CEYLON: KANDY DISTRICT: Amba-gamuwa, Jan. 1960, *Jayaweera 2120* (PDA), Feb. 1960, *Jayaweera 2128* (PDA). NUWARA ELIYA DISTRICT: Horton Plains, Sept. 1890, *s. coll. s.n.* (PDA); Kandapola, May 1959, *Jayaweera 6 (2)* (AMES); Nuwara Eliya, May 1960, *Jayaweera 2172, 1975* (PDA), Apr. 1922, *Stedman s.n.* (PDA). BADULLA DISTRICT: Namunukula, Mar. 1907, *J.M. Silva s.n.* (PDA). LOCALITY UNKNOWN: *s. coll. C.P. 3160* (K, holotype, PDA in part); *s. coll. C.P. 632* (K); *Evans s.n.* (K). ENGLAND: cultivated, 1889, Hort. Kew (K); Cambridge, Bot. Gard., July 1891, *R.I. Lynch s.n.* (K).

10. Bulbophyllum macraei (Lindl.) Reichb. f. in Walp. Ann. 6: 263. 1861. —**Fig. 51.**

Cirrhopetalum macraei Lindl., Gen. et Sp. Orch. 59. 1830; Trimen, Handb. Fl. Ceylon 4: 158. 1898.
Cirrhopetalum walkerianum Wight, Ic. Pl. Ind. Or. 5 (1): 7, pl. 1657. 1851.

Epiphyte with pseudobulbous stems on a creeping rootstock; roots fibrous and filiform; pseudobulbs 1.3–2.5 cm long, 0.5–1.4 cm diameter, ovoid, smooth, crowded together, surrounded by the remains of old leaf sheaths. Leaves petioled, solitary at the top of pseudobulbs, lamina 7.5–13.5 × 2.5–4.5 cm, petiole 1.5–3.5 cm long, oblong to linear-oblong, acute, very coriaceous, grooved along the midrib. Flowers yellow, tinged brownish-purple, 4.5–5.5 × 0.6 cm in 4- or 5-flowered umbels; peduncle 18 cm long, very slender with four linear, appressed, sterile bracts; floral bracts 6.8–7.6 × 2.8–3.2 mm, ovate, acuminate, acute, 7-veined; dorsal sepal 1.5 cm × 4.8–5.4 mm, lanceolate-ovate, acuminate, acute, 5-veined, hooded over the column; lateral sepals 4.4–4.7 cm × 4.2 mm, parallel, linear-ovate, 5-veined, free or curved inwards and cohering along their outer edges in the midline; petals falcately ovate, 8.2 × 2.8–3 mm, apiculate, 3-veined; lip small, 6 × 2.4 mm, thick, strongly recurved, tongue-shaped, obtuse, about 3-veined; column 2.4 mm high, 2.2 mm broad, oblong; columnar arms about 2 mm long, spreading, crenate on one side and protruding beyond the summit. Anther terminal, 2-loculed, 1 mm long and as broad; pollinia 4, pyriform, disc-shaped, collateral in pairs; the larger pollinia 0.7 × 0.5 mm. Ovary with pedicel 1.3 cm long. Fruit an ellipsoid capsule, 3.5 × 1 cm.

Distr. Endemic. Rather common, growing on trees in the tropical wet evergreen forests between 915 and 1372 m alt. Hantane on *Antidesma bunius* (L.) Spreng. and *Schefflera emarginata* Harms., Hewaheta, Pundaluoya, Ritigala, etc.

Ecol. Flowers June, July–October.

Illustr. PDA, drawing from *C.P. 2362*; Curtis, Bot. Mag. pl. 4422.

Note. This species is distinguished by the solitary leaved pseudobulbs,

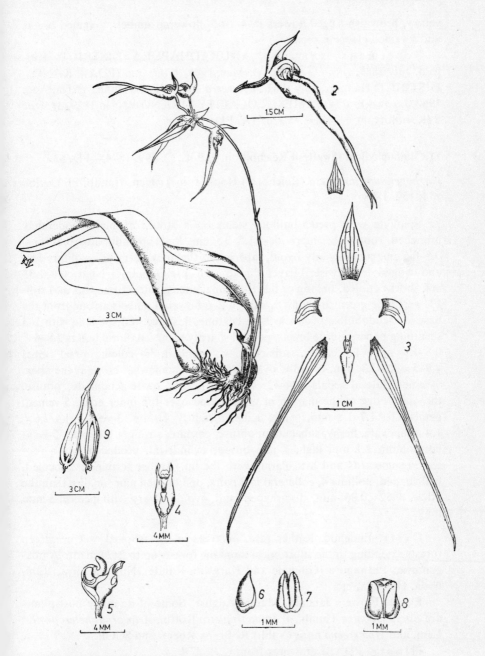

Fig. 51. *Bulbophyllum macraei* (Lindl.) Reichb. f. 1, plant with inflorescence. 2, flower from side. 3, bract, sepals, petals and lip spread out from front, column from inside. 4, column from front. 5, column and lip from side, anther removed. 6, pollinia from side. 7, pollinia from front. 8, operculum from inside. 9, fruits.

yellow, brownish-tinged flowers in 4- or 5- flowered umbels, 7-veined bracts and 5-veined glabrous sepals.

S p e c i m e n s E x a m i n e d. ANURADHAPURA DISTRICT: Riti-gala, July 1887, *s. coll. s.n.* (PDA), Mar. 1905, *Willis s.n.* (PDA). KANDY DISTRICT: Hantane, July 1963, *Jayaweera 2302* (PDA); Hunnasgiriya, Aug. 1960, *Jayaweera 6 (4)* (AMES). LOCALITY UNKNOWN: in 1829, *Macrae 8* (K, holotype), *s. coll. C.P. 2363* (K, PDA).

11. Bulbophyllum thwaitesii Reichb. f. in J. Bot. 12: 199. 1874.—**Fig. 52.**

Cirrhopetalum thwaitesii (Reichb. f.) Hook. f. in Trimen, Handb. Fl. Ceylon 4: 159. 1898.

Epiphyte with pseudobulbous stems on a stout, creeping, moderately branched rootstock; internodes 1.5–3.5 cm long; pseudobulbs 0.8–1.3 × 0.5–0.6 cm, subglobosely ovoid, tapering to the apex, carrying a solitary leaf and ridged lengthwise. Leaves one to each pseudobulb, 3.7–6.6 × 0.6–1.35 cm, short-petioled, oblong or linear-oblong, emarginate, coriaceous and stiff. Flowers pale greenish-yellow, small, in 2–6-flowered umbels arising from the base of pseudobulbs; peduncle 2.5–5 cm long, flexuous, red-streaked with 1–3 sheathing papery sterile bracts; pedicel sharply recurved; floral bracts 2.8–4 × 0.8–1.6 mm, lanceolate, subacute or rounded, 5-veined; dorsal sepal 4.9–5 × 3.2–3.3 mm, broadly ovate, acute and somewhat erose at the apex, 5-veined; lateral sepals 11.4–12 × 3.1 mm, falcate, ovate-acuminate, obtuse, the outer edge of the margin of each folded over the inner edge, 5-veined; petals 2.6 × 1.7–1.8 mm, ovate, acute, distantly serrate, 3-veined; lip 2.6 × 1.4 mm, ovate, fleshy, subacute or obtuse, cordate, strongly recurved, 5-vein-ed; column 2.1 mm high, 1 mm broad, cylindrical, produced into a foot curving upwards and articulating with the lip. Anther terminal, 2-loculed, bell-shaped; pollinia 4, collateral in 2 pairs, one of each pair smaller than the other, 0.52 × 0.36 mm, disc-shaped and ovoid. Ovary with pedicel 5 mm long.

D i s t r. Endemic. Rather rare, on trees in the tropical wet evergreen forests extending to the subtropical montane forests up to 2134 m alt. Amba-gamuwa, Ratnapura (Gilimale and Karawita Kande), Nuwara Eliya, Ram-boda, Hakgala, etc.

E c o l. Flowers January, March, August. Some of its many host plants are *Eurya japonica* Thunb., *Wormia triquetra* Rottb., *Artocarpus heterophyllus* Lam. and *Holarrhena mitis* (Vahl.) R. Br. ex Roem. and Schult.

I l l u s t r. PDA, 2 drawings from *C.P. 2740.*

N o t e. This species is distinguished by the solitary-leaved pseudobulbs, greenish-yellow flowers with claret-coloured veins in 2–6-flowered umbels and 5-veined glabrous sepals with the lateral sepals divergent.

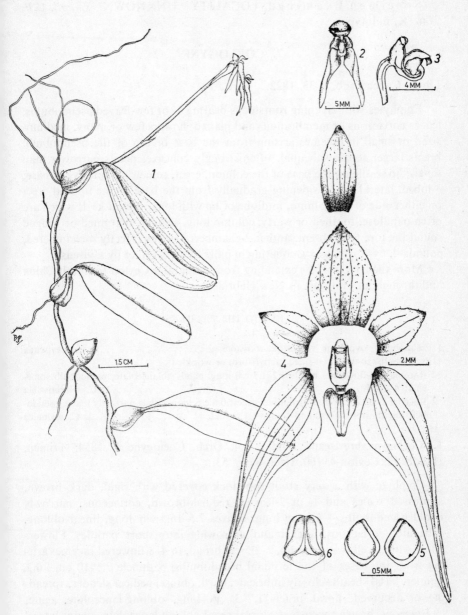

Fig. 52. *Bulbophyllum thwaitesii* Reichb. f. 1, plant with inflorescence. 2, flower from front. 3, lip, column and foot from side. 4, bract, sepals, petals and lip spread out from front, column from inside. 5, pollinia from side. 6, operculum, magnified.

Specimen Examined. LOCALITY   UNKNOWN: *s. coll. C.P. 2740* (K, holotype).

7. COELOGYNE

Lindl., Collect. sub. t. 33. 1822.

Epiphytes with creeping rootstocks bearing 1- or few-leaved pseudobulbs; leaves coriaceous or membranous and plaited; flowers few or many, medium-sized or small in racemes arising from the base or top of the pseudobulb; bracts large; sepals subequal, often strongly concave; petals narrower than sepals; lip sessile on the base of the column, erect, somewhat concave at base, 3-lobed, lateral lobes widening gradually from the base of the lip and erect on either side of the column, midlobe of lip with longitudinal keels which are often papillose, toothed or warty; column long, slender, margined or winged round the top, foot absent; anther 2-chambered or imperfectly 4-chambered, pollinia 4, pyriform, waxy, cohering in pairs or all together by a viscus.

More than 150 species extending from India and Ceylon to South China and throughout Malaysia to New Hebrides.

KEY TO THE SPECIES

1 Pseudobulbs ovoid on very stout rootstock......................**1. C. breviscapa**
1 Pseudobulbs somewhat 4-sided, obpyriform or wrinkled
   2 Raceme 2–4-flowered, bracts 1.2–1.7 cm long, petals oblanceolate, pseudobulb somewhat 4-sided...**2. C. odoratissima**
   2 Raceme 1- or 2-flowered, drooping; bracts 0.6 cm long, petals narrowly linear, pseudobulb small, obpyriform and somewhat wrinkled....................**3. C. zeylanica**

1. Coelogyne breviscapa Lindl., Fol. Orch. Coelogyne 4. 1854; Trimen, Handb. Fl. Ceylon 4: 160. 1898.—**Fig. 53.**

Epiphyte with a very stout rootstock covered with rigid, dark brown, appressed scales and 1- or 2-leaved, reddish-brown, coriaceous, narrowly ovoid pseudobulbs 4–6.5 cm long. Leaves 7.5–16.5 cm long, linear-oblong, subacute, coriaceous, keeled and narrowing into short petioles. Flowers white with a yellow-tinged lip, 2–2.5 cm broad, in 4–8-flowered racemes aris-ing from the bases of the terminal pseudobulbs; peduncle 7.5–10 cm long, slender, basal sheaths closely imbricate, hard, obtuse; pedicel slender, spread-ing or decurved; floral bracts 1.7–3 cm long, oblong-lanceolate, acute, chartaceous, brown, persistent; dorsal sepal oblong-lanceolate, acute; lateral sepals ovate-oblong; petals linear-oblong; lip sessile on the base of the column, erect, as long as the sepals, 3-lobed, lateral lobes short, embracing the column midlobe orbicular-ovate, retuse or apiculate; disc with two thickened ridges and a medium slender one; column long, slender, winged, crenate at the top,

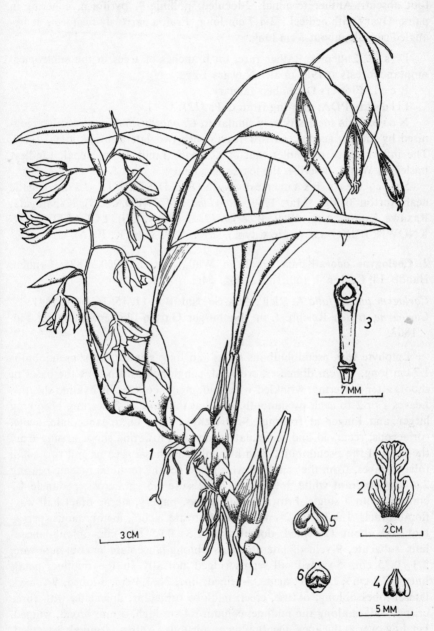

Fig. 53. *Coelogyne breviscapa* Lindl. redrawn from a drawing of *C.P. 3121* in PDA.
1, plant with raceme. 2, lip from front. 3, rostrum from front. 4, pollinia. 5, operculum from inside. 6, young operculum.

foot absent. Anther terminal, 2-loculed; pollinia 4, pyriform, cohering in pairs. Ovary with pedicel 1.2–1.7 cm long. Fruit a narrowly fusiform, acute-angled capsule, about 3 cm long.

D i s t r. Endemic. Rather rare, on branches of trees in the subtropical montane forests at 1981 m alt. Nuwara Eliya.

E c o l. Flowers December–January.

I l l u s t r. PDA, drawing from *C.P. 3121*.

N o t e. This species is very similar to *C. odoratissima* and readily recognised by the coriaceous, narrow leaves with two lateral longitudinal folds. The inflorescence resembles that of *C. ovalis* Lindl. from Nepal. Lindley, misled by Wight, describes the leaves as solitary.

S p e c i m e n s E x a m i n e d. KANDY DISTRICT: Laxapanagalle near Norton Bridge, Mar. 1969, *Hoogland 11477* (PDA, US); Kabaragala, Raxawa Estate, Aug. 1969, *Wheeler 12251* (PDA, US). LOCALITY UNKNOWN: *Walker s.n.* (K, lectotype), *s.coll. C.P. 3121* (K, PDA).

2. Coelogyne odoratissima Lindl. in Wall., Cat. n. 1960. 1828; Trimen, Handb. Fl. Ceylon 4: 160. 1898.—**Fig. 54.**

Coelogyne angustifolia A. Rich., Ann. Sc. Nat. Bot. 11. 15: 16, pl. 6. 1841.
Coelogyne trifida Reichb. f. in Hamburger Garten-Blumenzeitung 19: 546. 1863.

Epiphyte with pseudobulbous stems and long slender roots; pseudobulbs 1.7 cm long, 1.4 cm diameter, crowded, subglobose, formed at the bases of shoots after flowering, wrinkled when old, green, covered by hyaline sheaths. Leaves 1 or 2 to each pseudobulb, small at the time of flowering, becoming larger and longer at fruiting, 3–10 × 0.8–1.3 cm, linear-lanceolate, acute, coriaceous, recurved and punctulate beneath. Flowering shoot arising from the base of the pseudobulb, with five imbricate basal sheaths and two small foliage leaves, from the centre of which emerges the terminal raceme bearing 2–4 very fragrant white flowers which measure 3.5 cm across; peduncle 4.5 cm long with a single, brown, membranous, papery, sterile bract half-way; floral bracts 1.3–1.6 × 1.2 cm, orbicular-ovate, acute, membranous, persistent and about 12-veined; dorsal sepal 2.3 × 0.95–1.05 cm, oblong-lanceolate, subacute, 9-veined; lateral sepals oblong-lanceolate or oblong-ovate, 2.3 × 0.75 cm, 5-veined; all sepals ridged dorsally in the midline; petals linear, 2.2 cm × 2.6 mm, acute, 3-veined; lip 2.2 × 1.4 cm, 3-lobed, 9-veined; lateral lobes oblong, obtuse, erect; midlobe orbicular, apiculate, with three crisped ridges along the midline; column 1.4 cm high, 3 mm broad, winged, bending over at the apex, mentum inconspicuous. Anther terminal, 2-loculed, 2.4 × 2 mm; pollinia 4, cohering in two pairs, 1.4 × 1 mm, depressed inside. Ovary with pedicel 9 mm long. Fruit a capsule, 1.5–2.7 × 1–1.4 cm, ellipsoid, 6-ribbed, pendulous at the ends of thick, elongated peduncles.

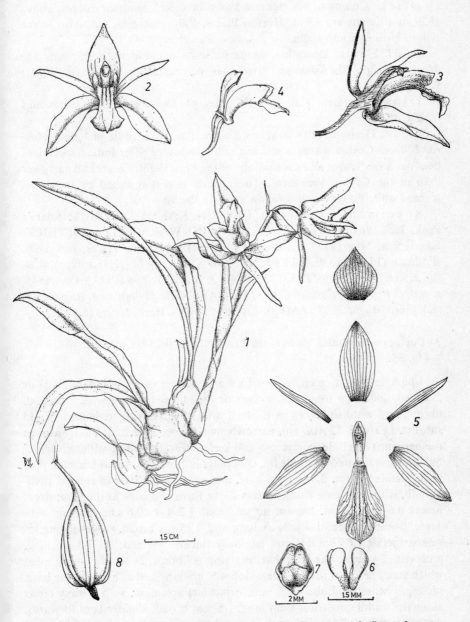

Fig. 54. *Coelogyne odoratissima* Lindl. 1, plant with inflorescence. 2, flower from front. 3, longitudinal section of a flower. 4, lip and column from side. 5, bract, sepals, petals, lip and column spread out from front. 6, pollinia. 7, operculum from inside. 8, fruit.

Distr. Common, on trees in the subtropical montane forests above 1829 m alt. Nuwara Eliya, Horton Plains, Pidurutalagala, etc. Also in the Nilgiri Hills in South India.

Ecol. Flowers December, January. Some of its many host plants are *Memecylon* sp., *Glochidion* sp. *Syzygium* sp., *Adinandra lasiopetala* (Wight) Choisy, etc.

Illustr. Trimen, Handb. Fl. Ceylon pl. 89. 1894; PDA, 2 drawings from *C.P. 518*.

Note. Herb. Lindley contains 3 collections from India including *Macrae* 14 from Ceylon which is selected as the lectotype. The Indian specimens bear narrower leaves and the midlobe of the lip is slightly acute and narrower than in the Ceylon specimens. This species is distinguished by its sweet-scented white flowers with a yellow stain on the lip.

Specimens Examined. CEYLON, KANDY DISTRICT: Adam's Peak, Jan. 1961, *Jayaweera 1976* (PDA). NUWARA ELIYA DISTRICT: Kandapola, May 1959, *Jayaweera 7 (2)* (AMES); Horton Plains, Jan. 1906, *Willis s.n.* (PDA). LOCALITY UNKNOWN: *Macrae 14* (K, lectotype), *Walker 359* (K), *Gardner 851* (K), Jan. 1846, *s. coll. C.P. 666* (PDA), Dec. 1845, *s. coll. C.P. 667* (K), *s. coll. C.P. 518* (PDA). INDIA: Nilgiris, *A. Richard s.n.* (K), Herb. *Wight 2965* (AMES), *Perrottet 79* (K); Herb. *Heyne* (K).

3. Coelogyne zeylanica Hook. f. in Trimen, Handb. Fl. Ceylon 4: 161. 1898. —Fig. 55.

Epiphyte with a creeping rootstock and slender roots; pseudobulbs 1- or 2-leaved, 1–1.2 cm long, obpyriform or ovoid, green, somewhat wrinkled, fibrous and reddish-brown at the base with the decaying remnants of old sheaths. Leaves 7–12 × 0.7 cm, narrowly linear-lanceolate, acute, narrowing at the base into a petiole, coriaceous and keeled. Flowers white with two ochreous spots on the middle of the lip, drooping, in 1- or 2-flowered fascicles; peduncle slender, erect, 2.5–3.7 cm long, arising from the base of the old pseudobulb, with imbricate basal sheaths in the form of a cone at the base; floral bracts 0.6–1 × 0.5 cm, brown; dorsal sepal 1.2–1.8 × 0.6 cm, oblong, subacute, 5-veined; lateral sepals as long and 0.45 cm broad, ovate-oblong, 5-veined; petals 1.65 cm × 1 mm, narrowly linear, 3-veined; lip 1.8 cm long, recurved, 3-veined, the lateral veins giving off branches to the lateral lobes which stand erect on the lip; lateral lobes 5 mm long and as broad at the base, oblong, obtuse; midlobe 8 × 7 mm, orbicular, apiculate, with 3 wavy crests along the middle; rostrum 1 cm long, 1.5 mm broad, slightly bent forwards. Anther terminal, 2-loculed; pollinia 4, cohering in two pairs, each 0.87 × 0.43 mm. Ovary with pedicel 1 cm long. Fruit a fusiform or spindle-shaped capsule, 1.7 × 1 cm, 6-ribbed, with the remains of the rostrum.

Distr. Endemic. Very rare, collected (Thwaites) from a tree at Amba-

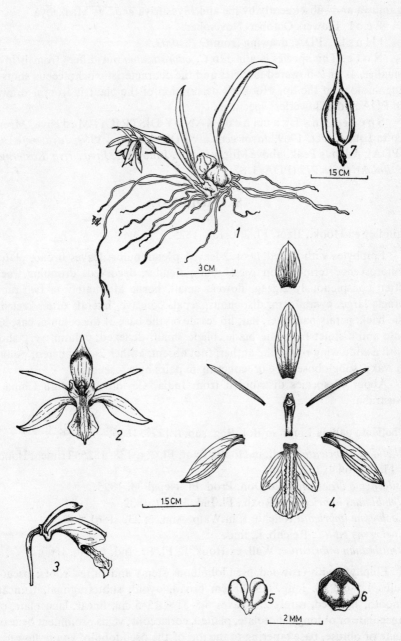

Fig. 55. *Coelogyne zeylanica* Hook. f. 1, group of pseudobulbs with leaves and an inflorescence. 2, flower from front. 3, lip, column, and ovary from side. 4, bract, sepals, petals, lip and column spread out from front. 5, pollinia. 6, operculum showing loculi. 7, fruit.

gamuwa and subsequently by me and Jayasuriya *et al.* at Maskeliya.

E c o l. Flowers October–November.

I l l u s t r. PDA, drawing from *C.P. 4003.*

N o t e. This species is allied to *C. odoratissima* but differs from it in the smaller, 1- or 2-flowered fascicles and the characteristic ochraceous spots on the midlobe of the lip. Hooker's description of the plant is from a drawing in PDA and a flowerless specimen.

S p e c i m e n s E x a m i n e d. KANDY DISTRICT: Maskeliya, Meeria-cotta Estate, Oct. 1969, *Jayaweera 3087* (PDA), Nov. 1969, *Jayaweera 3090* (PDA); Adam's Peak, above Moray Estate, June 1971, *Jayasuriya, Kostermans & Balakrishnan 217* (PDA, US).

8. PHOLIDOTA

Lindley ex Hook., Exot. Fl. 2: t. 138. 1825.

Epiphytes with tufted 1- or 2-leaved pseudobulbs; leaves broad, plaited; inflorescence terminal on pseudobulb, slender, decurved, drooping, rachis often conspicuously zigzag; flowers small, borne alternately in two ranks; bracts large, cymbiform, distichous; sepals concave, laterals often keeled at the back; petals narrower, flat; lip sessile on the base of the column, base saccate and distinct from the blade, blade small, deflexed; column very short, with a wide wing round the anther; foot absent; anther 2-chambered; pollinia 4, waxy, subglobose, free or cohering in pairs by a viscus.

About 40 species distributed from India, Ceylon and South China to Australia.

Pholidota pallida Lindl. in Bot. Reg. sub. t. 1777. 1836.—**Fig. 56.**

Pholidota imbricata Lindl. in Hook., Exot. Fl. 2: t. 138. 1825; Trimen, Handb. Fl. Ceylon 4: 162. 1898.

Ptilocnema bracteatum D. Don, Prod. Fl. Nepal 33. 1825.

Cymbidium imbricatum. Roxb., Fl. Ind. 3: 460. 1832.

Coelogyne imbricata Reichb. f. in Walp. Ann. 6: 238. 1861.

Coelogyne pallida Reichb. f., ibid.

Ornithidium imbricatum Wall. ex Hook. f., Fl. Br. Ind. 5: 846. 1890.

Epiphyte with crowded pseudobulbous stems and tufted roots; pseudobulbs 1.5–6.5 cm long, 0.9–2.8 cm broad, ovoid, subtetragonal, truncate, smooth, 1-leaved, rarely 2. Leaves 6.5–31 × 1.5–5 cm, linear, lanceolate, oblanceolate or oblong-lanceolate, plaited, coriaceous, veins prominent beneath, acute or obtuse, base tapering to the top of the pseudobulb; young flowering shoot with two brown scale leaves at the base, and enveloped in four green sheaths. Flowers pinkish-white, 6 mm broad in very slender, drooping axillary racemes, peduncle 10–11 cm long, naked, very slender and decurved.

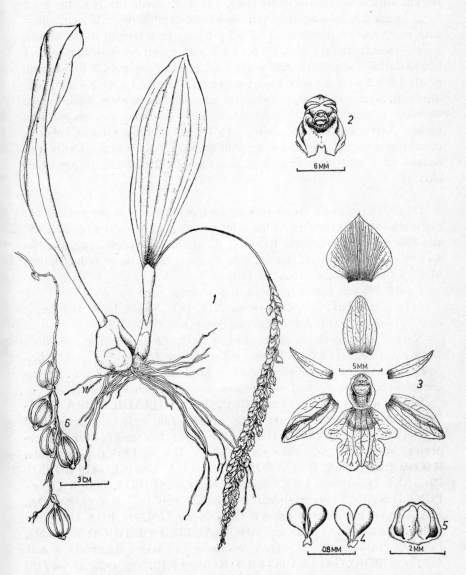

Fig. 56. *Pholidota pallida* Lindl. 1, plant with inflorescence. 2, flower from front. 3, bract, sepals, petals and lip spread out from front, column from inside. 4, pollinia. 5, operculum from inside. 6, fruits.

Flowering portion of the raceme 5–12 cm long, many-flowered, carrying 3–6 brown, distichous, closely imbricating, equitant, sterile bracts at the base; floral bracts 6.8–9.4 × 5.6–9.2 mm, distichous, cymbiform, orbicular, cuspidate, many-veined; dorsal sepal 5.4–6.8 × 4.4–5.1 mm, broadly ovate, obtuse, 3- or 5-veined; lateral sepals 7–8.6 × 3.6–5 mm, ovate, cymbiform, ridged or keeled dorsally, slightly connate at the base, acute or subacute, 3- or 5-veined; petals 5.4–6.2 × 1.5–1.9 mm, linear, subacute, 1-veined; lip 8 × 8.4 mm, panduriform, 5-veined, saccate between the lateral lobes, midlobe bifid, lobules rounded; column 3.6 mm high, 3 mm broad, orbicular-ovate, winged, foot absent. Anther terminal, 2-loculed, 1.1 × 1.8 mm, pollinia 4, equal, cohering in pairs by a viscus, subglobose or pyriform, waxy, 0.6 × 0.5 mm. Ovary with pedicel 4.8–6 mm long. Fruit a globose capsule, 2 × 1.5 cm, in pendulous chains.

D i s t r. Commonly found growing on trees or rocks in the tropical wet evergreen forests, extending to the subtropical montane forests between 457 and 1524 m alt. Ratnapura, Rangala, Ramboda, Watawala, Laggala, Nawalapitiya, Hunnasgiriya, Hatton, Adam's Peak, etc. Also in India, Burma, Malaya, China, Java, Celebes and Borneo.

E c o l. Flowers January, March, June–August.

I l l u s t r. Lindl., Bot. Reg. 14: pl. 1213, 1828; Wight, Ic. Pl. Ind. Or. 3: pl. 907. 1843–45; PDA, 2 drawings one being from *C.P. 3187*.

N o t e. This species is represented in Herb. Lindley by the collections *Hooker & Thomson 78* from Khasia Hills, *Macrae 32* from Ceylon and *Griffith's* from Assam. It is distinguished by the 1-leaved pseudobulbs, lanceolate, plaited, stiff leaves and its brownish, drooping, axillary racemes.

S p e c i m e n s E x a m i n e d. CEYLON, ANURADHAPURA DISTRICT: Ritigala, Mar. 1905, *Willis s.n.* (PDA), Jan. 1973, *Jayasuriya 1055* (PDA). KANDY DISTRICT: Hantane, in 1903, *Schlechter 65* (AMES); Peradeniya, Mar. 1904, *Schlechter s.n.* (AMES), *Macrae 32* (K); Kabaragala, Raxawa Estate, Aug. 1969, *Wheeler 12244* (PDA, US). KEGALLE DISTRICT: Kitulgala, Nov. 1975, *Sohmer & Waas 10567* (PDA, US). RATNAPURA DISTRICT: Warukandeniya, Sinharaja, Feb. 1977, *Waas 1999* (PDA, US), Apr. 1972, *Mueller-Dombois & Balakrishnan 72042311* (PDA, US); Ginigathena, *Senaratne s.n.* (PDA). NUWARA ELIYA DISTRICT: Watawala, July 1959, *Jayaweera 2036* (PDA), *Jayaweera 9* (AMES); Ramboda, *s. coll. C.P. 3187* (PDA). GALLE DISTRICT: Kottawa F.R., Aug. 1926, *Alston 1372* (PDA). INDIA: West Himalaya, Aug. 1900, *Duthie 24124* (K); Khasia Hills, 3000–5000 ft. alt., *J.D. Hooker & T. Thomson s.n.* (K, AMES); *Hooker & Thomson 78* (K); Sikkim Himalaya, Aug. 1892, *Pantling 30* (AMES); Sikkim, *J.D. Hooker* (K, AMES, PDA); 1857, *T. Thomson* (PDA); Malabar & Konkan, *Wallich 1991* (K, AMES); Coonoor, Nilgiris & Kurg, *G. Thomson* (PDA); Assam, Jawai, July 1899, *Prain's Collector 24* (AMES); Naga Hills, Apr. 1886,

Moti Ram Thappa 25 (AMES), July 1886, *Prain* (PDA), 1886, *Prain 25* (K); Mishmis, Brahma Kund, 1844, *Griffith* (K). ANDAMAN ISLANDS: *Kurg s.n.* (PDA). BURMA: Nov. 1922, *Rock 7457* (AMES). MALAY PENINSULA: Jan. 1885, *King's Collector 7218* (AMES). Singapore, Selangor, Nov. 1937, *Corner 34386* (AMES). THAILAND: North Thailand, Doi Sutep, July 1909, *Kerr 233* (AMES). INDO-CHINA: Laos, Nov. 1910, *Xieng-khouang 2280* (AMES); Annam, Jan. 1931, *Poilane 18266* (AMES). COCHIN CHINA: *Pierre s.n.* (AMES). CHINA: Yunnan Prov., *Forrest s.n.* (AMES); Szemoa, *Henry 12973c* (AMES). JAVA: July 1920, *Bakh 4303* (AMES). BORNEO: Sarawak, *Native Collector 1331* (AMES). CELEBES: Nov. 1909, *Schlechter 20443* (AMES). NEW HEBRIDES: Dillon's Bay, June 1928, *Kajewski 390* (AMES).

9. ADRORHIZON

Hook. f. in Trimen, Handb. Fl. Ceylon 4: 161. 1898.

Herb with a creeping rootstock producing many long, stout, vermiform roots clothed with loose inflated epidermis; pseudobulbs absent or narrowly ovoid, 1-leaved; leaves narrow, coriaceous; peduncle from base of stem or pseudobulb, erect, 1–3-flowered; sepals linear-oblong; petals narrowly sparulate; lip sessile on the base of the column, erect, spathulate, entire, base saccate, tip crenulate, disc smooth; column narrowly winged, top dilated with toothed sides; foot absent; anther imperfectly 4-chambered; pollinia 4, free, waxy, narrowly pyriform, two of them larger than the others; fruit narrowly oblong or pyriform, strongly 6-ribbed.

Monotypic, in Ceylon and India including Andaman Islands.

Adrorhizon purpurascens Hook. f. in Trimen, Handb. Fl. Ceylon 4: 161. 1898. —**Fig. 57.**

Dendrobium purpurascens Thw., Enum. Pl. Zeyl. 298. 1861.
Coelogyne purpurascens Hook. f., Fl. Br. Ind. 5: 842. 1890.

Epiphyte with non-pseudobulbous stems and long, stout, vermiform roots covered with a loose, pale, inflated epidermis; stem terete, clothed with 3–5 membranous, ovate, reticulate scales. Leaves erect, one to each stem (or pseudobulb if any), petiolate, 3–10 × 0.3–1.2 cm, linear-oblong or oblanceolate, acute or subacute, base tapering to the petiole, coriaceous, often purplish beneath, margins recurved when dry, midrib prominent. Flowers white, 1.2–2 cm across, in slender 1–3-flowered cymes; peduncle 5–10 cm long, with 3 sterile, sheathing bracts; pedicel curved when young, later becoming straight; floral bracts 2 × 3.5 mm, broadly triangular-ovate, annular, sheathing the rachis, acute, 1-veined; dorsal sepal 8 × 2.3 mm, linear-oblong or oblanceolate, obtuse, 3-veined; lateral sepals 9 × 2.3 mm, oblanceolate, acute, 3-veined;

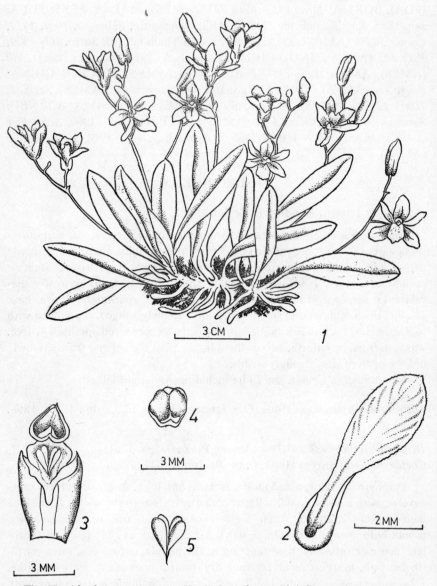

Fig. 57. *Adrorhizon purpurascens* Hook. f. 1, plants with inflorescences. 2, young lip from front. 3, rostrum with operculum opened out showing pollinia. 4, operculum from inside. 5, pollinia.

petals 8 × 1 mm, linear or linear-spathulate, subacute, 1-veined; lip sessile, 9 ×
3 mm, spathulate, emarginate, crenulate, saccate at the base, 5-veined, disc
smooth; foot absent; column erect, 5 mm high, 2 mm broad, club-shaped,
purple at the top, sides toothed. Anther terminal, imperfectly 4-loculed, 1.6 ×
1.5 mm, purple; pollinia 4, free, pyriform, two longer and narrower; larger
pollinia 1.1 × 0.4 mm, smaller pollinia 0.8 × 0.45 mm. Ovary with pedicel 0.8
cm long. Fruit a narrow, oblong, 6-ribbed capsule, 1.2–1.6 cm long.

D i s t r. Endemic. Rather common, on trunks of trees and on rocks by
streams in the submontane or mid-country tropical wet evergreen forests
from 548 to 1829 m alt. Rangala (Corbet's Gap), Adam's Peak, Nuwara
Eliya, Westward-Ho, Hatton (Duke's Nose), Hunnasgiriya, Balangoda,
Ambagamuwa, Hantane, etc.

E c o l. Flowers September–November. Some of its many host plants
are *Calophyllum trapezifolium* Thw., *Kurrimia ceylanica* Arn., *Eugenia* spp.,
Pygeum wightianum Bl. ex Walp., *Scolopia* sp., *Memecylon* sp. and *Eurya
japonica* Thunb. vars.

I l l u s t r. Hook., Ic. pl. 2110. 1894; PDA, drawing from *C.P. 2352.*

N o t e. It is reported that this species also occurs in Travancore and in
Andaman Islands but I have not seen any specimens from these locations.
This species is allied to the Himalayan genus *Panisea* from which it differs in
the absence of the long sigmoid claw of the lip. It is distinguished by the non-
pseudobulbous, 1-leaved stems strongly tinged with purple and pure white
flowers in slender 1–3-flowered cymes and the absence of the foot in the flower.

S p e c i m e n s E x a m i n e d. MATALE DISTRICT: Kalupahana, July
1973, *Jayasuriya & Subramaniam 1228* (PDA, US). KANDY DISTRICT:
Hantane, Jan. 1903, *Schlechter s.n.* (AMES); Rangala, Feb. 1960, *Jayaweera
8* (AMES); Adam's Peak, May 1906, *A.M. Silva s.n.* (PDA), Aug. 1960, *Jayaweera 1967* (PDA), June 1972, *Cramer 3803* (PDA, US). LOCALITY UN-
KNOWN: Nov. 1859, *s. coll. C.P. 2352* (K, holotype, PDA).

10. CHRYSOGLOSSUM

Blume, Bijdr. 337. 1825.

Terrestrial herb with creeping rhizomes and erect, pseudobulbous, 1-
leaved stems; leaf large, petioled, ovate or eillptic, membranous, plaited; inflorescence terminal on pseudobulb; sepals subequal, lateral sepals connate
with the short foot of the column forming with the lip a short mentum, so
that the column-foot may be termed saccate; petals smaller; lip erect, 3-lobed,
hinged to the column-foot, 2- or 3-keeled; column incurved, foot short,
margins with 2 wings or arms; anther 2-chambered; pollinia 2, without caudicles, pyriform, waxy and free.

About 25 species distributed from India, Ceylon through Malaya to China
and Formosa and southwards to Java, Borneo, Celebes and Fiji Islands.

Chrysoglossum maculatum (Thw.) Hook. f., Fl. Br. Ind. 5: 784. 1890; Trimen, Handb. Fl. Ceylon 4: 163. 1898.—Fig. 58.

Ania maculata Thw., Enum. Pl. Zeyl. 301. 1861.

Terrestrial herb with a stout, creeping rootstock and thick, vermiform roots; stem erect, narrowly pseudobulbous, about 30 cm high with a few distant, tubular, obliquely mouthed sheaths and a solitary leaf. Leaves 25 × 9 cm, ovate, shortly petioled, acute, 7-veined and quite glabrous. Flowers 2.5 cm diameter, pale green with a white lip and yellow spur, purple or red-spotted in lax-flowered racemes which measure 15 cm in length; floral bracts lanceolate, shorter than the slender pedicels and the ovaries; dorsal sepal oblong, erect, obtuse; lateral sepals larger than the dorsal, spreading, recurved, narrowly oblong, falcate, 5-veined, connate with the short foot of the column; mentum short, conical, obtuse, formed by the union of the sepals and lip on the foot; petals as broad as the sepals, 3-veined; lip erect, 3-lobed, base auricled, disc 3-lamellate, lateral lobes oblong, midlobe concave; column incurved with triangular auricles. Anther terminal, 2-loculed; pollinia 2, pyriform, waxy and free. Fruit an oblong-clavate, pendulous, strongly ribbed capsule, 3 cm long.

D i s t r. Rare, under the shade of trees in the lower altitudes of the subtropical montane forests between 1220 and 1829 m. Haputale, Kotiyagala, Dickoya, etc. Also in South India.

E c o l. Flowers March, April, June and December.

I l l u s t r. Hook. Ic. Pl. 21: pl. 2064. 1891.

N o t e. This species is more nearly allied to *Chrysoglossum erraticum* Hook. f. than to *Chrysoglossum assamicum* Hook. f. and having as large flowers. But it differs in the elliptic leaf with shorter petiole, short pedicels, conical mentum, shorter and straight lateral lobes of the lip, larger midlobe, lamellae of the lip being nearly equal in length and in the longer auricles of the column.

S p e c i m e n s E x a m i n e d. CEYLON, BADULLA DISTRICT: Haputale, Apr. 1856, *s. coll. C.P. 3515* (K, holotype, PDA). INDIA: Kodaikanal Region, Pulneys, June 1898, *Bourne 1841* (K), Dec. 1898, *Bourne 2939* (K), June 1897, *Bourne 539* (K); Tinnevelly, June 1901, *Barber 3045* (K).

11. ERIA

Lindl. in Bot. Reg. 11: t. 904. 1825.

Epiphytes with erect, branching stems or with pseudobulbs which are tufted or crowded on a creeping rootstock; leaves membranous or coriaceous, sessile or petiolate; inflorescences lateral or apparently terminal with one to

Fig. 58. *Chrysoglossum maculatum* (Thw.) Hook. f. redrawn from a drawing in PDA. 1, plant with 1-leaved pseudobulb and flowering racemes. 2, flower from side. 3, open flower from top. 4, column from side. 5, pollinia, enlarged. 6, operculum, enlarged. 7, fruits.

many flowers, hairy or hairless; sepals subequal, lateral sepals adnate to the foot of the column forming a saccate mentum; petals linear or oblong; lip sessile on the foot of the column, entire or 3-lobed; column long or short; anther imperfectly 4- or 8-chambered, pollinia 8, with caudicles in two groups all together attached to a viscus by their narrow bases.

About 650 species distributed in India, Ceylon through Burma, Malaya, Thailand, Cambodia, China, Japan, southwards to Java, Sumatra, Borneo, Celebes, New Guinea and as far as the Philippine Islands. Also in Australia and New Zealand.

KEY TO THE SPECIES

1 Plants pseudobulbous
  2 Pseudobulbs small, less than 1 cm long
    3 Flowers large, 1–3, pedicelled on top of the pseudobulb, sepals 5-veined...........
    ....**1. E. braccata**
    3 Flowers minute, many in zig-zag spikes
      4 Sepals and petals 3-veined.....................................**2. E. muscicola**
      4 Sepals veinless, petals faintly 1-veined...........................**3. E. articulata**
  2 Pseudobulbs large, elongate, over 7 cm long
    5 Pseudobulbs fusiform; leaves tufted on top of the pseudobulb
      6 Lip entire or nearly so; peduncles arising from axils of old leaf-sheaths...........
      ....**4. E. bicolor**
      6 Lip 3-lobed; peduncles arising from nodes of the stem...............**5. E. tricolor**
    5 Pseudobulbs clavate at the top, long and tuberous at the base; disc of lip hairy with
      2 calli between the side lobes.......................................**6. E. lindleyi**
1 Plants not pseudobulbous; stem branched, terete with woolly scales......**7. E. thwaitesii**

1. Eria braccata Lindl., J. Linn. Soc. Bot. 3: 46. 1859; Trimen, Handb. Fl. Ceylon 4: 165. 1898.—**Fig. 59.**

Dendrobium braccatum Lindl., Gen. et Sp. Orch. 75. 1830.

Dwarf epiphyte with depressed, globose, pseudobulbous stems on a branched rootstock; roots long, filiform; pseudobulbs 0.5–1.3 cm diameter, pale green, young pseudobulbs when about to flower enclosed in 3 sheaths at the base carrying a pair of imbricating leaves at the top. Leaves 2, 2.7–2.9 × 0.75–1.1 cm, oblong or oblong-lanceolate, obtuse, apiculate, minutely serrulate at the apex, bases sheathing, 15–19-veined, pale bright green. Flowers 1–3, creamy-white, 2.7 cm broad, pedicelled on top of the pseudobulb. Bracts small, sheathing the pedicels at the base, 5.5 × 2.7 mm, obovate-oblong, obtuse and serrate at the apex; pedicel 1.7–2 cm long, slender; floral bracts inserted between ovary and pedicel, 6 × 8 mm, broadly ovate, mucronate, 9-veined, cymbiform and incumbent on the dorsal sepal; dorsal sepals 1.6 × 0.55 cm, linear-oblong, obtuse or rounded, 5-veined; lateral sepals 1.7 × 1 cm at the base, lanceolate-falcate, subacute or obtuse, adnate to the curved foot of the

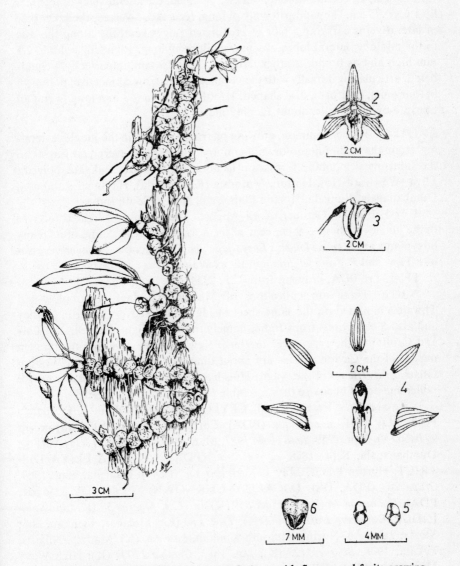

Fig. 59. *Eria braccata* Lindl. 1, colony of plants with flowers and fruits growing on the bark of a tree. 2, flower from front. 3, lip, column and foot from side. 4. sepals, petals, lip and column together with a portion of foot spread out from front. 5, pollinia from side. 6, operculum from front.

column, 5-veined, lateral veins branching; mentum incurved, broad; petals
1.5 × 0.5 cm, lanceolate-oblong, obtuse, 3-veined, the lateral veins branching;
lip 1.6 × 0.75 cm, subpanduriformly oblong, recurved, 5-veined, the inner pair
of lateral veins carrying a pair of crenulated ridges ventrally along the disc
to the midlobe; lateral lobes obscure, midlobe oblong, rounded; column 2.5
mm high and as broad. Anther terminal, 3.5 × 2.3 mm, imperfectly 4-cham-
bered, articulating dorsally with the column by a narrow connective; pollinia 8
in four pairs, pyriform, disc-shaped, 1.1 × 1 mm. Ovary 3 mm long. Fruit an
obovate-ovoid capsule, about 1.2 cm long.

D i s t r. Rather common, growing on trunks of trees in the jungles extending from the submontane or mid-country tropical wet evergreen forests to
the subtropical montane forests up to about 1829 m alt. Hakgala, Nuwara
Eliya (Westward-Ho), Hatton, Maturata (Kabaragala), Hantane, Ramboda,
Dumbanagala, Rangala, Horton Plains, etc. Also in South India.

E c o l. Flowers October, April–August. The amount of light it receives
in the jungles is about 2–9 per cent of the normal sunlight. Some of its many
host plants are *Memecylon* sp., *Eurya japonica* Thunb. vars., *Axinandra zeylanica* Thw. and *Pygeum wightianum* Bl. ex Walp.

I l l u s t r. PDA, drawing from *C.P. 2356*.

N o t e. There are collections of Macrae, Gardner, Champion and
Thwaites mounted on the same sheet inside the type cover in Herb. Lindley
and also 5 collections from India, namely those of Wight, Dalzell, 2 of Law
and Griffith in the type cover in Herb. Kew. Lindley says that the "pollen
masses of the Ceylon species are about quarter that of those from Western
Ghats. *Eria reticosa* of the Nilgiri Hills has a 3-lobed lip and probably longer
pollen masses. Otherwise they resemble *Eria braccata* very closely".

S p e c i m e n s E x a m i n e d. CEYLON: KANDY DISTRICT: Adam's
Peak, May 1891, *s. coll. s.n.* (PDA); Corbet's Gap, Jan. 1954, *Jayaweera
991* (PDA), Sept. 1959, *Jayaweera 1987*, Mar. 1959, *Jayaweera 12(1)* (AMES);
Dumbanagala, Sept. 1888, *s. coll. s.n.* (PDA). NUWARA ELIYA DIS-
TRICT: Horton Plains, May 1906, *Willis s.n.* (PDA); Hakgala, Sept. 1969,
Grupe 263 (PDA, US). LOCALITY UNKNOWN: *s. coll. C.P. 2356* (K,
PDA), *Champion 36* (K), *Gardner 859* (K), in 1829, *Macrae 53* (K, holotype).
INDIA: Bombay, *Dalzell s.n.* (K), *Law s.n.* (K); Malabar, Konkan, etc.,
Stocks, Law, etc. North and South Konkan, *Law s.n.* (K). Madras, Nilgiris,
Pykara, 1908, *Bourne 5123* (K), Jan. 1883, *Gamble 12004* (K); High Wavy
Mountains, May 1917, *Blatter & Halberg 338* (K); Herb. *Griffith s.n.* (K);
Herb. *Wight s.n.* (K).

2. Eria muscicola Lindl., J. Linn. Soc. Bot. 3: 47. 1859; Trimen, Handb. Fl.
Ceylon 4: 165. 1898.—**Fig. 60.**

Dendrobium muscicola Lindl. in Wall., Cat. n. 2017. 1829.

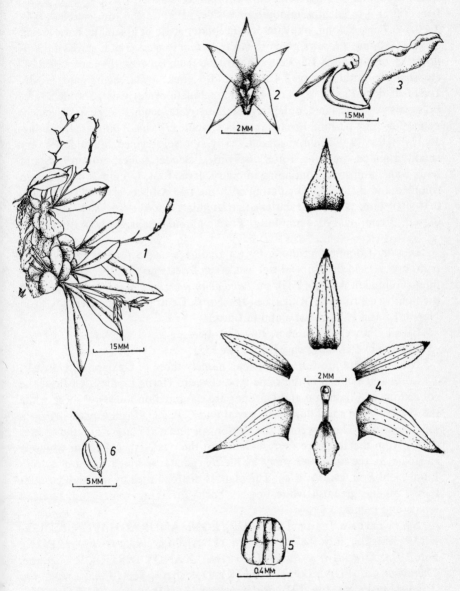

Fig. 60. *Eria muscicola* Lindl. 1, plants with inflorescence. 2, flower from front. 3, lip, column and foot from side. 4, bract, sepals, petals, lip and column together with a portion of foot spread out from front. 5, operculum from inside. 6, fruit.

132 ORCHIDACEAE

Dwarf epiphyte with crowded pseudobulbous stems on a creeping root-stock; pseudobulbs 1 cm long, 0.5 cm broad or smaller, flat, oval and green. Leaves 2 or 3 to each pseudobulb on a side, never on the top, petioled, 0.4–2 × 0.3–0.7 cm, oblong, obovate or lanceolate, acute or apiculate, dark green, bases sheathing. Flowers greenish-white, 4 mm long, 2–3 mm across in 3–6-flowered zigzag spikes 1.5–3 cm long arising from between the leaves; peduncle slender; floral bracts 2.4–3.1 × 1.5–1.6 mm, ovate, acuminate, acute, 1-veined; dorsal sepal 4.3–4.6 × 1.6 mm, subulate-ovate, acute, 3-veined; lateral sepals 4.3 × 2–2.4 mm, obliquely subulate-ovate, acuminate, acute, 3-veined; petals 3.6–3.7 × 1.1 mm, linear-lanceolate, acute, 3-veined; lip sessile, pandurate, 2.4–2.8 × 1.2–1.5 mm, recurved, fleshy, obtuse, 3-veined, lateral lobes very small, rounded, midlobe ovate, disc with 3 slender ridges; column 0.6 mm high, broad and stout continuing into a recurved foot, 1–6 mm long; mentum rounded and incurved, articulating with the lip. Anther terminal, 4-loculed, 0.34 × 0.4 mm, pollinia 8, flattened, triangular, disc-shaped, each pollinium 0.2 × 0.13 mm; ovary 1.4 mm long. Fruit a globular capsule, 3.6 × 2.6 mm.

D i s t r. Common, groming by watercourses in the jungle, epiphytic on trunks of trees in the tropical wet evergreen forests up to 2124 m alt. Ratna-pura (Gilimale), Adam's Peak on *Palaquium rubiginosum*, Nillowe Kande in the Southern Province, Ritigala in the North Central Province, etc. Also in Nepal, Khasia Hills in India and in Burma.

E c o l. Flowers November, July–October.

I l l u s t r. PDA, drawing from *C.P. 2355*.

N o t e. There are four collections namely those of Champion, Gardner, Thwaites and Wallich in the same type cover in Herb. Lindley. Of these the collections of Champion and Gardner are mounted on the same sheet while the Wallich type collection from Nepal and *C.P. 2355* from Ceylon are on a separate sheet. The flowers of the Ceylon specimen are larger and the species differs from the Burmese representative in the ovate-lanceolate lip which is subacute at the apex and wavy at the margin. It is allied to *Eria dalzelli* Lindl., and *Eria nana* A. Rich. The plant is distinguished by its small pseudo-bulbs, minute greenish white flowers borne in zigzag spikes and 3-veined sepals and petals.

S p e c i m e n s E x a m i n e d. CEYLON, ANURADHAPURA DIST-RICT: Ritigala, July 1887, *s. coll. s.n.* (PDA), Mar. 1905, *Willis s.n.* (PDA), Feb. 1973, *Jayasuriya & Burtt 1152* (PDA). KANDY DISTRICT: Hantane, *Champion s.n.* (PDA), *Gardner 854* (K); Dolosbage, Sept. 1885, *s. coll. s.n.* (PDA); Maskeliya, Jun. 1971, *Balakrishnan 584* (PDA, US). MATALE DIS-TRICT: Kabaragala, Raxawa Estate, Aug. 1969, *Wheeler 12252* (PDA). NUWARA ELIYA DISTRICT: Pidurutalagala, Aug. 1884, *s. coll. s.n.* (PDA), Oct. 1974, *Davidse & Sumithraarachchi 8059* (PDA, US), Sept. 1970, *Fernando s. n.* (PDA). NEPAL: *Wallich 2017* (K, holotype). INDIA: Sikkim

Himalaya, July 1897, 4000 ft alt. *Pantling 163* (K); Khasia Hills, Oct. 1886, *Clarke 45059* (K); Herb. *Griffith 5141* (K), 1850, *J.D. Hooker & T. Thomson* (K); Assam, Jan. 1899, *Prain's Collector 145* (K). BURMA: Moulmein, *Parish 320* (K).

3. Eria articulata Lindl. in J. Linn. Soc. Bot. 3: 47. 1859.—**Fig. 61.**

Alvisia tenuis Lindl., Fol. Orch. 1859; Trimen, Handb. Fl. Ceylon 4: 168. 1898.

Epiphyte with small pseudobulbous stems on a slender rootstock; pseudobulbs 0.6–0.8 cm long, ellipsoid or subglobose, adhering end-to-end like a chain. Leaves 1 or 2, sessile, 1.2–2.5 cm long, broadly oblong or oblanceolate, apiculate, 5-veined, membranous and dark green. Flowers small, orange-salmon-coloured in long flexuous, terminal, zigzag spikes; peduncle with the spike 2.5–7.5 cm long; floral bracts very small, membranous, cymbiform, sheathing the ovary; dorsal sepal small, lanceolate, obtuse or rounded, thickened in the middle, recurved; lateral sepals lanceolate, veinless, almost sigmoid with upcurved tips, bases confluent with the foot of the column in a broad, deep, incurved mentum with a rounded tip; petals small, lanceolate or linear-oblong, faintly 1-veined; lip horseshoe shaped, inserted on top of the very long foot within the margins of the connate lateral sepals; column minute, depressed, with two projecting incurved arms in front. Anther terminal, minute, 2-loculed; pollinia 8, obovoid, waxy and free.

D i s t r. Endemic. Rare, on trees in the tropical wet evergreen forests below 610 m alt. Ambagamuwa, Kothmale, Ratnapura (Karawita Kande), etc.
E c o l. Flowers February, March.
I l l u s t r. PDA, drawing from *C.P. 2655.*
N o t e. This species is allied to *Eria muscicola* Lindl. from which it differs in the venation of the sepals and petals.
S p e c i m e n s E x a m i n e d. KANDY DISTRICT: Ambagamuwa, Alu Oya, Feb. 1853, *s. coll. C.P. 2655* (K, holotype, AMES, PDA). RATNAPURA DISTRICT: Karawita Kande, Mar. 1881, *s. coll. s.n.* (PDA); Weddagala, Mar. 1972, *Fernando s.n.* (PDA).

4. Eria bicolor Lindl. Gen. et Sp. Orch. 65. 1830; Trimen, Handb. Fl. Ceylon 4: 166. 1898.—**Fig. 62.**

Tufted epiphyte with erect, pseudobulbous stems on a crowded rootstock; pseudobulbs fusiform, consisting of many nodes and internodes, 8–13.5 cm long, 0.9–1.5 cm diameter; internodes 2–2.7 cm long, smooth when young, longitudinally wrinkled when old, cylindrical, covered with brown, papery sheaths. Leaves forming a cluster at the top of the pseudobulb, 4–25 × 1.2–2.2 cm, linear-lanceolate, acute or obtuse, thinly coriaceous, shining on the upper

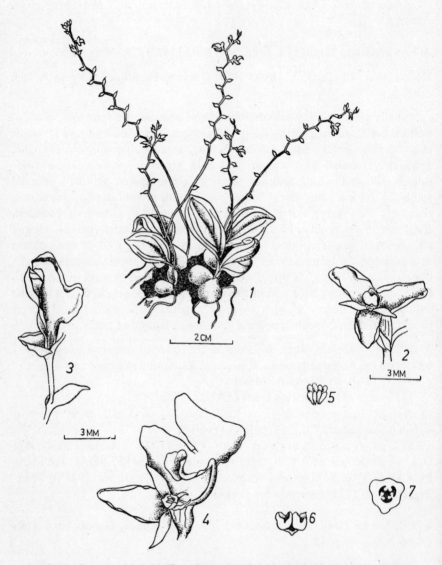

Fig. 61. *Eria articulata* Lindl. redrawn from a drawing of *C.P. 2655* in PDA.
1, plant with inflorescences. 2, flower from front, opened out. 3, flower from side.
4, flower from front with the sepals opened out showing petals, lip and foot. 5, pollinia,
enlarged. 6, operculum from inside, enlarged. 7, transverse section of ovary, enlarged.

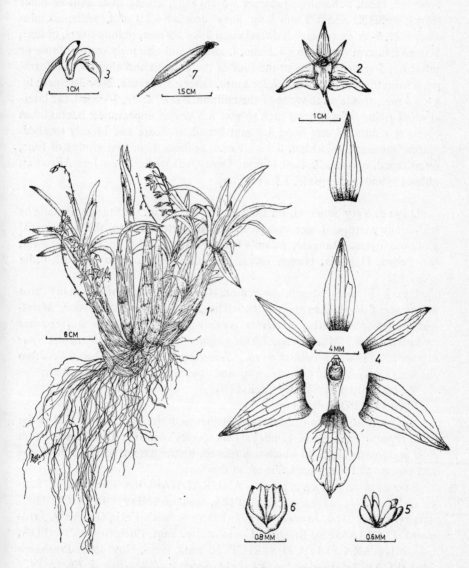

Fig. 62. *Eria bicolor* Lindl. 1, clump of pseudobulbs with inflorescences. 2, flower
from front. 3, lip, column and foot from side. 4, bract, sepals, petals, lip and
column together with portion of foot spread out from front. 5, pollinia. 6, operculum from inside. 7, fruit.

surface, many-veined. Flowers white, 2.3 cm broad when spread out, in many-flowered, erect, puberulous racemes 3–5 cm long, arising from axils of older leaves; peduncle about 8 mm long; floral bracts 8×2.9 mm, ovate, acuminate, acute, 5- or more-veined; dorsal sepal 8.4×2.9 mm, oblong-ovate, obtuse, 5-veined; lateral sepals 9.6×4.2 mm, falcately and obliquely ovate, obtuse or subacute, 5-veined, adnate to the foot of the column and along with it forming a saccate mentum; petals 7.2×2 mm, lanceolate, acute, 2- or 3-veined; li 8×5.3 mm, sessile on the foot of the column, ovate, acute, 3-veined, the lateral veins giving off a branch each to give a 5-veined appearance; lateral lobes obscure; column 3 mm high, 1.8 mm broad, truncate and bluntly toothed. Anther terminal, 4-loculed, 0.9×1.1 mm, pollinia 8, in two groups of four, disc-shaped, obovate, 0.4×0.44 mm. Ovary with pedicel 1 cm long. Fruit an oblong cylindrical capsule, 1.9×0.35 cm.

D i s t r. Very common, on trees above 1067 m alt. in the submontane or mid-country tropical wet evergreen forests extending to the subtropical montane forests. Rangala, Adam's Peak, Nuwara Eliya, Laggala, Maturata, Mt. Pedro, Hakgala, Hunnasgiriya, Namunukula etc. Also in South India (Alston).

E c o l. Flowers March, September–October. Some of its many host plants are: *Calophyllum trapezifolium* Thw., *Kurrimia ceylanica* Arn., *Myristica dactyloides* Gaertn, *Apodytes gardnerana* Miers., *Litsea* sp., *Ostodes zeylanica* (Thw.) Muell. Arg., *Litsea gardneri* (Thw.) Hook. f., *Semecarpus nigroviridis* Thw., *Memecylon* sp., *Semecarpus gardneri* Thw., *Neolitsea fuscata* (Thw.) Alston, *Glochidion* sp. and *Pygeun wightianum* Bl. ex Walp.

V e r n. Lily of the Valley Orchid (E).

I l l u s t r. PDA, drawing.

N o t e. Collections of Macrae, Gardner and Hooker are included in the same type cover in Herb. Lindley. This species is readily distinguished from *Eria mysorensis* Lindl. to which it is related, by the narrow leaves, stout scape and raceme and the remarkable sac at the base.

S p e c i m e n s   E x a m i n e d. ANURADHAPURA DISTRICT: Ritigala, Jun. 1974, *Jayasuriya 1738* (PDA, US). KANDY DISTRICT: Hunnasgiriya, Oct. 1960, *Jayaweera 1987* (PDA); Adam's Peak, Oct. 1959, *Jayaweera 12 (3)* (AMES); Rangala, Looloowatte, Sept. 1969, *Grupe 234* (PDA, US). NUWARA ELIYA DISTRICT: Nuwara Eliya, Nov. 1963, *Jayaweera 2363* (PDA); Pidurutalagala, Oct. 1973, *Sohmer, Jayasuriya & Eliezer 8423* (PDA, US), Oct. 1974, *Davidse & Sumithraarachchi 8060* (PDA, US); Hakgala, Jan. 1911, *J.M. Silva s.n.* (PDA), Oct. 1975, *Sohmer & Sumithraarachchi 10126* (PDA, US), Apr. 1906, *A.M. Silva s.n.* (PDA); Horton Plains, Oct. 1973, *Waas 131* (PDA, US), Oct. 1974, *Davidse 7628* (PDA, US), Nov. 1971, *Balakrishnan 1042* (PDA, US), Oct. 1976, *Jayasuriya 2397* (PDA, US), Nov. 1973, *Sohmer, Jayasuriya &Eliezer 8602* (PDA, US), Sept. 1970, *van Beusekom*

1405 (PDA, US); Kandapola, Oct. 1973, *Sohmer, Jayasuriya & Eliezer 8356* (PDA, US); Pattipola, Nov. 1973, *Sohmer, Jayasuriya & Eliezer 8526* (PDA, US). BADULLA DISTRICT: Namunukula, *J.M. Silva s.n.* (PDA). LOCALITY UNKNOWN: *Macrae 43* (K, holotype), *Gardner 840* (K), *J.D. Hooker 68* (K), *s. coll. C.P. 2782* (PDA).

5. Eria tricolor Thw., Enum. Pl. Zeyl. 429. 1864; Trimen, Handb. Fl. Ceylon 4: 166. 1898.—Fig. 63.

Epiphyte with tufted, erect, fleshy, pseudobulbous stems rooting at base; pseudobulbs 7–12 cm long, fusiform, consisting of many cylindrical internodes clothed with brown sheaths and carrying terminal tufts of leaves. Leaves many, 15–20 × 1.2–1.6 cm, distichous, recurved, linear-lanceolate, strongly veined, bases shortly sheathing. Flowers creamy-white with a pink and yellow lip, 1.6 cm broad, in laxly many-flowered racemes which measure 7–10 cm in length; peduncle short, arising from the nodes of the pseudobulb with few sterile bracts; floral bracts small, broadly ovate, obtuse, green, shorter than the ovary; dorsal sepal broadly ovate-oblong, scurfy, obtuse; lateral sepals falcately-ovate, subacute, scurfy; mentum rounded; petals ovate-oblong, glabrous, obtuse; lip sessile on the foot of the column, 3-lobed; lateral lobes erect, subfalcate, obtuse; midlobe orbicular, reflexed; disc with a central ridge; column long, truncate. Anther terminal, 2-loculed; pollinia 8, in two groups of 4. Ovary with pedicel 0.6 cm long.

D i s t r. Endemic. Very rare, on trees in subtropical montane forests, more elevated parts of the Central Province and at Namunukula in Uva Province.

E c o l. Flowers April.

I l l u s t r. PDA, drawing from *C.P. 3840.*

N o t e. The only specimen in Herb. Kew is Hunt's collection with no locality. Others available were collections made from cultivated plants. Herb. Peradeniya contains the original collection *C.P. 3440* and J.M. Silva's subsequent collection from Namunukula. This species resembles *E. bicolor* in habit but differs from it in the scurfy sepals and colour of the lip which is 3-lobed.

S p e c i m e n s E x a m i n e d. CEYLON, BADULLA DISTRICT: Namunukula, Apr. 1924, *J.M. Silva s.n.* (PDA). LOCALITY UNKNOWN: Dec. 1887, *Hunt s.n.* (K), *s. coll. C.P. 3840* (PDA, holotype). ENGLAND: cultivated, Hort. Kew 224–14 (K); Gatton Park, Jan. 1909, *Sir Jeremiah Coleman s.n.* (K).

6. Eria lindleyi Thw., Enum. Pl. Zeyl. 299. 1861; Trimen, Handb. Fl. Ceylon 4: 167. 1898.—Fig. 64.

Dendrobium bicolor Lindl. Gen. et Sp. Orch. 90. 1830.

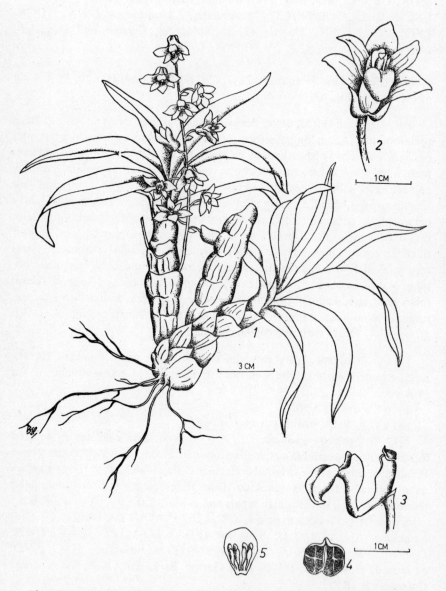

Fig. 63. *Eria tricolor* Thw. redrawn from a drawing of *C.P. 3840* in PDA. 1, plant
with inflorescence. 2, flower from front. 3, lip, column and foot from side.
4, 5, pollinia. operculum from inside, enlarged.

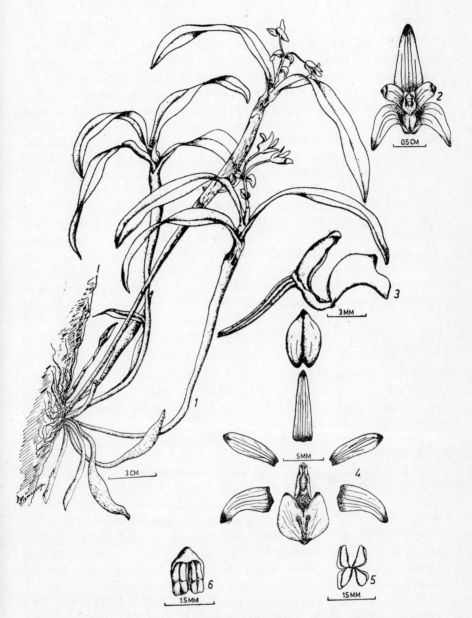

Fig. 64. *Eria lindleyi* Thw. 1, plant with inflorescences. 2, flower from front. 3, lip, column and foot from side. 4, bract, sepals and petals, spread out from front; lip, natural position, column from inside. 5, pollinia from side. 6, operculum from inside.

140 ORCHIDACEAE

Eria bicolor Lindl., J. Linn. Soc. Bot. 3: 58. 1859 (not of Gen. et Sp. Orch.). *Eria ephemera* Reichb. f. in Walp. Ann. 6: 272. 1861.

Densely tufted epiphyte with pseudobulbous stems rooting at their bases; stems 15–45 cm long, clavate at the top and tuberous at the base; internodes many, terete, clothed with short, acute sheaths. Leaves crowning the terminal internode, sessile, 7.5–11 cm long, oblong-lanceolate, obtuse, many veined, midrib prominent, bases partially sheathing. Flowers large, white, about 1.2 cm across in 2- or 3-flowered scapes; peduncle 2–3.5 cm long, glabrous, bearing 2 or 3 sterile bracts sheathing the base and another higher up midway; floral bracts large, green or yellow, 0.9–1.8 cm × 5.5–7.5 mm, broadly oblong, obtuse or mucronate, slightly cordate at the base, recurved, 15-veined; dorsal sepal 8.5–13 × 3.5–4 mm, ovate-oblong, obtuse, 7-veined; lateral sepals 8–11 × 4.5–5 mm, falcately ovate-oblong, obtuse, adnate to the foot of the column, 7-veined; mentum rounded; petals 7.5–11 × 2.7–3.3 mm, generally 3-veined with the lateral veins bifurcating at the base; lip 6 × 7 mm, 3-lobed, 3-veined, lateral veins reticulate; lateral lobes broad, subacute, a little longer than the truncate or subacute or rounded midlobe; disc hairy with 2 calli; column 4.5 mm long, narrowing towards the apex, 2.3 mm broad at the base. Anther terminal, 1.4 × 1.1 mm, obscurely 4-loculed with two pollinia in each loculus like a pair of cotyledons in a bean seed; each pollinium 0.6–0.7 × 0.45 mm, wedge-shaped. Ovary with pedicel 0.8–2 cm long. Fruit a narrowly clavate capsule, 2.5 cm long.

D i s t r. Endemic. Rather common, on trees towards the higher altitudes in the submontane or mid-country tropical wet evergreen forests extending to the subtropical montane forests up to 2134 m alt. Rangala, Laggala, Hunnasgiriya, Ritigala, etc.

E c o l. Flowers March, April, September–December.

I l l u s t r. PDA, 2 drawings from *C.P. 2761*.

N o t e. Collections of Macrae and Thwaites are in separate type covers under *Dendrobium bicolor* Lindl. and *Eria bicolor* Lindl. respectively in Herb. Lindley. *Macrae 18* is selected as the lectotype. Lindley says that the lip of this species is much like that of *Eria pauciflora* Wight but with a shorter midlobe which is rather pulverulent. Also there is a small orange-coloured process at the base of the column. This species is distinguished by the long clavate pseudobulbous stems, large glabrous white flowers in 2- or 3-flowered scapes, large green or yellow floral bracts and 7-veined sepals.

S p e c i m e n s E x a m i n e d. ANURADHAPURA DISTRICT: Ritigala, Mar. 1905, *Willis s.n.* (PDA). KANDY DISTRICT: Hantane, May 1903, *Schlechter s.n.* (AMES); Rangala, Mar. 1960, *Jayaweera 2198* (PDA), Oct. 1960, *Jayaweera 1988* (PDA), Sept. 1959, *Jayaweera 12 (5)* (AMES). LOCALITY UNKNOWN: *s. coll. C.P. 2761* (K, PDA), *Macrae 18* (K, lectotype).

7. Eria thwaitesii Trimen, Cat. 88. 1885; Trimen, Handb. Fl. Ceylon 4: 167. 1898—Fig. 65.

Eria velutina Thw., Enum. Pl. Zeyl. 299. 1861, not of Lodd.

Rhizomatous, softly pubescent epiphyte with non-pseudobulbous, branched, terete stems and short, 3–7-leaved branches; roots pubescent; branches 4–8 cm long, internodes short, clothed with silky sheaths, leafy at the top. Leaves 3.5–9 × 1.2 cm, oblong-lanceolate or subfalcate, obtuse or subacute, notched at the apex, base sheathing, thickly coriaceous and silky-pubescent on both surfaces; leaves lower down shorter, those at the base almost reduced to sheaths. Flowers subsessile, dull yellow, 0.9 cm broad, suberect, pubescent all over, in lax-flowered, woolly spikes which with the peduncles measure 3–10 cm in length; floral bracts 0.75 × 0.6 cm, broadly ovate, fleshy, obtuse, woolly-pubescent on both surfaces, 8–9-veined; dorsal sepal 6 × 3 mm, oblong, obtuse, hairy on both surfaces, 3-veined; lateral sepals 6.5 × 5.5 mm, broadly ovate-oblong, obtuse, 5-veined, adnate to the foot of the column, hairy on both sides; petals 5.5 × 1.8 mm, linear-oblong, subacute, pubescent on both sides, 3-veined; mentum rounded, incurved; lip 6.2 × 3 mm, shorter than sepals, fleshy, tongue-shaped or oblong-lanceolate when spread out, recurved, tomentose, 5-veined with the extreme lateral veins branching; lateral lobes obscure, rounded; midlobe small, broadly ovate, obtuse, column 2.6 mm high, 2.3 mm broad, hairy on the dorsal surface at the apex. Anther terminal, 4-loculed, 1.6 × 1.5 mm, pollinia 8, 4 larger, oval, and 4 pyriform; larger pollinia 0.6 × 0.4 mm, smaller pollinia 0.53 × 0.36 mm. Ovary 0.5–0.7 cm long.

D i s t r. Endemic. Rare, on trees at higher altitudes in the tropical wet evergreen forests from 610 to 1829 m alt. Adam's Peak, Ratnapura (Kuruwita Kande), Dolosbage, Hakgala, Balangoda, etc.

E c o l. Flowers March, October–January.

I l l u s t r. PDA, 2 drawings from *C.P. 2349*.

N o t e. This species is very characteristic by its non-pseudobulbous rhizomatic hairy stems, silky-pubescent leaves and woolly spikes of yellow pubescent flowers.

S p e c i m e n s E x a m i n e d. KANDY DISTRICT: Dolosbage, Dec. 1854, *s. coll. C.P. 2349* (PDA, holotype); Peradeniya, Bot. Gard, Cultd., Jan. 1963, *Jayaweera 2195* (PDA). KEGALLE DISTRICT: Kitulgala, Nov. 1974, *Davidse & Sumithraarachchi 8534* (PDA, US). RATNAPURA DISTRICT: foot of Adam's Peak, Oct 1960. *Jayaweera 1990* (PDA); Balangod , Bulathgama, Sept. 1895, *s. coll. s.n.* (PDA). NUWARA ELIYA DISTRICT: Hakgala, Oct. 1886, *Nock s.n.* (PDA).

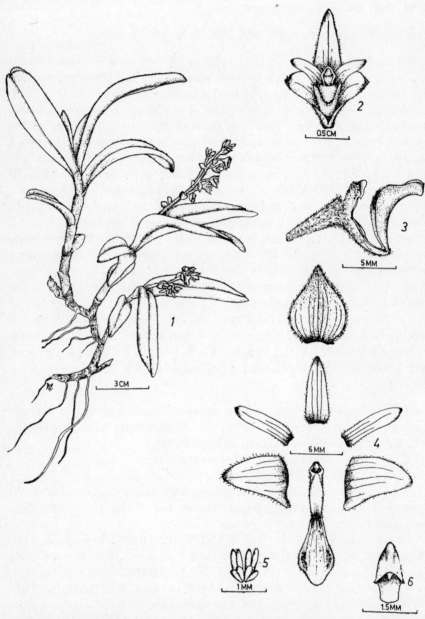

Fig. 65. *Eria thwaitesii* Trimen. 1, plant with inflorescences. 2, flower from front.
3, lip, column and foot from side. 4, bract, sepals, petals, lip and column together
with portion of foot spread out from front. 5, pollinia. 6, operculum from front.

12. AGROSTOPHYLLUM

Blume, Bijdr. 368, t. 53. 1825.

Epiphytes with tufted, flattened, stiff stems rooting at the base only; pseudobulbs absent; leaves distichous, vertical, linear or linear-oblong, sheaths overlapping and persistent; flowers very small, crowded in a sessile terminal head, mixed with paleaceous bracts; sepals and petals similar, petals narrower; lip adnate to the foot of the column which is hardly developed, erect, entire or trifid; column short, stout, thickened above, anther 2-chambered; pollinia 8, waxy, all attached to a single disc.

About 60 species distributed from India, Ceylon through Malaya to the islands of the Pacific and Indian Ocean including Java, Sumatra, and Borneo.

Agrostophyllum zeylanicum Hook. f., Fl. Br. Ind. 5: 825. 1890; Trimen, Handb. Fl. Ceylon 4: 171. 1898—**Fig. 66.**

Appendiculata longifolia Blume, Bijdr. 304. 1825; Thw., Enum. Pl. Zeyl. 306. 1861.

Tufted epiphyte with non-pseudobulbous, flattened, stiff stems 20–40 cm long and fibrous roots, perched on tops of very tall trees; stems ensheathed by the petiolar leaf bases throughout, the lower portion by dry, whitish-brown, truncate, distichous, equitant sheaths, the lamina having fallen off, and the top portion by green, basal sheaths with laminae; internodes 1.4–2.2 cm long. Leaves distichous, equitant, lamina 4.5–12.5 × 0.9–1.6 cm, linear, retuse, apiculate, thinly coriaceous, midrib slender; petiolar sheaths 4.5 × 1–1.5 cm, green while attached to laminae. Flower heads 1.3–2.2 cm diameter, sessile, consisting of a large number of spikelets surrounded by an involucre of large, papery, brown scarious bracts; spikelets 1.5 cm long, with 2–4 sterile bracts at the base and 3- or 4-flowered towards the apex; flowers straw-coloured, sessile, 4.2 mm long and 2.8 mm broad; floral bracts scarious, 5.8–7.4 × 3 mm, subulate-ovate, obtuse, with many veins of which 3–5 are prominent; dorsal sepal 3–3.2 × 1.5 mm, oblong-ovate, cuspidate, acute, 3-veined; lateral sepals 3.3 × 1.5 mm, oblong, cuspidate, acute, 3-veined, dorsal sepal appressed on them; petals 2.3–2.4 × 1.2–1.34 mm, ovate cuspidate, acute, 1-veined; lip 2.2–2.3 × 1.3–1.4 mm, ovate, erect, similar to petals, subacute, slightly constricted about 2/3 way from the base, appressed on the column and adnate to its foot, 3-veined; column 2.4 mm high, 1.2 mm broad, slightly bending and faintly 3-ridged. Anther terminal, 2-loculed, 0.4 × 0.6 mm; pollinia 8, pyriform, waxy, seated on a viscus in groups of four, 0.38 × 0.2 mm; stigma on top of the column just underneath the anther, pollinia detached with difficulty, cleistogamy apparent.

D i s t r. Endemic. Very rare, on tops of trees in the tropical wet ever-

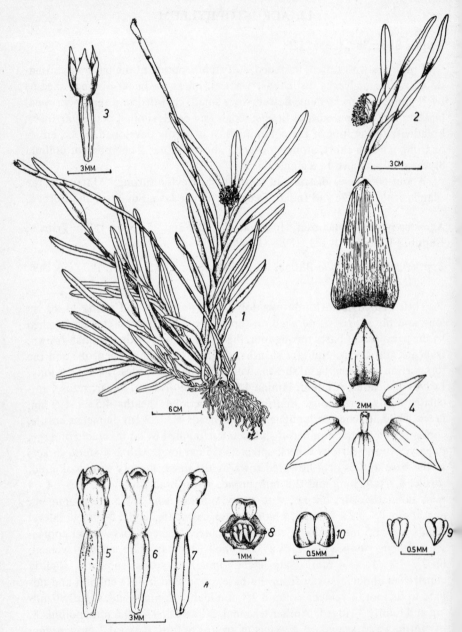

Fig. 66. *Agrostophyllum zeylanicum* Hook. f. 1, plant with inflorescence. 2, inflorescence with an involucre of bracts from side. 3, flower, natural position. 4, bract, sepals, petals, lip and column spread out from front. 5, 6, 7, column, ovary and anther in natural position from front, back and side respectively. 8, column from top with operculum flapped over exposing pollinia. 9, pollinia. 10, operculum from inside.

green forests from 213 to 610 m alt. Foot of Adam's Peak near Ratnapura, Eratne, Karawita Kande, Ambagamuwa, Balangoda, etc.

E c o l. Flowers January–March, September.

I l l u s t r. PDA, drawing.

N o t e. Herb. Kew contains the collections of Mackenzie and Walker from Ceylon in the same type cover. Mackenzie's collection is selected as the lectotype. It is very doubtful that Hooker's collection from Sikkim belongs to this species. This species does not resemble any of the Indian species. Though it resembles *Agrostophyllum callosum* Reichb. f. from Eastern Himalayas in habit and foliage, it differs in the somewhat radially symmetrical flowers, lip resembling the lateral sepals and the column slightly bent. The pollinia are lodged at the top of the column in the Ceylon species and no not possess the subbasal callus of *A. callosum*.

S p e c i m e n s E x a m i n e d. RATNAPURA DISTRICT: Foot of Adam's Peak, in 1839, *Mackenzie s.n.* (K, lectotype); Dotalugala Kande, Feb. 1927, *J.M. Silva s.n.* (PDA); Horagulankande, Sinharaja, Feb. 1977, *Waas 2011* (PDA, US); Gilimale, Feb. 1892, *s. coll. s.n.* (PDA), Sept. 1960, *Jayaweera 1969* (PDA), Jun. 1960, *Jayaweera 16* (AMES); Mar. 1919, Tittaweraluwa Kotha, *s. coll. s.n.* (PDA). GALLE DISTRICT: Kanneliya, Feb. 1976, *Waas 1515* (PDA, US). LOCALITY UNKNOWN: *Walker s.n.* (K), *s. coll. C.P. 3108* and *1856* (PDA).

13. ACANTHEPHIPPIUM

Blume. Bijdr. 353. 1825.

Terrestrial herb with rather long pseudobulbs and a few leaves near the top; leaves large, short-petioled, plaited; flowers few, rather large in lateral racemes from the middle nodes of the pseudobulb; sepals connate to form a swollen tube with short, free, recurved tips; lateral sepals adnate to the long curved foot of the column forming a large, saccate mentum; petals and lip enclosed in the sepal tube; petals narrow, erect as long as sepals; lip very small, hinged movably at the end of the column-foot, strongly 3-lobed, side-lobes erect, midlobe recurved, disc lamellate; anther 4-chambered, pollinia 8, waxy, in two bundles of 4 each, one pair of each bundle smaller, all seated on one granular viscus.

About 8 species distributed in India, Ceylon, Malaya, Java, Samatra, Borneo, Celebes and in the Philippine Islands.

Acanthephippium bicolor Lindl., Bot. Reg. 20: pl. 1730. 1835; Trimen, Handb. Fl. Ceylon 4: 164. 1898.—**Fig. 67.**

Large terrestrial herb with pseudobulbous stems and vermiform roots; pseudobulbs ovoid or fusiform, 5–14 cm long, 2–5 cm diam., crowded together,

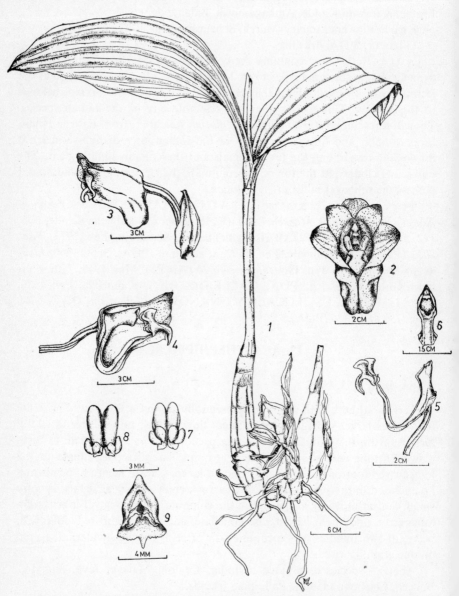

Fig. 67. *Acanthephippium bicolor* Lindl. 1, plant with inflorescence. 2, flower from front. 3, flower and bract from side. 4, flower with half perianth removed. 5, lip, column and foot from side. 6, column from inside. 7, pollinia, front view. 8, pollinia, back view. 9, operculum from inside.

each consisting of about 6 nodes and internodes, the uppermost ones sheathed by leaf petioles. Leaves 2 or 3, 18–45 × 4–13.5 cm, lanceolate to oval, acuminate, acute, narrowed to sheathing petioles, strongly veined underneath. Flowers large, yellow, pitcher-like, tips of petals and sepals purplish-red, 4.5 cm long, 3.5 cm across in 3–7-flowered racemes arising from the tops of new pseudobulbs, enveloped in 6 imbricating scaly sheaths; peduncle about 3 cm long, erect, with a sterile bract; floral bracts large, 3.5 cm long and as broad, cymbiform, striate, pale purple, 9–11-veined; sepals fusing to form a pitcher-like calyx-tube, gibbously inflated, base intruded, mouth oblique; dorsal sepal 3.2 × 1.1 cm, oblong, obtuse, fused 2/3 way up with the lateral sepals; lateral sepals as long as but broader than the dorsal sepal, fused with the foot along their inner edges forming the base of the pitcher, obtuse and recurved at the apex; petals free, erect, fleshy, 3.1 × 1.5 cm, spathulate, obtuse; lip small, 3-lobed, 1.5 × 2 cm, jointed to a long, inflexed, recurved foot 4.5 cm long; lateral lobes erect, rounded; midlobe recurved, oblong-spathulate, obtuse; disc 3-lamellate; column 1.3 cm high, 5.5 mm broad, stout, semicylindrical, truncate. Anther terminal, 4-loculed, 5.4 × 4.4 mm; pollinia 8, oblong or oval, in two bundles of four, one pair of each bundle smaller, all attached to a granular viscus; larger pollinia 2.6 × 1.2 mm and the smaller ones 1.4 × 1 mm. Ovary with pedicel 4 cm long.

D i s t r. Rare, found growing in shady jungles at higher altitudes of the tropical wet evergreen forests up to 610 m Nilambe, Kandy (Udawatte Kelle), Gampola, Bogawantalawa, etc. Also in the Pulney Hills in South India.

E c o l. Flowers January, March, May, July, October.

I l l u s t r. Lindl., Bot. Reg. 20: pl. 1730. 1835.

N o t e. This species is easily distinguished by its large pitcher-shaped, bright yellow flowers arising in short racemes from the tops of new pseudo-bulbs.

S p e c i m e n s   E x a m i n e d. CEYLON: KANDY DISTRICT: Hantane, *s. coll. C.P. 2365* (PDA, lectotype); Nilambe, Dec. 1959, *Jayaweera 11* (AMES); Udawattakele, Oct. 1960, *Jayaweera 1968* (PDA); Peradeniya, Apr. 1859, *Watson s.n.* (K); Botanic Garden, Peradeniya, cultd., July 1961, *Jayaweera 2175* (PDA). INDIA: Lower Pulneys, Machar Shola, May 1899, *Bourne 1843* (K).

14. TAINIA

Blume, Bijdr., 354. 1825.

Terrestrial herbs with a creeping rootstock bearing 1-leaved, tuberous pseudobulbs; leaf solitary, stalked, coriaceous; inflorescences arising from base of pseudobulb, rather long with few to many, well spaced, fairly large flowers; sepals narrow, lateral sepals falcate, adnate to the column-foot (when

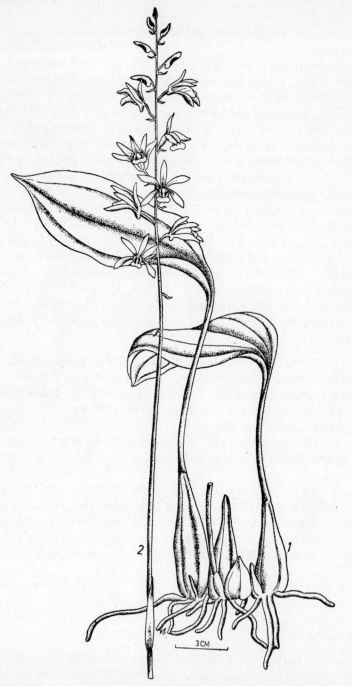

Fig. 68. *Tainia bicornis* Reichb, f. redrawn from a drawing of *C.P. 3190* in PDA.
1, plant with one-leaved pseudobulbs. 2, inflorescence.

present) or saccate base of the lip forming a mentum with it; petals linear, falcate, spreading; lip hinged to the end of the column-foot or not hinged but spurred, entire or 3-lobed with keels on the upper surface; column slender, incurved, with or without a foot; anther 2-chambered, often with two short horns; pollinia 8, waxy, united in fours by a granular viscus, subequal, globosely pyriform.

About 64 species distributed in India, Ceylon, Burma, Malaya, China and extending southwards to Java, Sumatra, Borneo and the Philippine Islands.

Tainia bicornis Reichb. f. in Bonplandia 5 : 54. 1857; Trimen, Handb. Fl. Ceylon 4: 169. 1898.—**Fig. 68.**

Ania bicornis Lindl., Bot. Reg. 28: Misc. 37. 1842; 30: pl. 8. 1844.
Ania latifolia Wight, Ic. Pl. Ind. Or. 3 (2): 10, pl. 914. 1844–1845.
Mitopetalum wightii Blume, Ann. Mus. Bot. Lugduno Batavum 2: 185. 1856.
Mitopetalum bicorne Blume, ibid.
Eria bicornis Reichb. f. in Walp. Ann. 6: 269. 1861.
Eria wightii Reichb. f., ibid. 270.

Terrestrial herb with a fusiform or narrowly pyriform, 1-leaved, tuberous pseudobulb on a creeping rootstock and stout vermiform roots; pseudobulb 3.7–6.2 cm long. Leaves solitary, 10–15 × 5–5.5 cm, oblong or ovate-oblong, acute or acuminate, coriaceous, many-veined; petiole 7.5–12.5 cm long, slender, erect, naked. Flowers pale olive-green stained with purple, 2.5–3 cm broad, in tall, slender, erect, many-flowered racemes; peduncle with the raceme 20–40 cm long with a few membranous, spreading bracts; floral bracts small, lanceolate and spreading; dorsal sepal linear-oblong, obtuse, erect; lateral sepals linear-spathulate, falcately decurved, obtuse; petals similar to lateral sepals; lip obovate, adnate to the foot of the column, 3-lobed; midlobe of lip short and broad, subquadrate, emarginate; disc with 2 lamellae between the side lobes and 3-lamellate on the midlobe; column slender, incurved, base produced into a short foot. Anther terminal, 2-loculed, bearing 2 short horns; pollinia 8, pyriform, united in fours by a glandular viscus. Ovary with pedicel 0.6 cm long.

D i s t r. Rare, under the shade of trees in moist conditions in the submontane or mid-country tropical wet evergreen forests at about 915 m alt. Hantane, Pundaluoya, etc. Also on the Pulney Hills in South India and probably in Northern Thailand and Java.

E c o l. Flowers January–March.

I l l u s t r. PDA, drawing from *C.P. 3190.*

N o t e. This species was imported to England from Ceylon by Rev. J. Clowes who flowered it in March 1842. Probably Lindley's specimen came from this collection and hence it is selected as the lectotype. The collection of *Wallich 3741* is also in Herb. Lindley as a type under *Ania latifolia* Wight. According to Hooker both Lindley's and Wight's figures do not represent the true *Tainia bicornis*. This species is distinguished by the one-leaved, tuberous, terrestrial pseudobulbs, and olive green flowers, stained purple, in erect racemes.

Specimens Examined. CEYLON: KANDY DISTRICT: Hantane, *s. coll. C.P. 3190* (PDA). INDIA: Courtallam, 1836, Herb. *Wight s.n.* (K). BANGLADESH: Sylhet, *Wallich 374* (K). THAILAND: Northern Thailand, Feb. 1912, in evergreen jungle by stream, lip yellow with purple veins on side lobes, rest of the flower green, *Kerr 295* (K, AMES). ENGLAND: cult., *Clowes s.n.* (K, lectotype).

15. IPSEA

Lindl., Gen. et Sp. Orch. 124. 1831.

Terrestrial pseudobulbous herbs with 1 or 2 long, narrow, plicate leaves; scape tall, erect, sheathed, few-flowered; flowers large, bracts spathaceous; sepals subequal, spreading, lateral sepals ovate-oblong, adnate to the base of the column; petals narrower; lip sessile at the base of the column forming a mentum, side lobes oblong, erect, midlobe obovate, disc crested; column slender, clavate above, foot absent; anther 4-chambered; pollinia 8, pyriform, waxy, in groups of 4 each, one pair of each group smaller, each group with a caudicle.

Three species found in India and Ceylon.

Ipsea speciosa Lindl., Gen. et Sp. Orch. 124. 1831; Trimen, Handb. Fl. Ceylon 4: 171. 1898.—**Fig. 69**.

Pachystoma speciosum Reichb. f., Bonplandia 3: 250. 1855.

Terrestrial herb with pseudobulbous stems, the whole plant puberulous; pseudobulbs 2–3 cm long, 1.2–2.5 cm diameter, clustered, depressed, broadly ovoid with long, filiform roots from their bases. Leaves usually single, occasionally two, 15–25 × 0.5–2.2 cm, narrowly or lanceolately linear, acuminate, narrowed at the base to a slender petiole, 3-veined and puberulous. Flowers large, puberulous all over, 5–6.6 cm across, bright golden-yellow in tall, erect, slender, sheathed, few-flowered scapes; peduncle 15–40 cm long, slender, with a few, oblong-lanceolate, loose, white sheaths; pedicel decurved; floral bracts 1.8–2 × 0.9–1.2 cm, ovate, acuminate, 17-veined; dorsal sepal 2.7–3 × 1.2–1.7 cm, oblong, subacute, 13-veined; lateral sepals 3–3.5 × 0.9–1.4 cm, ovate-oblong, subacute, spreading, adnate to the base of the column, 9–11-veined; petals 2.8–3.1 × 0.8–1 cm, spathulate, obtuse, 5-veined; lip

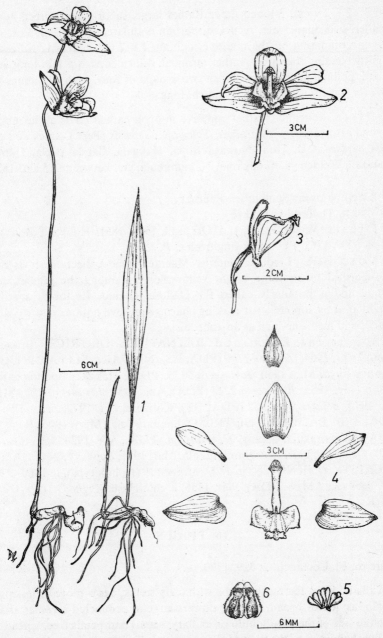

Fig. 69. *Ipsea speciosa* Lindl. 1, plant with inflorescence. 2, flower from front. 3, lip and column from side. 4, bract, sepals and petals spread out from front; lip and column, natural position, slightly spread out from front. 5, pollinia. 6, operculum from inside.

3–3.2 × 2.7–2.9 cm, 3-lobed; lateral lobes large, suborbicular, erect; midlobe smaller, orbicular-ovate, recurved, margin undulate, disc with 3–5 crenulate ridges terminating on the midlobe; column 1.9–2 cm, narrowly winged and slightly bending forward. Anther terminal, 4-loculed, 3–3.5 mm long and as broad; pollinia 8, pyriform, flat in two groups of four, each pollinium 1.5 × 0.8 mm. Ovary with pedicel 1–1.5 cm long.

D i s t r. Endemic. Rather common in open patana lands in the montane zone in association with grasses, *Spiranthes sinensis* (Pers.) Ames and *Satyrium nepalense* D. Don. Nuwara Eliya, Hakgala, Bandarawela, Hantane, Maturata, Teldeniya, Galagama, Namunukula, etc. between 915 and 1829 m alt.

E c o l. Flowers September–February.

V e r n. Daffodil Orchid (E).

I l l u s t r. Wight, Ic. Pl. Ind. Or. 5: pl. 1663. 1851; Hook. f., Bot. Mag. 94: pl. 5701. 1868; PDA, drawing from *C.P. 2364.*

N o t e: Herb. Lindley contains Macrae's type collection. It is easily distinguished by its large bright yellow flowers among the grasses in the patana and is popularly called the Daffodil Orchid. Its tubers are much sought after by sorcerers for making charms and love potions and by village quacks and medicine-men as an aphrodisiac.

S p e c i m e n s   E x a m i n e d. RATNAPURA DISTRICT: Brampton Group Apr. 1964, *Grierson 1140* (PDA, US). NUWARA ELIYA DISTRICT: Nuwara Eliya, May 1960, *Jayaweera 2173* (PDA); Hakgala Botanic garden, cultd., Nov. 1955, *Jayaweera 2247* (PDA), Apr. 1959, *Jayaweera 17* (AMES), Jan. 1970, *Balakrishnan 622* (PDA, US); Kotmale, Oct. 1972, *Jayasuriya 971* (PDA, US). BADULLA DISTRICT: Bandarawela, Mar. 1906, *Willis s.n.* (PDA); Namunukula, Sept. 1907, *Willis s.n.* (PDA), Apr. 1924, *J.M. Silva s.n.* (PDA); between Passara & Namunukula, Mar. 1971, *Robyns 7324* (PDA, US). LOCALITY UNKNOWN: in 1829, *Macrae 19* (K, holotype), in 1860, *s. coll. C.P. 2364* (K, AMES, PDA), Mar. 1836, *s. coll.* Herb. *Wight s.n.* (K); *Walker 206* (K).

16. PHAIUS

Loureiro, Fl. Cochinch. 2: 529. 1790.

Tall and stout terrestrial herbs with leafy stems; bases more or less pseudobulbous; leaves broad, plaited; flowers large in peduncled racemes arising from the side of the pseudobulb or axillary; sepals and petals free, spreading; lip slightly jointed to the base of the column and embracing it, 3-lobed, more or less saccate or spurred at the base with longitudinal ridges on the upper surface; column long, slender; foot absent or very short; anther incompletely 4-chambered; pollinia 8, waxy, in two groups of 4 with a caudicle.

About 85 species extending from tropical Africa and Madagascar through India, Ceylon, Burma, China and southwards into Java, Sumatra, Borneo, Celebes, New Guinea as far as the Philippine Islands and Australia.

KEY TO THE SPECIES

1 Peduncle arising from base of pseudobulb; flowers large, many, with strongly incurved spur; column not toothed..**1. P. tancarvilleae**
1 Peduncle arising from lower leaf axils; flowers small, few, with very short spur or mentum; top of column toothed...**2. P. luridus**

1. Phaius tancarvilleae (Banks ex L'Her.) Blume, Orch. Java 1: 2. 1858–1859.—**Fig. 70.**

Limodorum tancarvilleae Banks in L'Her., Sertum Anglicum 17. 1788.
Bletia tankervilliae Ait. f., Hort. Kew (ed. 2) 5: 205. 1813.
Pachyne spectabilis Salisb., Trans. Hort. Soc. London 1: 299. 1820 (3rd ed.).
Limodorum incarvillei Blume. Bijdr. 374. 1825.
Phaius blumei Lindl., Gen. et Sp. Orch. 127. 1830.
Phaius bicolor Lindl., ibid. 128.
Phaius wallichii Lindl., in Wall., Pl. As. Rar. 2: 46, pl. 158. 1831; Trimen, Handb. Fl. Ceylon 4: 172. 1898.
Limodorum tankervilliae Roxb., Fl. Ind. 3: 466. 1831. (not of Ait. f.).
Phaius grandifolius Lindl. in Wall., Cat. n. 3747. 1831.

Large terrestrial herb with pseudobulbous, leafy stems and vermiform roots; pseudobulbs about 8 cm long, 2.5–3 cm diameter, annulate, internodes greenish-white. Leaves 2–4 to each pseudobulb, 3–11.8 dm long from the base of petiolar end to apex, 4.5–13.5 cm broad, lanceolate or oblong-lanceolate, acuminate, strongly ribbed, veins prominent beneath, bases sheathing or petioled. Flowers varying in colour from purplish orange to pale orange-yellow with an orange-yellow to purplish-white lip, 6–11 cm across, in long-peduncled, many-flowered racemes; peduncle 40 cm or more long, green with five acute, sterile bracts each 2.5–5.5 cm long. Floral bracts 4.5 × 2.5 cm, orbicular-ovate, acuminate or cuspidately acute, 11-veined; dorsal sepals 4–5.2 × 0.9–1.3 cm, lanceolate, acute, 7-veined; lateral sepals 4.1–5.4 × 0.8–1.3 cm, lanceolate, acuminate, acute, 7-veined; petals 3.7–5.2 × 0.8–0.9 cm, lanceolate or oblong-lanceolate, acute or subacute, 7-veined; lip 3.5–5 cm long, erect, 3-lobed, adnate to the base of the column, and embracing it by the convolute and recurved, crenate, lateral lobes, midlobe orbicular, also crenate, posteriorly produced into a curved, horn-like spur, sometimes bifid; column 1.8–2.3 cm high, 5.5–6.5 mm broad, more or less straight without a foot; apex produced into an apiculate rostellum. Anther terminal, incompletely 4-loculed, 2.4 × 2.7 mm, pilose; pollinia 8, flat, clavate, waxy, in superposed pairs, lower pairs slightly

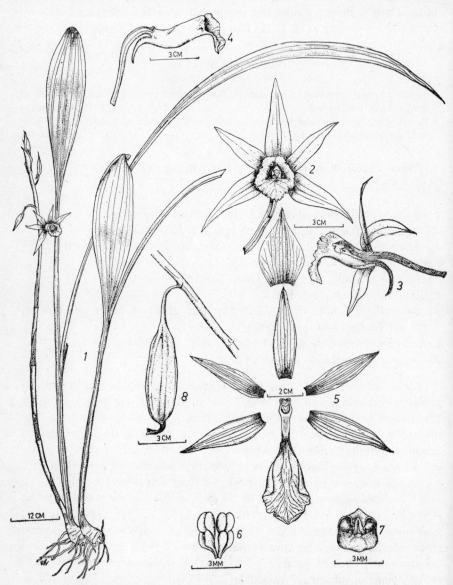

Fig. 70. *Phaius tancarvilleae* (Banks ex L'Herit) Blume. 1, plant with inflorescence.
2, flower from front. 3, longitudinal section of flower. 4, lip and spur from side,
lateral lobes of the lip embracing column. 5, bract, sepals, petals, lip and column
spread out from front. 6, pollinia. 7, operculum from inside. 8, fruit.

smaller; larger pollinia 1.8 × 1.3 mm, and the smaller ones 1.5 × 1.1 mm. Ovary with pedicel 2.5–5 cm long. Fruit an oblong capsule, 6 × 2 cm.

D i s t r. Rather common, under the shade of trees in the submontane or mid-country tropical wet evergreen forests extending on to the subtropical montane forests between 915 and 2134 m alt. Rangala, Nuwara Eliya, Hakgala, Adam's Peak, Mahacoodagala, Kabaragala, Laggala, etc. It also occurs in Sikkim Himalaya, Assam, Burma, Java, Sumatra, Borneo, New Guinea, Formosa and the Samoan and Fiji Islands.

E c o l. Flowers February, April–June, September–November.

I l l u s t r. Wall., Pl. As. Rar. 2: pl. 158. 1831; Paxton's Mag. Bot. 6: pl. 193. 1839; Hook. Bot. Mag. pl. 4078. 1844; Hook. f., Bot. Mag. 114: pl. 7023, 1888; Lindley, Sert. Orch. pl. 23. 1838; Wight, Ic. Pl. Ind. Or. 5: pls. 1659–60. 1851; King & Pantling, Ann. R. Bot. Gard. (Calcutta) 8: pl. 1150. 1898; PDA, 6 drawings.

N o t e. The flower varies much in colour but the species is distinguished by the scapes arising from the base of the pseudobulb. Dr. Fothergill sent the first plant to England from probably China and it flowered in 1776. In Herb. Lindley there are four collections under different synonyms. Of these *Macrae 24* from Ceylon is selected as the lectotype. This species has been cultivated in the U.S.A., Brazil and England. The collections reported from Cuba and Jamaica are probably escapes from cultivation and naturalized.

S p e c i m e n s   E x a m i n e d. CEYLON: KANDY DISTRICT: Rangala, Apr. 1932, *Simpson 9424* (PDA); Hunnasgiriya, Oct. 1960, *Jayaweera 2038* (PDA); Adam's Peak, Feb. 1973, *Jayasuriya, Burtt & Townsend 1117* (PDA, US); Maskeliya, Jan. 1973, *Cramer 4035* (PDA, US). RATNAPURA DISTRICT: Dotalugala Forest, Aug. 1976, *Waas 1346* (PDA, US). NUWARA ELIYA DISTRICT: Nuwara Eliya, May 1960, *Jayaweera 2171* (PDA), Aug. 1959, *Jayaweera 2039* (PDA), Feb. 1960, *Jayaweera 18 (1)* (AMES); Ambewela, Mar. 1906, *Willis s.n.* (PDA). BADULLA DISTRICT: Fort Macdonald, Mar. 1906, *A.M. Silva s.n.* (PDA). LOCALITY UNKNOWN: *Gardner 865* (K), *Macrae 24* (K, lectotype), *s. coll. C.P. 2368* (PDA). N. AMERICA: Missouri, Bot. Gard., cultd., Apr. 1915, *Thomson 235* (AMES). New York, Bot. Gard., cultd., May 1901, *Schafer 1711* (AMES). CUBA: Nipe Mts., Mar. 1928, in swamp near brook under trees at 2000 ft alt., *Michell 13* (AMES). JAMAICA: Feb. 1920, in dense forest on the upper slopes of Mt. Diabolo at 500–800 m alt., *Maxon & Killip 430* (AMES). S. AMERICA: Brazil, cult., Dec. 1914, *Dusen 15750* (AMES). ENGLAND: cultd., Oct. 1889, Hort. Kew (K); E. Sheen, May 1892, *F. Wigan* (K); Wisely, Jun. 1890, *Mrs. Evans* (K). INDIA: Oct. 1872, *Gamble* (K). Khasia Hills, at 4000 ft alt., *Hooker & Thomson 162* (K), 1844, *Griffith* (K). Sikkim Himalaya, 1891, *Pantling 139* (AMES), 1892, *Pantling 120* (AMES). Assam, *Jenkins* (PDA). BANGLADESH: Sylhet, *Wallich 374* (K). SUMATRA: Feb. 1820,

Binnemeyer 8253 (AMES); Jan. 1932, on side of volcano near Redelong, 3600–6000 ft alt., *Bangham 909* (AMES). BRITISH NORTH BORNEO: Feb. 1933, *Carr 26262* (AMES); Sept. 1933 at 6000–13500 ft alt., *Clemens 40460* (AMES). NEW GUINEA: Jan. 1955, at 5000 ft alt., *Womersley & Miller 7801* (AMES). FIJI ISLANDS: Venua Levu, Nov. 1933, *Smith 398* (AMES); Wainamo Creek, Aug. 1937, *Williams 18242* (AMES). SAMOA: Paia, July 1931, *Christophersen & Hume 2085* (AMES). COOK ISLAND: 1929, *Wilder 8* (AMES).

2. Phaius luridus Thw., Enum. Pl. Zeyl. 300. 1861; Trimen, Handb. Fl. Ceylon 4: 173. 1898.—**Fig. 71**.

Terrestrial, somewhat pseudobulbous herb with leafy stems about 60 cm high, clothed with large, lanceolate, acuminate, green sheaths; roots vermiform. Leaves 30–45 × 7.5–12.5 cm, lanceolate or oblong-lanceolate, acuminate, strongly ribbed beneath, petioles sheathing. Flowers yellow, striped with red lengthwise, 5 cm broad, in few-flowered, long racemes arising from the lower axils of leaves or leaf sheaths; peduncle 20–25 cm long, erect. Floral bracts oblong, acute, pubescent and caducous; sepals oblong-lanceolate, acuminate; petals narrower and broader above, oblong-lanceolate, acute, sepals and petals spreading; lip cucullate, obscurely 3-lobed, adnate to the base of the column and embracing it, undulate, hairy above with 2 contiguous wrinkled ridges, glabrous beneath, base forming a short spur or mentum; column short, stout, toothed at the apex. Anther terminal, hairy, incompletely 4-loculed; pollinia 8, in superposed pairs but in two bundles of four, lower pairs smaller. Fruit a fusiform capsule, about 5 cm long.

D i s t r. Endemic. Rare, in the shade in moist regions of the low country. Pasdun Korale, Raigam Korale, Rakwana, Hewessa, Sabaragamuwa Province, etc.

E c o l. Flowers August, September.

I l l u s t r. PDA, 3 drawings one of which is from *C.P. 613*.

N o t e. This species is distinguished from *Phaius tancarvilleae* Bl. in that the pseudobulb is inconspicuous and the scape arises from the top of the pseudobulb. Further, the flowers are smaller, greenish-yellow and rufous with two red blotches on its yellow lip. *C.P. 613* appears to be the only collection made from Ceylon. I have not come across this species in a live state.

S p e c i m e n s E x a m i n e d. COLOMBO DISTRICT: Pasdun Korale, Aug. 1865, *s. coll. C.P. 613* (K, holotype, PDA).

17. CALANTHE

R. Br. in Bot. Reg. 7. sub t. 573. 1821.

Terrestrial herbs with leafy stems; bases of stems pseudobulbous; leaves

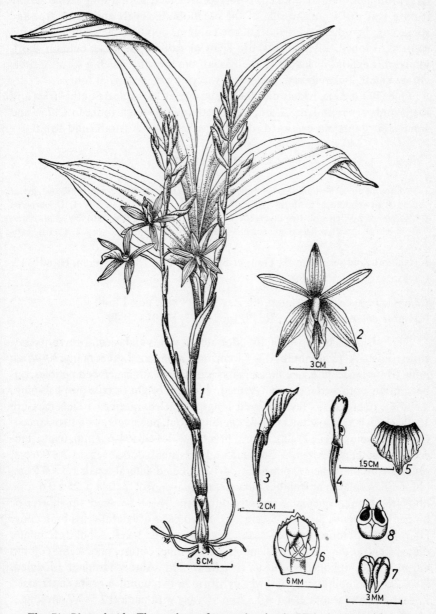

Fig. 71. *Phaius luridus* Thw. redrawn from a drawing in PDA. 1, plant with inflo-rescences. 2, flower from front. 3, lip embracing the column, side view. 4, column and ovary from side. 5, lip spread out from front. 6, top of the column from front. 7, pollinia. 8, operculum from front.

large, thin and plaited, stalked; inflorescence erect, with a long scape arising from a leaf axil from the side of the pseudobulb; sepals and petals free and spreading; lip adnate to the top of the column, opposite the stigmatic cavity, spurred, 3-lobed, often with short keels or calli at the base; column short, joined throughout its length to the base of the lip with which it forms a tube; anther small, 2-chambered; pollinia 8, waxy, in two groups of four.

Over 300 species, widely distributed, occurring in tropical South Africa and the islands of the Indian Ocean, and continuing through India to China and Japan and also south-eastwards through Malaysia to Australia and Tahiti.

KEY TO THE SPECIES

1 Midlobe of lip obcordate; leaves pubescent on both sides; disc prominently warted at base; fruit pendulous, fusiform...1. C. purpurea
1 Midlobe of lip cleft into two divergent lobes; leaves glabrous; disc with few small warts; fruit ellipsoid with a decurved pedicel.............................2. C. triplicatis

1. Calanthe purpurea Lindl., Gen. et Sp. Orch. 249. 1833; Trimen, Handb. Fl. Ceylon 4: 174. 1898.—**Fig. 72.**

Calanthe masuca Thw., Enum. Pl. Zeyl. 308. 1861, non Lindl.
Calanthe emarginata Wight, Ic. Pl. Ind. Or. 3: pl. 918. 1849.

Terrestrial herb with erect, pseudobulbous stems and vermiform roots on a stout rootstock; pseudobulbs 1.3–1.8 cm long, annulate. Leaves many, 30–45 cm long, ovate-lanceolate, acuminate, tapering into sheathing, ribbed petioles, pubescent on both surfaces and 7-veined. Flowers bright or pale purplish-pink, 2.5–3.7 cm broad, in few-flowered long-peduncled racemes which measure 12–20 cm in length; peduncle 20–45 cm long, stout, pubescent, with two lanceolate, pubescent, sterile bracts. Floral bracts 1.3–1.8 cm × 4–6.5 mm, ovate-lanceolate, acute, pubescent, 3–7-veined and persistent; dorsal sepal 1.3 × 0.6 cm, oblong-lanceolate, acute, pubescent, 4- or 5-veined; lateral sepals 1.5 × 0.5 cm, oblong-lanceolate, apiculate, pubescent, 3–5-veined; petals 1.25 × 0.6 cm, obovate-oblong, apiculate, sparsely pubescent, 4- or 5-veined; lip shorter or longer than sepals, 3-lobed, 5-veined, the two pairs of lateral veins branching; lateral lobes oblong, obtuse, falcate; midlobe broad, 2-cleft, lobules crenulate, disc warted at the base; spur slender, 2.5 cm long, obtuse, pubescent; column 4.5 mm high, obliquely truncate, rostellum bifid. Anther terminal 2-loculed, 2.8 × 2.3 mm; pollinia 8, narrowly pyriform in two bundles, pairs superposed in each bundle, stipitate, 1.7 × 0.5 mm. Ovary with pedicel 2.5–3.7 cm long.

D i s t r. Endemic. Rather common under the shade of trees in higher elevations in the submontane or mid-country tropical wet evergreen forests up to 1829 m alt. Rangala, Maturata, Mahacoodagala, Nuwara Eliya, Ambagamuwa, Hunnasgiriya, etc.

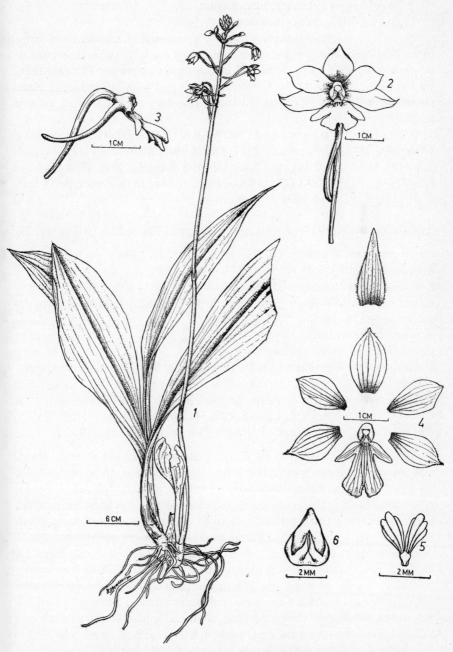

Fig. 72. *Calanthe purpurea* Lindl. 1, plant with inflorescence. 2, flower from front. 3, lip, column and spur from side. 4, bract, sepals, petals, lip and column spread out from front. 5, pollinia. 6, operculum from inside.

E c o l. Flowers February, July, August.

I l l u s t r. PDA, 2 drawings from *C.P. 2366*.

N o t e. This species is very similar to *C. masuca* of Lindley from India but differs from it in that the leaves are downy on both surfaces, especially beneath, while the leaves of the Indian species are glabrous. The only illustration which agrees with the Ceylon species is that of Wight in Icones Plantarum, pl. 918 while all others illustrated elsewhere are those of *C. masuca* Lindl.

S p e c i m e n s E x a m i n e d. NUWARA ELIYA DISTRICT: Nuwara Eliya, Sept. 1960, *Jayaweera 1977* (PDA), Jul. 1960, *Jayaweera 19 (1)* (AMES). KANDY DISTRICT: between Knuckles and Rilagala, Nov. 1974, *Davidse 8259* (PDA, US). LOCALITY UNKNOWN: *Hooker 18* (K, lectotype); *s. coll. C.P. 2366* (K, PDA); *Walker 1790* (K).

2. Calanthe triplicatis (Willemet) Ames, Philipp. J. Sci. 2: 326. 1907.—**Fig. 73.**

Orchis triplicata Willemet, Ann. Bot. (Usteri) 18: 52. 1796.
Limodorum veratrifolium Willd., Sp. Pl. 4: 122. 1805.
Limodorum ventricosum Steud., Nom. Bot. ed. 2, 481. 1820.
Calanthe veratrifolia R. Br., Bot. Reg. 9: pl. 720. 1823; Trimen, Handb. Fl. Ceylon 4: 174. 1898.
Amblyglottis flava Blume, Bijdr. 64. 1825.
Amblyglottis veratrifolia Blume, ibid. 370.
Calanthe furcata Bateman ex Lindl., Bot. Reg. 24: Misc. 34. 1838; Abeywick., Cey. J. Sci., Biol. Sci. 2 (2): 148. 1959.
Calanthe perrottetii A. Rich., Ann. Sc. Nat. Bot. 11. 15: 68. 1841.
Calanthe comosa Reichb. f., Linnaea 19: 374. 1847.
Bletia quadrifida Buch.-Ham. ex Hook. f., Fl. Br. Ind. 5: 851. 1890.

Large terrestrial herb with leafy, pseudobulbous stems on a stout, horizontal rootstock; roots vermiform. Leaves 3 or 4 to a pseudobulb, 28–38 × 5–10.5 cm, oblong-lanceolate, acuminate, plaited, glabrous, 5–7-veined; petioles 10–26 cm long, sheathing. Flowers white, 2.5 cm broad in terminal, long-peduncled racemes; peduncle about 65 cm long, stout, pubescent, green with four green, sterile bracts. Floral bracts 0.8 × 0.6 cm, oblong-ovate, suddenly acuminate, acute, green, pubescent, margin wrinkled; dorsal sepal 1.1 cm × 7.5 mm, broadly-ovate or oblong, acute or truncate or faintly apiculate, pubescent outside, 5-veined; lateral sepals 1.2 cm × 6.5 mm, obliquely obovate-oblong, obtuse or crenate-apiculate, pubescent outside, 5-veined; petals 1.1 cm × 6 mm, obovate or obovate-oblong, rounded, puberulous outside towards the base, 3-veined; lip 1.1 cm long, 3-lobed; lateral lobes of lip oblong, 7 × 2–4 mm, obtuse; midlobe cleft half way into two falcate diverging lobules, each 5 × 4 mm, crenate with a few small warts at the base; column 5 mm high and 4 mm broad, rostellum bifid with the glands of pollinia lodged in the fork.

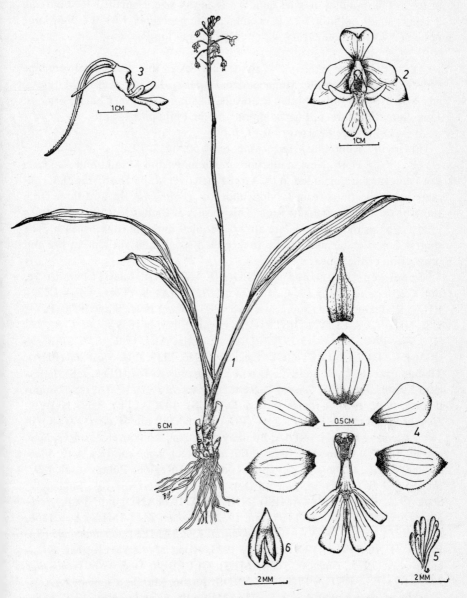

Fig. 73. *Calanthe triplicatis* (Willem.) Ames. 1, plant with inflorescence. 2, flower from front. 3, lip, column and spur from side. 4, bract, sepals, petals and lip spread out from front, column from inside. 5, pollinia. 6, operculum from inside.

Anther terminal, 2-loculed, 2.6 × 2 mm, pollinia 8, club-shaped, in two bundles of four each; pollinia in each bundle varying in size, 1 small, 1 medium and 2 large; small pollinia 1.2 × 0.36 mm, medium pollinia 1.3 × 0.4 mm, large pollinia 1.7 × 0.6 mm. Ovary with pedicel 3.5 cm long.

D i s t r. Rather rare, in the shade of trees in the subtropical montane forests up to 2134 m alt. Mahacoodagala, Hakgala, Mt. Pedro, Maturata, etc. Also in South India, Malay Peninsula, Thailand, Cochin, China, Formosa, Java, Sumatra, Borneo, Fiji, Solomon and the Philippine Islands.

E c o l. Flowers February–April, July.

I l l u s t r. Rumphius, Herb. Amb. 6: pl. 52, fig. 2. 1750.

N o t e. In Herb. Kew, collections of Cuming from Manila and *Junghuhn 308* from Java are included in the same type cover while Herb. Lindley contains two collections from Ceylon under *C. veratrifolia* Br. and three from India under *C. perrottetii* A. Rich. This species is similar to *Calanthe masuca* Lindl. in habit but its leaves are always petioled and glabrous beneath. The spur is more slender and the lip longer than sepals and variable in size and proportion of the lobes.

Specimens Examined. CEYLON: KANDY DISTRICT: Peradeniya, Bot. Gard. cultd., May 1954, *Jayaweera 1181* (PDA). RATNAPURA DISTRICT: Walukandeniya, Sinharaja, Feb. 1977, *Waas 1994, Wass 1974* (PDA, US). NUWARA ELIYA DISTRICT: Nuwara Eliya, in 1859 *s. coll. C.P. 1371* (K), May 1960, *Jayaweera 1979* (PDA); Hakgala, Aug. 1926, *J.M. Silva s.n.* (PDA). BADULLA DISTRICT: Uma Oya, Dec. 1927, *J.M. Silva 268* (PDA); Thangamalai F.R., June 1972, *Maxwell & Jayasuriya 767* (PDA, US); Fairyland Estate, Oct. 1975, *Sohmer & Sumithraarachchi 10201* (PDA, US); Namunukula, Nov. 1974, *Cramer 4734* (PDA, US). LOCALITY UNKNOWN: *Hooker 10* (K), *s. coll. C.P. 2367* (PDA); at 6000 ft alt. *Walker 193* (K); in 1845, *Thomson s.n.* (K). INDIA: Bombay, Malabar, Konkan etc., *Stocks, Law, etc. s.n.* (PDA). Coonoor: Nilgiris, *Wight 182* (K), *Lobb s.n.* (K), Aug. 1886, at 7000 ft alt., *Gamble 18030* (K). Kodaikanal Region: Pulneys, Jul. 1897, *Bourne 677* (K). Mysore, *Law 55* (K). MALAY PENINSULA: Singapore: Sept. 1921, *Burkill 6564* (AMES). NORTH THAILAND: Jan. 1914, *Herb. Kerr s.n.* (AMES). SUMATRA: Jan. 1932, *Bangham 783* (AMES), Oct. 1868, *Pierre 127* (AMES). JAVA: 1920 *Bakhuizen 4566* (AMES); *Junghuhn 308* (K). BRITISH NORTH BORNEO: May 1923, *Wood 1748* (AMES); Mt. Kinabalu, Nov. 1915, *Clemens 343* (AMES). CELEBES: Dec. 1909, *Schlechter 20528* (AMES). PHILIPPINE ISLANDS: Luzon: Manila, *Cumings s.n.* (K); Rizal Prov., Sept. 1909, *Loher 14605* (AMES); Pengasinam, Nov. 1917, *Fenix 29894* (AMES). Sorsogon Prov., Nov. 1915, *Elmer 14973* (AMES). Laguna Prov., Feb. 1913, *Ramos 20451* (AMES); Jul. 1929, *Quisumbing 5140* (AMES); Benguet Subprov., May 1911, *Merrill 7694* (AMES), Mar. 1904, *Elmer 5993* (AMES). Mindoro, Baco River, Mar. 1905, *Merrill 4065* (AMES); Jul. 1913,

Escritor 21310 (AMES). Panay, Antique Prov., May–Aug. 1918, *McGregor 32355* (AMES). Leyte, Apr. 1913 *Wenzel 71* (AMES). Negros, May 1908, *Elmer 10052* (AMES). Mindanao, Davao Prov., *Ramos & Edano 49607* (AMES); Zamboagna Dist., Sept.–Oct. 1915, *Reillo 16450* (AMES); Misamis Prov., 1906, *Mearns & Hutchinson 4602* (AMES). GUAM: Apr. 1936, *Bryan 1225* (AMES); Oct. 1911, *McGregor 575* (AMES). SOLOMON ISLANDS: Ysabel, *Brass 'C'* (AMES). FIJI ISLANDS: Feb. 1928, *Gillespie 4644* (AMES); Feb. 1941, *Degener 14635* (AMES); Feb. 1934, *Smith 961* (AMES). SAMOA: Oct. 1931, *Christophersen 2851* (AMES); Jan. 1905, *Vaupel 409* (AMES).

18. ARUNDINA

Blume, Bijdr. 401. 1825.

Terrestrial erect herbs; stems close together, elongate, rigid, bearing many grass-like leaves; leaves narrow, distichous, flat, jointed on their sheathing bases; flowers large in terminal, erect, few-flowered racemes; petals wider than sepals, spreading horizontally; lateral sepals close together behind the lip; lip large, embracing the column, trumpet-shaped; disc lamellate; column long, slender, narrowly winged, foot absent; anther 4-chambered; pollinia 8 in two superposed unequal groups of 4, flat, the caudicles covered with granular pollen.

About 18 species in India, Ceylon, Malaya, Cambodia, China and extending southwards to Java, Sumatra, Borneo, Celebes and the Pacific Islands.

KEY TO THE SPECIES

1 Leaves 5–7.5 cm long; capsule 2.5–3.7 cm..............................**1. A. minor**
1 Leaves 20–30 cm long; capsule 5–6.2 cm.........................**2. A. graminifolia**

1. Arundina minor Lindl., Gen. et Sp. Orch. 125. 1831; Trimen, Handb. Fl. Ceylon 4: 170. 1898.—**Fig. 74.**

Terrestrial, erect herb with non-pseudobulbous stems, on a hard rootstock; roots fibrous and matted. Stems tufted, 30–60 cm long, terete, leafless below, internodes 1–1.9 cm long. Leaves many, towards the top of canes, erect, distichous, 5–7.5 cm × 4.5–6 mm, linear, acute, appressed, bases sheathing. Flowers pale pink with yellow lips, 3.3 cm broad in 3- or 4-flowered, terminal racemes which measure 5–7.5 cm in length; peduncle and rachis stout. Floral bracts 1.1 cm long and as broad when spread out, infundibular-ovate, acute, 9-veined; dorsal and lateral sepals 2 cm × 4.6 mm, lanceolate-oblong, subacute, 7-veined; petals 2.5 × 1.17 cm, oblong, subacute, 5–7-veined; lip large, about 3 cm long, sessile on the base of the column, embracing it by its lateral lobes; midlobe flat, crisped, bifid; disc lamellate; column long,

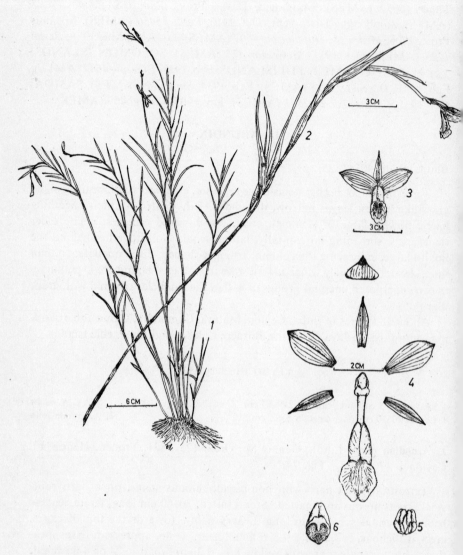

Fig. 74. *Arundina minor* Lindl. 1, clump of canes with inflorescences. 2, single cane with a flower. 3, flower from front. 4, bract, sepals and petals spread out from front, lip drawn out from the enveloping position of the column, not spread out, column from front. 5, pollinia, enlarged. 6, operculum, enlarged, from inside.

slender, narrowly winged, foot absent. Anther terminal, 4-loculed; pollinia 8 in two groups of 4, united by a viscus. Ovary with pedicel 1.8 cm long.

D i s t r. Endemic. Rather common, gregarious, growing in moist marshy open patanas up to 1220 m alt. Dolosbage, Ramboda, Galagama, Etampitiya, Uva Prov., foot of Adam's peak, etc.

E c o l. Flowers January, February, August. Grows in marshy land in the patanas.

I l l u s t r. PDA, drawing from *C.P. 485.*

N o t e. This is allied to *A. chinensis* from which it differs in the shorter, suberect small leaves that are acuminate or subacute with an apiculus. It is easily distinguished as a dwarf cane orchid with large pale pink flowers and distichous leaves.

S p e c i m e n s E x a m i n e d. KANDY DISTRICT: Moray Estate, Maskeliya, Mar. 1974, *Sumithraarachchi & Jayasuriya 179* (PDA, US), Oct. 1971, *Balakrishnan & Dassanayake 928* (PDA, US), Nov. 1974, *Davidse & Sumithraarachchi 8593* (PDA, US), Mar. 1974, *Jayasuriya & Sumithraarachchi 1565* (PDA, US), Nov. 1973, *Sohmer & Waas 8725* (PDA, US); Rajamally Estate, Feb. 1973, *Cramer 4052* (PDA, US); Adam's Peak, Aug. 1959, *Jayaweera 15* (AMES). BADULLA DISTRICT: Etampitiya, Jan. 1888, *s. coll. s.n.* (PDA). LOCALITY UNKNOWN: *s. coll. C.P. 485* (K, AMES, PDA); *Walker 295* (K).

2. Arundina graminifolia (D. Don) Hochreutiner, Bull. New York Bot. Gard. 6: 270. 1910; Alston in Trimen, Handb. Fl. Ceylon 6: 275. 1931.—**Fig. 75.**

Bletia graminifolia D. Don, Prod. Fl. Nepal. 29. 1825.
Limodorum graminifolium (Buch.-Ham.) D. Don, ibid.
Arundina bambusifolia Lindl., Gen. et Sp. Orch. 125. 1830.
Cymbidium bambusifolium Roxb., Fl. Ind. 3: 460. 1832.
Arundina speciosa Blume, Bijdr. 401. 1825.
Arundina densa Lindl., Bot. Reg. 28: pl. 38. 1842.
Arundina densiflora Hook. f., Fl. Br. Ind. 5: 851. 1890.

Tufted, terrestrial herb with grass-like stems and leaves; stems about 130 cm tall, 1 cm diameter. Leaves 20–28 × 1.5–2.3 cm, linear-lanceolate, acuminate, attenuate, sheathing, 5–9-veined. Flowers rose-purple, large, about 7.5 cm broad, in terminal racemes; rachis of the inflorescence green or yellowish-green. Floral bracts small, 7–8 × 9 mm, broadly ovate, acute, persistent; sepals 4.5 × 1.2–1.3 cm, linear-lanceolate, acute, spreading, 9–11-veined; petals 4.5 × 2.1 cm, oblong-lanceolate, acute, 3-veined, the lateral veins much branched at base; lip 5 × 3.7 cm when spread out; lateral lobes rounded, embracing the column; midlobe subrotund, margins curled; disc with 3 fimbriated ridges along the centre, lateral ridges with a callus each at the base continuing forward as far as the middle of the midlobe, the mid-ridge stop-

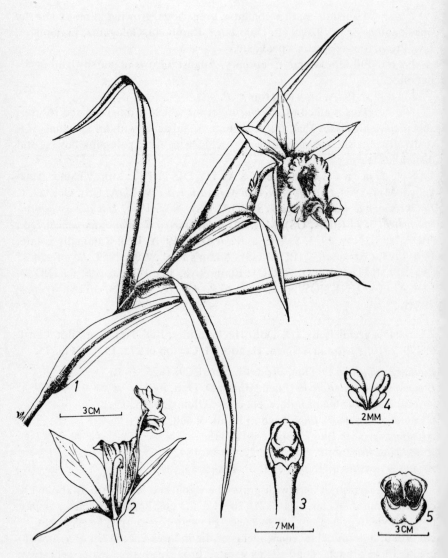

Fig. 75. *Arundina graminifolia* (D. Don) Hochreutiner. 1, portion of the stem with a flower. 2, longitudinal section of flower. 3, column from front. 4, pollinia. 5, operculum from inside.

ping half-way; column 2.5 cm high, 0.5 cm broad, slender, narrowly winged at the apex, rostellum trifid; foot absent. Anther terminal, 4-loculed, 3.8×3 mm; pollinia 8, in two compressed, superposed, unequal groups of four, united by a viscus; larger pollinia 1.3×0.95 mm, ventricose in outline, flat, the lower ones smaller. Ovary with pedicel 3 cm long. Fruit a decurved, linear-oblong, 6-ribbed capsule, 5–6 cm long.

D i s t r. An escape from cultivation, in open places in the patana grass-lands at higher altitudes. Adam's Peak, Kabaragala, Hewaheta, Gonavy, etc. Also in Northern India, Khasia Hills, Assam, Burma, Malaya, China, Java, Sumatra and Borneo.

E c o l. Flowers October, December.

I l l u s t r. Wight, Ic. Pl. Ind. Or. 5: pl. 1661, 1852; PDA, drawing.

N o t e. Lindley distinguished this species as different from *Arundina densa* Lindl. which is now reduced to a synonym. It is easily distinguished as a grass-like terrestrial orchid with linear leaves and large rose-purple flowers in terminal racemes.

S p e c i m e n s E x a m i n e d. CEYLON: KANDY DISTRICT: Peradeniya Bot. Gard., cultd., May 1927, *Alston 352* (PDA), July 1928, *Senaratne 44* (PDA); Adam's Peak, Dec. 1969, *Jayaweera 15 (2)* (AMES); Kandy, Feb. 1972, *Burtt & Townsend 39* (PDA, US); Loolwatte, Nov. 1974, *Davidse 8473* (PDA, US). RATNAPURA DISTRICT: Kalawana, Aug. 1974, *Cramer 4296* (PDA, US); Kudawe, near Weddagala, Feb. 1969, *Hoogland 11452* (PDA, US); Rassagala, Jul. 1969, *Read 2191* (PDA, US). NUWARA ELIYA DISTRICT: Hewaheta, Dec. 1912, *s. coll. s.n.* (PDA); Watawala, Apr. 1950, *Senaratne s.n.* (PDA). GALLE DISTRICT: Hiniduma, Sept. 1969, *Cramer 2679* (PDA). INDIA: Khasia Hills *J.D. Hooker & T. Thomson* (AMES, PDA). Sikkim, at 3000–5000 ft alt., *J.D. Hooker* (AMES, PDA), May–Sept. 1891, *Pantling 17* (K, AMES). BANGLADESH: Silhet, *Wallich 3751B* (PDA). Assam, Jaintia Hills, Jun. 1899, *Prain's Collector 263* (AMES); Lushai Hills, Jul. 1927, *Parry 247* (K), Aug. 1945, *Bullock* (AMES), *Jenkins s.n.* (PDA). BURMA: *Prazer 102* (AMES); Makawk Zup, Jul. 1958, *McKee 6306* (AMES). MALAY PENINSULA: Malasia, Perak, Mar. 1913, *Robinson* (AMES); Pulau Penang, Aug. 1915, *Haniff* (AMES); Kedah Peak, at 3000 ft, *Robinson & Kloss 5982* (AMES); Phang, 1891, *Ridley 2052* (AMES); Malacca, Mt. Ophir, *Ridley 642* (AMES). Singapore, Jan. 1960, *Bels 212* (AMES). THAILAND: North Thailand, *Herb. Kerr s.n.* (AMES); Kopoh-Bangsack, Dec. 1917, *Haniff 2941* (AMES). INDO-CHINA: Tam Wong Shan & vicinity, Sept. 1939, *Tsang 2954* (AMES); Saigon, May 1921, *Poilane 1979* (AMES). COCHIN-CHINA: 1862–66, *Thorel 987* (AMES). SUMATRA: Fort de Koch, May 1927, *Yates 2407* (AMES), 1933, *Boeea 5992* (AMES), 1936, *Boeea 10352* (AMES), Nov.–Dec. 1932, *Krukoff 4439* (AMES), Aug. 1941, *Asdat 23* (AMES); East Coast, 1921, *Yates 7* (AMES); Jan. 1932, on side of volcano near Redelong, alt. 3600–6000 ft, *Bangham 910* (AMES), Dec.

---

168 ORCHIDACEAE

1931, *Bangham 622* (AMES). JAVA 1910, *Moussel 63* (AMES). KRAKATAU: May 1908, *Backer s.n.* (AMES). BORNEO: Kinabalu, 1916, *Haslam s.n.* (AMES); Selangor, Nov. 1937, *Henderson 3441* (AMES).

19. EULOPHIA

R. Brown ex Lindley in Bot. Reg. 8: t. 686. 1823.

Terrestrial herbs with pseudobulbous or tuberous rootstocks; leaves thin and grass-like and plaited; scapes or peduncles lateral or terminal on pseudo-bulb or rootstock, erect, racemose or loosely paniculate above; sepals and petals free, spreading; lip erect from the base or foot of the column, base saccate or spurred, side lobes embracing the column, midlobe spreading or recurved, disc cristate or lamellate; column long, base produced into a foot or not; anther 2-chambered, operculate, pollinia 2, globose, waxy, attached by a short broad strap to a disciform gland.

Over 200 species, numerous in Africa, and extending over to India, Ceylon, Malaya, Java, Sumatra, Polynesia, the Philippine Islands and Australia.

KEY TO THE SPECIES

1 Column not produced into a foot; leaves many, grass-like
  2 Pseudobulb epigeal
    3 Sepals linear-oblong, yellowish-green.........................**1. E. epidendraea**
    3 Sepals lanceolate, acuminate, greenish..........................**2. E. graminea**
  2 Rootstock tuberous, hypogeal...............................**3. E. macrostachya**
1 Column produced into a foot
  4 Leaves produced at flowering together with the raceme; sepals greenish-purple, petals white...**4. E. nuda**
  4 Leaves produced after flowering, sepals and petals dull purplish red....**5. E. sanguinea**

1. Eulophia epidendraea (Retz.) C.E.C. Fischer in Gamble, Fl. Pres. Madras 1434. 1928; Alston in Trimen, Handb. Fl. Ceylon 6: 276. 1931.—**Fig. 76.**

Serapias epidendraea Koenig in Retzius, Obs. Bot. 6: 65. 1791.
Limodorum virens Roxb., Pl. Corom. 1: 31, pl. 38. 1795.
Limodorum epidendroides Willd., Sp. Pl. 4: 124. 1805.
Aerobion carinatum Spreng., Syst. Veg. 3: 718. 1826.
Eulophia virens Spreng., ibid. 720.
Eulophia carinata Lindl., Gen. et Sp. Orch. 183. 1833.
Eulophia viridiflora Steud, Nom. Bot. ed. 2. 1: 605. 1841.
Limodorum carinatum Willd., Sp. Pl. 4: 124. 1805.

Large, terrestrial herb with pseudobulbous stems and vermiform roots; pseudobulbs 4.5–10.5 cm long, 3–6.5 cm diameter, conico-ovoid, covered with broad, membranous, basal sheaths. Leaves many, 17–51 × 0.9–1.7 cm, linear,

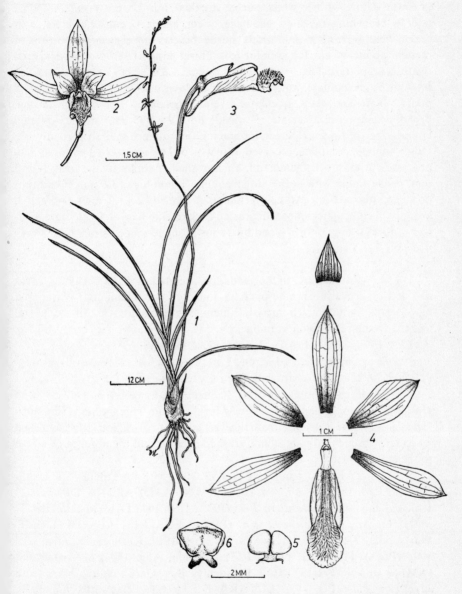

Fig. 76. *Eulophia epidendraea* (Retz.) C.E.C. Fischer. 1, plant with inflorescence. 2, flower from front. 3, lip, spur and column from side. 4, bract, sepals and petals spread out from front, column and lip drawn out from front. 5, pollinia with strap. 6, operculum from inside.

acuminate, keeled, 5–9-veined, bases sheathing the pseudobulb. Flowers greenish-yellow with a white purple-streaked lip, 3.5 cm broad, in long, lateral, branching racemes; peduncle terete, about 47 cm long, erect, ash-green, bearing nine membranous sterile bracts; flower-bearing portion of raceme about 34 cm long, branched. Floral bracts 7.8–9.9 × 3.8–5.4 mm, ovate, acuminate, acute, 7-veined; dorsal sepal 1.85–2.2 cm × 5–6 mm, lanceolate-oblong, acuminate, apiculate, 5-veined; lateral sepals 1.8–2.1 cm × 5–5.8 mm, obovate-lanceolate, apiculate, 5-veined; petals 1.4–1.85 cm × 5–7.5 mm, broadly lanceolate, apiculate, 5-veined; lip 1.9 × 1.35 cm, obovate-oblong; lateral lobes of lip small, erect, embracing the column; midlobe broadly oblong, rounded, crenulate, recurved; disc with 5–7 ridges, crested with subulate processes; spur short, cylindrical, thick-walled, parallel to the ovary, 7 × 2 mm, inside tinted with purple dots; column 8 mm high, 3.6 mm broad, not produced into a foot. Anther terminal, 2-loculed, 2 × 1.9 mm; pollinia 2, broadly obconicular-globose, depressed towards the base, 0.9 × 0.7 mm, connected to a large disciform gland by a short, tongue-shaped strap. Ovary with pedicel 1.7–1.8 cm long.

D i s t r. Rather rare, in the shade, on accumulations of decaying leaves and soil on rocks in the intermediate and dry zone. Dambulla, Wariapola, Kurunegala, Puttalam, Chunnavil, Bintenne, Trincomalee, etc. Also in Bengal and the Deccan Peninsula in India.

E c o l. Flowers February, June, August, October.

I l l u s t r. Wight, Ic. Pl. Ind. Or. 3: pl. 913. 1843–45; J. Brown, Bot. Mag. 92: pl. 5579, 1866; PDA, drawing from *C.P. 2369*.

N o t e. Herb. Lindley contains 3 collections, namely *Wallich 7364, J.D. Hooker 221* from India and *Macrae 34* from Ceylon. This species is similar to *Eulophia euglossa* Reichb. f. from the west coast of Africa and is distinguished by its large pseudobulbous stems, grass-like leaves and the absence of a foot to the column.

S p e c i m e n s E x a m i n e d. CEYLON: JAFFNA DISTRICT: Chunnakavil, Feb. 1890, *s. coll. s.n.* (PDA). ANURADHAPURA DISTRICT: Ritigala, Jan. 1973, *Jayasuriya 1095* (PDA, US). PUTTALAM DISTRICT: Puttalam, Aug. 1883, *s. coll. s.n.* (PDA). KURUNEGALA DISTRICT: Wariyapola, Aug. 1959, *Jayaweera 20 (1)* (AMES); Kurunegala, *Jayaweera 1993* (PDA). MATALE DISTRICT: Nalanda, Aug. 1904, *Schlechter s.n.* (AMES). KANDY DISTRICT: Peradeniya Bot. Gard., cultd., Mar. 1950, *Jayaweera 1114* (PDA). KALUTARA DISTRICT: Pelauwatte, Jan. 1970, *Cramer 2808* (PDA, US). BADULLA DISTRICT: Between Mahiyangana and Padiyatalawa, May 1975, *Jayasuriya 2117* (PDA, US). GALLE DISTRICT: Buana Vista, Mar. 1970, *Cramer 2908* (PDA, US). LOCALITY UNKNOWN: in 1829, *Macrae 24* (K, PDA); *Gardner 874* (K); *s. coll. C.P. 2369* (K, PDA). INDIA: Madras, Nilgiris & Coorg, *G. Thomson* (AMES, PDA),

EULOPHIA 171

J.D. Hooker 221 (K), *Wallich 7369* (K), Feb. 1912, *Bourne 5949* (K); Nellore,
Ramayapatnam, Dec. 1917, *Fischer 4289* (K). Kerala: Travancore, 1904,
Barber 6764 (K). Pen. Ind. Or., *Herb. Wight 2972* (K, AMES, PDA), *Herb.
Wight 2074* (K).

2. Eulophia graminea Lindl. in Wall., Cat. n. 7372. 1832; Trimen, Handb. Fl.
Ceylon 4: 176. 1898.—Fig. 77.

Eulophia inconspicua Griff., Notul. Pl. As. 3: 349. 1851.
Eulophia sinensis Miq., J. Bot. Neerl. 1: 91. 1861.
Eulophia decipiens Griff, J. Asiat. Soc. Bengal 47 (2): 155. 1876.
Eulophia ramosa Hayata, Mater. Fl. Formosa 332. 1911.

Terrestrial herb with conical pseudobulbous stems clothed in membranous
sheaths; roots vermiform. Leaves grass-like, 15–25 cm long, linear, finely
acuminate, bases sheathing. Flowers greenish with white lip, tessellate, in
slender, erect, branching, lax-flowered, racemose panicles; peduncle 30–60 cm
long. Floral bracts small, spreading, lanceolate, persistent; sepals 1.2 cm
long, lanceolate, acuminate; petals broader than sepals, elliptic-lanceolate,
acute, tessellate; lip obovate-oblong, lateral lobes small, erect, embracing the
column, midlobe obovate, apex rounded; disc with five ridges crested with
hooked processes; spur short, subcylindrical or conical, incurved; column
long, not produced into a foot. Anther terminal, 2-loculed; pollinia 2,
globose, attached to a large gland by a short broad strap. Ovary with pedicel
1.2–2.5 cm long. Fruit a clavate capsule, 2.5–3 cm long.

Distr. Rare, in open places under partial shade in the dry regions.
Dambulla, Marawila near Chilaw, etc. Also in India, Burma, Siam, Malaya,
China, Formosa and the Philippine and Nicobar Islands.

Ecol. Flowers March, April.

Illustr. Griff., Ic. Pl. Asiat. 3: pl. 326. 1851; King & Pantling, Ann. R.
Bot. Gard. (Calcutta) 8: pl. 238. 1898; PDA, drawing from *C.P. 3958.*

Note. This species is much similar to *E. epidendraea* in habit and
colour of the flower but for its shorter leaves, smaller flowers and the cylindrical spur with a clavate tip. The formosan *E. ramosa* differs very slightly
from this species and *E. sinensis* in the spur which in *E. ramosa* is shorter and
slightly contracted towards the apex while in *E. graminea* it is clavate or
saccate.

Specimens Examined. CEYLON: ANURADHAPURA DIS-
TRICT: Ritigala, Apr. 1970, *Gould 13628* (PDA, US). MATALE DISTRICT:
Dambulla, near bridge, Mar. 1868, *s. coll. C.P. 3958* (K, PDA). PUTTA-
LAM DISTRICT: Marawila, Apr. 1881, *Nevill s.n.* (PDA). INDIA: Sikkim
Himalaya: Dooars, Mar. 1896, *Pantling 438* (K, AMES), Mar. 1868, *Clarke
6672* (K). Bihar: *J.D. Hooker & T. Thomson 221* (K). Madras: *Wallich 7372*

Fig. 77. *Eulophia graminea* Lindl. redrawn from a drawing in PDA. 1, plant with inflorescence. 2, apical portion of a raceme.

(K, holotype); Chingleput Dist., Jul. 1885, *Gamble 16315* (K). BURMA: Amherst, 1834, *Griffith 343* (K); Maymyo, May 1932, *Dickason 5775* (AMES); Moulmein, Apr. 1872, *Parish 205* (K). NICOBAR ISLANDS: Feb. 1875, *S. Kurz 26009* (K). MALAY PENINSULA: Johore, Jul. 1934, *Ngadiman 36769* (AMES). INDO-CHINA: Annam, Mar.-Apr. 1932, *Squires 842* (AMES). CHINA: Kwangtung: Ting Woo Shan, Jul. 1932, *Lau 20175* (AMES). PHILIPPINE ISLANDS: Luzon: Union Prov., Dec. 1918, *Lete 467* (AMES).

3. Eulophia macrostachya Lindl., Gen. et Sp. Orch. 183. 1833; Trimen, Handb. Fl. Ceylon 4: 176. 1898.—**Fig. 78.**

Eulophidium pulchrum (Thuoars) Summerhayes in Bull. Rijkspl. Bruxelles 27: 400. 1957.
Limodorum pulchrum Thouars, Orch. Iles. Austr. Afr. pls. 43, 44. 1822.
Eulophia pulchra (Thouars) Lindl., Gen. et Sp. Orch. 182. 1833.
Eulophia emarginata Blume, Orch. Archip. Ind. 180. 1858.
Graphorchis pulchra (Thouars) Kuntze, Rev. Gen. Pl. 662. 1891.
Graphorchis macrostachya (Lindl.) Kuntze, l.c. 662. 1891.
Graphorchis blumeana Kuntze, l.c. 663. 1891.
Eulophia striata Rolfe, J. Linn. Soc. Bot. 29: 53. 1891.
Eulophia guamensis Ames, Philipp. J. Sci. 9: 12. 1914.
Eulophia rouxii Kranzl. in Sarasin & Roux, Nova Caled. 1: 82. 1914.
Lissochilus pulcher (Thouars) H. Perrier in Humbert, Fl. Madag. Orch. 2: 41. 1914, non Schlechter.

   Terrestrial herb with pseudobulbous stems and vermiform roots; pseudo-bulbs 5–15 cm long, 1.2 cm diameter, tufted, terete or narrowly fusiform, consisting of 2 or 3 internodes; young pseudobulbs sheathed with membranous, acuminate, scaly leaves. Leaves 2–4, petioled, 15–25 × 5–6.2 cm, oblong-lanceolate, acuminate, 3–7-veined; petiole channelled, 10–20 cm. Flowers greenish-yellow with purple-veined lip, arising from the base of pseudobulbs in large stout, many-flowered racemes which measures 60–75 cm in length; peduncle long and stout with about five reddish-brown, membranous, sheathing, sterile bracts. Floral bracts 5.5–8.5 × 1.9–3.7 mm, linear-lanceolate, persistent, 5–7-veined; dorsal sepal 1.3 cm × 3.9 mm, lanceolate, acuminate, acute, arching over, 3-veined; lateral sepals 1.6 cm × 3.7 mm, falcate-lanceolate, acuminate, acute, 3–5-veined, spreading; petals oblong-lanceolate, 1.1 × 0.5 cm, acuminate, acute, erect, 4- or 5-veined; lip very broad, 1.1 × 1.7 cm when spread out, 5-veined, veins branching, saccate, with erect, rounded lateral lobes and a short, recurved, obcordate, rounded, deeply cleft midlobe; spur short, globose or ampulliform, faintly bilobed; disc with 2 short lamellae and three crenate ridges but with no true crests or hair-like outgrowths; column 5 mm high, 2.9 mm broad, stout, base not produced into a foot. Anther terminal, umbonate, 2-loculed, 1.9 × 2.1 mm; pollinia 2, obconical or trapeziform,

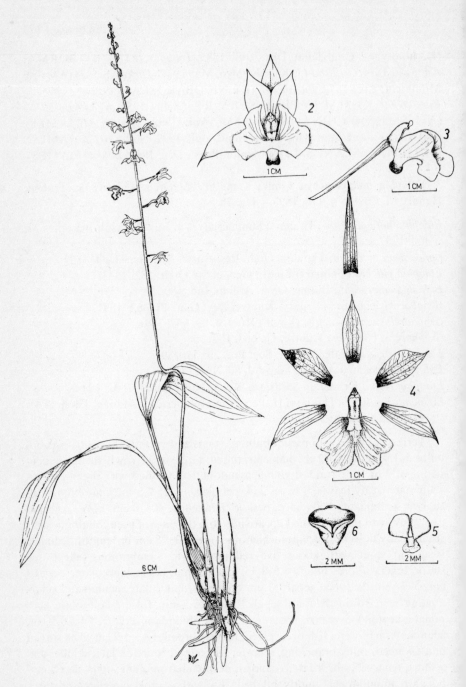

Fig. 78. *Eulophia macrostachya* Lindl. 1, plant with old pseudobulbs and inflorescence. 2, flower from front. 3, column and lip from side. 4, bract, sepals, petals, lip and column spread out from front. 5, pollinia with strap and gland. 6, operculum from inside.

connected to a large, orbicular, purple gland by a short, broad, strap; pollinia 0.9 × 0.8 mm. Ovary with pedicel 1.8 cm long.

D i s t r. Rare, in shady places in the submontane or mid-country tropical wet evergreen forests up to 610 m alt. Ambagamuwa, foot of Adam's Peak, Heneratgoda, etc. Also in Madagascar, Reunion, Comoro Is., Travancore and Nilgiri Hills in India, Malaysia, Philippines, New Guinea, New Caledonia, New Hebrides and Fiji Islands.

E c o l. Flowers September.

I l l u s t r. Lindl., Bot. Reg. 23: pl. 1972. 1837; Wight, Ic. Pl. Ind. Or. 5: pls. 1667 & 1668. 1851; Hook. Bot. Mag. 102: pl. 6246. 1876; PDA, two drawings one of which is from *C.P. 3188.*

N o t e. Herb. Lindley contains Macrae's collection 27 from Ceylon in its type cover. It was first introduced to Kew Gardens in 1837 and subsequently specimens sent by Thwaites. It is characterised by its petioled leaves and the disc of the lip carrying no true crests or hair-like outgrowths.

S p e c i m e n s E x a m i n e d. CEYLON: KANDY DISTRICT: Ambagamuwa, Dec. 1960, *Jayaweera 1992* (PDA), Sept. 1960, *Jayaweera 20 (3)* (AMES). RATNAPURA DISTRICT: Karawita Kande, Sept. 1926, *J.M. Silva s.n.* (PDA). LOCALITY UNKNOWN: in 1829, *Macrae 27* (K); *Gardner 867* (K). INDIA: Madras, *Herb. Wight 2971* (K). PHILIPPINE ISLANDS: Luzon: Camarines Prov., Mt. Isarog, Dec. 1913, *Ramos 22217* (AMES); Sorsogon Prov., Mt. Bulusan, Apr. 1916, *Elmer 15691* (AMES); Laguna Prov., San Antonia, Oct. 1913, *Ramos 21976* (AMES). Samar, Catubig River, Feb. 1916, *Ramos 24263* (AMES). Leyte: Palo, Jan. 1906, *Elmer 7277* (AMES); Dagami, Patoc, Sept. 1913, flower purple, green, yellow and flesh colour, *Wenzel 206* (AMES). Palawan: Brooks Point, Oct. 1923, *Taylor 81146* (AMES). Mindanao: Zamboanga Prov., Oct. 1919, *Ramos & Edano 36807* (AMES); Mambajao, Nov. 1912, *Elmer 14215* (AMES). GUAM: Oca Point, Jan.-Mar. 1945, *Glassman 46* (AMES); Oct. 1911, *McGregor 376* (AMES). FIJI ISLANDS: Viti Leon, May 1942, hills east of Navua River, *Greenwood 997* (AMES); Apr. 1941, *Degener 15211* (AMES); Waiyevo, Feb. 1928, *Gillespie 4702* (AMES).

4. Eulophia nuda Lindl., Gen. et Sp. Orch. 180. 1833; Trimen, Handb. Fl. Ceylon 4: 177. 1898.—**Fig. 79.**

Cyrtopera plicata Lindl. in Wall., Cat. n. 7362. 1832.
Dipodium roniate Hamilton ex Wall., Cat. n. 7371. 1832.
Dipodium plicatum Hamilton, ibid. n. 7362.
Eulophia bicolor Dalzell in Hooker's J. Bot. Kew Gard. Misc. 3: 343. 1851.
Cyrtopera fusca Wight, Ic. Pl. Ind. Or. 5 (1): pl. 1690. 1851.
Eulophia fusca Blume, Orch. Archip. Ind. 182. 1858.
Cyrtopera mysorensis Lindl., J. Linn. Soc. Bot. 3: 32. 1859.

Fig. 79. *Eulophia nuda*. Lindl. 1, plant with tuber and part of inflorescence. 2, apical portion of inflorescence. 3, flower from front. 4, longitudinal section of flower. 5, lip and column from side. 6, bract, sepals and petals spread out from front; lip and column, natural position, from front. 7, pollinia with strap and gland. 8, operculum from inside. 9, fruit.

Cyrtopera gardneri Thw., Enum. Pl. Zeyl. 302. 1861.
Cyrtopera laxiflora Gardner ex Thw., Enum. Pl. Zeyl. 320. 1861.
Cyrtopera nuda Reichb. f., Flora 55: 274. 1872.
Cyrtopodium fuscum Trimen, Cat. 89. 1885.

Terrestrial herb with large, tuberous, slightly branched rootstock and long, vermiform roots. Leaves 2 at flowering, afterwards more, 30–60 × 2.5–3.5 cm, linear-lanceolate, plaited, acuminate, base narrowing into a long sheath and attaching to the short stem. Flowers greenish-purple with a white to purplish-pink lip, 1.2 cm across, in erect, lax-flowered racemes, arising from the base of stem; peduncles 40–60 cm long, erect, with 3 or 4 distant, sheathing, sterile bracts. Floral bracts 1.4 × 0.4 cm, subulate-lanceolate, acuminate, acute, membranous, 7-veined; dorsal sepal 1.9 × 0.6 cm, oblong, acute, 7-veined; lateral sepals 2 × 0.55–0.6 cm, oblong, acute, 7-veined adnate to the foot of the column; petals 1.4 × 0.75–0.8 cm, oval-oblong, obtuse, 7-veined; lip 2.2 × 1.2 cm, ovate-oblong, obtuse, recurved; lateral lobes of lip erect, rounded, incurved, embracing the column, margin crisped; midlobe oblong, bifid, undulate, many-veined; column 1 cm high, 0.45 cm broad, acute, broadening to the base and continuing into the foot; mentum dark purplish-green, conical; disc with many crested ridges. Anther umbonate, 2-loculed, 2.8 × 2.4 mm; pollinia 2, hemispherical, connected to a large gland by a short, stout strap; each pollinium 0.96 × 1 mm. Ovary with pedicel 2.2 cm long and purplish. Fruit a fusiform, ridged capsule, 5–5.5 × 1.5–1.8 cm.

D i s t r. Rare, under the shade of trees in the tropical wet evergreen forests up to 915 m alt., particularly in areas which have been recently cleared and planted with rubber. Ratnapura, Hantane, Mirigama, Dolosbage, etc. Also in India, Burma, Thailand and China.

E c o l. Flowers February–June.

U s e s. The tuberous rootstock is used medicinally.

I l l u s t r. King & Pantling, Ann. R. Bot. Gard. (Calcutta) 8: pl. 243. 1898; PDA, 4 drawings one of which is from *C.P. 2370*.

N o t e. Herb. Lindley contains the collection *Wallich 7362* under *Cyrtopera plicata* Lindl. There is considerable variation in the colour of the flower. The Burmese specimens have pale mauve fiowers with a splash of yellow on the lip, some being tinged yellow throughout. The Siamese specimens on the other hand have dark crimson or reddish-brown flowers with pale purple lip or light green flowers with a pure white lip (*Kostermans 545*).

S p e c i m e n s E x a m i n e d. CEYLON: KANDY DISTRICT: Hantane, May 1924, *J.M. Silva s.n.* (PDA); Peradeniya, May 1913, *Braine s.n.* (PDA); Ambagamuwa, Mar. 1961, *Jayaweera 1991* (PDA); Between Norton and Watawala, Apr. 1972, *Jayasuriya, Dassanayake & Balakrishnan 758* (PDA, US). NUWARA ELIYA DISTRICT: Pussellawa, May 1926, *Alston s.n.* (PDA); Ramboda, Feb. 1972, *Balakrishnan & Dassanayake 1228* (PDA, US).

RATNAPURA DISTRICT: Kuruwita Kande, Apr. 1960, *Jayaweera 20 (4)* (AMES). INDIA: North India: Uttar Pradesh, Gonda, May 1890, *Harsukh s.n.* (AMES). Madhya Pradesh, Surguja, May 1938, *Mooney 777* (K); Jashpur, Aug. 1936, *Mooney 111* (K). Maharashtra: Bombay, *Richie 708* (K). Malabar, Konkan, etc., *Stocks, Law,* etc. (PDA). Orissa: May 1936, *Mooney 71* (K); Sambalpur, Jun. 1950, *Mooney 3818* (K). Coonoor: Nilgiris, May 1884, *Gamble 14530* (K); Nilgiris & Coorg, *Thomson* (AMES); *Stocks* (AMES). Andhra Pradesh: Visakhapatnam, May 1914, *Lushington* (K). Assam: Manipur, May 1882, *Watt 7133* (K). Pen. Ind. Or., Herb. *Wight* (K), Herb. *Wight 2973* (AMES); Morang Hills, Apr. 1810, *Wallich 7371* (K-holotype). BURMA: Shingaw, May 1938, *Kermode 17378* (AMES). THAILAND: North Thailand: May 1911, *Kerr 35A* (AMES); Pu Mano, May 1932, *Kerr 0991B* (AMES); Tripagodas, May 1946, *Kostermans 545* (AMES); *Kostermans 546* (AMES). CHINA: Yunnan, Apr. 1933, *Tsai 53272* (AMES). Hainan: Yaichow, Feb. 1933, *How & Chun 70182* (AMES).

5. Eulophia sanguinea (Lindl.) Hook. f., Fl. Br. Ind. 6: 8. 1890; Trimen, Handb. Fl. Ceylon 4: 177. 1898.—**Fig. 80.**

Cyrtopera sanguinea Lindl., J. Linn. Soc. Bot. 3: 32. 1859.
Cyrtopera rufa Thw., Enum. Pl. Zeyl. 302. 1861.
Cyrtopodium rufum Trimen, Cat. 89. 1885.

Terrestrial herb with a horizontal, tuberous rootstock and very stout, vermiform roots; leaves appearing after flowering. Flowers dull purplish-red, about 3.7 cm across in very stout erect, lax-flowered racemes; peduncle about 40–50 cm long, green or red, with a few, broad, brown, semi-amplexicaul, sterile, bracteolar sheaths 2.5 cm long; flower-bearing portion about 15 cm long. Floral bracts subulate-lanceolate, flexuous, as long as the ovary and persistent; dorsal sepal 2.5 cm long, erect, ovate-lanceolate, acuminate; lateral sepals as long as the dorsal sepal, obliquely ovate, acuminate, inserted on the foot of the column and spreading; mentum short, conical and incurved; petals 1.7 cm long, obovate, spreading, minutely notched and apiculate; lip saccate, 3-lobed, shorter than the sepals; lateral lobes small, obtuse; midlobe small, broadly ovate, recurved and apiculate; column long, base produced into a foot. Anther terminal, umbonate, 2-loculed; pollinia 2, subglobosely ovoid on a short strap with a large gland. Ovary with pedicel 1.2–2.5 cm long. Fruit an ellipsoid, pendulous capsule, about 6 cm long.

D i s t r. Rare, in open places in mid-country elevations up to 1220 m alt. Hantane, Moneragala, Haputale, Mirigama, etc. Also in the Eastern Himalayas, Khasia Hills, Bhutan and hills in Sikkim in India.

E c o l. Flowers January–April.

I l l u s t r. Hook. f., Bot. Mag. 101: pl. 6161. 1875; King & Pantling, Ann. R. Bot. Gard. (Calcutta) 8: pl. 242. 1898; PDA, two drawings one of

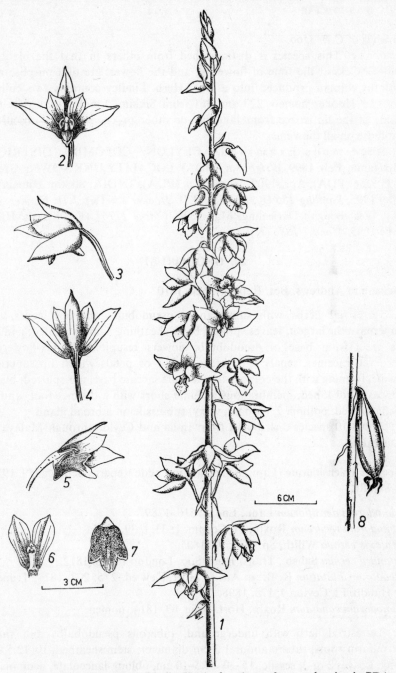

Fig. 80. *Eulophia sanguinea* (Lindl.) Hook. f. redrawn from a drawing in PDA.
1, inflorescence. 2, flower from front. 3, flower from side. 4, flower from behind.
5, longitudinal section of flower. 6, column and petals from front. 7, lip spread out
from front. 8, fruit.

6 CM

3 CM

which is of *C.P. 3566.*

N o t e. This species is distinguished from others in that the plant is
quite leafless at the time of flowering and the flowers are dull purplish-red
with the column produced into a foot. Herb. Lindley contains two collections of Hooker namely 223 and 361 from Sikkim. Lindley says that the
inside of the lip is free from lamellae or other processes but is obscurely
papillose on all the veins.

S p e c i m e n s   E x a m i n e d.   CEYLON: COLOMBO DISTRICT:
Mirigama, Feb. 1899, *Wright s.n.* (PDA). LOCALITY UNKNOWN: *s. coll.*
C.P. 3566 (PDA); Apr. 1909, *s. coll. s.n.* (PDA). INDIA: Sikkim Himalaya,
May 1895, *Pantling 186* (K, AMES); *J.D. Hooker s.n.* (K), *J.D. Hooker 361*
(K). West Bengal: Darjeeling, May 1870, *Clarke 11767* (K). Khasia Hills,
June 1885, *Mann 7/1886* (K).

20. GEODORUM

Jackson in Andrews, Bot. Repos. t. 626. 1810.

Terrestrial herbs with subterranean pseudobulbs and few leaves, the
uppermost the largest; leaves stalked, bases sheathing, lamina plaited; peduncle erect from base of pseudobulb; flowers resupinate in lax-flowered,
decurved racemes; sepals and petals similar or petals wider; lip superior,
sessile, forming with the column-foot a short saccate base, not spurred; blade
concave, not lobed, membranous; column short with a distinct foot; anther
2-chambered; pollinia 2, globose, waxy, subsessile on a broad gland.

About 10 species distributed from India and Ceylon through Malaya to
Australia.

Geodorum densiflorum (Lam.) Schlechter in Fedde Repert. Beih. 4: 259. 1919.
—Fig. 81.

Limodorum densiflorum Lam., Enc. 3: 516. 1789.
Limodorum recurvum Roxb., Pl. Corom. 1: 33, t. 39. 1795.
Malaxis cernua Willd., Sp. Pl. 4: 93. 1805.
Otandra cernua Salisb., Trans. Hort. Soc. London 1: 298. 1812.
Geodorum dilatatum R. Br. in Ait. f., Hort. Kew ed. 2. 5: 207. 1813; Trimen,
   Handb. Fl. Ceylon 4: 178. 1898.
Limodorum candidum Roxb., Hort. Beng. 63, 1814, nomen.

Terrestrial herb with underground, tuberous pseudobulbs and thick
vermiform roots; tubers about 1.3 cm diameter; stem sheathed, 10–12.5 cm
long. Leaves 2 or 3, sessile, 15–30 × 7.5–10 cm, oblong-lanceolate, acuminate,
with narrowed base, bright green and shining above, 3–5-ribbed beneath.
Flowers white with yellow and pink lip in rather closely 10–12-flowered,
sharply decurved racemes; peduncle 40–50 cm high, stout, with a few tubular

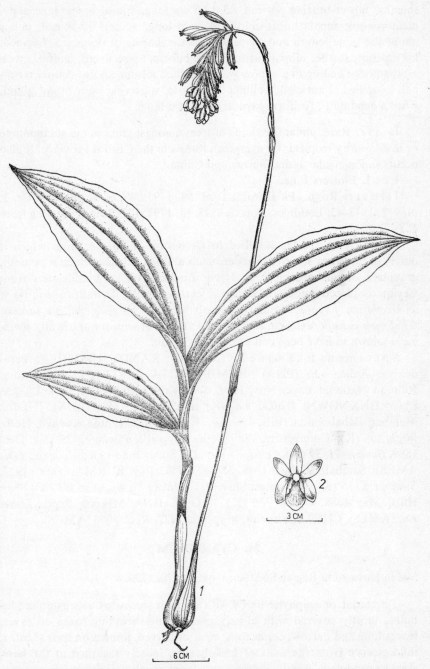

Fig. 81. *Geodorum densiflorum* (Lam.) Schlechter, redrawn from a drawing in PDA.
1, plant with inflorescence. 2, flower from front.

sheaths; flower-bearing portion 7.5–12.5 cm long. Floral bracts lanceolate, membranous; sepals linear-oblong, 1.2 cm long, acute, 3–5-veined; petals about the same length and shape as sepals, subacute or obtuse, 5–7-veined; lip superior, sessile, subpanduriform, cymbiform, tip recurved, undulate with a broad ridge ending in a yellow warted callus; column short. Anther terminal, 2-loculed, 2-auricled; pollinia 2, globose, subsessile on a broad gland. Fruit a pendulous, fusiform capsule, 1.7–2 cm long.

D i s t r. Rare, under the shade of trees amongst grass in the submontane or mid-country tropical wet evergreen forests in the Central Province. It also occurs in Peninsular India, Burma and China.

E c o l. Flowers June.

I l l u s t r. Roxb., Pl. Corom. 1: pl. 39. 1795; Wight, Ic. Pl. Ind. Or. 3: pl. 912. 1843–45; Loddiges, Bot. Cab. 18: pl. 1797. 1831; PDA, drawing from *C.P. 3196.*

N o t e. This species is allied to *Geodorum purpureum* from which it differs in the lower stature, broader petals and lip, the disc which is smooth, granulate or subcaruncled. In Herb. Lindley, Walker's collection from Ceylon is placed under *Geodorum dilatatum*, whilst Thwaites identifies it as *Geodorum furcatum* Lindl. It is probable that this specimen is a form of *Geodorum densiflorum* Sch. as Thwaites never met with it nor are any specimens known to have been collected from Ceylon.

S p e c i m e n s E x a m i n e d. CEYLON: KANDY DISTRICT: Peradeniya, *Braine s.n.* (PDA). HAMBANTOTA DISTRICT: Rugamtota, Ruhunu National Park, Nov. 1969, *Cooray 69111402* (PDA, US). LOCALITY UNKNOWN: *Walker s.n.* (K); *s. coll. C.P. 3196* (PDA). INDIA: Malabar: Bababoodun Hills, *Law s.n.* (K). Madras: Kantha Kudavu, Herb. *Wight s.n.* (K); Coimbatore, Vallapath, July 1910, *Fischer 2035* (K); Dec. 1889, *Gamble 21539* (K). Orissa: Athmallih State, June 1936, *Mooney 58* (K, AMES); Sambalpur, June 1946, *Mooney 2682* (K). BURMA: Sept. 1927, *Swinhoe K116* (K); Wa States, May 1937, *Maung Po Khant 15343* (K); Shan Hills, May 1888, *Collett 746* (K). INDO-CHINA: Mekong Expd., *Thorel s.n.* (AMES). CHINA: Yunnan, May-Jun. 1922, *Rock 5067* (AMES).

21. CYMBIDIUM

Sw. in Nova Acta Regiae Soc. Sci. Upsal. 6: 70. 1799.

Terrestrial or epiphytic herbs with short or somewhat elongate pseudobulbs, mostly covered with closely overlapping sheathing bases of leaves; leaves long and narrow, coriaceous, erect or curved, jointed on their sheaths; inflorescence from the axils of leaf-sheaths, loosely sheathed at the base, erect or pendulous, usually long; flowers large, sepals and petals free, narrow, widespreading, about equal; lip small, sessile on the base of the column and embracing it by its side lobes, base saccate, midlobe recurved, disc lamellate or ridged; column long, foot absent or very short; anther 1- or imperfectly 2-chambered; pollinia 2, cleft, subglobose, waxy, joined by a common caudicle and seated on a broad disc or gland.

About 50 species distributed from Madagascar through India, Ceylon to Japan and south-eastwards through Malaysia to Australia.

KEY TO THE SPECIES

1 Leaf loriform, coriaceous, tip unequally 2-lobed; raceme pendulous; pollinia 2, sessile..
....**1. C. aloifolium**
1 Leaf ensiform, membranous, conduplicate; raceme suberect; pollinia 4, in pairs, one of each pair smaller..............................**2. C. ensifolium** var **haematodes**

1. Cymbidium aloifolium (L.) Sw., Nova Acta Regiae Soc. Sci. Upsal. 6: 73. 1799.—**Fig. 82.**

Epidendrum aloifolium L., Sp. Pl. 953. 1753.
Cymbidium pendulum Sw. & Lindl., Nova Acta Soc. Regiae Sci. Upsal. 6: 73. 1799.
Aerides borassi J.E. Smith in Rees, Cyclop. Suppl. 39: n. 8. 1819.
Cymbidium aloefolium Blume, Bijdr. 378, pl. 19. 1825.
Cymbidium bicolor Lindl., Gen. et Sp. Orch. 164. 1833; Trimen, Handb. Fl. Ceylon 4: 179. 1898.
Cymbidium erectum Wight, Ic. Pl. Ind. Or. 5 (1): 21, pl. 1753. 1851.
Cymbidium mannii Reichb. f., Flora 55: 274. 1872.

Tufted epiphyte with short, stout, fleshy stems clothed in membranous sheaths embracing the leaf bases; roots vermiform, giving off aerial roots standing out of the clump as thin needles. Leaves 2 or 3, loriform, 20–48 × 1.8–2.4 cm, coriaceous, tip unequally and obtusely 2-lobed, sheaths 5–8 cm long, very stout, strongly ribbed, green. Flowers cream-coloured, stained reddish-purple down the middle of the sepals and petals with a purple blotched lip, in laxly many-flowered, pendulous racemes about 28 cm or more long; rachis stout, terete; peduncle 12–14 cm long, stout, clothed with imbricating, acute sheaths at the base. Floral bracts 2.5 × 3 mm, broadly ovate, fleshy, rounded at the apex, 3-veined; dorsal sepal 2–2.2 cm × 4.5–6 mm, linear-oblong, suddenly acuminate or apiculate, obtuse, 7–9-veined; lateral sepals 1.8–2.1 cm × 5–6 mm, linear-oblong, falcate, obtuse, 7–9-veined; petals 1.8–2.1 cm × 6.5–7.5 mm, lanceolate, erect, subacute or apiculate, 3-veined, the lateral veins branching from the base, each producing 2 branches, giving a 7-veined appearance; lip 1.5–1.6 × 1.15 cm, sessile on the base of the column and embracing it by its lateral lobes, 5-veined, the two extreme lateral veins branching, supplying the midlobe as well as the lateral lobes, base saccate with 2 ridges and calli; lateral lobes lanceolate, acute; midlobe broadly oblong,

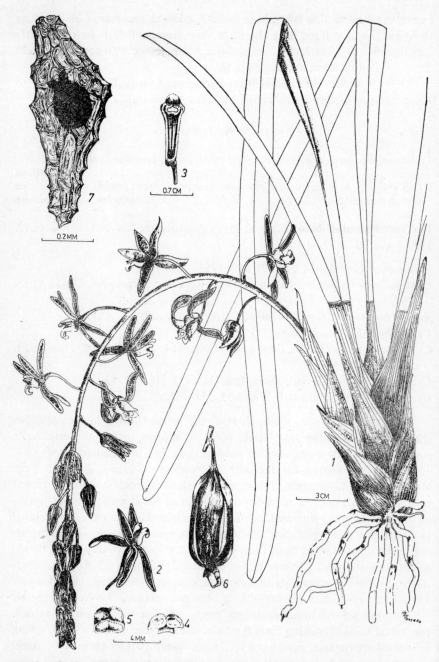

Fig. 82. *Cymbidium aloifolium* (Linn.) Swartz. 1, plant with inflorescence. 2, flower from side, three quarters view. 3, column from front. 4, pollinia with gland. 5, operculum from front. 6, fruit. 7, seed.

rounded, revolute, finely hairy or papillate on the inner surface; column 1.1 cm high, 3 mm broad, incurved, continuing into a very short foot at the base. Anther terminal, 2-loculed, 2×2.8 mm; pollinia 2, ovoid, 1.7×1.2 mm, unequally bifid, sessile on a semilunar gland. Ovary with pedicel 1.8–2.7 cm long. Fruit a pyriform capsule 5–6 cm long.

Distr. Very common, on trunks of trees in the tropical wet evergreen forests extending to the mid-country up to an alt. of 1220 m commonly found epiphytic on *Borassus flabellifer* L. in the northern and north-western provinces. Rangala, Ambagamuwa, Kurunegala, Naula, Galewela, Ratnapura, Hunnasgiriya, Weragantota, Kegalle, Rattota, Jaffna, Puttalam, etc. Also in India, Burma, China and Borneo.

Ecol. Flowers March, April. Some of its many host plants are *Abizzia falcata* (L.) Back., *Wormia triquetra* Rottb., *Artocarpus nobilis* Thw., *Artocarpus heterophyllus* Lam., *Cassia nodosa* Ham., *Grevillea robusta* Cunn. ex R. Br. *Samanea saman* (Jacq.) Merr., *Eugenia* sp., *Garcinia* sp., *Terminalia arjuna* (Roxb.) Wight & Arn., *Mangifera indica* L., *Turpinia malabarica* Gamble and *Ouratea zeylanica* (Lam.) Alston.

Illustr. Blume, Tabellen en Platen Jav. Orch. pl. 19. 1825; Curtis Bot. Mag. 11: pl. 387, 1797; PDA, 2 drawings from *C.P. 3379.*

Note. The species is recognised as a large apparently non-pseudobulbous epiphyte with pendulous racemes of cream-coloured flowers stained with reddish-purple down the middle of the sepals and petals. Herb. Lindley contains collections *J.D. Hooker 228* and *Wallich 7375* from India, *Macrae 54* from Ceylon and Cumings from the Philippine Islands. Lindley recognised *Cymbidium bicolor* as a separate species from *C. aloifolium* but the characters are not sufficiently distinct to maintain this separation.

Specimens Examined. CEYLON: JAFFNA DISTRICT: Point Pedro, Chempianpathi Road, Sept. 1974, *Tirvengadum, Cramer & Waas 488* (PDA, US). ANURADHAPURA DISTRICT: Ritigala, Jan. 1973, *Jayasuriya 1024* (K, PDA). KANDY DISTRICT: Peradeniya, *s. coll. C.P. 3379* (PDA), Nov. 1926, *Alston 819* (PDA); Peradeniya, Bot. Gard. Apr. 1960, *Jayaweera 22 (1)* (AMES); Pallewatte, Kalugala, Mar. 1974, *Jayasuriya 1553* (PDA, US). NEPAL: Apr.1900, *Inayat 23865* (AMES). INDIA: Khasia Hills, *J.D. Hooker & T. Thomson 1866* (K). Sikkim, *Clarke 11811* (K), May 1891, *Pantling 268* (AMES), Herb. *Wight 2987* (AMES), *J.D. Hooker 228* (K). Kodaikanal Region: Pulneys, Jun. 1898, *Bourne 1201* (K). Assam: Cachar, May 1929, *Parry 714* (K). BANGLADESH: Sylhet, *Wallich 7352* (K); *Wallich 7375* (K); East Bengal, Herb. *Griffith 5263* (PDA). BURMA: Mar. 1938, *Dickason 7179* (AMES). ANDAMAN ISLANDS: *S. Kurz s.n.* (K). INDOCHINA: *Petelot 2279* (AMES). BRITISH NORTH BORNEO: Banguay Islands, 1923, *Castro & Melegrito 1417* (AMES). PHILIPPINE ISLANDS: *Cumings s.n.* (K).

2. Cymbidium ensifolium var. **haematodes** (Lindl.) Trimen, Cat. 89. 1885;
Trimen, Handb. Fl. Ceylon 4: 180. 1898.—**Fig. 83.**

Limodorum longifolium Roxb., Hort. Beng. 63. 1814.
Cymbidium cyperifolium Wall., Cat. n. 7353. 1832.
Cymbidium haematodes Lindl., Gen. et Sp. Orch. 162. 1832–1833.
Cymbidium viridiflorum Griff., Itin. notes 2: 126. 1848.
Cyperorchis wallichii Blume, Orch. Archip. Ind. 92,'1858.

Tufted epiphyte with very short, non-pseudobulbous stems clothed with
brown, ovate-lanceolate sheaths; roots many, thick, vermiform. Leaves many,
all radical, the lowest short, membranous, conduplicate and the upper more
or less erect, curving like blades of grass, 50–70 cm × 8–10 mm, linear-ensiform, acute, 3–5-veined beneath, margins scabrous. Flowers sweet-scented,
dull yellow with pink veins and pale yellow lip spotted and stained with dark
pink, 6.5 cm broad, in many-flowered, suberect racemes about 30 cm or more
long, rachis stout; peduncle 25 cm long, with about 5 sterile bracts. Floral
bracts 2.1 cm × 8.5 mm, green, lanceolate, acute, 7-veined; sepals subequal
3.7 cm × 9 mm, oblong-lanceolate, acute or subacute, 7-veined; petals 3 × 1.1
cm, lanceolate, acute, 9-veined; lip 2.4 cm × 9.5 mm, sessile on the base of the
column, base slightly saccate, lateral lobes rounded, midlobe orbicular,
revolute, tapering to an obtuse apex, 5-veined; column 1.35 cm high, incurved, foot absent. Anther terminal, hemispheric, 2-loculed, 2.1 × 1.9 mm; pollinia 4, sessile in pairs on a semilunar gland, 1.3 mm long and as broad,
triangular, wedge-shaped, one of each pair smaller. Ovary with pedicel 2 cm
long.

D i s t r. Rather common in open places in the submontane or mid-coun-
try tropical wet evergreen forests up to 1524 m alt. Hantane, Kondagala,
Bogawantalawa, Peradeniya (cultivated), etc. Also in Sikkim, Khasia Hills,
China and Japan.

E c o l. Flowers December, April.

I l l u s t r. Trimen, Handb. Fl. Ceyl. pl. 90. 1893; PDA, 2 drawings one of
which is from *C.P. 3694.*

N o t e. The collections of *Macrae 12* from Ceylon and *Wallich 7353*
from Sylhet are in Herb. Lindley. Of these *Macrae 12* is selected as the lectotype as there seems to be some confusion by Hooker in reference to the type
specimen.

S p e c i m e n s E x a m i n e d. CEYLON: KANDY DISTRICT: Hantane,
Jan. 1895, *s. coll. s.n.* (PDA); Peradeniya, Bot. Gard., cultd., Mar. 1961,
Jayaweera 2400 (PDA). RATNAPURA DISTRICT: Balangoda, Sept. 1895,
s. coll. s.n. (PDA). LOCALITY UNKNOWN: in 1829, *Macrae 12* (K, lecto-
type); Apr. 1863, *s. coll. C.P. 3694* (K, PDA). INDIA: Oct. 1850, *J.D.
Hooker & T. Thomson 2496* (K). Khasia Hills, *J.D. Hooker & T. Thomson 267*

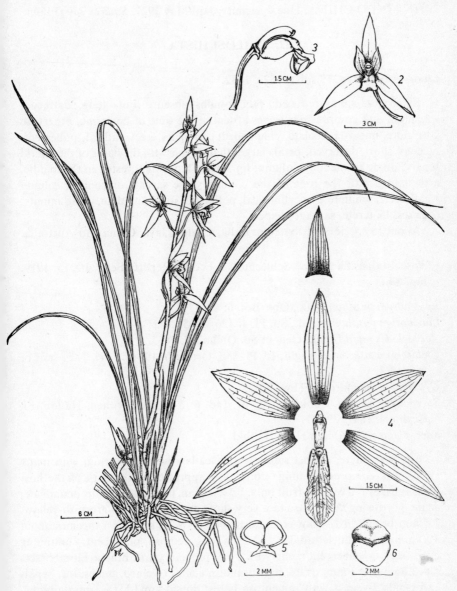

Fig. 83. *Cymbidium ensifolium* var. *haematodes* (Lindl.) Trimen. 1, plant with inflorescence. 2, flower from front. 3, lip and column from side. 4, bract, sepals, petals, lip and column spread out from front. 5, pollinia with gland. 6, operculum from inside.

(K, PDA). BANGLADESH: Sylhet. *Wallich 7353* (K). BHUTAN: *Griffith s.n.* (K). INDO-CHINA: Hue & vicinity, Jan.-May 1927, *Squires 289* (PDA).

22. CHILOSCHISTA

Lindl. in Bot. Reg. 18 sub t. 1522. 1832.

Epiphytes; stems reduced; pseudobulbs absent; roots long, flattened, spreading and compressed; leaves absent at the time of flowering, otherwise 2 or more, linear-lanceolate, channelled; peduncles erect, radical, pubescent; racemes short, decurved, petals larger than sepals with the bases of the lateral sepals adnate to the long column; lip sessile, bipartite, crested in the middle, articulating with the foot of the column, base saccate or conical; column small, erect, semiterete or cylindrical; pollinia 2, stipes subulate, gland minute; fruit sessile, terete, sausage-shaped.

About 13 species distributed in India, Ceylon, Java, China and Australia.

Chiloschista pusilla (Retz.) Schlechter in Fedde, Repert. Beih. 4: 275. 1919. —Fig. 84.

Epidendrum pusillum Retz., Obs. Bot. 6: 49. 1791.
Limodorum pusillum Willd., Sp. Pl. 4: 126. 1805.
Aeceoclades retzii Lindl., Gen. et Sp. Orch. 237. 1833.
Chiloschista usneoides Wight, Ic. Pl. Ind. Or. 5 (1): 19, pl. 1741. 1851 (not of Lindl.).
Cymbidium minimifolius Thw., Mss.
Sarcochilus wightii Hook. f., Fl. Br. Ind. 6: 37. 1890; Trimen, Handb. Fl. Ceylon 4: 184. 1898.
Sarcochilus minimifolius Hook. f., ibid.

Small epiphyte, almost stemless and leafless when flowering, with many vermiform, compressed, long, stout roots appressed to the bark of the host plant. Leaves 1–3 when in fruit only, 1.3 × 0.6 cm, linear-lanceolate, acuminate, acute, narrowing at the base to a very short petiole. Flowers greenish-yellow, 7.5 mm broad, in 2–4-flowered, decurved spikes or spiciform racemes about 3.5 cm high; peduncle radical, 1–2.2 cm long, reddish, pubescent, continuing into a zig zag, pubescent rachis with 2 or 3 tubular, sterile bracts. Floral bracts 1.8–2.6 × 1.8–2.2 mm, ovate, membranous, acute, 1-veined, pubescent; sepals and petals 3-veined with tomentose bases; dorsal sepal 5.7 × 3 mm, oblong, rounded; lateral sepals 4.8 × 2.4 mm, oblong-oval, obtuse, attached to the foot of the column; petals 4 × 2.4 mm, oblong, rounded or faintly truncate, also attached to the foot of the column; lip 3 × 8 mm, transversely oblong or 2-winged, on the foot of the column, 5-veined; lateral lobes of lip vertical, oblong; midlobe obscure, depressed and the apex bluntly dividing into two, base

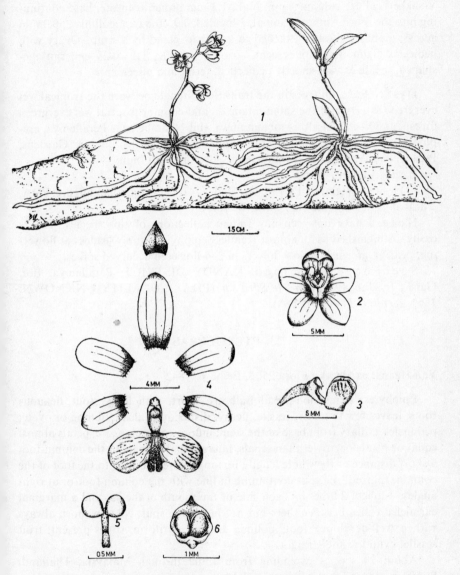

Fig. 84. *Chiloschista pusilla* (Retz.) Schlechter. 1, plants with inflorescence and fruits on twig. 2, flower from front. 3, lip and column from side. 4, bract, sepals, petals and lip spread out from front, column from inside. 5, pollinia with strap and gland. 6, operculum from inside.

shortly saccate, pubescent; disc pubescent with a thick, scurfy, glandular V-shaped callus; column 1 mm high, 1.3 mm broad, truncate, base continuing into the foot. Anther terminal, 2-loculed, 0.9×0.8 mm; pollinia 2, 0.3 mm across, globose, sulcate, attached to a narrow gland by a strap. Ovary with pedicel 2.5 mm long, pubescent. Fruit a capsule, 1.1×0.25 cm, sausage-shaped, sessile or very shortly pedicelled, terete and pubescent.

D i s t r. Rare, on trees in the transitional jungle between the tropical wet evergreen forests and the submontane or mid-country tropical wet evergreen forests at 305–915 m alt. Ambagamuwa and Nilambe near Peradeniya, epiphytic on *Artocarpus noblis* Thw., and on trees in the Botanic Gardens, Peradeniya, Wattegoda, Hantane, etc. Also in South India.

E c o l. Flowers March, June.

I l l u s t r. Wight, Ic. Pl. Ind. Or. 5: pl. 1741. 1851, right hand figure; PDA, 2 drawings one of which is from *C.P. 4017*.

N o t e. I have not seen any Indian collections of this species. This is easily distinguished as an almost stemless epiphyte entirely leafless at flowering, bearing greenish-yellow flowers in 2–4-flowered decurved spikes.

S p e c i m e n s E x a m i n e d. KANDY DISTRICT: Peradeniya, Bot. Gard., fr., Jun. 1927, *F.W. de Silva s.n.* (PDA). LOCALITY UNKNOWN: 1869, *s. coll. C.P. 4017* (PDA).

23. PTEROCERAS

Van Hasselt ex Hassk., Flora 25: 2, Beibl. 6. 1842.

Epiphytes; stems non-pseudobulbous, short, with long, stout, flexuous roots; leaves few to many, sessile, fleshy, distichous, falcate-oblong or ovate; peduncles axillary from base of the stem; inflorescence elongate; petals almost equal or petals narrower than sepals, lateral sepals adnate to the column-foot a short distance or the whole length; lip long-clawed, jointed to the foot of the column, spurred, the spur continuing in line with the column-foot or at right angles, 3-lobed, 2 lobes on each side of the mouth of the sac and a marginal caruncled callus between them but not inside the spur; column short, always with a well-developed foot; pollinia 2, cleft, pyriform; stipes present; fruit sessile, cylindric and straight.

About 24 species extending from India through Malaysia, Thailand, Sumatra, Borneo to the Philippine Islands.

Pteroceras viridiflorum (Thw.) Holttum in Kew Bull. 14: 272. 1960.—**Fig. 85.**

Sarcochilus viridiflorus (Thw.) Hook. f., Fl. Br. Ind. 6: 38. 1890; Trimen, Handb. Fl. Ceylon 4: 184. 1898.
Aerides viridiflora Thw., Enum. Pl. Zeyl. 430. 1864.

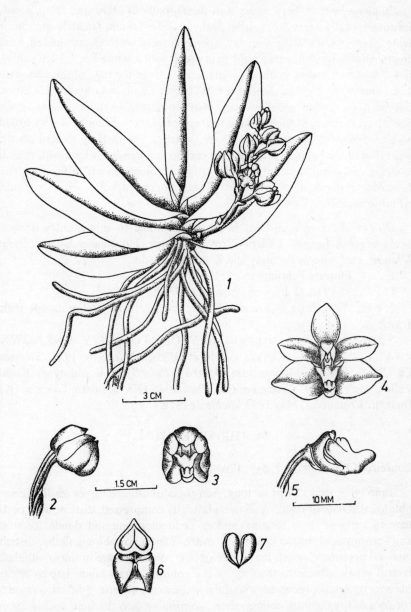

Fig. 85. *Pteroceras viridiflorum* (Thw.) Holttum, redrawn from a drawing of *C.P. 3385* in PDA. 1, plant with inflorescence. 2, partially opened flower from side. 3, partially opened flower from front. 4, fully opened flower from front. 5, lip, foot and column from side. 6, top of the column from front showing the operculum flapped over, enlarged. 7, pollinia, enlarged.

Epiphyte with a very short non-pseudobulbous stem and long, stout, flexuous roots. Leaves 3–6, sessile, fleshy, 5–7.5 × 1.6 cm, falcately oblong or ovate, nerveless, all facing one way, apex obliquely notched or rounded, base shortly sheathing. Flowers bright pale green with a white lip, 1.2 cm across, in 4–8-flowered spikes; peduncle short, arising from the base of the stem with 2 or 3 sterile, bracteolar sheaths. Floral bracts small, broadly ovate, obtuse, membranous; dorsal sepal broadly oval, rounded, 3-veined; lateral sepals much larger, ovate, obtuse, adnate to the foot of the column by a very broad base, 3–5-veined; petals linear-oblong, obtuse, 1-veined; lip jointed on the short foot of the column, long-clawed, ending in a semilunar limb with rounded cusps, disc deeply saccate, midlobe reduced; column short; anther terminal, 2-loculed; pollinia 4, pyriform in closely appressed pairs. Fruit a sessile, cylindric capsule, 3.7 cm long.

D i s t r. Very rare on trees in the submontane or mid-country tropical wet evergreen forests. Central Province above Dunsinane Estate, Great Western, etc. Also in Bombay and Konkan in India.

E c o l. Flowers February.

I l l u s t r. PDA, 2 drawings from *C.P. 3385*.

N o t e. Very little is known of this species from Ceylon except from drawings.

S p e c i m e n s   E x a m i n e d. CEYLON: LOCALITY UNKNOWN: *s. coll. C.P. 4016* (K, PDA); *s. coll. C.P. 3385* (PDA); Nov. 1923, *Stedman s.n.* (PDA). INDIA: Maharashtra, Bombay, *Dalzell s.n.* (K, holotype); Koina Valley, May 1892, *T. Cooke s.n.* (K), *Dalzell 26* (K). Konkan, *Law s.n.* (K); Oosheli, Chundivar, May 1853, *Richie 1426* (K).

24. THRIXSPERMUM

Loureiro, Fl. Cochinch. 2: 519. 1790.

Epiphytes; stems short or long, non-pseudobulbous; leaves sessile, linear-oblong, subulate or loriform; flowers laterally compressed, distichous in pectinate racemes or short terminal spikes; peduncles long and slender or stout and leaf-opposed; bracts lanceolate, ovate-subulate or oblong, fleshy, distichous and persistent; sepals lanceolate-oblong, oblong-ovate or linear-subulate, lateral sepals adnate to the foot of the column; petals lanceolate or linear-oblong, lip sessile, recurved, glandular-pubescent, saccate, 3-lobed, adnate to the foot of the column; column short, continuing into the foot; anther terminal, 2-loculed, pollinia 2, bifid, or apparently 4, caudicles very short; fruit capsules linear.

About 160 species from India, Ceylon through Malaya, Indo-China, Formosa and southwards to Java, Sumatra, Borneo, Celebes and the Philippine Islands.

KEY TO THE SPECIES

1 Flowers in terminal spikes
  2 Lip orbicular-ovate, recurved, 3-lobed, glandular-pubescent..........**1. T. pulchellum**
  2 Lip cymbiform, obscurely 3-lobed, pubescent...................**2. T. pugionifolium**
1 Flowers in distichous pectinate racemes.........................**3. T. complanatum**

1. Thrixspermum pulchellum (Thw.) Schlechter in Orchis 5: 57. 1911.—Fig. 86.

Dendrocolla pulchella Thw., Enum. Pl. Zeyl. 430. 1864; Alston in Trimen,
  Handb. Fl. Ceylon 6: 276. 1931.
Sarcochilus pulchellus Trimen, Cat. 89. 1885; Handb. Fl. Ceylon 4: 185. 1898.
Cylindrochilus pulchellus Thw., Enum. Pl. Zeyl. 307. 1861.

Epiphyte with non-pseudobulbous, flexuous stems, sharply and suddenly
bent at the terminal ends; roots long, slender, tortuous and branched. Leaves
sessile, distichous, 5–9 × 0.7–1.2 cm, linear-oblong, loriform or falcate, fleshy,
coriaceous, rounded, obliquely 2-lobed at apex, grooved along the midrib on
the upper surface. Flowers white, 1.2 cm across, in short, terminal spikes,
borne at the ends of long, slender peduncles; peduncle 2.5–9 cm long, broader
towards the end with 1 or 2 minute, sterile bracts. Floral bracts 2.4–3.2 × 2.4–
3 mm, acuminate, spiny, 1-veined; dorsal sepal 7 × 3.6 mm, lanceolate-oblong,
obtuse, 5-veined; lateral sepals 7–8 × 3.9–4 mm, broadly lanceolate-oblong,
subacute, 5-veined, adnate to the foot of the column; petals 7 × 2.8 mm, lanceolate, 3-veined; lip 5 × 8 mm, orbicular-obovate, recurved, 7-veined, glandular
pubescent; lateral lobes of lip rounded and blunt, bent inwards; midlobe short,
blunt and sometimes bifid, with a thick, scurfy callus between the mouth of
the sac and outer margin; column 3.2 mm high, 1.1 mm broad, continuing
into a foot. Anther terminal, 2-loculed, broader than long; pollinia 2, attached by a short strap to a small gland; each pollinium 0.7 × 0.5 mm, divided
longitudinally, cutting off a small flap; ovary 6–9 mm long. Fruit a long
cylindrical capsule, 7.5 cm × 3.5 mm.

D i s t r. Endemic. Rather common, abundantly on trees in the Gardens at
Peradeniya and Heneratgoda, Hantane, Kadugannawa, Kurunegala, etc. to
an alt. of 610 m.

E c o l. Flowers April–June. Some of its many host plants are: *Magnolia
sphenocarpa* Roxb., *Psidium guajava* L., *Eriobotrya japonica* Lindl., *Brownea
coccinea* Jacq.

I l l u s t r. PDA, drawing from *C.P. 2354*.

N o t e. This species is easily distinguished by the stems suddenly bent at
the terminal ends, white flowers borne in terminal spikes at the ends of long
slender peduncles and long slender capsules.

S p e c i m e n s   E x a m i n e d. KANDY DISTRICT: Peradeniya, May
1903, *Schlechter s.n.* (AMES); Peradeniya Bot. Gard., Aug. 1968, *Jayaweera*

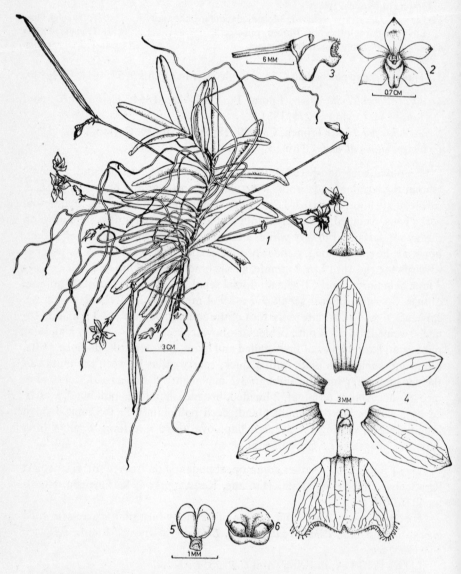

Fig. 86. *Thrixspermum pulchellum* (Thw.) Schlechter. 1, plant with inflorescences and fruits. 2, flower from front. 3, lip and column from side. 4, bract, sepals, petals, lip and column spread out from front. 5, bifid pollinia with strap and gland from behind. 6, operculum from inside, enlarged.

2768 (PDA); Kadugannawa, Aug. 1884, *s. coll. s.n.* (PDA). COLOMBO DISTRICT: Heneratgoda, Nov. 1884, *s. coll. s.n.* (PDA). LOCALITY UNKNOWN: *s. coll. C.P. 2354* (K, holotype, PDA); *Gardner 1439* (K).

2. Thrixspermum pugionifolium (Hook. f.) Schlechter, Orchis 5: 57. 1911.
—**Fig. 87.**

Dendrocolla pugionifolia (Hook. f.) Ridley, J. Linn. Soc. Bot. 32: 380. 1896; Alston in Trimen, Handb. Fl. Ceylon 6: 277. 1931.
Sarcochilus pugionifolius Hook. f., Fl. Br. Ind. 6: 196. 1890 (*pugionifolia*).

Epiphyte with very short, non-pseudobulbous, compressed stems and simple tortuous roots. Leaves few, 3–6.5 × 0.3–0.4 cm, linear-subulate, acuminate, fleshy, green, thick, coriaceous, channelled on the upper surface, rounded at the back, tip setaceous, base shortly sheathed. Flowers pale yellow, 1.8 cm across, in very short, terminal spikes with a thickened rachis; peduncle 2–6 cm long, rather stout, glabrous, green and dotted with red. Floral bracts 2.2 × 1.6 mm, ovate-subulate, fleshy, persistent, obtuse, 1-veined; dorsal sepal 4.5–6 × 3.3–5 mm, oblong or oblong-ovate, subacute, 3-veined; lateral sepals 7 × 4.5 mm, falcately and broadly oblong, gibbous on the lower margin, obtuse, 5-veined, adnate to the foot of the column; petals 6 × 2 mm, linear-oblong, obtuse, 3-veined; lip sessile on the foot, transversely oblong when spread out, otherwise cymbiform, 8 × 7.6 mm, obscurely 3-lobed, pubescent, deeply saccate on the disc and ciliate with a small caruncle at the base of the midlobe; sac broad, incurved, 2-lobed; column 1.5–2 mm high and as broad. Anther terminal, membranous, 2-loculed, 0.9 × 1.2 mm, resembling the two eyes of a fly; pollinia 2, unequally 2-partite or almost 4, larger lobe of each pollinium 0.65 × 0.4 mm, the smaller lobe 0.55 × 0.3 mm, lobes strongly appressed. Ovary 6.5 mm long. Fruit a linear, terete, straight capsule.

D i s t r. Endemic. Rare, on branches of trees overhanging irrigation reservoirs in the tropical dry mixed evergreen forests in the dry zone. Between Ganewatte and Maho, near Anuradhapura, Samanthurai (Eastern Province), Vilankulam, Vavuniya, etc.

E c o l. Flowers August, November.

I l l u s t r. PDA, 2 drawings.

N o t e. This species is distinguished by its non-pseudobulbous stems bearing a few fleshy leaves, pale yellow flowers borne in short terminal spikes nd the anther at the end of the column resembling the two eyes of a fly.

S p e c i m e n s E x a m i n e d. VAVUNIYA DISTRICT: Aug. 1890, *s. coll. s.n.* (K, holotype). AMPARAI DISTRICT: Samanthurai, Nov. 1885, *Nevill s.n.* (PDA).

3. Thrixspermum complanatum (Retz.) Schlechter, Orchis 5: 55. 1911; Alston in Trimen, Handb. Fl. Ceylon 6: 277. 1931.—**Fig. 88.**

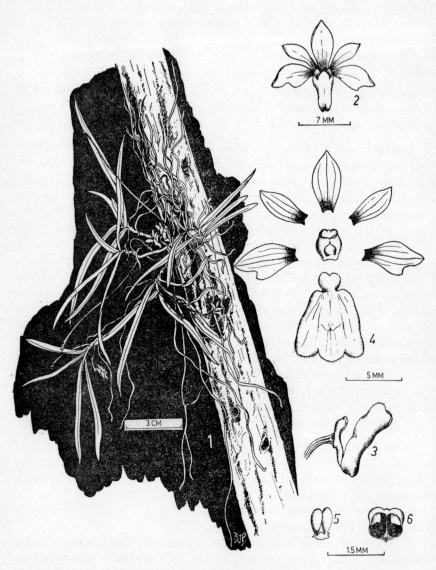

Fig. 87. *Thrixspermum pugionifolium* (Hook. f.) Schlechter. 1, plant with inflorescences on a twig. 2, flower from front. 3, lip and column from side. 4, sepals, petals, lip and column spread out from front. 5, pollinia from front. 6, operculum from inside.

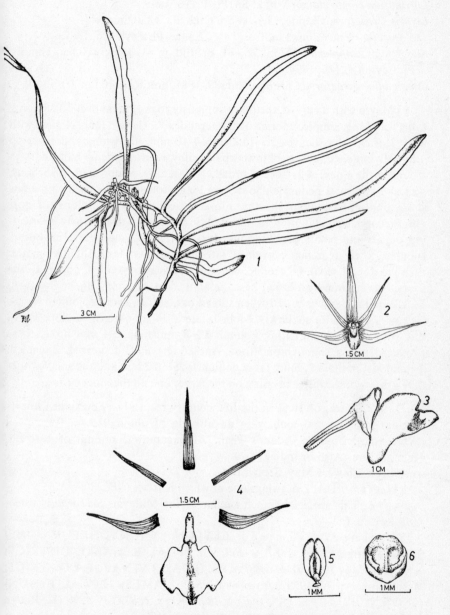

Fig. 88. *Thrixspermum complanatum* (Retz.) Schiechter. 1, plant with inflorescence.
2, flower from front. 3, lip and column from side. 4, sepals, petals, lip and column
spread out from front. 5, pollinia. 6, operculum from inside.

Epidendrum complanatum Koenig in Retz., Obs. 6: 50. 1791.
Limodorum complanatum Willd., Sp. Pl. 4: 126. 1805.
Liparis serraeformis Lindl., Gen. et Sp. Orch. 33. 1830, in part.
Dendrocolla serraeformis Lindl. ex Thw., Enum. Pl. Zeyl. 306. 1861.
Sarcochilus complanatus Hook. f., Fl. Br. Ind. 6: 41. 1890; Trimen, Handb.
　　Fl. Ceylon 4: 186. 1898.
Sarcochilus serraeformis Trimen, Cat. 89. 1885, non Reichb. f.

Epiphyte with a curved, tortuous, copiously rooting stem over 10 cm long;
roots very long, simple, unbranched; internodes 1.2–1.6 cm long, clothed with
short leaf-sheaths. Leaves 5.3–15.2 cm × 4–10 mm, loriform, coriaceous, tip
unequally notched, obtuse. Flowers pale yellow with a white lip blotched with
red near the apex, 4.2–4.6 cm broad, in laterally compressed, distichous,
pectinate racemes; peduncle about 3 cm long, stout, leaf-opposed with a few
short, obtuse, coriaceous sheaths. Floral bracts about 3 mm long, oblong,
obtuse, coriaceous, laterally compressed, incurved and distichously imbricating; sepals and petals membranous; dorsal sepal 2.2 cm × 3.5 mm, linear-
subulate, finely acuminate, 5-veined; lateral sepals 2 cm long, slightly broader
than the dorsal sepal, lanceolate, acuminate, falcate, 5-veined, adnate to the
foot of the column by a broad base; petals 1.7 cm × 1.5 mm, linear, 3-veined;
lip 1.7 cm long and as broad when spread out, sessile, saccate, jointed on the
foot of the column, shallowly 3-lobed, lateral lobes obtuse, midlobe thick,
disc with a prominent callus; column 7.2–8 mm high, 3.5 mm broad, base
produced into a short, broad foot. Anther terminal, depressed, 2-loculed,
1 mm long; pollinia 2, bifid; large pollinia 0.75 × 0.2 mm and the smaller ones
0.27 × 0.1 mm, the latter pressing on the larger one on the inner surface.

D i s t r. Rare, on trees in the low country tropical wet evergreen forests
extending to the mid-country to an altitude of about 915 m. Ratnapura
(Weragama), Foot of Adam's Peak, Ambagamuwa, summit of Ritigala,
Kalutara, etc. Also in India.

E c o l. Flowers May, September.

I l l u s t r. PDA, 2 drawings one of which is from *C.P. 2309.*

N o t e. This species is much similar to the Malayan *Sarcochilus arach-*
nites Reichb. f.

S p e c i m e n s　E x a m i n e d. CEYLON: ANURADHAPURA DIS-
TRICT: Ritigala, Jul. 1887, *s. coll. s.n.* (PDA). KEGALLE DISTRICT:
Kitulgala, May 1928, *J.M. de Silva s.n.* (PDA). RATNAPURA DISTRICT:
Ratnapura, Nov. 1959, *Jayaweera 25 (5)* (AMES). LOCALITY UN-
KNOWN: *Walker s.n.* (K), *Walker 1802* (K); *s. coll. C.P. 3209* (K, PDA).
INDIA: Herb. Rottler, 1872, *King's Collector s.n.* (K).

25. RHYNCHOSTYLIS

Blume, Bijdr. 285. t. 49. 1825.

Epiphytes; stems short and thick; pseudobulbs absent; leaves long, sessile, distichous, channelled, unequally bilobed and toothed at the tips; inflorescences erect or drooping, flowers densely crowded into long cylindric racemes; sepals and petals spreading, petals smaller than sepals, lateral sepals adnate to the column-foot; lip not hinged, joined to column-foot, with backward-pointing laterally flattened spur and forward-pointing unlobed or slightly 3-lobed blade; column and column-foot both short, lip merging into them; rostellum and anther long-pointed; pollinia 2, cleft, on a long slender caudicle, gland small.

About 5 species distributed through India, Ceylon, Malaysia, Burma, Thailand as far as the Philippine Islands.

Rhynchostylis retusa Blume, Bijdr. 286, pl. 49. 1825; Trimen, Handb. Fl. Ceylon 4: 187. 1898.—**Fig. 89.**

Epidendrum retusum L., Sp. Pl. 953. 1753.
Limodorum retusum Sw., Nova Acta Regiae Soc. Sci. Upsal. 6: 80. 1799.
Aerides retusum Sw., J. Bot. (Schrad.) 2: 233. 1799.
Aerides praemorsum Willd., Sp. Pl. 4: 130. 1805.
Rhynchostylis praemorsa Blume, ibid.
Aerides spicatum D. Don, Prod. Fl. Nepal 31. 1825.
Epidendrum hippium Hamilton ex D. Don, ibid. 32.
Sarcanthus guttatus Lindl., Bot. Reg. 17: pl. 1443. 1831.
Saccolabium guttatum Lindl. in Wall., Cat. n. 7308. 1832.
Aerides guttatum Roxb., Fl. Ind. 3: 471. 1832.
Saccolabium praemorsum Lindl., Gen. et Sp. Orch. 221. 1833.
Saccolabium spicatum Lindl., ibid.
Saccolabium blumei Lindl., Sert. Orch. pl. 47. 1838.
Saccolabium macrostachyum Lindl., ibid.
Saccolabium retusum Voight, Hort. Suburb. Calcutta 630. 1845.
Saccolabium rheedii Wight, Ic. Pl. Ind. Or. 5 (1): 19, pl. 1745–46. 1851.
Rhynchostylis guttata Reichb. f., Bonplandia 2: 93. 1854.
Saccolabium violaceum Reichb. f., ibid.
Saccolabium garwalicum Lindl., J. Linn, Soc. Bot. 3: 32. 1859.
Rhynchostylis garwalica Reichb. f. in Walp., Ann. 6: 888. 1861.

Stout epiphyte with a non-pseudobulbous stem and long, stout, aerial roots; stems 5–25 cm long, lower parts leafless with short internodes; often covered with the remains of old leaf sheaths. Leaves 15–37 × 1.6–2 cm, linear, strap-shaped, equitant, recurved, unequally lobed at the apex as if

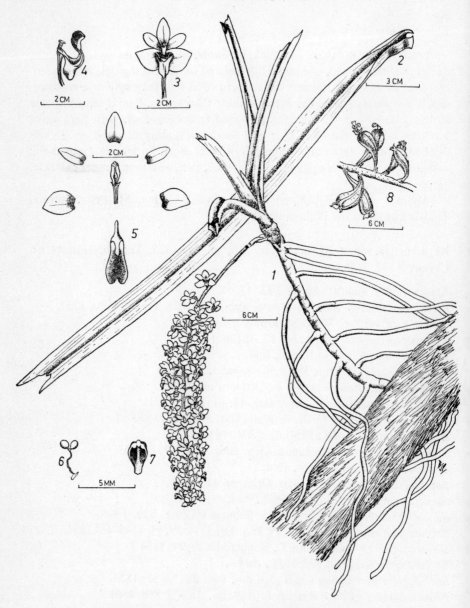

Fig. 89. *Rhynchostylis retusa* Blume. 1, plant with inflorescence. 2, leaf from above. 3, flower from front. 4, saccate lip and column from side. 5, sepals, petals, lip and column spread out from front. 6, pollinia with strap and gland. 7, operculum from inside 8, fruits.

bitten off, sheathing grooved above and coriaceous. Flowers white, tinged violet pink, 1.2–2 cm broad, in stout, compact, drooping, axillary racemes which measure 20–30 cm in length, 3.5–5 cm diameter; peduncle 9–10 cm long, stout, bearing two or more sterile bracts. Floral bracts 2.5 mm long and as broad, cordate, acute; dorsal sepal 12 × 8 mm, ovate or ovate-oblong, obtuse or emarginate; lateral sepals 12 × 9 mm, obliquely and broadly ovate, acute or subacute; petals 11.5 × 4.6 mm, oblong-ovate; lip 3-lobed, clawed; claw deflexed, deeply saccate or spurred beyond; lateral lobes obscure, mid-lobe elongated, inflexed, cuneiform; disc a 2-lobed, laterally compressed sac, or spur, tip rounded or emarginate, puberulous inside; column 5 mm high, 2 mm broad, rostellum shortly beaked. Anther terminal, 2-loculed, 2.6 × 1.4 mm; pollinia 2, globose or pyriform, waxy, slightly sulcate, attached to a small gland by means of a long, slender strap; caudicles short. Ovary with pedicel 1.3 cm long. Fruit an obovate or obconical, 6-ridged capsule, 2.8–4 × 1.5–1.8 cm.

D i s t r. Rather rare, usually on trees by streams in the tropical savannah in Uva and Eastern Provinces. Between Bibile and Ekiriyankumbura, Bint-enne, Batticaloa, Rugam Tank, etc. Also in tropical Himalayas, Bengal, Assam, Burma, Java and the Philippine Islands.

E c o l. Flowers January, April, July, November.

V e r n. Fox-tail Orchid, Batticaloa Orchid (E).

I l l u s t r. Blume, Tabellen en Platen Jav. Orch. pl. 49. 1825; PDA, drawing from *C.P. 2344*.

N o t e. This species is one of the most beautiful species of Ceylon orchids, referred to as the Fox-tail Orchid. It is easily recognised by the dense drooping racemes of pinkish-white flowers which contain a saccate spur in the lip. A white form of this species has been reported to be growing in these jungles. Herb. Lindley contains 8 collections many of which have been cited as type specimens under different synonyms.

S p e c i m e n s E x a m i n e d. CEYLON: KANDY DISTRICT: Perade-niya Bot. Gard., cultd., Jan. 1905, *Schlechter s.n.* (AMES), Jun. 1960, *Jayaweera 2047* (PDA), *Jayaweera 26* (AMES). AMPARAI DISTRICT: Bibile, Jan. 1888, *s. coll. s.n.* (PDA). BADULLA DISTRICT: Bintenne. Apr. 1858, *s. coll. C.P. 2344* (PDA). INDIA: Uttar Pradesh: Garhwal, *T. Thomson 181* (K); Dehra Dun, Jun. 1891, *Gamble 22786* (K). Sikkim Hima-layas: Tropical Valley, May 1892, *Pantling 442* (K, AMES); Hot Valley, *J.D. Hooker 184* (K); Junai Valley, *J.D. Hooker 185* (K). Madras: *Herb. Wight 3022* (K); East India Co., Herb. *Falconer 1064* (AMES); *Heyne s.n.* (K). BANGLADESH: Sylhet, Chittagong, etc. *Wallich 7308* (K); *Clarke 7119* (K). BURMA: Kachin Hills, Jun. 1899, *Shaik Mokin 6* (AMES); Chin Hills, Oct. 1923, *Daun 17* (K). Tavoy: May 1901, *Shaik Mokin 742* (AMES), JAVA: *Lobb s.n.* (K); *Loddiges s.n.* (K); Depok, *Beumee s.n.* (AMES). PHILIPPINE IS-

LANDS: Jul. 1945, *Lambert s.n.* (AMES), *Cumings s.n.* (K), Sept. 1908, *Lyon 13* (AMES). Luzon: Rizal Prov., East India Co., Jul. 1908, *Merrill 4190* (AMES), Aug. 1913, *Ramos 21334* (AMES), Aug. 1917, *Ramos & Edano 29476* (AMES); Bataan Prov., Apr. 1904, *Whitford 46* (AMES); Zambales Prov., Dec. 1916, *Edano 26781* (AMES).

26. PAPILIONANTHE

Schlechter in Orchis 9: 78. 1915.

Epiphytes with terete leaves and long flexuous simple roots; inflorescences axillary, 1- to few-flowered; flowers small to large, often showy; petals attached by a very broad base to the foot of the column; column short, stout, non-pyramidal, basally extended into a long and prominent foot which is continuous without articulation with the variously 3-lobed lip, the lateral lobes either parallel with or enfolding the column; pollinia 2, sulcate on broadly triangular to subquadrate stipes, viscidium large, rostellum elongate.

In India and Ceylon.

Papilionanthe subulata (Koenig) Garay, Bot. Mus. Leafl. 23 (10): 372. 1974. —Fig. 90.

Aerides cylindricum Lindl. in Wall., Cat. n. 7317. 1832; Trimen, Handb. Fl. Ceylon 4: 189. 1898.
Epidendrum subulatum Koenig in Retz., Obs. 6: 51. 1791.
Limodorum subulatum Willd., Sp. Pl. 4: 126. 1805.
Cymbidium cylindricum Heyne in Wall., Cat. n. 7317. 1832.
Cymbidium elegans Lindl. in Wall., Cat. n. 7354. 1832.

Terete epiphyte with non-pseudobulbous stems 30 cm or more long and long flexuous roots; internodes 2–3.5 cm long, cylindrical. Leaves terete, 7–8.7 cm long, 3 mm diameter, obliquely truncate-acute, petiolar sheaths annular, 2–2.5 cm long, sheathing the internodes above. Flowers creamish-white, fragrant, 3 cm broad, solitary or in twos at the apices of peduncles; peduncle 2.8–3.5 cm long, green, cylindrical, spotted, bearing 2 sterile bracts. Floral bracts 3.5–4 × 8 mm, triangular, emarginate, 3- or 5-veined; dorsal sepal 1.6 × 0.9 cm, oblong-lanceolate or oblong-oval, rounded or emarginate, 7-veined; lateral sepals 1.6 × 0.75 cm, obliquely oblong-lanceolate, subacute or rounded, 7-veined, adnate to the foot of the column; petals 1.6 × 1 cm, oval, obtuse or rounded, 7-veined, also attached to the foot; lip 1.5 cm long, sessile on the foot, infundibuliform, 3-lobed; lateral lobes oblong, obtuse, erect, conspicuously marked on the inside by a number of purple, parallel lines; midlobe tongue-shaped, recurved, obtuse, yellow in the centre, tipped dark purple, disc ridged; column stout, 5 mm high, 3.5 mm broad, incurved, truncate; rostellum obtuse. Anther terminal, 2-loculed, 3 mm long,

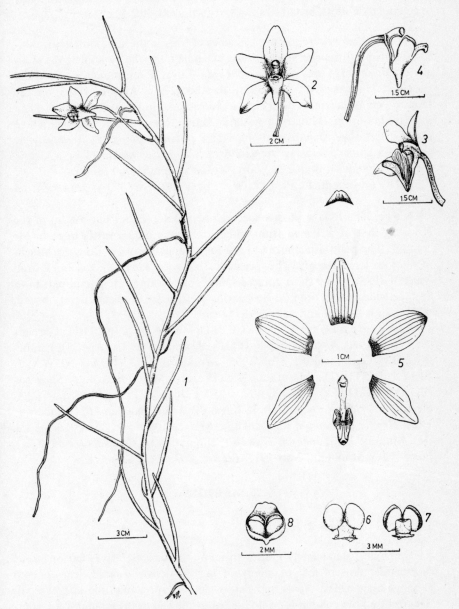

Fig. 90. *Papilionanthe subulata* (Koenig) Garay. 1, terminal portion of plant with inflorescence. 2, flower from front. 3, longitudinal section of flower. 4, lip, column and foot from side. 5, bract, sepals, petals and column spread out from front, lip from front not spread out. 6, pollinia with strap and gland from front. 7, pollinia from behind. 8, operculum from inside.

and as broad; pollinia 2, globose, 1.7 × 1.4 mm, depressed laterally, attached to a gland by a short, broad strap. Ovary with pedicel 2.5 cm long.

D i s t r. Rather rare, on top branches of trees in the submontane or mid-country tropical wet evergreen forests extending into the montane zone at an alt. of about 1524 m; Rangala, Nuwara Eliya, Pidurutalagala, Hakgala, Hantane, Hunnasgiriya, Maturata, Ramboda, etc. Also in India, in the Deccan Peninsula from Coorg Hills to Kerala and in Khasia Hills.

E c o l. Flowers January, February, March, May. Some of its many host plants are: *Calophyllum trapezifolium* Thw., *Stemonoporus* sp., *Actinodaphne* sp., *Syzygium* sp., *Rapanea robusta* Mez., *Neolitsea fuscata* (Thw.) Alston, *Pygeum wightianum* Blume ex Walp., *Aglaia* sp. and *Ficus retusa* L.

I l l u s t r. Wight, Ic. Pl. Ind. Or. 5: pl. 1744. 1853; PDA, drawing from *C.P. 2348.*

N o t e. The foliage of this species resembles a *Luisia* but the lip of the flower is that of a *Vanda* from which the genus differs in the foot of the column. The petal attachment to the foot is much broader than the attachment of the lateral sepals. The species is allied to *A. vandorum* Reichb. f. from which it differs in the short conical spur, broad ovate-acute lateral partitions and the wide, retuse, anterior lip bearing crests. The caudicula is very broad, whereas it is slender and narrow in *A. vandorum.*

S p e c i m e n s E x a m i n e d. CEYLON: KANDY DISTRICT: Corbet's Gap, Feb. 1960, *Jayaweera 1970* (PDA), *Jayaweera 28 (1)* (AMES); Perade-niya, Bot. Gard., cultd., Mar. 1956, *Jayaweera 1547* (PDA). NUWARA ELIYA DISTRICT: Maturata, High Forest, May 1906, *A.M. Silva s.n.* (PDA). LOCALITY UNKNOWN: *s. coll. C.P. 2348* (PDA, AMES). INDIA: Herb. *Rottlerianum s.n.* (K); Herb. *Wight 2984* (K); *Thomson 210* (K). Khasia Hills: *Hooker & Thomson s.n.* (AMES). Malabar: Wynaad, 1884, *Lawson s.n.* (K). Madras: 1877, *Johnson 1744* (K); Nilgiris, Apr. 1917, *Bourne 6390* (K); High Wavy Mountain, May 1917, *Blatter & Hallberg 25805* (K).

27. AERIDES

Lour., Fl. Cochincn. 2: 525. 1790.

Epiphytes; stems fairly long with many thick roots; leaves flat or terete, coriaceous; flowers few or many in lax or dense-flowered, leaf-opposed racemes or panicles; sepals and petals similar, spreading, the lateral sepals decurrent on the column-foot; lip hinged to the end of the column-foot, spur-red, 3-lobed; spur usually bent forwards with calli within; column short with a large foot; pollinia 2, waxy, globose, cleft on a rather short and broad or long narrow stipe.

About 90 species, throughout India, Ceylon, Malaya, Burma, Thailand,

Cambodia and China and southwards to Java, Sumatra, Borneo, Celebes as far as the Philippine Islands.

Aerides ringens (Lindl.) C.E.C. Fischer in Gamble, Fl. Pres. Madras 1442. 1928.—**Fig. 91.**

Saccolabium ringens Lindl. in Wall., Cat. n. 7313. 1832.
Saccolabium lineare Lindl., ibid. n. 7312.
Cymbidium lineare Heyne ex Wall., ibid.
Saccolabium wightianum Lindl., ibid. n. 7303, in part.
Aerides radicosum A. Rich., Ann. Sci. Nat. Bot. 11. 15: 65. 1841.
Saccolabium paniculatum Wight, Ic. Pl. Ind. Or. 5: pl. 1678. 1851.
Saccolabium rubrum Wight, ibid. pl. 1673.
Aerides lineare Hook. f., Fl. Br. Ind. 6: 47. 1890; Trimen, Handb. Fl. Ceylon 4: 189. 1898.

Epiphyte with a short, stout stem and stout, vermiform, branched roots. Leaves 17–18 × 1.4 cm, loriform and twisted, thickly coriaceous, keeled, unequally two-lobed, sides complicate, bases closely imbricating. Flowers whitish-pale pink, 2 cm long from the dorsal sepal to the tip of the spur, 7.5 mm broad, in secundly racemose, long, spreading branches of stoutly peduncles about 18 cm long; peduncle 12 cm long, stout, erect; pedicel decurved. Floral bracts 5 × 6 mm, triangular, acute, margins at apex irregularly serrate, 3-veined, persistent, sepals and petals adnate to the long foot of the column by their bases; dorsal sepal 7 × 3 mm, oblong or oval, subacute, 5-veined; lateral sepals as long as but broader than the dorsal sepal, broadly ovate or orbicular, obtuse, 7-veined; petals 6 × 4.8 mm, obovate, subacute, 3-veined; lip as long as the sepals or a little longer, sessile on the foot of the column, 3-lobed; lateral lobes of lip small, rounded, bordering the mouth of a large, subclavate spur; midlobe oblong-ovate, flat, rounded, base with fleshy, rounded callus at the mouth of the sac; column 4.8 mm high; foot with a long, broad, deep channel leading into the sac with raised, fleshy sides; rostellum shortly beaked. Anther terminal, imperfectly 2-loculed, 2 × 2.5 mm; pollinia 2, globose, 1.1 mm diameter, attached by a short strap to a large gland. Ovary with pedicel 1.3 cm long.

D i s t r. Rare, on trees in the moist semi-evergreen forests between the wet and dry zone extending to the tropical savannah. Between Bibile and Ekiriyankumbura it is very abundant, and also in Dumbara, Nalanda, the Seven Korales, etc. Also in South India, in the Ghats from Canara southwards.

E c o l. Flowers September, October.

I l l u s t r. Wight, Ic. Pl. Ind. Or. 5: pl. 1676. 1852; PDA, drawing.

N o t e. In Herb. Kew there are three specimens in the type cover under different synonyms. This species is distinguished by its typical flat vandaceous

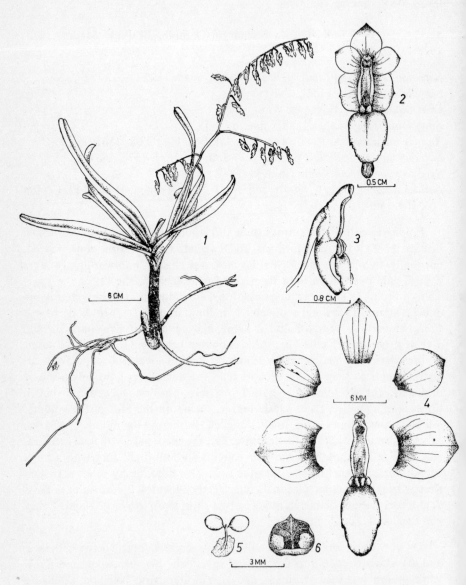

Fig. 91. *Aerides ringens* (Lindl.) C.E.C. Fischer. 1, plant with inflorescence. 2, flower from front. 3, lip, column and spur from side. 4, sepals, petals and lip spread out from front, column and foot from inside with the operculum flapped over. 5, pollinia with strap and gland. 6, operculum from inside.

leaves, its pale pink flowers spreading out in panicles and the presence of a foot and conical spur in the lip of the flower.

Specimens Examined. CEYLON: MATALE DISTRICT: Nalanda, Sept. 1885, *s. coll. s.n.* (PDA). AMPARAI DISTRICT: Bibile, Nov. 1959, *Jayaweera 28 (2)* (AMES). LOCALITY UNKNOWN: *s. coll. C.P. 3767* (PDA); Seven Korales, Oct. 1882, *s. coll. s.n.* (PDA). INDIA: East India: *Wallich 7303* (K); Courtallam, *Wight 903* (K). Kodaikanal Region: Pulney Hills, *Anglade s.n.* (AMES). Pen. Ind. Or., Herb. *Wight 3026* (AMES).

28. KINGIDIUM

P.F. Hunt in Kew Bull. 24: 97. 1970.

Epiphytes; stems short, stout, leafy without pseudobulb; leaves sessile, distichous, broad, coriaceous; peduncle leaf-opposed, simple or paniculately branched; sepals and narrower petals spreading, obovate or oblong, lateral sepals adnate to the base of the lip forming a short, conical, spur-like mentum from which the lobes are borne directly without an unguis, furnished with linear appendages, oblong, subfalcate; petals as long, linear-oblong; lip shortly clawed, 3-lobed, the apex broad and deeply cleft into two spreading teeth; column short, broad, margins winged, foot absent; anther low, acuminate, 2-locular; pollinia 2, waxy, strap long, slender, gland small.

Two species, distributed over China, India, Ceylon and Thailand.

Kingidium deliciosum (Reichb. f.) Sweet, Amer. Orchid Soc. Bull. 39: 1095. 1970.—**Fig. 92.**

Phalaenopsis decumbens (Griff.) Holttum, Gard. Bull. Singapore 11: 286. 1947.
Aerides decumbens Griff., Notul. Pl. As. 3: 365. 1851; Ic. pl. Asiat. 3: 320. 1851.
Phalaenopsis wightii Reichb. f., Bot. Zeitung 20: 214. 1832.
Phalaenopsis hebe Reichb. f., Hamburger Garten-Blumenzeitung 18: 35. 1862.
Aerides latifolium Thw., Enum. Pl. Zeyl. 429. 1864.
Doritis wightii Benth. & Hook. f., Gen. Pl. 3: 574. 1883; Trimen, Handb. Fl. Ceylon 4: 188. 1898.
Doritis latifolia Trimen, Cat. 89. 1885.
Kingiella decumbens Rolfe, Orchid Rev. 25: 197. 1917.

Epiphyte with a very short, non-pseudobulbous stem clothed in old leaf sheaths and bearing long vermiform roots. Leaves 3 or 4, sessile, 11–17 × 2.5–6.4 cm, distichous, oblong-lanceolate, obtuse or cuspidate, base jointed on short sheaths, coriaceous, margin undulate. Flowers white with a pink or violet-veined lip, 1.2 cm broad in racemose panicles; peduncle long, flexuous, green, branched, 15–45 cm long together with the panicle, bearing 2 or more sterile bracts, branches few, 7.5–10 cm long, spreading on stout rachis. Floral

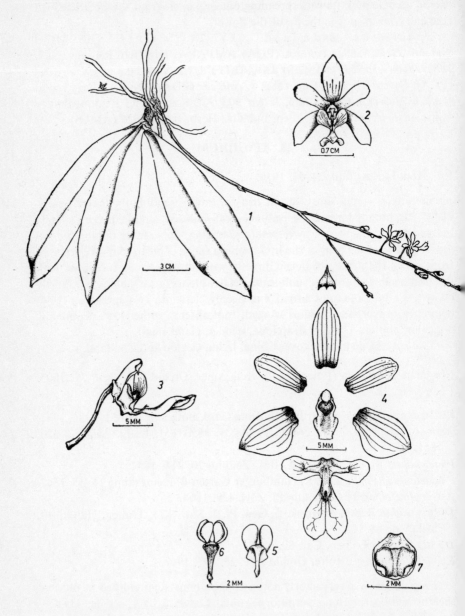

Fig. 92. *Kingidium deliciosum* (Reichb. f.) Sweet. 1, plant with inflorescence. 2, flower from front. 3, lip, column and foot from side. 4, bract, sepals, petals and lip spread out from front, column with foot from inside. 5, pollinia with strap and gland from front. 6, pollinia from behind. 7, operculum from inside.

bracts 1.2 × 1.7 mm, ovate, acute, ridged on the dorsal surface, 1-veined; dorsal sepal 9 × 4 mm, linear-oblong, obtuse or rounded, 5-veined; lateral sepals 8 × 5.5 mm, obliquely oblong, obtuse, 5-veined, adnate to the base of the column, lower margin reflexed; petals 7 × 3.8 mm, oblong, rounded, 3-veined, lateral veins bifurcate at base giving a 5-veined appearance; lip 8.5 × 11 mm when spread out, 3-lobed; lateral lobes when spread out 5 × 3 mm, obovate, rounded, with a thick inner ridge down the centre connecting them to the disc which carries a short conical mentum at the base and a bicuspidate callus; midlobe obcordate, 7 × 5.2 mm with the cusps of the calli pointing forward; column 3.3 mm high, 2.6 mm broad, foot absent; rostellum 3-lobed, midlobe short, triangular, acuminate, and the lateral lobes linear; anther terminal, 2-loculed, 1.6 mm long and as broad; pollinia 2, globular, bipartite, 0.8 × 0.65 mm, joined to a triangular acuminate strap which terminates in a small gland lodged in the rostellar lobes. Ovary with pedicel 1.05–1.2 cm long.

D i s t r. Rare, on trees in the tropical wet evergreen forests up to 305 m alt. Ratnapura, Ambagamuwa, Hiniduma, etc. It also occurs in Malabar, Sikkim and Bhutan Himalaya, Burma, Siam, and China.

E c o l. Flowers September.

I l l u s t r. Hook. f., Ann. R. Bot. Gard. (Calcutta) 5: pl. 59. 1895; King & Pantling, Ann. R. Bot. Gard. (Calcutta) 8: pl. 265. 1898; Smith, Atlas Orch., Java. pl. 417. 1908; PDA, 2 drawings, one of which is from *C.P. 3495.*

N o t e. The Ceylon species differs from the Indian species in that the flowers are white while the Indian species bears cream-coloured sepals and petals in the flower. Herb. Kew contains four collections under different synonyms. Two collections from Burma, Herb. *Griffith 5236* under *Aerides decumbens* and *Parish 175* under *Phalaenopsis wightii. Thwaites C.P. 3495* from Ceylon has been described under *Aerides latifolium* and Wight's collection from Quilon under *Doritis wightii.*

S p e c i m e n s E x a m i n e d. CEYLON: KANDY DISTRICT: Peradeniya, Bot. Gard., cultd., Nov. 1928, *Senaratne 139* (PDA), Sept. 1964, *Jayaweera 2640* (PDA). RATNAPURA DISTRICT: Ratnapura, *s. coll. C.P. 3495* (K, PDA), Oct. 1960, *Jayaweera 27* (AMES). INDIA: Sikkim Himalaya: Teesta Valley, Aug. 1894, *Pantling 94* (K). Kerala: Quilon, Herb. *Wight s.n.* (K). BURMA: Sept. 1857, *Herb. Griffith 5236* (K); Mandalay, 1926, *Swinhoe 61* (K); Moulmein, *Parish 175* (K, lectotype). THAILAND: Pungok, Dec. 1918, *Haniff 3875* (AMES). CHINA: Hainan: Loktung, June 1936, *Lau 27188* (AMES); Lin Fa Shan & Vicinity, Aug. 1927, *Tsang 264* (AMES); May 1932, *Liang 61748* (K, AMES).

29. LUISIA

Gaud. in Voy. Uranie & Physicienne 426. t. 37. 1827.

Epiphytes; stems fairly long, rigid, terete, not pseudobulbous; roots vermiform; leaves slender, terete; flowers spicate on a short, axillary peduncle, drooping; sepals and petals free, equal or the petals longer and narrower; lip fleshy, fixed immovably to the base of the column, entire or obscurely 3-lobed; column short, truncate; foot absent; pollinia 2, entire or cleft, globose or pyriform on a short broad strap or stipe; gland broad; fruit narrow, erect.

About 55 species distributed throughout India, Ceylon, Malaya, Burma, Thailand, China, Formosa, Japan and southwards through Java, Borneo, Celebes, New Guinea as far as the Philippine Islands.

KEY TO THE SPECIES

1 Lip with broadly obcordate short terminal lobe....:................1. **L. teretifolia**
1 Lip panduriform, tip with 2 divergent lobules.......................2. **L. tenuifolia**

1. Luisia teretifolia Gaud. in Voy. Uranie & Physicienne 426. t. 37. 1827; Trimen, Handb. Fl. Ceylon 4: 190. 1898.—**Fig. 93.**

Epidendrum triste Forster f., Fl. Insul. Austr. Prod. 60, n. 314. 1786.
Cymbidium triste Roxb., Fl. Ind. 3: 461. 1832, non Willd.
Luisia trichorrhiza Blume, Rumphia 4: 50. 1848.
Cymbidium tenuifolium Wight, Ic. Pl. Ind. Or. 5 (1): 8, pl. 1689. 1851.
Luisia occidentalis Lindl., Fol. Orch. 4: 97. 1853.
Luisia zeylanica Lindl., ibid. 3.
Luisia burmanica Lindl., ibid.
Luisia platyglossa Reichb. f. in Walp., Ann. 6: 622. 1861.
Luisia brachystachys var. *flaveola* Parish & Reichb. f., Trans. Linn. Soc. London 30: 144. 1874.
Luisia tristis Kuntze, Rev. Gen. Bot. 2: 672. 1891.

Epiphyte with non-pseudobulbous, rigid, terete, branching stems, 25–50 cm long, roots vermiform and branching, internodes 1–2 cm long. Leaves 8–25 cm long, terete, green, apex rounded, bases sheathing the internodes above and as long. Flowers small, 7 mm broad, purplish-green with a dark purple lip in few-flowered, short-peduncled axillary spikes emerging through the petiolar sheaths; pedicel sharply recurved. Floral bracts 2 mm long, 4 mm broad, broadly triangular or ovate and rounded; dorsal sepal 5.2–6 × 3.1 mm, oblong, rounded, concave and 5-veined; lateral sepals 6–6.8 × 3.2–3.5 mm, oblong-lanceolate, obtuse, 5-veined, concave with the margins incurved; petals 6.6–7.2 × 2.2–2.4 mm, linear-oblong, obtuse, 3-veined, the lateral veins branching from base, concave; lip 6.8 mm long, saccate at the base, hourglass-shaped; lateral lobes short, rounded, vertical; midlobe broadly ovate, or obscurely cordate, 5.2 mm broad. Column 3.8 mm high, 2.4 mm broad, with a purple stigma and purple-spotted apex; foot absent. Anther terminal, 2-loculed, 1.8 × 2 mm; pollinia 2, pyriform, connected to a shield-shaped gland

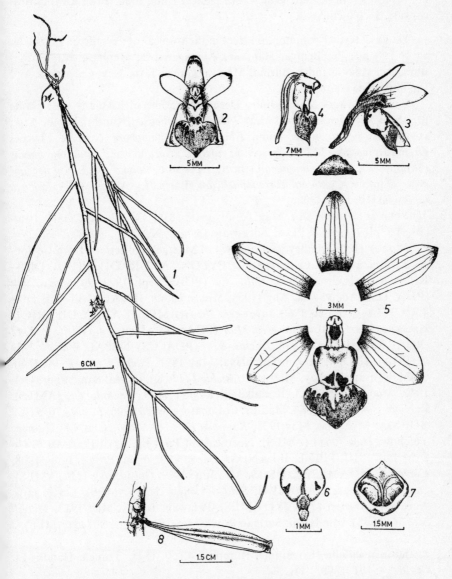

Fig. 93. *Luisia teretifolia* Gaud. 1, plant with inflorescence. 2, flower from front.
3, longitudinal section of flower. 4, lip and column from side, three quarters view.
5, bract, sepals, petals, lip and column spread out from front. 6, pollinia with
strap and gland. 7, operculum from inside. 8, fruit.

by means of a short, flat strap; each pollinium 1 × 0.7 mm, hollow and opening inwards from behind. Ovary with pedicel 7 mm long. Fruit a cylindrical capsule, 3 × 0.6 cm.

D i s t r. Rather common, on trees in the tropical wet evergreen forests up to 762 m alt. Peradeniya, Hantane, Ambagamuwa, Hunnasgiriya, Ratnapura, etc. Also in India, Burma, Malaya, China, Java, New Caledonia, and the Philippine Islands.

E c o l. Flowers March–June, December. Some of its many host plants are: *Samanea saman* (Jacq.) Merr., *Hevea brasiliensis* (Kunth.) Muell. Arg., *Artocarpus heterophyllus* Lam., *Cinnamomum camphora* Nees & Eberm., *Oreodoxa oleracea* Mart., *Crescentia cujete* L., *Gardinia* sp., *Antidesma bunius* (L.) Spreng., *Syzygium aqueum* (Burm. f.) Alston, *Randia* sp., *Litsea deceanensis* Gamble, *Canthium coromandelicum* (Burm. f.) Alston and *Madhuca longifolia* (L.) J.F. Macbr.

I l l u s t r. Hook. Bot. Mag. 65: pl. 3648. 1839; Ann. R. Bot. Gard. (Calcutta) 8: pl. 271. 1898; PDA, 2 drawings from *C.P. 2347.*

N o t e. Herb. Lindley contains two of Macrae's collections from Ceylon.

S p e c i m e n s E x a m i n e d. CEYLON: ANURADHAPURA DISTRICT: Ritigala, Mar. 1905, *Willis s.n.* (PDA), Sept. 1972, *Jayasuriya 909* (PDA, US); Andiyagala, Aug. 1958, *Senaratne s.n.* (PDA). MATALE DISTRICT: Laggala, Feb. 1960, *Jayaweera 20 (4)* (AMES). KANDY DISTRICT: Hantane, Dec. 1960, *Jayaweera 2196* (PDA); Peradeniya, *s. coll. C.P. 2347* (PDA); Rangala, Nov. 1974, *Davidse 8257* (PDA, US). NEPAL: *Wallich 7359 A* (PDA). INDIA: Sikkim Himalaya: May 1891, *Pantling 115* (K, AMES). Maharashtra: Bombay, May 1853, *Richie 1417* (K). Orissa: Sambalpur, Oct. 1940, *Mooney 1486* (K). Kodaikanal Region 1923, *Anglade s.n.* (AMES); Pulneys, *Bourne 2943* (K). Madras: Coimbatore, April 1906, *Fischer 1035* (K). BURMA: Myitkyna, May 1938, *Kermode 17333* (AMES). CHINA: Hainan: Yaichow, *How 70684* (AMES); Northeast of Po Ting, April 1932, *Ko 62416* (AMES). PHILIPPINE ISLANDS: Luzon: Sorsogon Prov., June 1908, *Curran 12248* (AMES); Zambales Mt., June 1929, *Quisumbing 5119* (AMES). Samar: Laquilacen, April 1948, *Sulit & Conese 5459* (AMES). Leyte: Jaro, April 1914, *Wenzel 422 & 583* (AMES). Palawan: Taytay, May 1913, *Merrill 9287* (AMES). Mindanao: Surigao Prov., May 1921, *Lopez 40146* (AMES).

2. Luisia tenuifolia (L.) Blume, Rumphia 4: 50. 1848; Trimen, Handb. Fl. Ceylon. 4: 191. 1898.—**Fig. 94.**

Epidendrum tenuifolium L., Sp. Pl. 952. 1753.
Cymbidium tenuifolium Lindl., Gen. et Sp. Orch. 167. 1833.
Birchea teretifolia A. Rich., Ann. Sc. Nat. Bot. 11. 15: 67, pl. 10. 1841.
Luisia birchea Blume, ibid.
Cymbidium triste Wight, Ic. Pl. Ind. Or. 3 (2): 10, pl. 911. 1844–1845, non

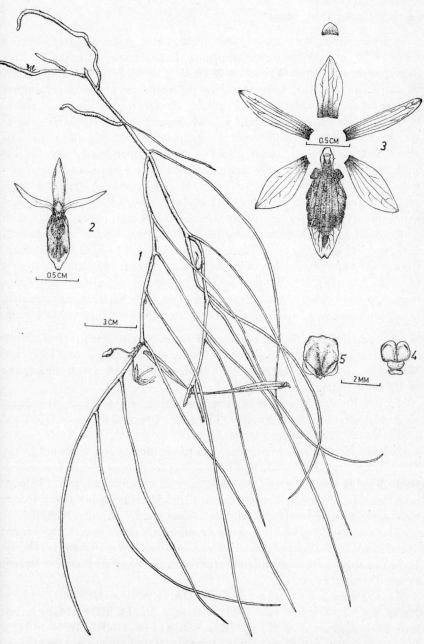

Fig. 94. *Luisia tenuifolia* (L.) Blume. 1, plant with inflorescence and fruits. 2, flower from front. 3, bract, sepals, petals, lip and column spread out from front. 4, pollinia with strap and gland. 5, operculum from inside.

Roxb., non Willd.
Luisia zeylanica Thw., Mss.

Tufted epiphyte with non-pseudobulbous, terete, green, slender, drooping stems 17–75 cm long and vermiform roots. Leaves terete, more slender than stems, green, straight or flexuous, 8–28 cm long, apex constricted and produced into a nail-like beak, bases sheathing the internodes above them; petiolar sheaths 2.8 cm long; internodes 3.2 cm long. Flowers few, 1.1 cm broad, sharply reflexed, pale yellowish-purple with a white-patched dark purple lip, in close spiciform racemes, opening one at a time, peduncle short, axillary, towards the ends of the drooping stems, about 6 mm long, emerging through the leaf sheaths. Floral bracts broadly crescent-shaped, 2×1.8 mm, rounded and persistent; dorsal sepal $6.2-7 \times 3.1-3.2$ mm, lanceolate-oblong, obtuse, 3- or 5-veined; lateral sepals lanceolate or oblong-lanceolate, $8.2-8.4 \times 3.6$ mm, subacute, concave and 4-veined; petals $9-9.8 \times 1.8-1.9$ mm, obtuse or rounded, 5-veined; lip $9.8 \times 4.4-4.6$ mm, panduriform, convex, bifid at apex, base 2-auricled, 7-veined, margin crenate; column 3.9 mm high, 2.4 mm broad, truncate and narrowed down to a purple blotched base; foot absent. Anther terminal, 2-loculed, 2.2×1.8 mm; pollinia 2, globose, each pollinium 0.96 mm long, 0.84 mm broad with a laterally depressed slit behind, opening inwards. Ovary with pedicel 1.2 cm long. Fruit a slender, fusiform capsule, 3×0.3 cm.

D i s t r. Rare, on trees in the tropical dry mixed evergreen forests extending to the mid-country tropical wet evergreen forests up to 915 m alt. Wariapola, Hewaheta, Hantane, etc. Also in the Western Ghats from Konkan to Kerala in India.

E c o l. Flowers March, May–June. Two other orchids which grow in association with it are *Vanda parviflora* Lindl. and *Oberonia thwaitesii* Hook. f.

I l l u s t r. PDA, drawing from *C.P. 3530*.

N o t e. Herb. Lindley contains Macrae's collection No. 67 from Ceylon. The two species *L. teretifolia* and *L. tenuifolia* seem to have been confused in Herb. Kew as Hooker cites *C.P. 2347* under *L. tenuifolia* whereas it belongs to *L. teretifolia*. He says that collection *C.P. 3530* is probably a new species while it has been correctly identified as *L. tenuifolia* by Thwaites himself.

This species along with *Sarcanthus peninsularis* Dalz. have been reduced to synonyms by Garay and placed under *Cleisostoma ternuifolium* (L.) Garay. These two species are quite different from each other and are therefore treated as two distinct species.

S p e c i m e n s E x a m i n e d. CEYLON: KANDY DISTRICT: Peradeniya, Bot. Gard. cultd., Mar. 1961, *Jayaweera 2014* (K, PDA); Mapitigama, Jun. 1960, *Jayaweera 29 (2)* (AMES). LOCALITY UNKNOWN: in 1829, *Macrae 67* (K); *s. coll. C.P. 3530* (K, PDA). INDIA: Coonoor: Nilgiri Hills, Jun. 1912, *Bourne 5979* (K); Nilgiris, May 1857, *Herb. Wight 2975* (K); Nilgiri & Coorg, *Thomson* (AMES, PDA). Kodaikanal Region: *C.A. Barber 7544*

(K); Malabar, Konkan, etc. Herb. *Stocks s.n.* (K); Pulneys, Jul. 1898, *Bourne 1847 & 1848* (K). Pen. Ind. Or., *Herb. Wight 2975* (AMES, PDA).

30. VANDA

R. Br., Bot. Reg. 6: 506. 1820.

Epiphytes; stems long with vermiform roots, non-pseudobulbous; leaves flat, distichous, recurved, thickly coriaceous, bilobed at apex or terete; inflorescence simple, more or less erect, of few large or medium-sized flowers, peduncle leaf-opposed; sepals and petals nearly equal, narrowed to the base, the edges more or less reflexed or crisped; lip smaller than sepals, attached immovably to a short column-foot; spur short, funnel-shaped, 3-lobed, often laterally flattened without calli; side lobes erect, close to the column; midlobe erect or recurved, narrow or broad with longitudinal ridges and 2 small calli at the base; column short, thick; foot short or absent; anther 2-chambered with 2 large, waxy, cleft pollinia on a short strap and gland.

About 80 species distributed throughout India, Ceylon, Malaya, Burma, Thailand, Cambodia, Indo-China and China, extending southwards into Java, Sumatra, Borneo, Celebes, Australia and the Philippine Islands.

KEY TO THE SPECIES

1 Leaves 10–26 cm long
  2 Flowers 1.8 cm across, light yellow, lateral lobes of lip obtuse.........**1. V. parviflora**
  2 Flowers 5 cm across, slate, pink or blue, lateral lobes of lip acute......**2. V. tessellata**
1 Leaves 5.5–10 cm long
  3 Plant not scandent, raceme 2- or 3-flowered, flowers yellow-green......**3. V. thwaitesii**
  3 Plant scandent, raceme, 4- or 5-flowered, flowers bright yellow.......**4. V. spathulata**

1. Vanda parviflora Lindl., Bot. Reg. 30: Misc. 45. 1844; Trimen, Handb. Fl. Ceylon 4: 192. 1898.—**Fig. 95.**

Vanda testacea (Lindl.) Reichb. f., Gard. Chron. 2: 166. 1877; Alston in Trimen, Handb. Fl. Ceylon 6: 277. 1931.
Aerides testaceum Lindl., Gen. et Sp. Orch. 238. 1833.
Aerides·wightianum Lindl., ibid.

Epiphyte with a stout, non-pseudobulbous stem 10–15 cm long, the lower portion covered over by the remains of old, brown leaf bases; roots large, thick, vermiform. Leaves 10–26 × 1.3–1.9 cm, linear-lorate, distichous, equitant, usually recurved in larger specimens, unequally lobed or toothed at the apex with the midrib forming the third tooth, coriaceous and keeled. Flowers 1.8 cm broad, cream-yellow with a white, purple or reddish-pink lip in erect many-flowered racemes measuring 6–15 cm in length; peduncle stout,

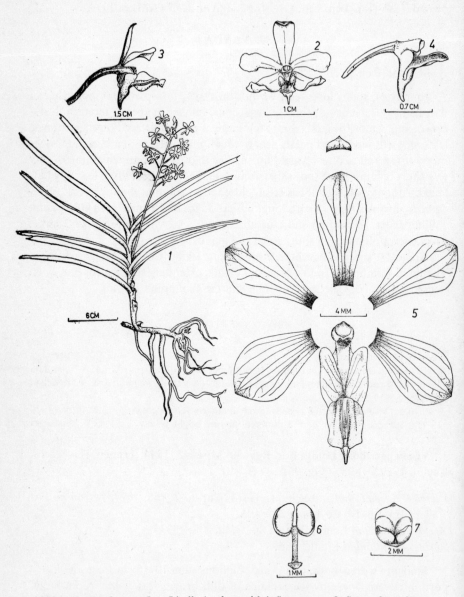

Fig. 95. *Vanda parviflora* Lindl. 1, plant with inflorescence. 2, flower from front.
3, longitudinal section of flower. 4, lip and column from side. 5, bract, sepals,
petals and column spread out from front, lip natural position. 6, pollinia with
strap and gland. 7, operculum from inside.

5–25 cm long, tinged red. Floral bracts 1.5–2 × 2.6–3 mm, broadly-ovate, acute; dorsal sepal 6–11.2 × 2.7–5.2 mm, obovate-spathulate, obtusely rounded and incurved at the apex; lateral sepals 5.6–9.2 × 2.8–5.4 mm, obovate-spathulate, obtusely rounded, incurved and twisted upwards laterally at the apex; petals 5.2–10.8 × 2.2–4.6 mm, spathulate, concave, narrow and twisted at the base downwards; lip 9.5 mm long with the spur, sessile, 3-lobed; lateral lobes oblong, obtuse, erect; midlobe 6.4 × 3.5 mm, subquadrate-oblong, recurved, dilated at the apex, emarginate, crenulate, disc with two broad, fleshy ridges; spur narrow, funnel-shaped, 3.1 mm long; column short, 2.8 mm high, 2.4 mm broad, truncate. Anther terminal, 2-loculed, 1.6 mm long and as broad; pollinia 2, oblong, bifid, 0.74 × 0.56 mm, attached to an orbicular gland by means of a short, broad strap. Ovary with pedicel 2.5 cm long. Fruit a long-pedicelled, clavate, capsule 2.5–3 cm long.

D i s t r. Rather common, on trees along roadsides and in the jungles of the tropical dry mixed evergreen forests, extending up to mid-country. Kurunegala, Dambulla, Anuradhapura, Hewaheta, Hunnasgiriya, Haragama, Peradeniya, Galle, etc. Also in the Eastern Himalayas, Western Peninsula from Konkan to Travancore and Assam in India, Nepal and Burma.

E c o l. Flowers February, March, September. Some of its many host plants are: *Vitex leucoxylon* L. f., *Samanea saman* (Jacq.) Merr., *Antidesma bunius* (L.) Spreng., *Madhuca longifolia* (L.) J.F. Macbr., *Manilkara hexandra* (Roxb.) Dubard; *Wormia triquetra* Rottb., *Ficus retusa* L., *Semecarpus gardneri* Thw. and *Grevillea robusta* Cunn. It has a wide range of tolerance of light intensity from 37 to 90 per cent of the normal light, a temperature of about 80°F and above, and relative humidity 36–41 per cent.

I l l u s t r. Wight, Ic. Pl. Ind. Or. 5: pl. 1669. 1851; Hooker, Bot. Mag. 85: pl. 5138. 1859; King & Pantling, Ann. R. Bot. Gard. Calcutta 8: pl. 286. 1898; PDA, 2 drawings from *C.P. 752.*

S p e c i m e n s   E x a m i n e d. CEYLON: ANURADHAPURA DISTRICT: Nachchaduwa Tank, Nov. 1973, *Sohmer 8954* (PDA, US); Dambulla-Anuradhapura Road, Oct. 1973, *Sohmer 8074* (PDA, US). KURUNEGALA DISTRICT: Melsiripura, Sept. 1959, *Jayaweera 30 (1)* (AMES). KANDY DISTRICT: Peradeniya, *s. coll. C.P. 752* (K, PDA); Bot. Gard., Mar. 1967, *Jayaweera 2061* (PDA). KALUTARA DISTRICT: Hewessa, *s. coll. s.n.* (PDA). COLOMBO DISTRICT: Henaratgoda, Bot. Gard. Jan. 1927, *A. de Silva s.n.* (PDA). MATARA DISTRICT: Deniyaya, Anningkande, *Waas 576* (PDA, US). INDIA: West Himalaya: Kush Kundlai, May 1922, *Inayat s.n.* (AMES). Punjab: Simla & Sivalik, 1885, *Drummond 22667* (K). Madhya Pradesh: Chota Nagpur, May 1955, *Kerr 2591* (K). Orissa: Sambalpur, Apr. 1940, *Mooney 1282* (K). Maharashtra: Bombay, *Law s.n.* (K). Madras: Cuddapah Dist., July 1884, *Gamble 15203* (K); Godavari Dist., Oct. 1920, *V. Narayanswami 558* (K); Herb. *Wight 3026* (K). NEPAL: Khairbhati, May 1902, *Inayat*

23866 (AMES). BURMA: Pegu, *S. Kurz 3242* (K). Moulmein: 1884, *Parish 22* (K).

2. Vanda tessellata (Roxb.) Lodd. ex G. Don in Loud., Hort. Brit. 372. 1832; Alston in Trimen, Handb. Fl. Ceylon 6: 277. 1931.—**Fig. 96.**

Epidendrum tessellatum Roxb., Pl. Corom. 1: 34. 1795.
Cymbidium tessellatum Sw., Nova Acta Regiae Soc. Sci. Upsal. 6: 75. 1799.
Vanda roxburghii R. Br., Bot. Reg. 6: pl. 506. 1820; Trimen, Handb. Fl. Ceylon 4: 192. 1898.
Cymbidium tesselloides Roxb., Fl. Ind. 3: 463. 1832.
Cymbidium alagnata Hamilton ex Wall., Cat. n. 7327. 1832.
Aerides tessellatum Wight in Wall., Cat. n. 7318. 1832.
Vanda unicolor Steud., Nom. Bot. ed. 2. 2: 744. 1841.
Epidendrum tesselloides Steud., ibid. 1: 558. 1841.
Vanda tesselloides Reichb. f. in Walp., Ann. 6: 864. 1861.

Stout epiphyte with non-pseudobulbous stems 30–60 cm long, and simple, branching roots; brown bases of the remnants of old leaves sheathing the internodes in the lower part of the stem. Leaves 15–20 × 1.7–2.4 cm, strapshaped, recurved, distichous, equitant, thick, coriaceous, obtusely keeled, praemorse with two unequal lobes and a short pointed one in between. Flowers large, 5 cm across, grey, greyish-blue, buff, red or yellow in 4- or 10-flowered racemes measuring 15–20 cm in length; peduncle stout, green, with two or more brownish-green, sterile bracts. Floral bracts 2.7 × 6.4 mm, broadly triangular-ovate, clasping the rachis, obtuse or rounded, 1-veined; dorsal sepal 2.4 × 1.4 cm, obovate, faintly trifid, margin waxy and many-veined; lateral sepals 2.5 × 1.8 cm, obovate, obtuse, wavy and many-veined; petals 2.4 × 1.5 cm, obovate, obtuse or subacute, wavy and many-veined; lip funnel-shaped, 3-lobed; lateral lobes erect, 1 cm × 4.5 mm, obliquely oblong, acuminate, acute; midlobe panduriform, 1.7 × 1.25 cm, constricted below the bifid apex; disc swollen with fleshy curved ridges; spur conical, short, 6–7 mm long, blunt and laterally compressed; column 9 mm high, 5 mm broad, fleshy, cylindrical. Anther terminal, 2-loculed, 4.2 × 4 mm; pollinia 2, globular, 1.6 × 1.3 mm, unequally bifid, attached to a large gland by a short and broad conical strap; ovary with pedicel 3.7 mm long. Fruit a clavate, ribbed capsule, 7.5–9 cm long with a short pedicel.

D i s t r. Rather common, on trees in the tropical dry mixed evergreen forests in the dry zone of the island and along the east coast. Jaffna, Batticaloa, Puttalam, Anuradhapura, Polonnaruwa, Hingurakgoda, Maha Illupalama, Wariapola, etc. Also in Bengal, Bihar and Konkan to Kerala in India, Nepal, Burma and China.

E c o l. Flowers January, March–August, December. Some of its many

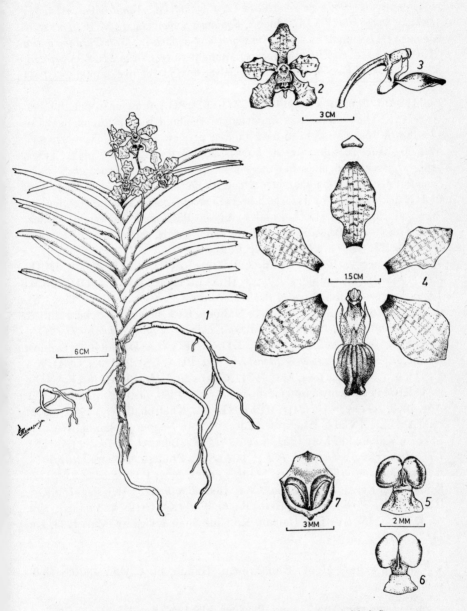

Fig. 96. *Vanda tessellata* (Roxb.) Lodd. ex G. Don. 1, plant with inflorescence. 2, flower from front. 3, lip and column from side. 4, bract, sepals, petals and column spread out from front, lip in natural position. 5, pollinia from behind with strap and gland. 6, pollinia from front. 7, operculum from inside.

host plants are: *Bauhinia tomentosa* L., *Eugenia* sp., *Tamarindus indica* L., *Madhuca longifolia* (L.) J.F. Macbr., *Samanea saman* (Jacq.) Merr., *Thespesia populnea* (L.) Soland. ex Corr., *Strychnos nux-vomica* L., *Manilkara hexandra* (Roxb.) Dubard, etc. Its tolerance of sunlight ranges from 27 to 93 per cent of normal sunlight, of temperature 79–88°F and relative humidity 31–44 per cent.

I l l u s t r. Sims, Bot. Mag. 48: *pl.* 2245. 1821; PDA, drawing from *C.P. 2346*.

N o t e. This species was imported to England by Sir Joseph Banks in 1819 but it does not seem to have thrived at Kew Gardens. There are well over 50 shades of colour in the flower ranging through reds, pinks, greys, yellows, greens and blues but the markings on the calyx and corolla are a constant distinguishing character which is inherited in all hybrids made with it. It is distinguished by its large flowers in erect racemes and the markings on the sepals and petals. Herb. Lindley contains Bateman's and Wight's collections without numbers and localities mounted on the same sheet and labelled *Wallich 7327*. They are Indian collections.

S p e c i m e n s E x a m i n e d. CEYLON: ANURADHAPURA DISTRICT: Maradankadawala, *s. coll. s.n.* (PDA). TRINCOMALEE DISTRICT: Trincomalee—Muthur Road, Jul. 1973, *Nowicke & Jayasuriya 281* (PDA, US). PUTTALAM DISTRICT: Wilpattu National Park, between Kokkara Villu & Kurutu Pandi Villu, June 1969, *Wirawan, Cooray & Balakrishnan 871* (PDA, US); Puttalam, *s. coll. s.n.* (PDA). KURUNEGALA DISTRICT: Doluwa Kande, June 1972, *Maxwell & Jayasuriya 820* (PDA, US). POLONNARUWA DISTRICT: Polonnaruwa, May 1971, *Ripley 433 & 434* (PDA, US). KANDY DISTRICT: Peradeniya, Bot. Gard., cultd., July 1960, *Jayaweera 2180* (PDA), Apr. 1960, *Jayaweera 30* (2) (AMES). NEPAL: Khairbhati, Apr. 1900, *Inayat s.n.* (AMES). INDIA: Madhya Pradesh: Chota Nagpur, Palandu, *A. Coore 148* (K); Kalanuddi, May 1853, *Richie 1425* (K). Bihar: *J.D. Hooker* (AMES), *J.D. Hooker & T. Thomson 169* (K). Andhra Pradesh: Nellore, July 1914, *Ramaswami 1337* (K). Mysore: South Canara, Nov. 1900, *Barber 2531* (K). Kodaikanal Region: Pulney Hills, May 1898, *Bourne 1851* (K). Pen. Ind. Or., Herb. *Wight 2976* (AMES); Herb. *Wight 2977* (K). CHINA: Yunnan: Jan. 1934, *Tsai 56757* (AMES). Hainan: Ka Chik Shan & vicinity, Mar. 1933, *Lau 1415* (AMES).

3. Vanda thwaitesii Hook. f. in Trimen, Handb. Fl. Ceylon 4: 193. 1898. —Fig. 97.

Aerides tessellatum Thw., Enum. Pl. Zeyl. 305. 1861, non Wight.

Epiphyte with a non-pseudobulbous stem 15–30 cm long; lower internodes covered with brown coriaceous sheaths. Leaves 7.5–10 cm long, thick, coriaceous, falcately recurving, bifid at apex and sheaths closely imbricating at the base. Flowers 3.7 cm broad, yellow-green, streaked and spotted with red and

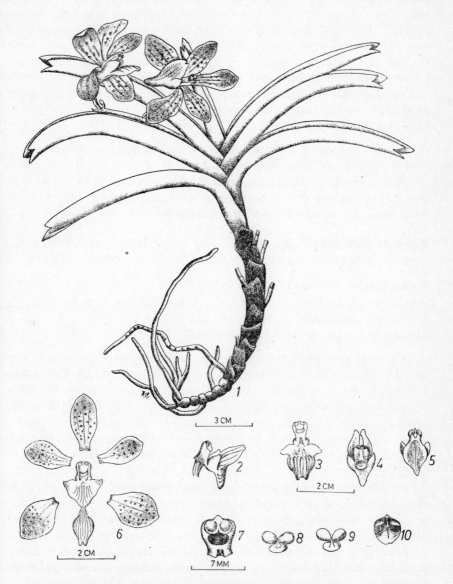

Fig. 97. *Vanda thwaitesii* Hook. f., redrawn from a drawing in PDA. 1, plant with inflorescence. 2, lip and column from side. 3, lip and column spread out from front. 4, lip and column from behind. 5, lip and column from front. 6, sepals, petals, lip and column spread out from front. 7, top of the column from front. 8, pollinia with strap and gland from behind. 9, pollinia from front. 10, operculum from front.

white or pale yellow, in 2- or 3-flowered stout racemes; peduncle green, 10 cm long. Floral bracts very small; dorsal sepal obovate-oblong, very obtuse; lateral sepals larger than dorsal sepal, orbicular-ovate and obtuse; petals as large as the dorsal sepal, obovate-oblong; lip shorter than the sepals, sessile on the base of the column, infundibuliform, 3-lobed; lateral lobes small, erect; midlobe broad, ovate, 2-lobulate; spur shorter than the lobes, straight, acute; column short stout; rostellum truncate. Anther terminal, depressed, 2-loculed; pollinia 2, obovoid, sulcate; strap short, subulate on a large orbicular gland. Ovary with pedicel 2.5 cm long.

D i s t r. Endemic. Very rare, on trees in the Hunnasgiriya district.
I l l u s t r. PDA, 2 drawings from *C.P. 3378.*
N o t e. Hooker's description is based on drawings made by Alwis. It is probably extinct now as no other collector has found it since and there are no specimens in the Peradeniya Herbarium nor in Kew.

4. Vanda spathulata (L.) Spreng., Syst. Veg. 3: 719. 1826; Trimen, Handb. Fl. Ceylon 4: 193. 1898.—**Fig. 98.**

Epidendrum spathulatum L., Sp. Pl. 952. 1753.
Aerides maculatum Buch.-Ham. ex Smith in Rees, Cyclop. 39: n. 9. 1813.
Cymbidium spathulatum Moon, Cat. 60. 1824.
Limodorum spathulatum Willd., Sp. Pl. 4: 125. 1825.

Scandent, non-pseudobulbous epiphyte with long, leafy stems 30–60 cm long and vermiform roots; internodes green, black-spotted, 2.5–3 cm long. Leaves 5.5–8.5 × 1.1–7 cm, keeled, distichous, recurved, coriaceous, emarginate with one-half of the apex shorter than the other, bases sheathing the internodes above, reddish-green, sometimes spotted on the upper surface. Flowers large, 3.7 cm across, yellow in long-peduncled 4- or 5-flowered apical racemes arising from the middle of the stem or the lower nodes; peduncle 30–45 cm long, erect, green with about four acute, papery, sterile bracts. Floral bracts 7.5 × 6 mm, broadly ovate, acute, 5–7-veined; dorsal sepal 1.9 × 1.1 cm, obovate-oblong, obtuse or rounded, 9-veined; lateral sepals 1.8 cm long, 1.15 cm broad, obovate-oblong, obtuse or rounded, 7-veined; petals 1.9 × 1.1 cm, obovate, rounded, 5-veined; lip 1.8 × 1 cm, 3-lobed; lateral lobes small, oblong, erect, laterally notched with a brown streak through the middle; midlobe reniform, ribbed fanwise in the middle, obtuse, contracted, emarginate or notched; spur conical, very short; column 0.7 cm high, 0.45 cm broad, stout, extending to a foot at the base. Anther terminal, 2-loculed, 4 × 3 mm; pollinia 2, oblong, depressed, 1.66 × 1.08 mm, attached to a large bifid gland by a short spathulate strap; ovary with pedicel 3.5–4.8 cm long, shorter in flowers towards the apex. Fruit a fusiform capsule, 3.7–6.5 cm long.

D i s t r. Rather common; Kundasale, Dambulla, Nalanda, Bibile, Wariya-

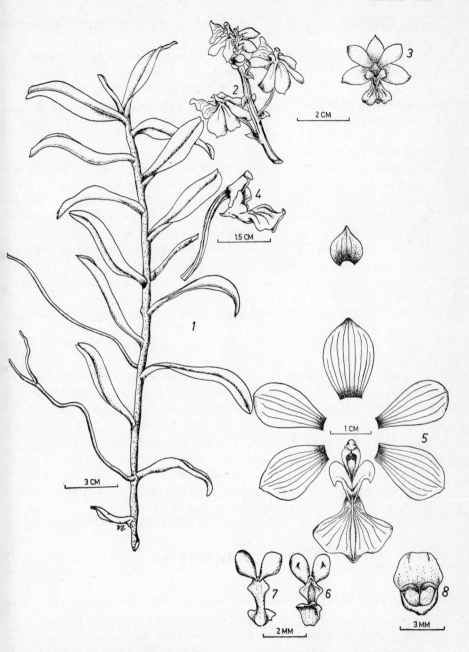

Fig. 98. *Vanda spathulata* (L.) Spreng. 1, terminal portion of a plant. 2, inflorescence. 3, flower from front. 4, lip, column and foot from side. 5, bract, sepals, petals and column spread out from front, lip in natural position. 6, pollinia from behind with strap and gland. 7, pollinia from front. 8, operculum from inside.

pola, Kurunegala, Vavuniya, etc. Also in South India from Malabar to Kerala.

E c o l. Flowers March–September, December. On succulent shrubs or trees in open, rocky patches in an association of its own in the dry zone and mid-country. The following is a list of shrubs and herbs in one such association in which *Euphorbia tortilis* Rottl. ex Wight was dominant, matting the other shrubs together: *Hibiscus micranthus* L. f., *Abrus precatorius* L., *Securinega leucopyrus* (Willd.) Muell. Arg. *Lantana mixta* L., *Barleria prionitis* L., *Dioscorea tomentosa* Heyne ex Roth., *Croton tiglium* L., *Sarcostemma* sp., *Cissus quadrangularis* L., *Tinospora* sp., *Pauzolsia* sp., *Lettsomia* sp., *Cissus* sp., *Coleus barbatus* (Andr.) Benth., *Gynura* sp., *Aerva lanata* (L.) Juss. ex Schult., *Ageratum conyzoides* L., *Cassia occidentalis* Linn., *Sansevieria zeylanica* (L.) Willd., *Commelina diffusa* Burm. f., *Vanilla walkerae* Wight, *Ochna* sp., *Vicoa indica* (L.) DC., etc. Other orchids found in this association are *Eulophia epidendraea* C.E.C. Fisher, *Vanda tessellata* (Roxb.) Lod. ex G. Don. and *Vanilla walkerae* Wight, growing in direct sunlight.

I l l u s t r. Wight, Ic. Pl. Ind. Or. 3: pl. 915. 1844–45; PDA, drawing from *Thwaites C.P. 2345*.

N o t e. This is the only indigenous hexaploid *Vanda* known in Ceylon. Herb. Lindley contains a collection from Herb. Wight without number. The plant is recognised by its scandent habit and yellow flowers on erect racemes.

S p e c i m e n s E x a m i n e d. CEYLON: KURUNEGALA DISTRICT: Wariyapola, Apr. 1953, *Senaratne 10090* (PDA). KANDY DISTRICT: Peradeniya, Bot. Gard., cultd., Aug. 1960, *Jayaweera 2060* (PDA), Nov. 1928, *Senaratne 138* (PDA). AMPARAI DISTRICT: Bibile, Oct. 1959, *Jayaweera 30 (4)* (AMES). HAMBANTOTA DISTRICT: Ruhuna National Park, Andunoruwa Wewa, Nov. 1969, *Cooray 69111615* (PDA, US). INDIA: Andhra Pradesh: Nellore, Oct. 1921, *Fischer 4684* (K). Madras: Cudappah Distr., Nov. 1885, *Gamble 17101* (K); Salem, Jun. 1932, *Mrs. Yeshode 179* (AMES); Kodaikanal Region: 1923, *Anglade s.n.* (AMES); Pen. Ind. Or., Herb. *Wight 2978* (K, AMES, PDA), Herb. *Wight 2076* (K), Herb. *Wight* (K).

31. DIPLOCENTRUM

Lindl., Bot. Reg. 18: sub. t. 1522. 1832.

Epiphytes; stems very short, non-pseudobulbous; roots long, flattened and stout; leaves distichous, narrow, fleshy, subterete or complicate; flowers small, subspicate in short-peduncled panicles; sepals spreading and incurved, lateral sepals larger; petals like the dorsal sepal; lip larger than sepals, tongue-shaped, jointed on to the base of the column, entire, shortly 2-spurred at base; spurs short, collateral; column very short, clavate, 2-auricled, truncate; foot absent; anther flat, 2-chambered, chambers very small at the broad end; pollinia 2, small, cleft, waxy; strap very large and broad with a broad gland.

Two or three species in India and Ceylon.

Diplocentrum recurvum Lindl., Bot. Reg. 18: sub. t. 1522. 1832; Trimen, Handb. Fl. Ceylon 4: 194. 1898.—**Fig. 99.**

Cymbidium aloefolium Heyne ex Wall., Cat. sub. n. 7331. 1832.
Diplocentrum longifolium Wight, Ic. Pl. Ind. Or. 5 (1): 10, pl. 1681. 1851.

Epiphyte with a short, stout, non-pseudobulbous, leafy stem 5–15 cm long, internodes short; roots very long and flattened. Leaves 10–15 × 0.6–0.8 cm, linear, recurved, keeled, coriaceous, unequally and obtusely bifid at the apex. Flowers pink, 4–6 mm broad, crowded towards the ends of branches, in shortly peduncled, branched, long-spreading, decurved, many-flowered panicles; peduncle together with the panicle 12.5–20 cm long. Floral bracts minute, acute, deciduous; dorsal sepal oblong, obtuse; lateral sepals larger, falcately and broadly oblong, 3-veined; petals similar to the dorsal sepal, 1-veined, lip ovate-oblong, longer than petals, entire, 2-spurred, lateral lobes obscure; disc fleshy with a median ridge; spurs collateral, short, conical, acute, incurved; column very stout, clavate; auricles incurved; rostellum inconspicuous; foot absent. Anther terminal, flat, 2-loculed; loculi very small; pollinia 2, small; strap of pollinia large, cuneiform, narrowed from the broad base upwards to the insertion of the pollinia. Fruit a clavate, strongly ribbed capsule, 1.2 cm long.

D i s t r. Very rare. Collected by Gardner somewhere in the Central Province with no locality given. It has not been collected since from Ceylon. Also in Nilgiri Hills and Kerala in India.

E c o l. Flowers May–July.

N o t e. This species is distinguished by the *Vanda*-like appearance of the plant, many-flowered panicles and the 2-spurred lip.

S p e c i m e n s   E x a m i n e d. CEYLON: LOCALITY UNKNOWN: *s. coll. C.P. 3192* (PDA). INDIA: Andhra Pradesh: Cuddapah Dist., Honlegkonda, *Gamble 15033* (K), Jul. 1894, *Gamble 15111* (K); Herb. *Rottler s.n.* (K). Madras: Coimbatore, Herb. *Wight* (K), May 1905. *Fischer 20* (K); Pen. Ind. Or. Herb. *Wight 2979* (K, AMES), *Wallich 733* (K).

32. ACAMPE

Lindl., Fol. Orch. 4: 95. 1853.

Epiphytes; stems thick, stout, covered with leaf sheaths; roots long, stout, vermiform; leaves distichous, lorate or ligulate, coriaceous, 2-lobed; panicle stoutly peduncled, leaf-opposed or supra-axillary, branches short or long;

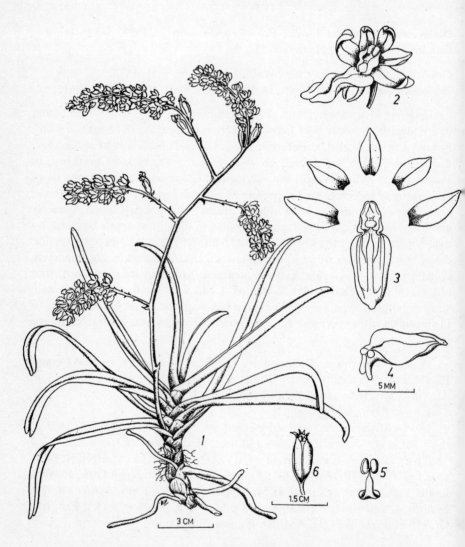

Fig. 99. *Diplocentrum recurvum* Lindl., redrawn from a drawing in PDA. 1, plant with inflorescence. 2, flower from front, three quarters view. 3, sepals, petals, lip and column spread out from front. 4, lip from side showing the two spurs. 5, pollinia with strap and gland. 6, fruit.

peduncle with cupular sheaths; flowers comparatively large; sepals and petals subequal or petals smaller, thick, barred; lip spurred or saccate, side lobes small, midlobe ovate, fleshy; column short, stout; foot absent; pollinia 2, entire or unequally bipartite, waxy; strap narrow, gland small.

About 20 species distributed in tropical Africa, India and Ceylon, extending through Malaya, Burma to South China and the Philippine Islands.

KEY TO THE SPECIES

1 Lip spurred, panicles slender, leaf-opposed; midlobe of lip with a fleshy tooth on each
  side of the base...**1. A. ochracea**
1 Lip saccate, panicles axillary; midlobe of lip entire
  2 Leaves 15–30 cm long...**2. A. rigida**
  2 Leaves 10–17 cm long..**3. A. praemorsa**

1. Acampe ochracea (Lindl.) Hochr., Bull. New York Bot. Gard. 6: 270. 1910.
—Fig. 100.

Saccolabium ochraceum Lindl., Bot. Reg. 28: Misc. 2. 1842; Trimen, Handb.
  Fl. Ceylon 4: 197. 1898.
Acampe dentata Lindl., Fol. Orch. 4: 95. 1853.
Saccolabium lineolatum Thw., Enum. Pl. Zeyl. 304. 1861.

Epiphyte with simple, non-pseudobulbous stems 30–76 cm long; internodes 2.4–3 cm long; roots vermiform, branched. Leaves 14.5–19.3 × 1.8–2.3 cm, lorate, distichous, keeled, thickly coriaceous, with 2 rounded lobes at the apex, articulating on short petiolar sheaths ensheathing internodes above. Flowers yellow with red transverse striae across the perianth segments and white lip, 1 cm across, in racemose panicles arising from the axils of petiolar sheaths and breaking through them; panicles as long as or longer than leaves; branches spiciform, 2–5.5 cm long, green and many-flowered. Floral bracts 1.2 × 2.6 mm, broadly ovate, mucronate, villous inside; dorsal sepal 5.6–6 × 2.8–3 mm, obovate-oblong or lanceolate-oblong, obtuse or emarginate, 3-veined; lateral sepals 5.2 × 2.1 mm, of the same shape as the dorsal sepal, obtuse and 3-veined; petals 5.2 × 1.8–2 mm, lanceolate-oblong, obtuse or rounded and 3-veined; lip 4.4 × 3.8 mm, saccate and hairy to the base inside; lateral lobes of lip short, recurved; midlobe ovate, acute, or rounded, undulate; spur 3.6 mm long, stout and rounded; column 1.6 mm high, 1.5 mm broad, with two straight arms at the apex laterally. Anther terminal, 2-loculed, 1.2 mm long and as broad; pollinia 2, globose, 0.56 × 0.46 mm, unequally bipartite, attached by a long, linear strap to a small gland. Ovary with pedicel 5.6 mm long. Fruit a fusiform, erect, short-pedicelled capsule 4.5 × 0.45 cm.

D i s t r. Rather rare; on trees by streams in the tropical wet evergreen forests 305–915 m alt. Ratnapura, Hunnasgiriya, Hewaheta, Negombo, etc.

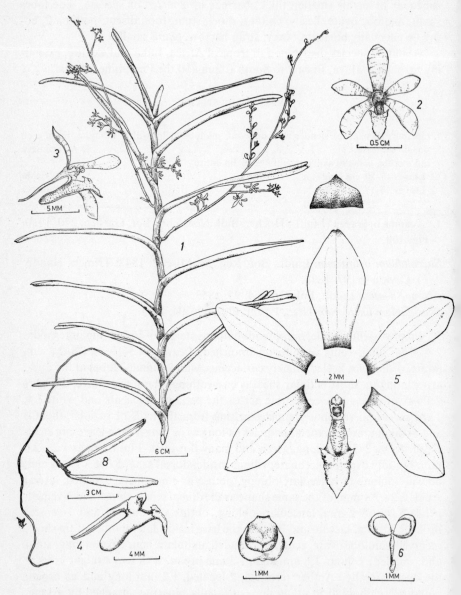

Fig. 100. *Acampe ochracea* (Lindl.) Hochr. 1, plant with inflorescence. 2, flower from front. 3, longitudinal section of flower through spur. 4, lip, column and spur from side. 5, bract, sepals, petals, lip and column spread out from front. 6, pollinia with strap and gland from behind. 7, operculum from inside. 8, fruits.

Also in the Eastern Himalayas, Sikkim, Khasia Hills, Assam, Bhutan, Burma, and Indo-China.

E c o l. Flowers January, September, October, December.

I l l u s t r. King & Pantling, Ann. R. Bot. Gard. (Calcutta) 8: pl. 291. 1898; PDA, drawing from *C.P. 2741.*

N o t e. Herb. Lindley contains Loddiges' collection from Ceylon, specimens sent to Loddiges nursery by Sir Wilmot Horton, the Governor of Ceylon at that time. The long slender panicle and the four teeth at the base of the lip are features peculiar to this species whose flower is about the size of *Acampe papillosa* Lindl.

S p e c i m e n s E x a m i n e d. CEYLON: ANURADHAPURA DISTRICT: Ritigala, Sept. 1975, *Jayasuriya, Premadasa & Foster 2280* (PDA, US). RATNAPURA DISTRICT: Gilimale, Jan. 1960, *Jayaweera 2054* (PDA); Ratnapura, Jan. 1960, *Jayaweera 32 (6)* (AMES). INDIA: Sikkim, Valley of Teesta, Aug. 1897, *Pantling 291* (AMES). COCHIN CHINA: 1890, *Pierre 653* (AMES); *Pierre 108* (AMES).

2. Acampe rigida (Buch.-Ham. ex J.E. Smith) P.F. Hunt, Kew Bull. 24 (1): 98. 1970.—**Fig. 101.**

Acampe longifolia Lindl., Fol. Orch. 95. 1853.
Vanda multiflora Lindl., Collect. Bot. pl. 38. 1821.
Vanda longifolia Lindl. in Wall., Cat. n. 7322. 1832.
Cymbidium praemorsum Buch.-Ham. ex Wall., Cat. n. 7325. 1832.
Acampe multiflora Lindl., Fol. Orch. 1: 95. 1853.
Saccolabium longifolium Hook. f., Fl. Br. Ind. 6: 62. 1890; Trimen, Handb.
   Fl. Ceylon 4: 198. 1898.

Epiphyte with very stout, non-pseudobulbous stems 60–90 cm long. Leaves 15–30 × 3.7 cm, lorate, thickly coriaceous, shortly 2-lobed. Flowers yellow, barred with red, 1.8 cm broad, in many-flowered stoutly peduncled panicles; peduncle with racemes 15–20 cm long, distantly branched, base with cupular sheaths, branches short. Floral bracts small, annular, rounded; sepals broadly oblong, obtuse; petals small, obovate-oblong; lip saccate, lateral lobes short, midlobe ovate, obtuse, channelled in the middle, sac short, rounded with a vertical hairy plate projecting in the hollow opposite the column; column short, stout; foot absent. Anther terminal, 2-loculed; pollinia 2, globose deeply bipartite.

D i s t r. Rare on trees in the submontane or mid-country tropical wet evergreen forests 305–915 m alt. Ambagamuwa, Kitulgala, etc. Also in tropical Sikkim Himalayas, Upper Assam, Burma, China and the Philippine Islands.

E c o l. Flowers September, October.

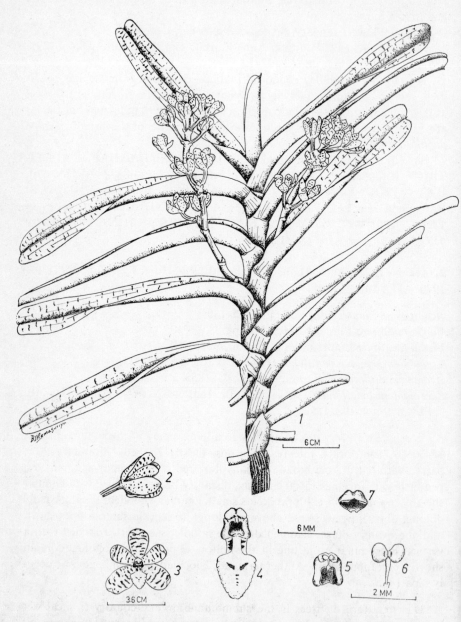

Fig. 101. *Acampe rigida* P.F. Hunt, redrawn from a drawing in Herb. PDA.
1, plant with inflorescences. 2, flower from side. 3, flower from front. 4, lip and
column from front. 5, column from front with operculum removed. 6, pollinia
with strap and gland. 7, operculum from side.

I l l u s t r. King & Pantling, Ann. R. Bot. Gard. Calcutta 8: Pl. 292. 1898; PDA, drawing.

N o t e. Herb. Lindley contains *Wallich 7322* from Burma and *Champion 528* from Hong Kong. This species is allied to *Acampe wightiana* from which it differs in its more robust growth and by the termination of its leaves which are rounded at the apex with a little point, not abruptly ternate. The flowers too are produced in greater abundance. The dorsal, erect, fleshy plate inside the cavity of the lip among numerous, yellow hairs recalls *Cleisostoma*.

S p e c i m e n s   E x a m i n e d. CEYLON: LOCALITY UNKNOWN: *s. coll. C.P. 3492* (PDA). INDIA: Sikkim Himalaya: May 1892, *Pantling 250* (K). Pen. Ind. Or., Herb. *Wight s.n.* (K), *Wallich 1849* (K). BURMA: Myit-kyina, 1926, *Swinhoe 66* (K). Tavoy: *Wallich 7322* (K). CHINA: Kwangtung: Ng-Tung Shan, *Tsui 256* (AMES). Kwansi: Sui-huk, *Tsang 21915* (AMES). Hainan: Pak Shik Ling & vicinity, *Lei 459* (AMES), *Lei 946* (AMES), *Lau 27665* (AMES). HONG KONG: *Champion 528* (K); *Taam 1986* (AMES). PHILIPPINE ISLANDS: *Loher, s.n.* (AMES).

3. Acampe praemorsa (Roxb.) Blatter & McCann, J. Bombay Nat. Hist. Soc. 35: 1495. 1932.—**Fig. 102.**

Acampe wightiana (Wight) Lindl., Fol. Orch. 2: 95. 1853.
Epidendrum praemorsum Roxb., Pl. Corom. 34. 1795.
Vanda wightiana Lindl. ex Wight, Ic. Pl. Ind. Or. 5 (1): 9. pl. 1670. 1851.
Vanda fasciata Gard. ex Lindl., Fol. Orch. 2: 95. 1853.
Saccolabium papillosum Dalzell & Gibson, Bombay Fl. 264. 1861.
Saccolabium wightianum Hook. f., Fl. Br. Ind. 6: 62. 1890; Trimen, Handb.
    Fl. Ceylon 4: 199. 1898.

Epiphyte with a simple, non-pseudobulbous stem; stem 60 cm long, thick, ensheathed in the petiolar leaf-bases, bearing long, stout roots. Leaves 16–17 × 2.5–2.7 cm, lorate, thickly coriaceous, unequally bilobed at the apex, lobes rounded. Flowers yellow, barred with red, 1.2 cm across, in stout, compact, spiciform racemes arising opposite leaves; peduncle short, stout, with sterile, scaly, cupular bracts. Floral bracts 2 × 4.4 mm, triangular, fleshy, rounded and spotted pink; sepals and petals thick, fleshy, barred pink or red on the inside and spotted outside; dorsal sepal 10 × 5 mm, oblong, obtuse; lateral sepals 9 mm long, 5 mm broad, obovate-oblong, obtuse; lip fleshy, saccate, 8 × 4 mm, lateral lobes of lip small, blunt; midlobe thick, ovate, white, barred light pink, obtuse and irregularly dentate; column short, thick. Anther terminal, 2-loculed, 1.5 × 2.3 mm; pollinia 2, globose, unequally bipartite; the larger section 0.7 × 0.8 mm, concave, and the smaller section 0.6 × 0.4 mm, wedged into the concavity; pollinia attached by short caudicles to a slender strap and a small gland. Ovary with pedicel 7–9 mm long. Fruit a fusiform, subsessile capsule, 4.6 × 0.9–1 cm.

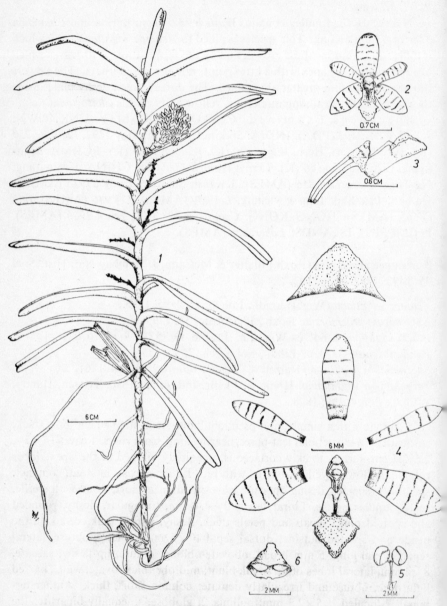

Fig. 102. *Acampe praemorsa* (Roxb.) Blatter & McCann. 1, plant with inflorescence and fruits. 2, flower from front. 3, lip and column from side. 4, bract, sepals, petals, lip and column spread out from front. 5, pollinia with strap and gland from behind. 6, operculum from side.

Distr. Rare; on branches of trees in the tropical wet evergreen forests and in the tropical savannah up to 915 m alt. Ratnapura, Bibile, Jaffna, Hantane, etc. Also in the Eastern Ghats from Konkan southwards and in Sikkim in India.

Ecol. Flowers September, November.

Illustr. PDA, 2 drawings from *C.P. 2342*.

Note. Herb. Lindley contains the holotype from Ceylon. Wight's drawing shows two tubulate horns as springing from the base of the lip. Probably they are tubercles as found in *Acampe congesta* Lindl.

Specimens Examined. CEYLON: MANNAR DISTRICT: Mannar, *Davidse & Sumithraarachchi 9178* (PDA, US). KURUNEGALA DISTRICT: Kurunegala, Dec. 1959, *Jayaweera 2176* (PDA). MONERAGALA DISTRICT: Bibile, Oct. 1959, *Jayaweera 2052* (PDA), *Jayaweera 32 (9)* (AMES). LOCALITY UNKNOWN: *Gardner 172* (K, holotype), *Thwaites C.P. 2342* (PDA). INDIA: Sikkim: Dec. 1898, *Pantling 243* (AMES). Kerala: Travancore, Jul. 1895, *Bourdillon 672* (K). Madras: Godavari Dist., Oct. 1910, *Narayanswami 514* (K). Pen. Ind. Or., Herb. *Wight 3021* (AMES).

33. POMATOCALPA

Breda, Gen. et Sp. Orch. et Asclep. Fasc. 3: t. 15. 1829.

Epiphytes with short or long stems, sometimes climbing; leaves oblong or narrow; inflorescence short or long, erect or decurved, often branched, usually densely many-flowered; flowers small, with lip at the top or pointing towards the apex of the inflorescence; sepals and petals almost equal, free or spreading; lip more or less bucket-shaped, 3-lobed, with a rounded saccate spur; lateral lobes small, broadly triangular; midlobe fleshy, straight or curved downwards, round or ovate-triangular; spur rounded, widening from the opening, the front wall with a fleshy thickening, back wall with an erect tongue reaching the mouth of the spur, often forked at the tip, sides joined to the wall of the spur. Column short, footless, to which the fleshy lip is immovably attached; rostellum bifid or hammer-shaped; anther shortly beaked; pollinia 2, each split into unequal halves on a slender stipe with a small disc.

About 30 species, Burma through Malaysia to the Pacific Islands.

KEY TO THE SPECIES

1 Flowers in axillary racemes, orange-yellow, spotted red with cream-yellow lip . . . .
. . . . **1. P. maculosum**
1 Flowers in paniculately branched spikes, lemon-yellow with crimson centres on sepals and petals . . . . **2. P. decipiens**

1. Pomatocalpa maculosum (Lindl.) J.J. Smith, Natuurw. Tijdschr. Ned. Indie 72: 35. 1912.—**Fig. 103.**

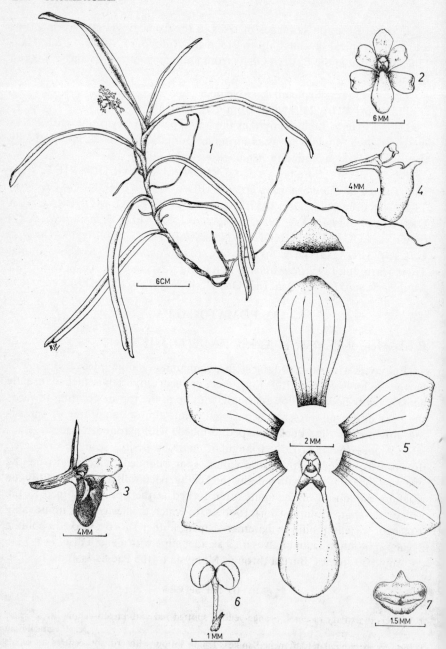

Fig. 103. *Pomatocalpa maculosum* (Lindl.) J.J. Smith. 1, plant with inflorescence. 2, flower from front. 3, longitudinal section of flower, through spur. 4, subcylindrical lip, spur and column from side. 5, bract, sepals, petals, lip, spur and column from front. 6, pollinia with strap and gland. 7, operculum from side.

Cleisostoma maculosum Lindl., Gen. et Sp. Orch. 227. 1833, non Blume ex Teysm. & Binn., Cat. Plant. Buitenz. 49, 1854, non Thw., Enum. Pl. Zeyl. 304. 1861; Trimen, Handb. Fl. Ceylon 4: 200. 1898.

Cleisostoma galeata Thw., ibid. 305.

Saccolabium galeatum Gardner ex Thw., ibid.

Saccolabium maculosum Alston in Trimen, Handb. Fl. Ceylon 6: 278. 1931.

Epiphyte with simple, non-pseudobulbous stems 30–45 cm long and very long roots; internodes 1.8–2.3 cm long. Leaves 15–18 × 1.5–2.1 cm, lorate, flat, coriaceous, unequally 2-lobed at the apex and rounded; bases articulating with petiolar sheaths, ensheathing the internodes above. Flowers 8.2 mm broad, orange-yellow, spotted red with a cream-yellow lip, in simple spicate, axillary racemes, emerging through the petiolar leaf sheaths; peduncle stout, green, 4.5–7.5 cm long with 4–6 sterile bracts, the lower ones annular. Floral bracts 1.5 × 2.8 mm, broadly triangular-ovate, acute, crenulate; sepals and petals thick, obovate-spathulate, obtuse and incurved; dorsal sepal 5.6 × 3 mm, 5-veined; lateral sepals 5.3 × 2.8 mm, 5-veined; petals 4.6 × 2.4 mm, 3-veined; lip a subcylindric, saccate, rounded spur, 5.2 × 2.8 mm; lateral lobes truncate; midlobe ovate, acute, retuse, imperfectly papillose within; column short, stout, 1.8 mm long, 2 mm broad. Anther terminal, 2-loculed, 1.6 mm long and as broad; pollinia 2, globose, waxy, attached by a linear strap to a small, narrow, bifid gland; each pollinium 0.6 × 0.46 mm and bipartite. Ovary with pedicel 3.8 mm long. Fruit a narrowly clavate capsule, 3.7 cm long.

D i s t r. Endemic. Rather rare, on trees by streams in the tropical wet evergreen forests up to 762 m alt. Ratnapura, Ambagamuwa, Ritigala, Hantane, Avissawella, etc.

E c o l. Flowers January–March. Some of its many host plants are *Ficus parasitica* Koen., *Artocarpus heterophyllus* Lam. and *Samanea saman* (Jacq.) Merr.

I l l u s t r. PDA, drawing from *C.P. 2343*.

N o t e. This species is distinguished as a large epiphyte with thick orange-yellow flowers and cream-yellow lip in short axillary racemes, absence of the lateral lobes of the lip and the mouth of the spur closed with calli. Herb. Lindley contains the type specimen and also *Gardner 2340* cited as type number under *Saccolabium galeatum* Gard. ex Thw.

S p e c i m e n s E x a m i n e d. ANURADHAPURA DISTRICT: Ritigala, Mar. 1905, *Willis s.n.* (PDA). RATNAPURA DISTRICT: Gilimale, Feb. 1962, *Jayaweera 2186* (PDA), Mar. 1960, *Jayaweera 34 (1)* (AMES). LOCALITY UNKNOWN: 1929, *Macrae 39* (K, holotype); *Walker s.n.* (K); *Gardner 2340* (K); *s. coll. C.P. 2343* (PDA).

2. Pomatocalpa decipiens (Lindl.) J.J. Smith, Natuurw. Tijdschr. Ned. Indie 72: 33. 1912.—**Fig. 104.**

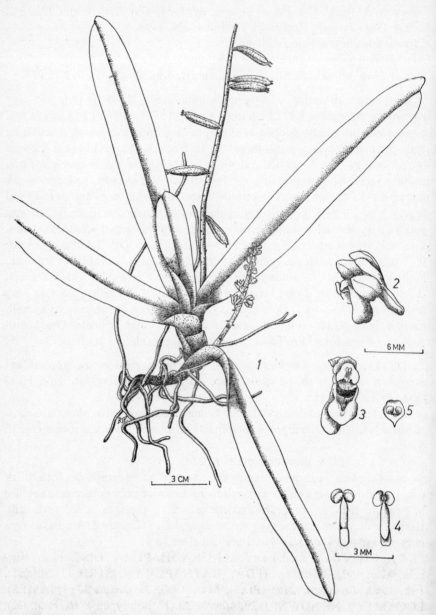

Fig. 104. *Pomatocalpa decipiens* (Lindl.) J.J. Smith, redrawn from a drawing in
PDA. 1, plant with inflorescence and fruits. 2, flower from side. 3, flower from front.
4, pollinia with strap and gland from front and behind. 5, operculum from front.

Cleisostoma decipiens Lindl., Bot. Reg. 30: Misc. 11. 1844; Trimen, Handb. Fl. Ceylon 4: 201. 1898.
Cleisostoma maculosa Thw., Enum. Pl. Zeyl. 304. 1861, non Lindl.
Cleisostoma thwaitesianum Trimen, J. Bot. 23: 244. 1885.
Saccolabium decipiens Alston in Trimen, Handb. Fl. Ceylon 6: 278. 1931.

Epiphyte with very short, stout stems and copiously tortuous roots. Leaves 12.5–25 × 1.2–2.5 cm, lorate, flat, unequally obtusely 2-lobed, speckled beneath with purple, sheaths very short. Flowers 4 mm broad, lemon-yellow with crimson centres on sepals and petals, in short-peduncled, paniculately branched spikes 12.5–15 cm long, branches flowering along their entire length. Floral bracts minute, subulate; sepals oblong, subacute; petals linear-oblong; lip a broad subcylindric sac, rounded at the tip, lateral lobes truncate, midlobe orbicular, dorsal callus broad, erect; column very short. Anther terminal, 2-loculed; pollinia 2, globose; strap linear, attached to an oblong gland. Fruit a sessile linear-oblong capsule, 1.8 cm long, spreading.

D i s t r. Endemic. Rather rare, on trees in the tropical wet evergreen forests in the low-country extending to the mid-country forests. Heneratgoda, Hunnasgiriya, Peradeniya, etc.

E c o l. Flowers January–March.

I l l u s t r. PDA, drawing from *C.P. 3193*.

N o t e. This species is very similar to *Saccolabium micranthum*, the one a genuine *Saccolabium* and the other a true *Cleisostoma*. In *S. micranthum* the tooth proceeds from the base of the blade of the labellum whereas in *C. decipiens* it springs from the back of the spur just below the column. Herb. Lindley contains a single specimen from Ceylon collected by one Mr. Fielding.

S p e c i m e n s E x a m i n e d. ANURADHAPURA DISTRICT: Ritigala, Jan. 1973. *Jayasuriya 1033* (PDA, US). COLOMBO DISTRICT: Heneratgoda, Feb. 1885, *s. coll. s.n.* (PDA). KANDY DISTRICT: Peradeniya, Bot. Gdn., Mar. 1893, *s. coll. s.n.* (K), *s. coll. 3193* (PDA). BADULLA DISTRICT: Talpitigala, Uma Oya, Sept. 1971, *Balakrishnan & Jayasuriya 838* (PDA, US).

34. TRICHOGLOTTIS

Blume, Bijdr. 6: t. 3. 1825.

Scandent epiphytes with long stems; leaves narrow, oblong or elliptic; inflorescence axillary, either fasciculate with one or several flowers in a cluster or loosely racemose or paniculate with many flowers, much exceeding the leaves; flowers small to large, wide-opening; sepals and petals usually yellowish with red-brown markings; lateral sepals joined at the base to the very short column-foot; lip firmly adnate to the base of the column, saccate or spurred, 3-lobed, the lateral lobes more or less fused with the basal sides of the column, midlobe simple or 3-lobed; from the dorsal wall of the spur or sac, a narrow ligulate or tongue-shaped, movable, often hairy lamella projects towards the midlobe so as to completely cover the entrance to the nectariferous cavity; column short with a foot-like extension to which the lip is firmly adnate; clinandrium shallow, often provided in front on both sides with hairy stelidia of various lengths; pollinia 2, each divided in equal halves on a distinct stipe, rostellum often vertically elongated below the tip of the anther.

About 16 species, throughout Malaysia and the Philippine Islands.

Trichoglottis tenera (Lindl.) Reichb. f., Gard. Chron. 699. 1872.—**Fig. 105.**

Cleisostoma tenerum (Lindl.) Hook. f., Fl. Br. Ind. 6: 73. 1890; Trimen, Handb. Fl. Ceylon 4: 201. 1898.
Oeceoclades tenera Lindl., Gen. et Sp. Orch. 236. 1833.
Oeonia alata A. Rich., Ann. Sci. Nat. Bot. 11. 15: 67. pl. 7. 1841.
Saccolabium tenerum Trimen, Cat. 89. 1885.

Scandent epiphyte with thin, non-pseudobulbous stems 30–60 cm long, green, speckled red; internodes 1–2 cm long, roots slender and flexuous. Leaves alternate, distichous, $1.7–4.5 \times 0.7–1.4$ cm, oblong or linear-oblong, recurved, apex notched, midrib produced beyond into a pointed spine, bases petiolar, sheathing the internodes above. Flowers small, 1–1.6 cm across when spread out, greenish-yellow with longitudinal red lines along the perianth segments and a white lip, in two flowered racemes, emerging through leaf-sheaths; peduncle stout, 0.5–1 cm long. Floral bracts 2 mm long, 2.6 mm broad, broadly ovate, speckled pink inside, obtuse and 1-veined; dorsal sepals 12×4 mm, oblanceolate, obtuse, 3-veined; lateral sepals 8.8×2.8 mm, obliquely oblanceolate, decurved, 3-veined; petals 8.8×3.4 mm, oblanceolate, obtuse, 3-veined; lip 6.8 mm long, 3-lobed; lateral lobes erect, crenulate, ovate, truncate or acute, 2-veined; midlobe 5.2 mm broad, obtusely trilobulate, ovate, fleshy, crenulate and 3-veined; spur 2.2×1.2 mm, blunt, septate vertically, hairy inside with a bifid callus at the throat running down into the cavity; column 3 mm high, 2.2 mm broad, extending into a short, inconspicuous foot; rostellum bifid. Anther terminal, 2-loculed, 1.8×1.94 mm; pollinia 2, globose, 0.8×0.66 mm, bifid, attached by a long, thin strap to a small gland. Ovary with pedicel 5–7 mm long. Fruit an erect, oblong, fusiform or subpyriform, strongly ribbed capsule, 2.5×0.9 cm.

D i s t r. Rather common, on trees in the submontane or mid-country tropical wet evergreen forests up to 1829 m alt. Nuwara Eliya, Laggala, Rangala, Hunnasgiriya, Maturata, Namunukula, etc. Also in the Nilgiri Hills in India.

E c o l. Flowers February, March, April. Some of its host plants are

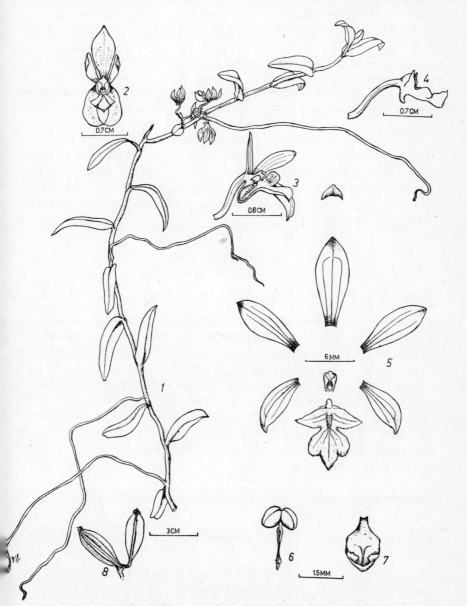

Fig. 105. *Trichoglottis tenera* (Lindl.) Reichb. f. 1, plant with inflorescences. 2, flower from front. 3, longitudinal section of the flower through spur. 4, lip and spur from side, column hidden between lateral lobes of lip. 5, bract, sepals, petals, lip and column spread out from front. 6, pollinia with strap and gland. 7, operculum from inside. 8, fruits.

Syzygium sp., *Rauvolfia densiflora* (Wall.) Hook. f., *Apodytes benthamiana* Wight, *Glochidion* sp., etc.

I l l u s t r. Wight, Ic. Pl. Ind. Or. 5: pl. 1683. 1852; PDA, 3 drawings from *C.P. 2983*.

N o t e. The species is distinguished as a large thin-stemmed epiphyte with small greenish-yellow flowers in 2-flowered racemes emerging through the leaf sheaths, white lip and the mouth of the spur closed with calli. Herb. Lindley contains the type collection. I have not seen specimens from Nilgiri Hills.

S p e c i m e n s E x a m i n e d. NUWARA ELIYA DISTRICT: Nuwara Eliya, Aug. 1962, *Jayaweera 2192* (PDA); Westward Ho, Feb. 1960, *Jayaweera 34 (2)* (AMES); Hakgala, Mar. 1889, *W. Nock s.n.* (PDA). BADULLA DISTRICT: Namunukula, Mar. 1907, *J.M. Silva s.n.* (PDA). LOCALITY UNKNOWN: 1829, *Macrae 66* (K, holotype); *Thwaites C.P. 2983* (AMES, PDA); *Walker 118* (PDA).

35. ANGRAECUM

Bory, Voy. 1: 359. t. 19. 1804.

Epiphytes; stems short or long, not pseudobulbous; leaves distichous, coriaceous or fleshy, articulated to persistent sheaths; inflorescence racemose, axillary; sepals and petals subequal, similar, free, spreading; lip affixed to the base of the column and continuous with it, produced at the base into a long spur; column very short, without wings and footless; anther convex, terminal, incumbent; pollinia 2, waxy, globose, grooved; stipes single, clavate or slender or absent, gland simple, scaly; fruit capsule oblong or fusiform, not beaked.

About 490 species widely distributed in Continental Africa, Madagascar and the islands of the Indian Ocean and the Philippine Islands. Also in Brazil and the West Indies.

Angraecum zeylanicum Lindl., J. Linn. Soc. Bot. 3: 40. 1859; Thw., Enum. Pl. Zeyl. 306. 1861.—**Fig. 106**.

Mystacidium zeylanicum (Lindl.) Trimen, Cat. 90. 1885; Handb. Fl. Ceylon 4: 202. 1898.

Epiphyte with simple, non-pseudobulbous stems 12–15 cm long, and long, tufted, vermiform, branched roots. Leaves few, distichous, 11–24 × 1.3–2.4 cm, linear-oblong, flat, many-veined, midrib conspicuous below, unequally two lobed at apex and one lobe shorter. Flowers yellowish-green, 1 cm broad, in slender 4- or 5-flowered, lax racemes measuring 3.5–7.5 cm in length; peduncle 5 cm long with 4 or 5 dark brown, sterile bracts. Floral bracts minute, membranous, truncate, dark brown when old; dorsal sepal 5.2 × 2.4 mm,

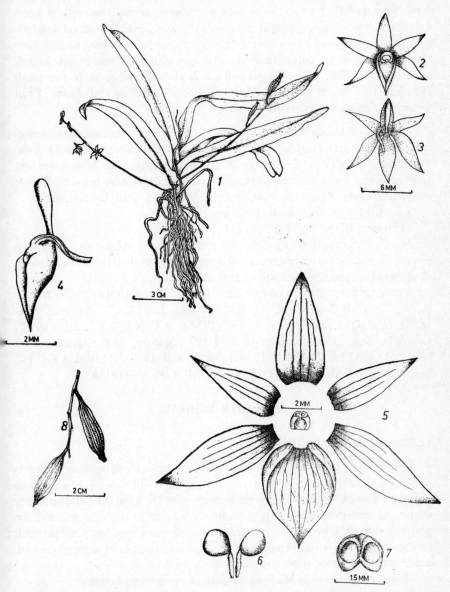

Fig. 106. *Angraecum zeylanicum* Lindl. 1, plant with inflorescence and fruits. 2, flower from front. 3, flower from behind. 4, lip, column and spur from side, three quarters view. 5, sepals, petals and lip spread out from front, column separated from lip from inside. 6, pollinia with straps. 7, operculum from inside. 8, fruits.

ovate-lanceolate, acute, 3-veined; lateral sepals 6 × 2 mm, lanceolate, acute, 5-veined; petals 4.8 × 1.8 mm, lanceolate, acuminate, acute, 3-veined; lip 4.6 × 4.8 mm, deltoid-ovate, cymbiform, acuminate-acute, entire, 9-veined and reticulate; base produced into a suberect, clavate spur 5.2 mm long standing behind the dorsal sepal; column globular, 1.1 mm high and 1 mm broad. Anther terminal, 2-loculed, 1.1 × 1.4 mm; pollinia 2, globular, attached to two small glands by two slender straps. Ovary with pedicel 7 mm long and twisted. Fruit a narrowly ellipsoid, pedicelled capsule, 1.5 cm long.

D i s t r. Endemic. Rare, on trunks of trees and large shrubs in the tropical wet evergreen forests up to 305 m alt. Ratnapura (Gilimale, Kuruwita Kande, Foot of Adam's Peak and Karawita Kande), epiphyte on *Memecylon* sp., *Gaertnera* sp., *Areca catechu* L. etc., Narawela, near Galle, between Matale and Kurunegala, Reigam Korale, Neluwa, Pelawatta near Hewesse, etc.

E c o l. Flowers September, October.

I l l u s t r. PDA, drawing from *C.P. 3693*.

N o t e. According to Lindley this species is very similar to *Angraecum caulescens* but the leaves are broad with one of the terminal lobes much longer than the other and the spur not inflated at the point.

S p e c i m e n s E x a m i n e d. ANURADHAPURA DISTRICT: Ritigala, Mar. 1905, *Willis s.n.* (PDA). KALUTARA DISTRICT: Hewessa, Pelawatta Mukalana, 1887, *s. coll. s n.* (PDA). RATNAPURA DISTRICT: Gilimale, Sept. 1960, *Jayaweera 2017* (PDA), Nov. 1959, *Jayaweera 35* (AMES). GALLE DISTRICT: Narawela, near Galle, *Champion s.n.* (K, holotype). LOCALITY UNKNOWN: *s. coll. C.P. 3693* (PDA).

36. GASTROCHILUS

D. Don, Prod. Fl. Nepal 32. 1825.

Epiphytes with usually short stems and few leaves close together; inflorescences often two at a node, short, each with up to 10 flowers, several open together; flowers rather fleshy, wide-opening with the lip at the base; lip basin-shaped to semiglobose with its sides firmly adnate to the column; midlobe pointing forwards, broad and round, nearly flat, sometimes hairy and fringed; column very short, stout, without a foot; pollinia 2, porate or slightly notched, never split on a linear stipe; rostellum short, bifid.

A few species, mostly confined to India, Ceylon and Malaysia.

Gastrochilus acaulis (Lindl.) Kuntze., Rev. Gen. Bot. 2: 661. 1891.—**Fig. 107.**

Saccolabium acaule (Lindl.) Hook. f., Fl. Br. Ind. 6: 61. 1890; Trimen, Handb. Fl. Ceylon 4: 198. 1898.
Cleisostoma acaule Lindl., Gen. et Sp. Orch. 227. 1833.

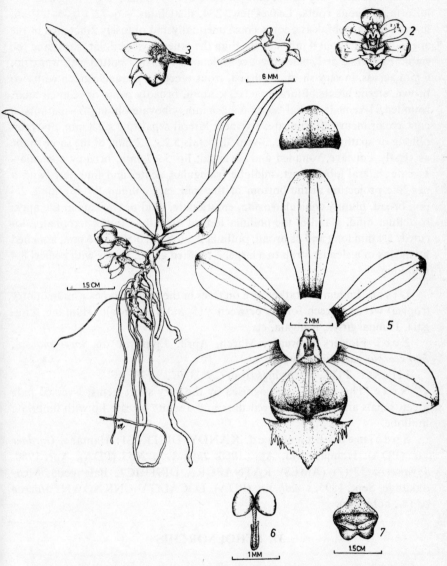

Fig. 107. *Gastrochilus acaulis* (Lindl.) Kuntze. 1, plant with inflorescence. 2, flower from front. 3, longitudinal section of flower. 4, lip, spur and column from side. 5, bract, sepals, petals, lip and column spread out from front. 6, pollinia with strap and gland. 7, operculum from side, three-quarters view.

Vanda fimbriata Gardner ex Thw., Enum. Pl. Zeyl. 305. 1861.

Epiphyte with very short, non-pseudobulbous stems 1–2 cm long and vermiform, flexuous roots. Leaves few, 2–4, distichous, 4.5–7.5 × 0.75–1.1 cm, linear-oblong, subfalcate, coriaceous, unequally and obtusely 2-notched at the apex, one-half about 4 mm shorter than the other, base petiolar, sheathing the stem. Flowers 2 or 3, pale green, conspicuously purple-spotted with white lip, 6 mm across, in very short, decurved, stout racemes; peduncle green with two brown, sterile bracts. Floral bracts 2 × 3 mm, broadly ovate or semi-circular, rounded, 1-veined; dorsal sepal 6 × 2.7 mm, obovate-oblong or spathulate, concave or incurved, truncate, 3-veined; lateral sepals 5.6 × 2.8 mm, obovate-oblong or spathulate, obtuse, 3-veined; petals 5.2 × 2.2 mm, of the same shape as sepals, concave, rounded and 3-veined; lip 5 × 7 mm, broadly conicular-saccate; lateral lobes short, midlobe triangular, acute, and fimbriate, with a peg-like projection at the bottom of the spur sac; column 1.7 mm high, 2.4 mm broad, bluntly conicular-ovate, emarginate, bifid or truncate at the apex; rostellum bifid, gland of the pollinia lodged dorsally. Anther terminal, 2-loculed, 1.4 mm long and as broad; pollinia 2, globose, 0.56 × 0.46 mm, attached by means of a slender strap to a large, 2-toothed gland. Ovary with pedicel 8.4 mm long.

D i s t r. Endemic. Rather rare on trees in the submontane or mid-country tropical wet evergreen forests between 915 and 1524 m alt. Hantane, Laggala, Hunnasgiriya, Rangala, etc.

E c o l. Flowers February, March, April. Epiphytic on *Saprosma* sp., *Semecarpus gardneri* Thw., etc.

I l l u s t r. PDA, 3 drawings from *C.P. 3191.*

N o t e. This species is recognised by the very short stems, 3-veined pale green sepals and petals with red dots and a white saccate lip with fimbriate midlobe.

S p e c i m e n s   E x a m i n e d. KANDY DISTRICT: Hantane, *Gardner s.n.* (PDA); Hunnasgiriya, Apr. 1960, *Jayaweera 2053* (PDA), Apr. 1960, *Jayaweera 32 (7)* (AMES). RATNAPURA DISTRICT: Balangoda, Meddakande, Sept. 1895, *s. coll. s.n.* (PDA). LOCALITY UNKNOWN: *Macrae 65* (K, holotype).

37. SCHOENORCHIS

Blume, Bijdr. 6: t. 3. 1825.

Epiphytes with erect or pendulous stems, often only branching and rooting at the base; leaves narrow; inflorescences simple or branched, bearing many very small flowers; sepals and petals similar, hardly spreading; lip 3-lobed, spurred, often with a callus at the entrance to the spur on the opposite side of the column; side lobes rounded, midlobe straight, fleshy, contracted at the base; spur cylindric or ellipsoid, pointing downwards or forwards without inside callosities; column short, footless, to which the lip is firmly jointed at the base; stigma at the base of the column, marginate. Rostellum prominent, long-acicular, distinctly bilobed; anther with a long beak, abruptly upcurved from the base; pollinia 2, each divided into more or less unequal halves on a rather slender stipe with long narrow disc; rostellum appearing as two long slender erect arms.

This genus consists of about 10 species distributed from the Himalayas to New Guinea.

KEY TO THE SPECIES

1 Flower small, white in leaf-opposed panicles, spur short, cylindric, pollinia 4
2 Leaves recurved; lip 2.1 mm long; pollinia-strap spathulate..............**1. S. nivea**
2 Leaves twisted clockwise or anticlockwise; lip 3–3.4 mm long; pollinia-strap lanceolate..**2. S. tortifolia**
1 Flowers yellow with orange veins in dense flowered racemes, pollinia 2..**3. S. chrysantha**

1. Schoenorchis nivea (Lindl.) Schltr., Fedde Repert. Beih. 1: 986. 1913.
—**Fig. 108.**

Saccolabium niveum Lindl., Gen. et Sp. Orch. 224. 1833; Trimen, Handb.
Fl. Ceylon 4: 195. 1898.

Epiphyte with simple, non-pseudobulbous stems; stems 1–9 cm long, curved upwards, remains of petiolar sheaths of older leaves ensheathing them at the base, leaf-bearing portion short with short internodes. Leaves semiterete, 4–9 × 0.5 cm, linear, distichous, spreading, recurved, fleshy, concave on the upper surface and rounded on the lower surface, notched, articulating on short petiolar sheaths. Flowers white, minute, 2 × 1.2 mm in slender, leaf-opposed, racemose panicles measuring 6–10 cm in length; peduncle 1.5–3.5 cm long, 2 mm broad, semiterete, green, concave on the upper surface, rounded below with one or more sterile bracts; each panicle consisting of 1–4 racemose or spiciform branches, 3–5.5 cm long. Floral bracts minute, 1.6–2.1 × 1.2–1.4 mm, triangular-ovate, acuminate, acute, green, papillate and 1-veined; dorsal sepal 1.5–0.7 mm, oblong, obtuse, 1-veined; lateral sepals 1.8 × 0.92 mm, obliquely ovate, rounded and 1-veined; petals 1.3 × 0.56 mm, oblong, truncate, 1-veined; lip white, fleshy, thick, 2.1 mm long; lateral lobes short, blunt and curved inwards; midlobe concave, spathulate, 1.3 × 0.74 mm; spur short-cylindric and rounded; column broader than tall, 0.3 × 0.5 mm, globular. Anther terminal, 2-loculed, 0.36 mm long and as broad, hemispheric; pollinia 4, unequal, oblong, in two appressed pairs; larger pollinia 0.26 × 0.14 mm; smaller ones 0.14 × 0.06 mm; pollinia attached by short caudicles to a spathu-

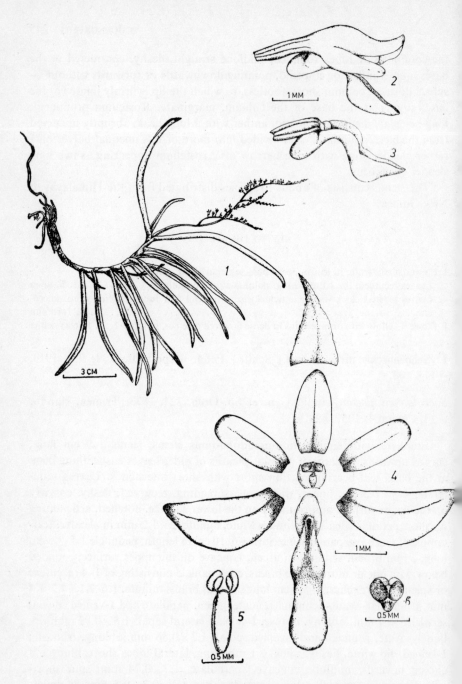

Fig. 108. *Schoenorchis nivea* (Lindl.) Schlechter. 1, plant with inflorescence.
2, flower from side. 3, lip with spur and column from side, three-quarters view.
4, bract, sepals, petals and lip spread out from front, column separated, seen from
front. 5, pollinia with enlarged strap. 6, operculum from inside.

late-oblong strap 0.44 × 0.16 mm and a large gland. Ovary with pedicel 2.2 mm long. Fruit a small capsule, 0.5 cm long.

D i s t r. Endemic. Common, on trees in the tropical wet evergreen forests. Ratnapura (Karawita Kande), Hunnasgiriya, Ritigala, Hantane, Hewaheta, Dolosbage, Adam's Peak, etc., from 305 to 915 m alt.

E c o l. Flowers July, September, October.

I l l u s t r. PDA, drawing from *C.P. 2340*.

N o t e. This species is distinguished by the semiterete, linear, distichous, recurved leaves and minute white flowers in leaf-opposed panicles. Herb. Lindley contains Macrae's and Thwaites' collections from Ceylon in the same type cover and another, *Hooker 2340*, separately, also from Ceylon.

S p e c i m e n s E x a m i n e d. ANURADHAPURA DISTRICT: Ritigala, Mar. 1905, *Willis s.n.* (PDA), May 1974, *Jayasuriya & Premadasa 1639* (PDA, US), Sept. 1975, *Jayasuriya, Premadasa & Foster 2311* (PDA, US), Nov. 1971, *Balakrishnan & Jayasuriya 1095* (PDA, US). KANDY DISTRICT: Hantane, Jan. 1957, *Watford s.n.* (PDA); Medamahanuwara Kande, *J.M. Silva s.n.* (PDA); Hunnasgiriya, Mar. 1960, *Jayaweera 2184* (PDA). RATNAPURA DISTRICT: Ratnapura, Nov. 1959, *Jayaweera 2055* (PDA), Nov. 1959, *Jayaweera 32 (1)* (AMES). LOCALITY UNKNOWN: in 1829, *Macrae 41* (K, holotype); *Walker s.n.* (K); *Gardner 872* (K); *Walker 1798* (K); *Hooker 2340* (K).

2. Schoenorchis tortifolia (Jayaweera) Garay, Bot. Mus. Leafl. 23 (4): 203. 1972.—**Fig. 109.**

Saccolabium tortifolium Jayaweera, Bot. Mus. Leafl. 20 (4): 111–114. 1963.

Tufted epiphyte with simple non-pseudobulbous stems; 3–15 cm long, 2 mm diameter, curving upwards in all directions, bases ensheathed in the remnants of old petiolar sheaths, the crowns carrying 7–18 ash-green, semiterete leaves, twisted clockwise or anticlockwise. Leaves 4–6 × 0.3 cm, linear, fleshy, distichous, notched, bases sheathing the internodes above. Flowers minute, white, in leaf-opposed racemose panicles, 13–14 cm long. Peduncle 6.5–7 cm long, flat, green with a number of short, membranous, sterile bracts; branches of the rachis few, 2.5–5.5 cm long and spiciform. Floral bracts 1.8–2.4 × 1.4–1.6 mm, triangular-ovate, acute, faintly undulate, 1-veined; dorsal sepal 2 × 1–1.1 mm, oblong, obtuse, 1-veined; lateral sepals 2.4–2.6 × 1.2–1.4 mm, obliquely oblong, rounded, 1-veined; petals 1.4–1.5 × 0.7–0.8 mm, obovate-oblong, truncate or faintly emarginate, 1-veined; lip fleshy, white, 3–3.4 mm long, notched halfway, concave and rounded dorsally; lateral lobes inconspicuous; midlobe 1.5 mm long, fleshy, spathulate; spur short, cylindrical and rounded; column 0.8 mm high, 0.6 mm broad, globular. Anther terminal, 2-loculed, 0.56 × 0.54 mm, stalked at the base; pollinia 4, unequal, collateral in two pairs; large pollinia 0.34 × 0.16 mm and the smaller ones 0.24 × 0.1

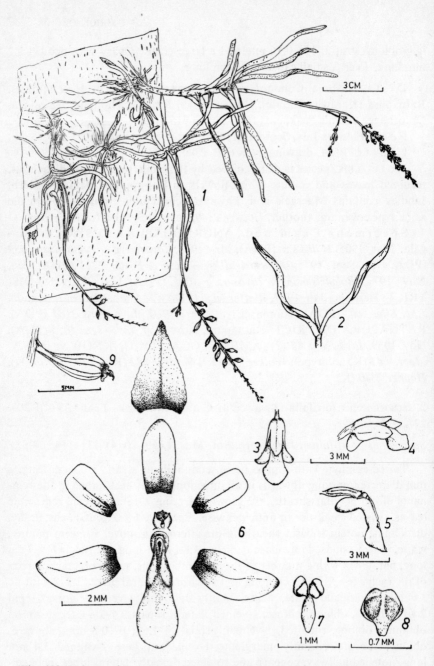

Fig. 109. *Schoenorchis tortifolia* (Jayaweera) Garay. 1, plants with inflorescences.
2, apical portion of shoot showing the twisted leaves. 3, flower from top. 4, flower from side. 5, lip, column (hidden between lateral lobes of lip) and spur from
side. 6, bract, sepals, petals, lip and column spread out from front. 7, pollinia
with strap. 8, operculum from inside.

mm, attached to a lanceolate stipe 0.44 × 0.2 mm by short, flat caudicles. Anther 0.56 × 0.54 mm, emarginate and stalked at the base. Ovary with pedicel 2.4–3.5 mm long. Fruit a small, spreading, clavate, pedicelled capsule, 4 mm long.

D i s t r. Endemic. Rare, on trees in the submontane or mid-country tropical wet evergreen forests up to 915 m alt. Hunnasgiriya, Daulagala, etc.

E c o l. Flowers April–August. Two of its many host plants are *Schefflera stellata* (Gaertn.) Bail. and *Macaranga peltata* (Roxb.) Muell. Arg.

I l l u s t r. Bot. Mus. Leafl. 20 (4): pl. 18. 1963.

S p e c i m e n s E x a m i n e d. KURUNEGALA DISTRICT: Doluwakande, Jan. 1972, *Jayasuriya & Subramaniam 550* (PDA, US). KANDY DISTRICT: Hunnasgiriya, Aug. 1959, *Jayaweera 1850* (PDA, holotype), *Jayaweera 1851* and *1852* (PDA); Daulagala, Jul. 1960, *Jayaweera 2185* (PDA).

3. Schoenorchis chrysantha (Alston) Garay, Bot. Mus. Leafl. 23 (4): 202. 1972.—Fig. 110.

Saccolabium chrysanthum Alston in Trimen, Handb. Fl. Ceylon 6: 277. 1931.
Schoenorchis juncifolia Thw., Enum. Pl. Zeyl. 304. 1861, non Blume.
Saccolabium filiforme Trimen, Handb. Fl. Ceylon 4: 196. 1898, non Lindl.

Pendulous epiphyte with simple, non-pseudobulbous, terete stems; stems slender, 14–45 cm long, purple-spotted, bending downwards and often upwards terminally, base naked but higher up ensheathed in remains of petiolar sheaths of older leaves; internodes 1.5–2 cm long; roots long, terete or flattened, older roots covered by a scurfy greenish-grey tomentum. Leaves 7–12.5 cm long, green, terete, with a ventral groove, acute, articulating with the petiolar sheaths which ensheath the internodes above. Flowers yellow with orange veins, 3 mm broad, conspicuous by their saccate spurs, in short-peduncled, simple, dense-flowered, stout racemes measuring 3 cm in length. Floral bracts 1.3 × 1.2 mm, ovate-acuminate; dorsal sepal 3.1–3.2 × 1.4 mm, oblong-lanceolate, erect, obtuse or rounded, 1-veined; lateral sepals 2.4 × 0.9–1.2 mm, obliquely subspathulate, obtuse, 1-veined; petals 2.4–2.8 × 2.2–2.4 mm, orbicular, crenate, rounded, 3-veined; lip a large, inflated spur, 3.6 × 1.9 mm, base of spur rounded; lateral lobes of lip erect and rounded; midlobe small, ovate, deflexed, subacute; column 1.2 mm high, 1 mm broad with two erect, curved arms at the top lodging the large gland of the pollinia in between; foot absent. Anther terminal, 2-loculed, 0.9 × 0.8 mm; pollinia 2, globose, whitish yellow; each pollinium 0.3 mm diameter, attached by a short linear strap to a gland. Ovary with pedicel 6.6 mm long. Fruit a fusiform ribbed capsule, 7 mm long, with a pedicel as long.

D i s t r. Rather common on trees in the subtropical montane forests up to 2134 m alt. Nuwara Eliya, Pidurutalagala. Epiphytic on *Apodytes* sp.,

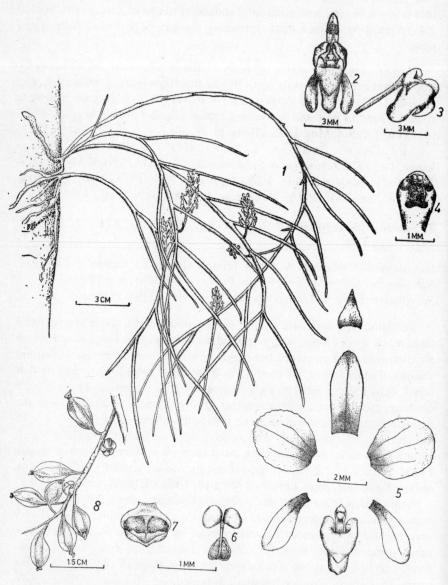

Fig. 110. *Schoenorchis chrysantha* (Alston) Garay. 1, plant with inflorescences growing on the bark of a tree. 2, flower from front. 3, lip, column and spur from side. 4, column from inside with operculum removed. 5, bract, sepals and petals spread out from front, lip and column natural position. 6, pollinia with strap and gland. 7, operculum from inside. 8, fruits.

Glochidion montanum Thw. etc. Also in South India.

E c o l. Flowers March, May.

I l l u s t r. PDA, 2 drawings one of which is from *C.P. 633*.

N o t e. This species is allied to *Saccolabium filiforme* Lindl. but differs from it in the orange coloured flowers.

S p e c i m e n s E x a m i n e d. NUWARA ELIYA DISTRICT: Nuwara Eliya, May 1959, *Jayaweera 32 (2)* (AMES), May 1959, *Jayaweera 2050* (PDA); Pidurutalagala, May 1960, *Jayaweera 2306* (PDA); Horton Plains, May 1960, *Jayaweera 2051* (PDA), May 1906, *A.M. Silva s.n.* (PDA). BADULLA DISTRICT: Namunukula, *J.M. Silva s.n.* (PDA). LOCALITY UNKNOWN: *s. coll. C.P. 633* (K, holotype, PDA); *Walker s.n.* (K); *Walker 69* (K).

38. ROBIQUETIA

Gaud., Voy. Uranie & Physcienne 426. 1829.

Epiphytes with stout, elongated, pendulous stems; leaves broadly oblong, inflorescence pendulous, unbranched with many crowded small flowers; sepals and petals spreading; lip 3-lobed, spurred, more or less joined to the base of the column; side lobes short with a fleshy thickening on the inside; midlobe straight, very small, fleshy, convex; spur large with a 2-lobed projection from the back wall and a fleshy callus on the front wall; column short, footless with a broad, well-developed, bifid rostellum; anther pointed; pollinia 2, notched on a more or less spathulate or often uncinate stipe; viscidium large; the pollinia on the rostellum projecting into the clinandrium; disc small.

About a dozen species, mostly in the eastern part of Malaysia, Ceylon and India.

KEY TO THE SPECIES

1 Flowers in long pendulous racemes, 10–15 cm long, lip a subincurved spur with a very oblique mouth..**1. R. gracilis**
1 Flowers in short, axillary, recurved racemes 2–4.2 cm long
  2 Lip or spur 9.8–10.5 mm long
    3 Spur oblong; racemes 4.2 cm long; sepals oblong, petals obovate-oblong...........
....**2. R. brevifolia**
    3 Spur lanceolate; racemes 2–2.5 cm long; sepals and petals lanceolate-oblong.......
....**3. R. virescens**
  2 Lip or spur 2.7 mm long and oblong................................**4. R. rosea**

1. Robiquetia gracilis (Lindl.) Garay, Bot. Mus. Leafl. 23 (4): 197. 1972. —**Fig. 111.**

Saccolabium gracile Lindl., Gen. et Sp. Orch. 225. 1833; Trimen, Handb. Fl. Ceylon 4: 196. 1898.

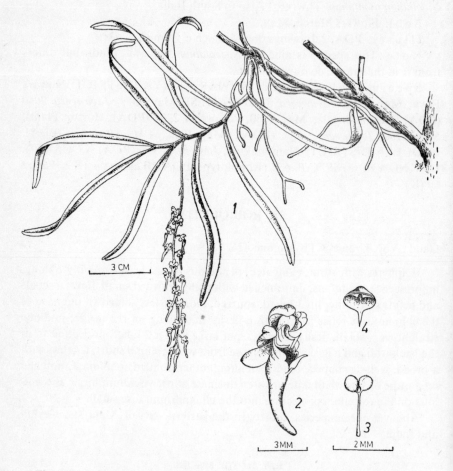

Fig. 111. *Robiquetia gracilis* (Lindl.) Garay, redrawn from a drawing of *C.P. 2528* in PDA. 1, plant with inflorescence. 2, flower from side, three quarters view. 3, pollinia with strap. 4, operculum from inside.

Epiphyte with non-pseudobulbous, zigzag or flexuous stems 5–20 cm long; internodes 0.6–1.2 cm long; roots slender, flexuous. Leaves 6.3–10 × 0.8 cm, elongate, linear-lanceolate, acuminate, flat, straight or falcate, narrowed at both ends; midrib obscure. Flowers white, 0.6 cm long, in pendulous, slender, many-flowered racemes 10–15 cm long. Floral bracts minute, subulate; sepals oblong, obtuse, 1-veined; lateral sepals larger; petals narrow, oblong, obtuse, 1-veined; lip a long subincurved, obtuse spur; lateral lobes absent; midlobe very small, ovate or lanceolate, acute; mouth of the spur very oblique; column short, foot absent. Anther terminal, depressed, 2-loculed; pollinia 2, globose; strap of pollinia very slender. Ovary with pedicel 2.5 mm long.

D i s t r. Very rare, on trees in the submontane or mid-country tropical wet evergreen forests up to about 1220 m alt. Hantane, Horton Plains, etc. Also in South India.

E c o l. Flowers May, July.

I l l u s t r. PDA, drawing from *C.P. 2528*.

N o t e. Herb. Lindley contains along with the type collection *Gardner 869* from Ceylon in the same cover. This species was thought to be endemic to Ceylon but collections from India prove to the contrary.

S p e c i m e n s E x a m i n e d. CEYLON: LOCALITY UNKNOWN: *Macrae 55* (K, holotype); *Gardner 869* (K); *s. coll. s.n.* (AMES); *s. coll. C.P. 2528* (K, PDA). INDIA: S. India: High Wavy Mountains, May 1917, *Blatter & Hallberg 26531* (K), *Wight* (K).

2. Robiquetia brevifolia (Lindl.) Garay, Bot. Mus. Leafl. 23 (4): 196. 1972. —**Fig. 112.**

Saccolabium brevifolium Lindl., Gen. et Sp. Orch. 225. 1833; Trimen, Handb. Fl. Ceylon 4: 196. 1898.

Scandent epiphyte with simple, non-pseudobulbous stems 15–25 cm long and long, slender, filiform roots; internodes 1.2–2 cm long, ensheathed by petiolar sheaths. Leaves 1.5–2 cm × 4.5–7 mm, linear-oblong, distichous, channelled along the middle, coriaceous, unequally two lobed at the apex. Flowers 11 mm long, 3.5 mm across, deep purple-red with the upper part of the lip yellow, in recurved racemes 4.2 cm long; peduncle short, about 6 mm long with sterile, scaly bracts. Floral bracts small, triangular-ovate, acute or subacute; dorsal sepal 3 × 1.7 mm, oblong, obtuse, 1-veined; lateral sepals about the same size and shape as the dorsal sepal but slightly oblique, obtuse, 1-veined; petals 3 × 1.8 mm, obovate-oblong, rounded, 1-veined; both petals and sepals concave and incurved; lip a nearly straight, saccate, laterally compressed spur, 10.5 mm long, running parallel to the ovary; lateral lobes absent and the midlobe a minute, subacute or obtuse tooth; column short. Anther terminal, 2-loculed; pollinia 2, globose, purple, bipartite, one-half much smaller than the other, attached by short caudicles to a slender strap and a large, oblong, bifid gland. Ovary with pedicel 11 mm long. Fruit a fusiform capsule, 1.5 × 0.6 cm.

D i s t r. Endemic. Common, on branches of trees in the submontane or mid-country tropical wet evergreen forests extending to the subtropical montane forests up to 1829 m alt. Rangala, Hakgala, Ramboda, Maturata, Mahacoodagala, Hunnasgiriya, Sita Eliya, Namunukula, etc.

E c o l. Flowers February–April, September. Some of its many host plants are *Semecarpus nigroviridis* Thw., *Calophyllum calaba* L., *Eugenia* sp., *Stemnoporus* sp. and *Michelia nilagirica* Zenk.

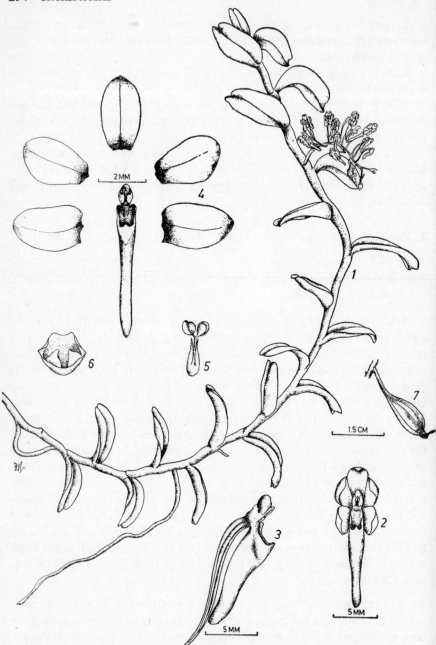

Fig. 112. *Robiquetia brevifolia* (Lindl.) Garay. 1, plant with inflorescence. 2, flower from front. 3, saccate lip, spur and column from side. 4, sepals, petals, lip and column spread out from front. 5, pollinia with strap and gland, enlarged. 6, operculum from inside, enlarged. 7, fruit.

I l l u s t r. PDA, five drawings of which four are from *C.P. 2341*.

N o t e. This species differs from *Robiquetia rosea* Lindl. in the longer lip or spur and from *Robiquetia virescens* in the longer racemes and oblong sepals and petals. Herb. Lindley contains the holotype and the collection *Gardner 871* both from Ceylon in the same type cover.

S p e c i m e n s E x a m i n e d. KANDY DISTRICT: Hunnasgiriya, Apr. 1891, *Farmer s.n.* (PDA); Slopes of Adam's Peak, Nov. 1974, *Davidse & Sumithraarachchi 8662* (PDA, US), Oct. 1975, *Sohmer & Sumithraarachchi 9935* (PDA, US); Corbet's Gap, Mar. 1961, *Jayaweera 2048* (PDA); Between Knuckles & Rilagala, Nov. 1974, *Davidse 8272* (PDA, US). RATNAPURA DISTRICT: Kunadiyaparavata, Dec. 1917, *Lewis s.n.* (PDA). NUWARA ELIYA DISTRICT: Horton Plains, Oct. 1974, *Davidse 7629* (PDA, US), Oct. 1973, *Waas 139* (PDA, US), *Fernando s.n.* (PDA); Between Nuwara Eliya & Ramboda, Mar. 1907, *J.M. Silva s.n.* (PDA); Sita Eliya, Oct. 1906, *A.M. Silva s.n.* (PDA); Hakgala, Oct. 1906, *A.M. Silva s.n.* (PDA), Sept. 1969, *Grupe 204* (PDA, US). BADULLA DISTRICT: Namunukula, Mar. 1907, *J.M. Silva s.n.* (PDA). LOCALITY UNKNOWN: *Macrae 42* (K, holotype); *Gardner 871* (K).

3. **Robiquetia virescens** (Gard. ex Lindl.) Jayaweera, comb. nov.—**Fig. 113.**

Saccolabium virescens Gard. ex Lindl., J. Linn. Soc. Bot. 3: 35. 1859.

Epiphyte with non-pseudobulbous stems; leaves 2.7–7 × 0.8–1 cm, linear-oblong with short petioles 0.9–1 cm long, sheathing the internodes above. Flowers green or white, 1.2 × 3.5 mm, in short racemes 2–2.5 cm long; peduncle slender and short, 2.2–2.5 cm long with 3–5 brown, sterile bracts; floral bracts 0.8 × 1.7 mm, triangular, acute, margin spiny; dorsal sepal 3.9 × 2.1 mm, lanceolate-oblong, obtuse or truncate; lateral sepals 3.8 × 1.8 mm; petals 3.8 × 1.7 mm, lanceolate-oblong, truncate, crenulate; lip a saccate lanceolate spur 9.8 mm long, base of the sac acute, broadening towards the middle and tapering to the mouth, column green or white, 2.1 mm high, 1.2 mm broad; rostellum straight, 2-toothed; anther depressed, 0.9 × 1 mm, ellipsoid and purple in colour; pollinia 0.56 × 1.36 mm.

D i s t r. Endemic. There are two forms of this species, both common on branches of trees in the submontane or mid-country tropical wet evergreen forests. Rangala at 1296 m alt.

E c o l. Flowers February–March.

N o t e. This species is distinguished by the linear-oblong leaves, green or white flowers and the lanceolate spur of the flower.

S p e c i m e n s E x a m i n e d. KANDY DISTRICT: Corbet's Gap, Mar. 1961, *Jayaweera 2048* (PDA); Adam's Peak, Dec. 1975, *Bernardi 15769* (PDA, US). LOCALITY UNKNOWN: *s. coll. C.P. 488* (K, holotype).

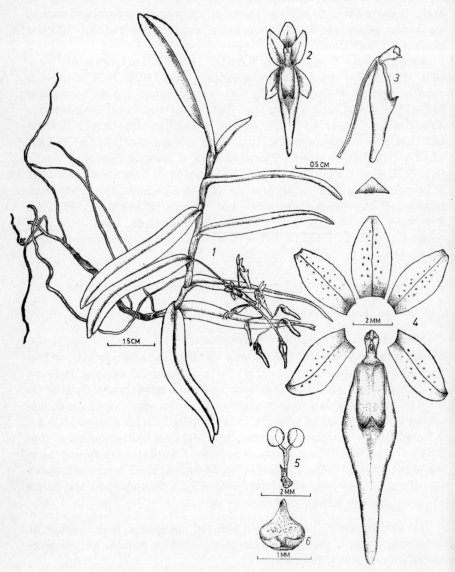

Fig. 113. *Robiquetia virescens* (Gardner ex Lindl.) Jayaweera. 1, plant with inflorescence. 2, flower from front. 3, lip with spur and column from side. 4, bract, sepals, petals, lip and column spread out from front. 5, pollinia with strap and gland. 6, operculum from inside.

4. Robiquetia rosea (Lindl.) Garay, Bot. Mus. Leafl. 23 (4): 197. 1972. —Fig. 114.

Saccolabium roseum Lindl., Gen. et Sp. Orch. 225, 1833; Trimen, Handb. Fl. Ceylon 4: 197. 1898.
Sarcanthus walkerianus Wight, Ic. Pl. Ind. Or. 5 (1): 11, pl. 1686. 1851.
Saccolabium walkerianum Reichb. f. in Walp. Ann. 6: 887. 1861.

Epiphyte with a non-pseudobulbous stem and long, slender roots; stem 8–20 cm long, internodes 0.6 cm long. Leaves 2–7.5 × 0.3–0.4 cm, narrowly linear or linear-oblong, flat, recurved, unequally notched at the apex, bases sheathing the internodes above, thickly fleshy, channelled along the centre. Flowers 3 mm diameter, pale or dark purple with the tip of the lip green, in slender, few-flowered, axillary racemes measuring 2–3.7 cm in length; peduncle short. Floral bracts 1.2 × 1 mm, triangular-ovate, acute or rounded; dorsal sepal 1.8 × 1 mm, lanceolate-oblong, obtuse, 1-veined; lateral sepals 1.9 × 1 mm, lanceolate-oblong, obtuse, 1-veined; petals 1.7 × 1.1 mm, orbicular-oblong, obtuse, 1-veined; lip a large, incurved, laterally compressed spur, 2.7 mm long, rounded at the tip; lateral lobes absent, midlobe reduced to a blunt tooth; column 1 mm high; rostellum a flat, blunt beak; foot absent. Anther terminal, 2-loculed, 1 mm long and as broad; pollinia 2, bipartite, globose, 0.5 × 0.37 mm, purple, attached by a slender strap to a large gland. Ovary with pedicel 4 mm long. Fruit a slender, pedicelled, subpyriform capsule, 0.6–0.8 cm long.

D i s t r. Endemic. Common on trees at higher elevations of the submontane or mid-country tropical wet evergreen forests extending to the subtropical montane forests up to 1829 m alt. Rangala, Hunnasgiriya, Matale, Hantane, Ambagamuwa, Hakgala, Maturata, Laggala, etc.

E c o l. Flowers March, April and September. Some of its many host plants are *Semecarpus gardneri* Thw., *Euodia lunuankenda* (Gaertn.) Merr., *Michelia nilagirica* Zenk., *Eurya japonica* Thunb., *Diospyros* sp., *Syzygium aqueum* (Burm. f.) Alston, *Podadenia thwaitesii* (Baill.) Muell., *Schefflera emarginata* (Seem.) Harms. and *Canthium coromandelicum* (Burm. f.) Alston.

I l l u s t r. PDA, drawing from *C.P. 489.*

N o t e. This species differs from others in the slender stems, short racemes and shorter lip or spur. Herb. Lindley contains the type collection.

S p e c i m e n s   E x a m i n e d. MATALE DISTRICT: Laggala, Mar. 1960, *Jayaweera 32 (5)* (AMES). KANDY DISTRICT: Hunnasgiriya, Apr. 1960, *Jayaweera 2160* (PDA). NUWARA ELIYA DISTRICT: Hakgala, *s. coll. s.n.* (PDA), Oct. 1906, *A.M. Silva s.n.* (PDA), Sept. 1960, *Jayaweera 2182* (PDA), Oct. 1975, *Sohmer & Sumithraarachchi 10082* (PDA, US). LOCALITY UNKNOWN: *Macrae 64* (K, holotype); *s. coll. C.P. 489* (PDA); Apr. 1906, *s. coll. s.n.* (AMES).

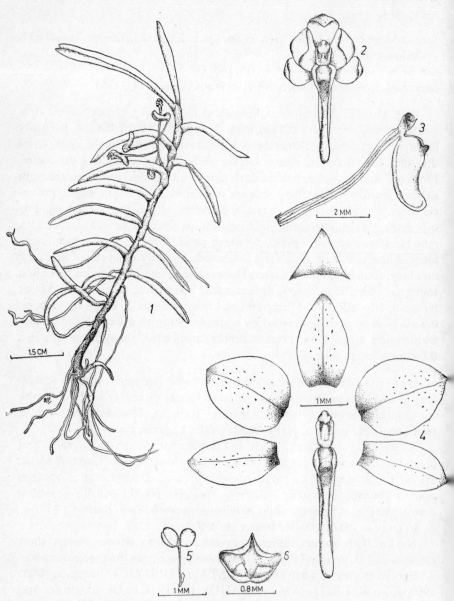

Fig. 114. *Robiquetia rosea* (Lindl.) Garay. 1, plant with inflorescence. 2, flower from front. 3, spur and column from side. 4, bract, sepals, petals, spur and column from front. 5, pollinia with short caudicles, strap and gland. 6, operculum from inside.

39. AERANGIS

Reichb. f., Flora 48: 190. 1865.

Epiphytes with erect, short, or elongate stems, sometimes stemless; leaves distichous, articulate with the leaf sheaths; inflorescence axillary, racemose; sepals and petals free, spreading to reflexed; lip reflexed with the blade much shorter than the slender spur; column short, somewhat dilated towards the base; rostellum simple and elongate; pollinia 2, on a single elongate stipe.

Aerangis hologlottis (Schltr.) Schltr., Beih. Bot. Centralbl. 36 (2): 117. 1918. —**Fig. 115.**

Angraecum hologlottis Schlechter, Fedde Repert. 3: 82. 1906; Alston in Trimen, Handb. Fl. Ceylon 6: 278. 1931.

Stemless and non-pseudobulbous epiphyte with cylindrical, vermiform roots. Leaves 4.5–9 × 1.1–1.7 cm, oblong-lanceolate, falcate, coriaceous, dark green and shining above, paler beneath, unequally bilobed at apex, midrib prominent below and lateral veins conspicuously reticulated. Flowers white, 1.1–1.4 cm broad in conspicuously bracteated, semierect, many-flowered racemes 13.5–16.5 cm long, opening irregularly; first flowers to open at the base or towards the middle of the raceme; peduncle 4.5–6.8 cm long, cylindrical, dark green, bearing a number of dark brown, sterile bracts. Floral bracts 2.6 × 3.8 mm, ovate, narrowing suddenly halfway, apiculate, almost sheathing the rachis, splitting in two as the flower bud emerges; dorsal sepal 7.1 × 2.6 mm, lanceolate, acute, 3-veined; lateral sepals 8 × 2 mm, oblanceolate, acute, 3-veined; petals 7.2 × 2.6 mm, oblong-lanceolate, acute, 3-veined; lip 8.4 × 3.4 mm, lanceolate-spathulate, apiculate, 5-veined, with a cylindrical spur 5.4 mm long at the base parallel to the ovary; column 1.2 mm high, 1.6 mm broad, truncate; foot absent. Anther terminal, 2-loculed, 1 × 1.16 mm; pollinia 2, globular or pyriform, 0.56 mm diameter and depressed on one side. Ovary with pedicel 7 mm long. Fruit a fusiform capsule, 1.5–1.8 cm × 3.5–4 mm.

D i s t r. Endemic. Rare on trees in the submontane or mid-country tropical wet evergreen forests at an alt. of about 457 m and extending to the intermediate zone of the tropical dry mixed evergreen forests. Botanic Gardens, Peradeniya, Nalanda, Aluthgama (between Galewela and Matale), etc.

E c o l. Flowers January, February, March–April.

I l l u s t r. PDA, 2 drawings.

N o t e. This plant was discovered growing on trees in the Botanic Gardens, Peradeniya by Dr. Schlechter, on his visit to Ceylon in 1903. He thinks that it is an isolated form. In Herb. Kew *C.P. 2352* is labelled erroneously as

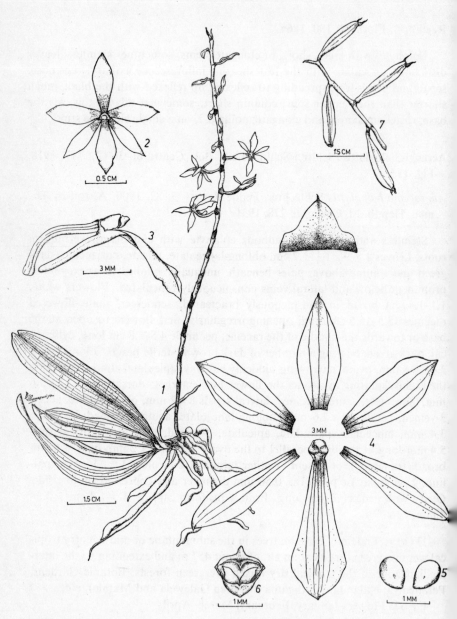

Fig. 115. *Aerangis hologlottis* (Schlechter) Schlechter. 1, plant with inflorescence. 2, flower from front. 3, lip, column and spur from side. 4, bract, sepals, petals, lip and column spread out from front. 5, pollinia. 6, operculum from side, three-quarters view. 7, fruits.

Mystacidium zeylanicum (*Angraecum zeylanicum* Lindl.). This species differs from it in the falcate leaves, white flowers with 3-veined lateral sepals, lanceo-late-spathulate 5-veined lip and cylindrical spur.

Specimens Examined. KURUNEGALA DISTRICT: Aluthgama, between Matale & Galewela, *Jayaweera 37A* (AMES). MATALE DISTRICT: Nalanda, Feb. 1960, *Jayaweera 37* (AMES). KANDY DISTRICT: Peradeniya, Bot. Gard., Jun. 1974, *Sumithraarachchi 380* (PDA, US). LOCALITY UNKNOWN: *s. coll. C.P. 2352* (K), in part.

40. COTTONIA

Wight, Ic. Pl. Ind. Or. 5: 21. t. 1755. 1852.

An epiphyte; stems elongate, leafy, clothed with appressed dark green leaf-sheaths; roots stout and vermiform; leaves lorate, coriaceous, keeled, jointed on leaf-sheaths, unequally 2-lobed; peduncle long, leaf-opposed, slender, simple or paniculately branched, flowering at the ends of branches; sepals subequal; petals narrower and spreading or reflexed; lip sessile on the base of the column, much longer than sepals, subpanduriform, base 2-auricled with interposed calli, margin villous, disc with a tooth-like callus; column very short, foot absent; anther short, 2-chambered; pollinia 2, deeply bipartite giving the appearance of 4; strap long, gland small.

Two species in S.W. India and Ceylon.

Cottonia peduncularis (Lindl.) Thw., Enum. Pl. Zeyl. 303. 1861; Alston in Trimen, Handb. Fl. Ceylon 6: 278. 1931.—**Fig. 116.**

Vanda peduncularis Lindl., Gen. et Sp. Orch. 216. 1833.
Cottonia macrostachya Wight, Ic. Pl. Ind. Or. 5 (1): 21, pl. 1755. 1851; Trimen, Handb. Fl. Ceylon 4: 203. 1898.

Epiphyte with non-pseudobulbous, stout, leafy stems 10–43 cm long, roots long, stout, vermiform; petiolar bases of leaf sheaths ensheathing the short internodes; terminal ends of stem together with leaves sharply recurving. Leaves 12–24 × 1.5–2.3 cm, lorate, coriaceous, jointed at petiolar sheaths, recurved, apex truncately 2-lobed, one lobe a little longer than the other and more rounded, with a spiny sinus in between. Flowers greenish-brown, 2.4 cm long, 1.5 cm broad, with a conspicuous, dark purple lip resembling a bee, in long-peduncled, racemose panicles; rachis 30–90 cm long, green, red-mottled; raceme with its peduncle 15–30 cm long, flowers borne terminally. Floral bracts 1.2 × 2.4 mm, ovate or semilunar, rounded, 1-veined; dorsal sepal 9–9.5 × 4 mm, obovate-oblong, obtuse or rounded, 7-veined; lateral sepals 8 × 4.5 mm, obovate-oblong, obtuse or rounded, 7-veined; petals 8–9 × 3 mm, linear-oblong, obliquely truncate, 3-veined, the lateral pair branching;

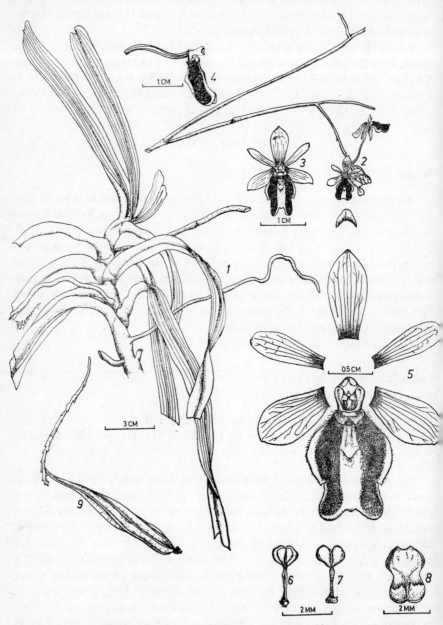

Fig. 116. *Cottonia peduncularis* (Lindl.) Thw. 1, top portion of a stem. 2, inflorescence. 3, flower from front. 4, lip and column from side. 5, bract, sepals, petals and lip spread out from front, column from inside. 6, pollinia with strap and gland from behind. 7, pollinia from front. 8, operculum from inside. 9, fruit.

lip 1.2 × 1 cm, thick, subpanduriform, villous, adnate to the base of the column, 2-auricled at the base with interposed calli; lateral lobes conspicuously fringed with greenish-yellow in colour; midlobe trifid, lateral lobules large and rounded, and the midlobule small; column 4.6 mm long, 4 mm broad, muricate, 3-toothed. Anther terminal, 2-loculed, 2.4 × 1.8 mm, panduriform; pollinia 2, waxy, pyriform, attached to a small gland by a slender, linear strap; each pollinium 0.8 × 0.64 mm, unequally bipartite. Ovary with pedicel 2 cm long. Fruit a fusiform, ridged, twisted capsule, 7 × 1.2 cm.

D i s t r. Rare, on trees by streams or on rocks in the tropical dry mixed evergreen forests and in the tropical savannah. Ekiriyankumbura, Doluwa-kande, Hantane, Peradeniya, etc. Also in India in the Deccan Peninsula and Western Ghats from Konkan southwards.

E c o l. Flowers March, April.

I l l u s t r. Hook., Bot. Mag. 116: pl. 7099. 1890; PDA, drawing.

N o t e. Distinguished by its characteristic flower which resembles a female bee.

S p e c i m e n s E x a m i n e d. CEYLON: ANURADHAPURA DISTRICT: Ritigala, Mar. 1905, *Willis s.n.* (PDA), Aug. 1977, *Jayasuriya 1299* (PDA, US). MATALE DISTRICT: Laggala, Sept. 1893, *s. coll. s.n.* (PDA). KANDY DISTRICT: Peradeniya, Bot. Gard., cultd., Mar. 1961, *Jayaweera 2399* (PDA). MONERAGALA DISTRICT: Bibile, Oct. 1959, *Jayaweera 36* (AMES). LOCALITY UNKNOWN: *Macrae 40* (K, holotype), *Walker s.n.* (K), *s. coll. C.P. 2361* (PDA). INDIA: Bombay, Soopa Kala Nuddi, 1853, *Richie 1424* (K); Malabar, Konkan, etc., *Herb. Stocks s.n.* (K); South Konkan, 1878, *Dalzell* (K). Madras, Annaimalai Hills, Apr. 1912, *Fischer 3358* (K).

41. DIPLOPRORA

Hook. f., Fl. Br. Ind. 6: 26. 1890.

An epiphyte; stems short, stout, non-pseudobulbous, curved, leafy, with long vermiform roots, lower internodes clothed with leaf-sheaths; leaves sessile, distichous, coriaceous, jointed on sheaths; tip unequally 2-toothed; peduncle leaf-opposed, stout, erect, few-flowered and somewhat zigzag; flowers small, spicate; sepals spreading, keeled; petals smaller, ovate or obovate-oblong; lip shorter or longer than the lateral sepals, margins adnate to the sides of the column, cymbiform, sigmoidly curved, suddenly narrowed into a compressed, 2-caudate lip; disc with a fleshy keel; column very short; foot absent; anther hemispheric, beaked, 2-chambered; pollinia 2, deeply bipartite unequally, giving the appearance of 4, strap short, linear, gland small.

Monotypic. Distributed in India, Ceylon, Burma and Hong Kong.

Diploprora championi Hook. f., Fl. Br. Ind. 6 (1): 26. 1890; Trimen, Handb. Fl. Ceylon 4: 204. 1898.—**Fig. 117.**

Cottonia championii Lindl., J. Bot. 7: 35. 1855.
Luisia bicaudata Thw., Enum., Pl. Zeyl. 302. 1861.
Vanda bicaudata Thw., ibid. 429. 1864.
Diploprora bicaudata (Thw.) Schlechter, Fedde Repert. Beih. 4: 281. 1919.

Pendulous epiphyte with terminal ends of the stems bending upwards; stems non-pseudobulbous, leafy, 5–37 cm long, roots long, vermiform. Leaves sessile, distichous, twisted, all facing one side, 7.5–10.5 × 1.3–2.4 cm, oblong, slightly falcate in seedlings, thinly coriaceous, bright green with a prominent midrib, unequally 2-toothed at apex, wavy, bases jointed to sheaths ensheathing internodes above. Flowers greenish-yellow, 1.2–2 cm across, in leaf-opposed, stout-peduncled, green, few-flowered, erect, sometimes zigzag, racemes 3–11 cm long. Floral bracts 3.5–4 × 3–3.4 mm, ovate, acute, base tinged purple, keeled dorsally, margin spiny, 1-veined; dorsal sepal 11.5 × 6 mm, broadly lanceolate-oblong, obtuse, keeled dorsally, 7-veined; lateral sepals 9 × 5.7 mm, obliquely obovate, obtuse, 7-veined, keeled dorsally; petals 9 × 4.5 mm, obovate-lanceolate, obtuse, 5-veined, not keeled dorsally; lip small, smaller than sepals and petals, 7 × 4 mm, cymbiform, 3-lobed and adnate to the base of the column, lateral lobes short; midlobe abruptly contracted, compressed and incurved, terminating in two long, filiform branches; disc fleshy and keeled; column 3 mm high and as broad, truncate, and together with its lip resembling the head of an insect cleaning its proboscis with its two front feet; foot absent. Anther terminal, 2-loculed, 2 mm long as broad, beaked; pollinia 2, globose, bipartite, larger portion 0.8 × 0.7 mm, smaller portion 0.6 × 0.3 mm, appressed to the flat inner surface of the larger one; pollinia attached by a narrow strap 1.2 mm long to a small gland. Ovary with pedicel 8 mm long. Fruit a fusiform, 6-ribbed capsule, 5 × 0.8 cm.

D i s t r. Rare, growing on branches of trees overhanging watercourses in the submontane or mid-country tropical wet evergreen forests up to 610 m alt. Ratnapura, Ambagamuwa, Karawita Kande, Balangoda, etc. It also occurs in the Himalayan regions, Khasia Hills, Sikkim in India and Burma and China.

E c o l. Flowers February, June, August, December.

I l l u s t r. Hook. f., Ic. Pl. 22: pl. 2120. 1892; King & Pantling, Ann. R. Bot. Gard. (Calcutta) 8: pl. 274. 1898; PDA, 2 drawings from *C.P. 3494*.

N o t e: This species has been referred to three genera *Luisia, Vanda* and *Cottonia*. It is closest to *Vanda* from which it differs in habit, membranous leaves, smaller flowers, broad bases of the sepals and the remarkable semi-cymbiform lip with a process at the extremity like a bowsprit ending in two setiform forks. The membranous leaves distinguish it from *Luisia* while it is totally different from *Cottonia* in habit and the large, flat lip.

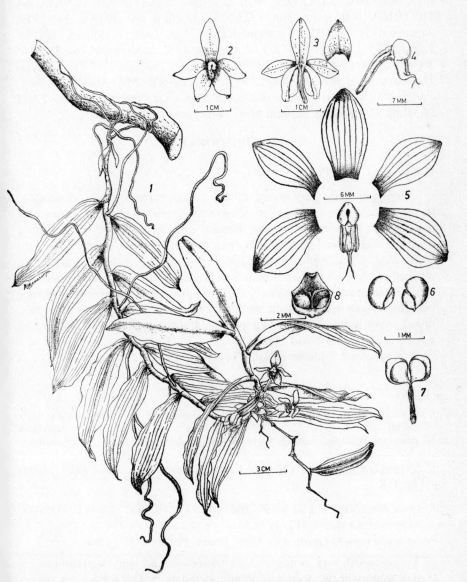

Fig. 117. *Diploprora championi* Hook. f. 1, plant with inflorescence and fruit, hanging down from a twig of the host plant. 2, flower from front. 3, flower from behind. 4, lip and column from side. 5, bract, sepals, petals, lip and column spreadout from front. 6, pollinia from front. 7, pollinia with strap and gland from behind. 8, operculum from inside.

Specimens Examined. CEYLON: KANDY DISTRICT: Peradeniya, Bot. Gard. cultd., Feb. 1963, *Jayaweera 1986* (PDA). RATNAPURA DISTRICT: Ratnapura, Jun. 1925, *J.M. de Silva s.n.* (PDA), Dec. 1959, *Jayaweera 38* (AMES); Kuruwita Kande, Jun. 1895, *s. coll. s.n.* (PDA). LOCALITY UNKNOWN: *s. coll. C.P. 3494* (K, holotype, PDA). INDIA: Khasia Hills: Churra, 1850, *J.D. Hooker & T. Thomson 1110* (K). Sikkim Himalaya: Aug. 1893, *Pantling 284* (K, AMES). BURMA: Moulmein, 1868, *Parish 277* (K). CHINA: Kwansi: Shap Man Shan, Jun. 1933, *Tsang 22435* (AMES). Hong Kong: Saiwan, Mar. 1941, *Taam 1980* (AMES).

42. SIRHOOKERA

Kuntze, Rev. Gen. Pl. 2: 681. 1891.

Epiphytes; stems very short, tufted, pseudobulbous; roots vermiform; leaves solitary, petioled, coriaceous; peduncle slender, paniculately branched, much longer than leaves; flowers terminal or subterminal on the branches, bracts subulate, persistent, shorter than pedicels; flowers small; sepals subequal, oblong, connivent, concave, base subsaccate; petals same as sepals; lip inserted on the base of the column, base recurved, concave, side lobes short, rounded, incurved, midlobe small, rounded, disc with a transverse membrane between the side lobes and the midlobe; column erect, as long as the sepals, broad above; anther 2-chambered; pollinia 4, waxy, pyriform, all attached by a short caudicle to a broad gland.

Two species distributed in South India and Ceylon.

KEY TO THE SPECIES

1 Leaves oblong-lanceolate, peduncle 15–20 cm long; midlobe of lip subquadrately rounded...1. S. lanceolata
1 Leaves oval or oblong, peduncle 10–15 cm long; midlobe of lip ovate....2. S. latifolia

1. Sirhookera lanceolata (Wight) Kuntze, Rev. Gen. Pl. 2: 681. 1891. —Fig. 118.

Josephia lanceolata Wight, Ic. Pl. Ind. Or. 5 (1): 19, pl. 1742. 1851; Trimen, Handb. Fl. Ceylon 4: 182. 1898.
Polystachya ramosa Gardner ex Thw., Enum. Pl. Zeyl. 307. 1861.

Epiphyte with very short pseudobulbous stems and long vermiform roots. Leaves solitary or two to a pseudobulb, petiolate, 5–11 × 1.5–3.3 cm, oblanceolate, coriaceous, base continuing into the petiolar sheath which when young is surrounded by four green, purple-veined sheaths, later becoming papery and matted; lower surfaces of young leaves purple-spotted and the lower scaly sheaths blotched purple especially along the veins. Flowers pale purple, in compound, racemose continuously flowering spikes which measure

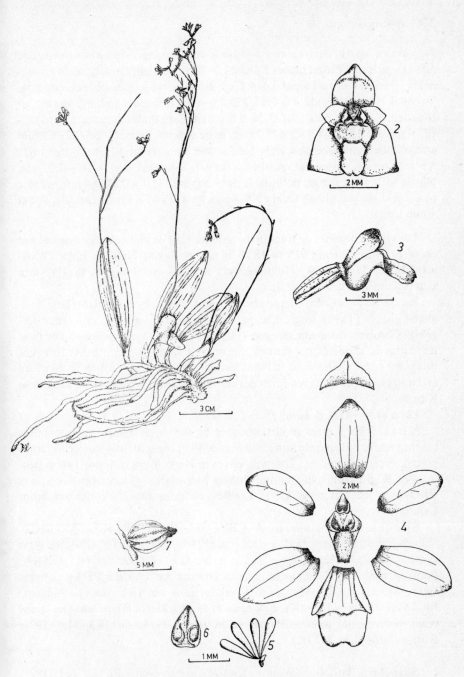

Fig. 118. *Sirhookera lanceolata* (Wight) Kuntze. 1, plant with inflorescences and
stout roots. 2, flower from front. 3, lip and column from side. 4, bract, sepals,
petals and lip spread out from front, column from inside with operculum flapped
over. 5, pollinia with gland. 6, operculum from inside. 7, fruit.

7–23 cm in length, each spike 1.5–5 cm long, carrying 2–10 flowers; peduncle 5.5–11 cm long. Floral bracts 1.4–2 × 1.2–2 mm, broadly ovate, acute or subacute, 1-veined; dorsal sepal 3.4–4.2 × 2–2.6 mm, lanceolate-oblong, concave, 3-veined; lateral sepals 3.6–3.8 × 2.2–2.6 mm, obliquely oblong, obtuse or rounded, 3-veined; petals 3.1–3.2 × 0.6–0.8 mm, spathulate, truncate or rounded, 1-veined; lip 3.5–4.8 × 2.6–3.2 mm, panduriform, lateral lobes short, blunt and rounded, midlobe obscurely bifid at the apex; column 2.4–2.8 mm high, 1.8 mm broad, obconical. Anther terminal, 2-loculed, 1–1.4 × 0.8–1.2 mm, purple with white fringe; pollinia 4, club-shaped, 1–1.1 × 0.24–0.4 mm, adnate to a shield-shaped gland. Ovary 2.4–4 mm long. Fruit a sessile capsule, about 4 mm long.

D i s t r. Common, on trees in the submontane or mid-country tropical wet evergreen forests from 915 to 1829 m alt. Rangala, Nuwara Eliya (Westward-Ho) Adam's Peak, Hunnasgiriya, etc. Also in India in the Western Ghats from Konkan to Kerala.

E c o l. Flowers May–September. Some of its many host plants are *Palaquium grande* (Thw.) Engl., *Calophyllum trapezifolium* Thw., *Syzygium fergusoni* Gamble., *Gordonia speciosa* (Gardn.) Choisy, *Symplocos* sp. The light it receives is about 24 per cent of the normal sunlight. Two other forms of this plant occur in the same habitat: a white-flowered form which is very rare and a light purple-flowered form darker in colour than *Sirhookera lanceolata* Kuntze.

I l l u s t r. PDA, drawing from *C.P. 2358*.

N o t e. This species is distinguished by the 1- or 2-leaved pseudobulbs bearing small, pale purple flowers in Statice-like, continuously flowering, compound, racemose spikes. The type cover in Herb. Kew contains two collections of Wight from Nilgiris and Pulney Mountains. That from Nilgiris is selected as the lectotype. Herb. Lindley contains Stock's collection from Canara.

S p e c i m e n s E x a m i n e d. CEYLON: RATNAPURA DISTRICT: Sinharaja Forest, Sept. 1891, *s. coll. s.n.* (PDA). LOCALITY UNKNOWN: *s. coll. C.P. 2358* (K, PDA); *s. coll. s.n.* (AMES); *Walker s.n.* (K). INDIA: Bombay: Malabar, Konkan etc., *Stocks, Law* etc. *s.n.* (AMES, PDA); Canara, Herb. *Stocks 50* (K). Mysore & Konkan, *Law s.n.* (K). Madras: Nilgiris, Jul. 1884, *Gamble 14289* (K), *E. Barnes 1745* (K); Herb. *Wight s.n.* (K, lectotype). Kodaikanal Region: Pulney Hills, *Herb. Wight s.n.* (K); May 1927, *Blatter & Hallberg 333* (K).

2. **Sirhookera latifolia** (Wight) Kuntze, Rev. Gen. Pl. 2: 681. 1891. —**Fig. 119.**

Josephia latifolia Wight, Ic. Pl. Ind. Or. 5 (1): 19. pl. 1743. 1851; Trimen, Handb. Fl. Ceylon 4: 182. 1898.

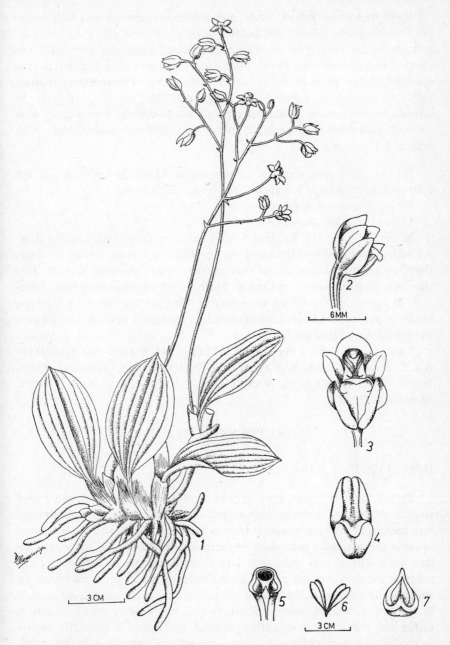

Fig. 119. *Sirhookera latifolia* (Wight) Kuntze, redrawn from a drawing in PDA.
1, plant with inflorescences. 2, flower from side. 3, flower from front. 4, lip from
front, natural position. 5, top of the column from front. 6, pollinia. 7, operculum
from inside.

Epiphyte with very short, hardy, pseudobulbous stems clothed with reticulate, membranous sheaths and bearing long vermiform roots. Leaves solitary, 5–7.5 cm long, oval or oblong, coriaceous, apiculate, narrowed into short channelled petioles. Flowers small in slender spreading panicles; peduncle 10–12.5 cm long, branches slender, spreading. Floral bracts minute, subulate, coriaceous; sepals 4 mm long, orbicular, 3-veined, concave, the laterals hardly saccate at the base; petals linear-oblong, 1-veined; lip with rounded lateral lobes and saccate in between, midlobe ovate. Ovary with pedicel 2.5 mm long.

D i s t r. Very rare, reported as growing at Ramboda by Nock and not collected since. Also in Kerala and the Nilgiri Hills in India.

E c o l. Flowers August.

I l l u s t r. PDA, drawing.

N o t e. Hooker (Fl. Br. Ind. 5: 823) mentions that it bears yellow flowers with purple stripes at the tip of the lip while in Trimen's Flora he states that they are of a deeper colour than in *Sirhookera lanceolata* Kuntze. This species is probably extinct in Ceylon. Herb. Lindley contains the type collection. It resembles *Sirhookera lanceolata* in habit but the leaves are broader, more coriaceous and flowers few in spreading panicles. I have not come across live specimens of this species.

S p e c i m e n s   E x a m i n e d. CEYLON: NUWARA ELIYA DISTRICT: Ramboda, 1896, *Nock s.n.* (PDA). INDIA: Kerala: Courtallam, Herb. *Wight 1743* (K, lectotype), *Wight 906* (K); Kavalay Cochin, Nov. 1909, *Meebold 12290* (K).

43. POLYSTACHYA

Hook., Exot. Fl. 2. t. 103. 1825.

Tufted epiphytes; stems leafy or pseudobulbous at the base or with a hard rootstock; roots vermiform; leaves few, distichous, coriaceous, contracted into sheaths at the base; peduncle terminal, erect, clothed with tubular membranous sheaths, apex paniculate or racemose; flowers small, resupinate; sepals connivent, dorsal sepal free, lateral sepals adnate to the foot of the column; mentum conical; petals like the dorsal sepal or often narrower; lip superior, articulated to the foot of the column, base contracted, entire or 3-lobed; disc pubescent; column short, broad, not winged, produced into a rather long foot at the base; anther terminal, operculate, hemispheric, imperfectly 2-chambered; pollinia 4, waxy, subsessile in pairs on a broad gland; capsule fusiform, elongated.

About 100 species distributed throughout tropical Africa and extending to Malaya through India and Ceylon.

Polystachya concreta (Jacq.) Garay and Sweet, Orquideologia 9 (3): 206. 1974.
—Fig. 120.

Polystachya zeylanica Lindl., Bot. Reg. 24: Misc. 78. 1838; Trimen, Handb.
Fl. Ceylon 4: 183. 1898.
Dendrobium polystachyum Thouars, Orch. Afr. pl. 85. 1822.
Polystachya luteola Lindl., Gen. et Sp. Orch. 73. 1830.

Epiphyte with a stout pseudobulbous stem, clothed with old leaf sheaths
and bearing vermiform roots; stems tufted, 15–25 cm long. Leaves 4–6, alternate, distichous, 10–20 × 1.2–3 cm, linear-oblong or oblanceolate, obtuse
with a minute incurved tooth at the apex, base sheathing, many-veined with a
distinct median vein, coriaceous, shining and slightly wavy along the margin.
Flowers pale yellow, 1 cm broad, resupinate in terminal panicles; peduncle
together with the panicle 15–42 cm long, rachis faintly tomentose; racemes
branching, 6–7 cm long, bearing numerous flowers. Floral bracts 5 × 3.6 mm,
ovate, acuminate, acute, 2–4-veined, persistent; dorsal sepal 3.9–4.1 × 2–2.1
mm, oblong-ovate, acuminate, 3-veined; lateral sepals 4.8–5 × 3.5–4 mm,
triangular-ovate, acuminate, inserted on the foot of the column, 3-veined but
one of the lateral veins bifurcate giving a 4-veined appearance; petals 3.2–3.5
× 0.8 mm, linear-oblong, subacute, 1-veined; lip 4 mm long and as broad,
cuneate-obovate, superior, joined to the foot of the column, 3-veined, the lateral veins trifurcate at the base, supplying the lateral lobes and the midlobe,
lateral lobes falcate, subacute; midlobe broadly oblong, rounded, fimbriate;
disc scurfy; column 1.9 mm high, 1.3 mm broad. Anther terminal, 2-loculed,
1 × 1.25 mm, pollinia 4, in two pairs, 0.5 × 0.4 mm, subglobose, attached to a
very short strap or gland. Ovary with pedicel 6 mm long. Fruit a small, fusiform capsule 1.2 × 0.35 cm.

D i s t r. Rather common, growing on trees in the submontane or mid-
country tropical wet evergreen forests up to 1677 m alt. Peradeniya, Rangala,
Ramboda, Melsiripura, Maturata, Ratnapura, Kabaragala, Ambagamuwa,
Nuwara Eliya (Westward-Ho), Hantane, Ritigala, Hunnasgiriya, Adam's
Peak, Laggala, etc.

E c o l. Flowers March, April, July–October. Some of its many host
plants are *Samanea saman* (Jacq.) Merr., *Mangifera indica* L., *Antidesma
bunius* (L.) Spreng., *Hevea brasiliensis* (Kunth) Muell.—Arg, *Artocarpus heterophyllus* Lam., *Diospyros walkeri* (Wight) Guerke, *Callicarpa tomentosa* (L.)
Murr., *Semecarpus gardneri* Thw., *Ficus retusa* L., *Canthium coromandelicum*
(Burm. f.) Alston, *Oreodoxa oleracea* Mart., *Eurya japonica* Thunb., *Glochidion* sp. and *Scolopia* sp. It receives about 54 per cent of normal sunlight.

I l l u s t r. PDA, two drawings of which one is from *C.P. 2360*.

N o t e. According to Lindley the frost-like mealiness of the lip is a curious modification of hairs also found in other plants. When undisturbed it
consists of threads with egg-shaped joints filled with air. "The surface of each

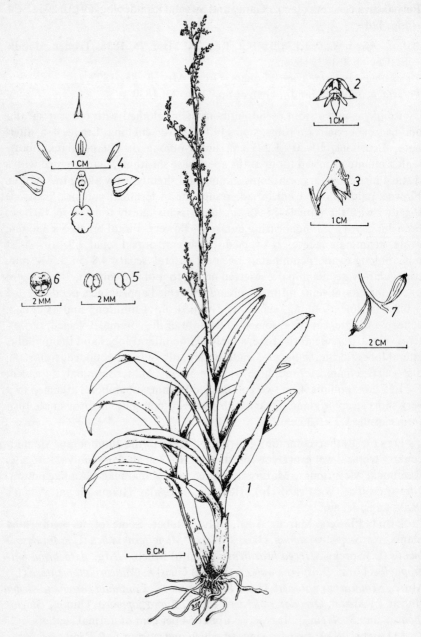

Fig. 120. *Polystachya concreta* (Jacq.) Garay and Sweet. 1, plant with inflorescence. 2, flower from front. 3, flower from side. 4, bract, sepals, petals and lip from front, column from front with portion of foot. 5, pollinia from front and from behind. 6, operculum from inside. 7, fruits.

joint is marked by wavy striae, and the interior uniformly contains a nucleus, to which there appears to belong a circulating apparatus of the same nature as that in the hairs of *Tradescantia* and other plants". The slightest touch destroys the cohesion between the joints. Herb. Lindley contains the collections of Macrae and Loddiges from Ceylon in the same type cover. *Macrae 16* is selected as the lectotype. I have not seen any African collections but Lindley says that it is the same as *Dendrobium polystachyum* Thours which is reduced to a synonym. This species is closely related to *Polystachya wightii* Reichb. f. of South India differing only in size in that the latter is smaller.

Specimens Examined. CEYLON: ANURADHAPURA DISTRICT: Ritigala, Mar. 1905, *Willis s.n.* (PDA), Aug. 1972, *Cramer 3835* (PDA, US), Aug. 1972, *Jayasuriya, Wheeler & Cramer 837* (PDA, US), *Jayasuriya 1091* (PDA, US). KANDY DISTRICT: Corbet's Gap, Sept. 1969, *Grupe 250* (PDA, US); Peradeniya, Bot. Gard., Aug. 1926, *Livera s.n.* (PDA), Jul. 1928, *Senaratne 51* (PDA), Aug. 1955, *Jayaweera 1432* (PDA); Hantane, May 1959, *Jayaweera 24* (AMES); Ambagamuwa, Jul. 1961, *Jayaweera 2183* (PDA); Hunnasgiriya, Oct. 1960, *Jayaweera 2040* (PDA); Rajamally, Oct. 1975, *Sohmer & Sumithraarachchi 9812* (PDA, US). KALUTARA DISTRICT: Moragala, June 1975, *Waas 1273* (PDA, US). NUWARA ELIYA DISTRICT: Hakgala, Apr. 1906, *A.M. Silva s.n.* (PDA). BADULLA DISTRICT: Haputale, Pita Ratmale Estate, Jul. 1969, *Wheeler 12185* (PDA, US). INDIA: Mysore: Coorg, Sept. 1934, *Barnes 895* (K). Madras: Annaimalai Hills, Aug. 1920, *Fischer 4480* (K).

44. SARCANTHUS

Lindl., Bot. Reg. 10. sub t. 817. 1824.

Epiphytes; stems short or long, erect or hanging, non-pseudobulbous; leaves flat or terete, articulate on a short sheath; inflorescences racemose or panicled, erect or pendulous, leaf-opposed and many-flowered, flowers rather small; sepals and petals similar, usually spreading; lip 3-lobed, spurred, joined to the foot of the column by the back edges of the side lobes, with a conspicuous callus at the entrance to the spur on its back wall and often another opposite to it; spur conical or cylindric, often longitudinally septate; column short with a short foot; pollinia 4, united in two round bodies, strap very slender, gland small.

About 168 species distributed over tropical Africa, India, Ceylon, Burma, Thailand to China and southwards to Java, Sumatra, Borneo, New Guinea and the Philippine Islands.

Sarcanthus peninsularis Dalzell in Hook. J. Bot. Kew Gard. Misc. 3: 247. 1857; Trimen, Handb. Fl. Ceylon 4: 200. 1898—**Fig. 121.**

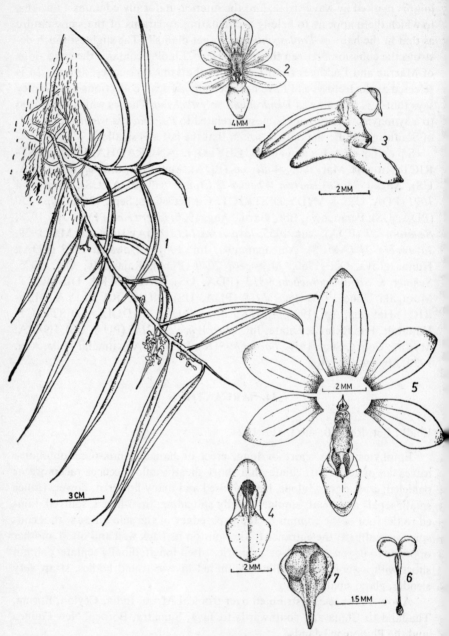

Fig. 121. *Sarcanthus peninsularis* Dalzell. 1, plant with inflorescences. 2, flower from front. 3, lip, column and foot from side. 4, lip and column from above. 5, sepals, petals, lip and column from front, lip not spread out, operculum flapped over showing the position of pollinia. 6, pollinia with strap and gland. 7, operculum from inside.

Sarcanthus pauciflorus Wight, Ic. Pl. Ind. Or. 5 (1): 20, pl. 1747. 1851.
Saccolabium acuminatum Thw., Enum. Pl. Zeyl. 304. 1861.
Saccolabium peninsulare (Dalzell) Alston in Trimen, Handb. Fl. Ceylon 6: 278. 1931.

Epiphyte with simple, non-pseudobulbous, flexuous stems 10–30 cm long; internodes 0.9–1.2 cm long, slightly flattened; roots vandaceous in the lower part of the stem, arising from internodes and emerging through the leaf sheaths of the lower nodes. Leaves 8–17 × 0.5–0.8 cm, linear-lanceolate, falcately recurved, dark green above and ash-green below, acuminate, keeled, coriaceous, bases sheathing the internodes above, 9-veined. Flowers small, 7 mm across, waxy, brownish-yellow with a white lip and pink wings, in stout, few-flowered, leaf-opposed racemes; peduncle 6–10 mm long; the flower-bearing portion of the raceme 1.2–1.7 cm long. Floral bracts minute, 1 × 1.6 mm, obtuse; dorsal sepal 4.8 × 2.7 mm, ovate-oblong, obtuse, concave, 5-veined; lateral sepals 3.8 × 2.2 mm, obliquely obovate-oblong, obtuse, 3-veined; petals 3.7 × 2.2 mm, obovate-oblong, rounded, 3-veined; lip along with the spur 4.6 mm long, 3-lobed; lateral lobes very short, erect, subacute; midlobe small, margins incurved; spur as long as the midlobe, conical, septate to near the mouth vertically; dorsal callus 2-lobed; column 1.4 mm high, 1.8 mm broad, extending to a very short foot. Anther terminal, 2-loculed, 2 × 1.4 mm; pollinia 4, subglobose, in two pairs; each pair consisting of a large pollinium 0.6 × 0.56 mm and a smaller and more spherical one 0.56 × 0.42 mm, attached by short caudicles to the broad bent-end of a linear, grooved strap and a small gland. Ovary with pedicel 4.6 mm long. Fruit a deflexed, fusiform capsule, 2 cm long.

D i s t r. Rare, on trees in the tropical wet evergreen forests up to 302 m alt. Ratnapura, Ambagamuwa, etc. Also in the Western Ghats from Konkan to Kerala in India.

E c o l. Flowers August–October. Some of its many host plants are *Wormia triquetra* Rottb., *Memecylon* sp., *Pometia tomentosa* (Bl.) Teys. and Binn., *Syzygium* sp., *Ouratea zeylanica* (Lam.) Alston. Other epiphytes associated with it besides mosses and lichens on a *Wormia triquetra* at Ambagamuwa are *Bulbophyllum thwaitesii* (Reichb. f.) Hook. f., *Cymbidium aloifolium* (L.) Sw., *Pholidota pallida* Lindl., *Vittaria elongata* Sw., *Nephrolepis exaltata* (L.) Schott., *Pothos scandens* L., *Drynaria* sp. and *Freycinetia pycnophylla* Solms.

I l l u s t r. PDA, drawing from *C.P. 3376.*

N o t e. Herb. Lindley contains the type collection *Dalzell 35.* Herb. Kew on the other hand contains four collections including *C.P. 3376* in the type cover. Thwaites says that the presence of the dorsal tooth within the labellum indicates an approach to *Cleisostoma.*

S p e c i m e n s E x a m i n e d. CEYLON: KANDY DISTRICT: Ambagamuwa, Sept. 1960, *Jayaweera 2056* (PDA), Oct. 1960, *Jayaweera 217* (PDA), Oct. 1959, *Jayaweera 33* (AMES). KEGALLE DISTRICT: Kitulgala Aug. 1937, *Alston 1940* (PDA). RATNAPURA DISTRICT: Mangala Oy Forest, Jun. 1976, *Waas 1689* (PDA, US); Panil Kande, Jul. 1975, *Wass 141* (PDA, US); Gilimale, Apr. 1960, *Jayaweera 2057* (PDA). INDIA: Kal Nuddi, May 1853, *Richie 1430* (K); Malabar, Konkan etc. *Stocks s.n* (K); Malabar, *Stocks s.n.* (AMES). Kerala: Quilon, Herb. *Wight s.n.* (K) Madras: Nov. 1867, *Johnson 1747* (K); Wynaad, Aug. 1905, *Barber 7408* (K) Pen. Ind. Or., Herb. *Wight 2987* (K).

45. PODOCHILUS

Blume, Bijdr. 295. t. 12. 1825.

Epiphytes with tufted, leafy, erect or diffuse, non-pseudobulbous, slende stems rooting at the base only; leaves short, distichous, closely imbricate equitant, laterally compressed, coriaceous, not jonited on the sheaths; flow ers small or minute in terminal or leaf-opposed spikes or racemes, resupin ate; petals smaller than sepals, lateral sepals adnate to the long, decurved foo of the column and forming with it a spur-like mentum; lip jointed on the ape of the foot of the column, narrow, entire, membranous; column short; rostel lum broad, erect, at length bifid; anther at the back of the column, erect, 2 chambered; pollinia 4, pyriform, waxy, pendulous in pairs from a small glan at the tip of the rostellum, each pair enclosed in a calyptriform membran that comes out with it.

About 140 species in India, Ceylon, Malaya, Burma, China and extending southwards to Java, Sumatra, Borneo, Celebes, New Guinea and the Philip pine Islands.

KEY TO THE SPECIES

1 Plants large, 13–30 cm long; leaves 1.4–2 cm long; flowers white or pink
  2 Flowers 5 mm broad, lip 4.6–5.2 mm long, spathulate-lanceolate; pollinia straps long
    and recurved...**1. P. falcatu**
  2 Flowers 3.2 mm broad, lip 2.8 mm long, oblong-lanceolate; pollinia straps short and
    not recurved...**2. P. malabaricu**
1 Plants small, 4–5.5 cm long; leaves 0.4–0.5 cm long; flowers yellow......**3. P. saxatili**

1. Podochilus falcatus Lindl., Gen. et Sp. Orch. 234. 1833; Trimen, Handb. Fl. Ceylon 4: 205. 1898.—**Fig. 122.**

Tufted, leafy epiphyte with slender, non-pseudobulbous stems 13–30 cm long, naked and bearing adventitious roots at the base. Leaves 1.5–2 × 0.5 cm, distichous, equitant, laterally compressed, subulate or ovate-subulate acute, subacute or obtuse, straight, erect, sheathing the stem at the base bu not jointed on sheaths. Flowers pink with a white spur, 5 mm broad in termi-

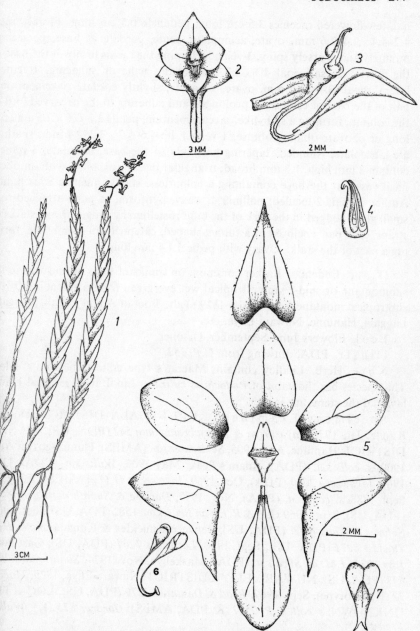

Fig. 122. *Podochilus falcatus* Lindl. 1, plants with inflorescences. 2, flower from front. 3, lip, column and foot from side, three-quarters view. 4, column from top showing the position of pollinia, enlarged. 5, bract, sepals, petals, lip and column spread out from front. 6, pollinia with their funnel-shaped calyptriform membranes, straps and gland, enlarged. 7, operculum from front, enlarged.

nal, few-flowered racemes 3.5 cm long; peduncle 0.5 cm long. Floral bract 4.2–4.4 × 2.4–2.6 mm, ovate, acuminate, acute, cordate at base, persistent minutely and sparsely spiny, 3-veined, clasping the rachis firmly at the base o the flower; dorsal sepal 4.1 × 2.7 mm, ovate, acute or subacute, 1-veined lateral sepals 3.7 × 2.6 mm, ovate, subacute, slightly cordate, 1-veined; one half of the base of each sepal prolonged and adhering to the decurved foot o the column, forming a spur-like, saccate mentum; petals 3.2–3.6 × 2.5 mm, ob long or obovate-oblong, obtuse, 1-veined; lip 4.6–5.2 × 2.2–2.4 mm, spathul ate-lanceolate, rounded, tapering narrowly to the base, undulate, 3-veinec column 2 mm high, 1.8 mm broad, triangular or conical, bifid, with an obcc nical vessel at the base containing a colourless, sticky, mucilaginous liquic Anther dorsal, 2-loculed; pollinia 4, waxy, pyriform, in pairs attached to small gland lodged in the fork of the bifid rostellum by long, springy stalks c straps; each pair enclosed in a funnel-shaped, calyptriform membrane, forn ing a part of the stalk. Ovary with pedicel 4.4 mm long.

D i s t r. Endemic. Rather common, on trunks of trees or on rocks in th submontane or mid-country tropical wet evergreen forests extending to tł subtropical montane forests, 610–1829 m alt. Foot of Adam's Peak, Rangal Laggala, Hantane, Nuwara Eliya, etc.

E c o l. Flowers June–September, October.

I l l u s t r. PDA, drawing from *C.P. 2527.*

N o t e. Herb. Lindley contains Macrae's type collection from Ceylo This species has the habit of *Podochilus cultratus* Lindl. from tropical Him laya but the stems are longer.

S p e c i m e n s E x a m i n e d. KURUNEGALA DISTRICT: Doluv Kande, Jan. 1972, *Jayasuriya & Balasubramaniam 542* (PDA, US). KAND DISTRICT: Hantane, Aug. 1905, *Schlechter s.n.* (AMES); Hunnasgiriya, Au 1900, *s. coll. s.n.* (PDA); Adam's Peak, May 1906, *Willis s.n.* (PDA), De 1960, *Jayaweera 2040* (PDA), Oct. 1959, *Jayaweera 41 (1)* (AMES); Rangaŀ Sept. 1888, *s. coll. s.n.* (PDA), Nov. 1977, *Davidse & Sumithraarachchi 86.* (PDA, US), Sept. 1969 *C.F. & R.J. Van Beusekom 1582* (PDA, US), Sept. 196 *Sohmer & Waas 8706* (PDA, US); Between Knuckles & Ritigala, Nov. 197 *Davidse 8271* (PDA, US), Sept. 1970, *Lazarides 7204* (PDA, US); Gartmor July 1924, *J.M. de Silva s.n.* (PDA); Maskeliya, Nov. 1974, *Sumithraarachc 547* (PDA, US). NUWARA ELIYA DISTRICT: Nuwara Eliya, 1829, *Macr 72* (K, holotype), Sept. 1969, *Read & Desuntels 2279* (PDA, US). LOCALIT UNKNOWN: *s. coll. C.P. 2527* (K, PDA, AMES); *Gardner 873* (K); *Walŀ 217* (K).

2. **Podochilus malabaricus** Wight, Ic. Pl. Ind. Or. 5 (1): 20, pl. 1748. f. 2. 18: Trimen, Handb. Fl. Ceylon 4: 206. 1898.—**Fig. 123.**

Podochilus falcatus var. *angustatus* Thw., nomen.

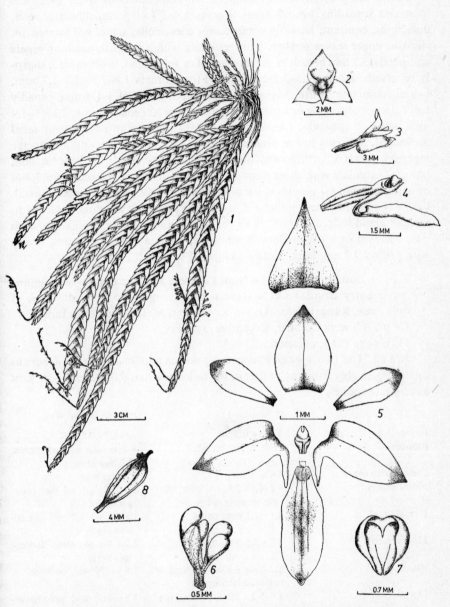

Fig. 123. *Podochilus malabaricus* Wight. 1, plant with inflorescences. 2, flower from front. 3, flower from side. 4, lip, column and foot from side. 5, bract, sepals, petals, lip and column spread out from front. 6, pollinia with their calyptriform membranes, straps and gland. 7, operculum from inside. 8, fruit.

Tufted leafy epiphyte with slender, non-pseudobulbous stems 14–28 cm long and spreading fibrous roots. Leaves 1.4–1.7 × 0.5 cm, subulate, erect, distichous, equitant, laterally compressed, coriaceous, acute, not jointed on sheaths; upper leaves smaller. Flowers white with a purplish patch on sepals and petals, 3.2 mm broad, in short terminal or subrotund, lax-flowered, sharply recurved racemes 2.5–3.5 cm long. Floral bracts 1.8–2.2 × 1.3–1.7 mm, ovate, acuminate, acute, 3-veined; dorsal sepal 1.8–2 × 1.3–1.4 mm, broadly lanceolate-ovate, acute or subacute; lateral sepals lanceolate-ovate, 2.2 × 1–1.4 mm, acute or subacute, 1-veined; one-half of the base of each lateral sepal prolonged, adhering to the decurved foot of the column forming a spur-like mentum; petals 1.8 × 0.76 mm, obovate, obtuse, 1-veined; lip 2.8 × 1.6 mm, oblong-lanceolate with three purplish blotches, obtuse, 3-veined, lateral lobes obscure; column 1.1 mm high, 0.9 mm broad; rostellum bifid. Anther dorsal, 0.8 × 0.5 mm, 2-loculed; pollinia 4, pyriform, waxy, in two pairs, attached to a small gland lodged in the fork of the rostellum by a very short strap, each pair enclosed in a calyptriform membrane; pollinia 0.44 × 0.24 mm. Ovary with pedicel 2.2 mm long. Fruit an ellipsoid capsule 5.2 × 2 mm.

D i s t r. Rather common, on trunks of trees and rocks in the submontane or mid-country tropical wet evergreen forests up to 1372 m alt. Foot of Adam's Peak, Rangala, etc. Also in Kerala and Malabar in South India.

E c o l. Flowers October, December, January.

I l l u s t r. PDA, drawing.

N o t e. The two species *Podochilus falcatus* and *Podochilus malabaricus* differ appreciably from each other in the following characters so as to be kept as separate species.

	P. falcatus Lindl.	*P. malabaricus* Wight
Leaves	1.5–2 × 0.5 cm	1.4–1.7 × 0.5 cm
Flowers	Pink, 5 mm broad	White with purple blotches, 3.2 mm broad
Pedicel with ovary	4.4 mm long	2.2 mm long
Floral bracts	4.2–4.4 × 2.4–2.6 mm, margin sparsely spiny	1.8–2.2 × 1.3–1.4 mm, margin entire
Dorsal sepal	4.1 × 2.7 mm, ovate	1.8–2 × 1.3–1.7 mm, lanceolate-ovate
Lateral sepals	3.7 × 2.6 mm, ovate	2.2 × 1–1.14 mm, lanceolate-ovate
Petals	3.2–3.6 × 2.5 mm, oblong or obovate-oblong	1.8 × 0.76 mm, obovate
Lip	4.6–5.2 × 2.2–2.4 mm, spathulate-lanceolate	2.8 × 1.6 mm, oblong-lanceolate
Column	2 mm high, triangular or conical	1.1 mm high, ellipsoid-conical
Strap (pollinia)	Long, recurved	Short, not recurved
Operculum	Triangular ovate	Broadly ovate

Specimens Examined. CEYLON: KANDY DISTRICT: Galage-
dera, Oct. 1882, *s. coll. s.n.* (PDA); Adam's Peak, *Jayaweera 2304* (PDA),
Jan. 1960, *Jayaweera 2042* (PDA), *Jayaweera 41(2)* (AMES); Moray Estate,
Rajamally, Oct. 1975, *Sohmer & Sumithraarachchi 9873* (PDA, US). LOCA-
LITY UNKNOWN: *s. coll. C.P. 3889* (PDA). INDIA: Kerala: Wynaad,
Feb. 1857, *Johnson s.n.* (K), Sept. 1900, *Barber 2034* (K).

3. Podochilus saxatilis Lindl., Gen. et Sp. Orch. 235. 1833; Trimen, Handb.
Fl. Ceylon 4: 206. 1898.—**Fig. 124.**

Small tufted epiphyte with non-pseudobulbous, leafy stems 4–5.5 cm long
with adventitious roots at their bases and also producing adventitious buds
with roots towards the ends of stems as means of vegetative propagation.
Leaves 4.4–5.2 × 1.8 mm, ovate, laterally compressed, distichous, slightly recurved and rounded at the apex. Flowers yellow, 1.8 mm broad, in 4–6-flow-
ered, terminal, recurved recemes about 1 cm long. Floral bracts 1.2 × 1.1
mm, ovate, acuminate, 3-veined; dorsal sepal 2 × 1.12 mm, oblong-ovate,
obtuse, 1-veined; lateral sepals 1.5 × 0.9 mm, ovate, obtuse, 1-veined, one-half
of the base of each sepal continuing down and adnate to the recurved foot of
the column forming a saccate, spur-like mentum; petals 1.6 × 0.8 mm, oblong-
lanceolate, obtuse or rounded, 1-veined; lip 2.4 mm long, spathulate, 3-veined,
adnate to the end of the foot; lateral lobes inconspicuous, linear and folded
in at the margins; midlobe ovate, 1 mm long, 0.72 mm broad, faintly and
bluntly apiculate; column short, bifid at apex. Anther dorsal, 2-loculed,
0.6 × 0.5 mm; pollinia 4, pyriform, waxy, in pairs attached to a shield-shaped
gland at the tip of the rostellum by filiform straps, a membranous conical
sheath enveloping each pair; each pollinium 0.5 × 0.2 mm. Ovary with pedicel
1.8 mm long. Fruit a small, globular capsule, 3.5 × 2.5 mm.

Distr. Endemic. Rare, on trunks of trees in the tropical wet evergreen
forests up to 915 m alt. Ratnapura (Gilimale, Kuruwita Kande and Karawita
Kande), Hantane, Ambagamuwa, Doluwa Kande, Ritigala, etc.

Ecol. Flowers March, October–December.

Illustr. PDA, drawing from *C.P. 3194.*

Note. This species is distinguished by the small size of the plant with
adventitious buds at the ends of stems and terminal yellow flowers in recurved racemes.

Specimens Examined. ANURADHAPURA DISTRICT: Ritiga-
la, Mar. 1905, *Willis s.n.* (PDA), Mar. 1905, *Schlechter s.n.* (AMES), Aug.
1972, *Wheeler 12732* (PDA, US), Jan. 1973, *Jayasuriya 1046* (PDA, US), Dec.
1975, *Bernardi 16122* (PDA, US). KURUNEGALA DISTRICT: Doluwa
Kande, Dec. 1883, *s. coll. s.n.* (PDA), Jan. 1972, *Jayasuriya & Subramanium
543* (PDA, US). KANDY DISTRICT: Peradeniya, 1829, *Macrae 52* (K, holotype). KALUTARA DISTRICT: Hewessa, Nov. 1894, *s. coll. s.n.* (PDA).

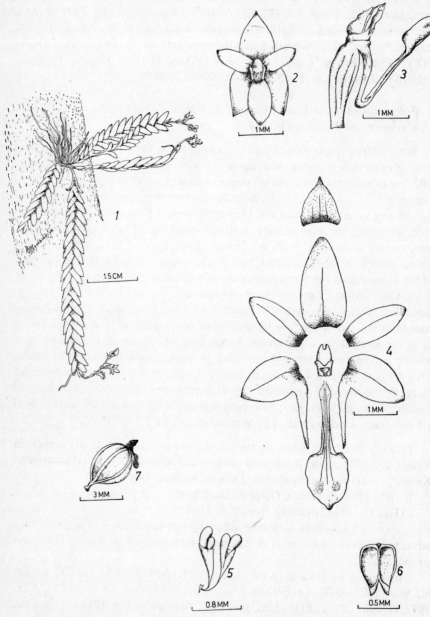

Fig. 124. *Podochilus saxatilis* Lindl. 1, plant with inflorescences. 2, flower from front. 3, lip column and foot from side. 4, bract, sepals, petals, lip and column spread out from front. 5, pollinia with their calyptriform membranes, straps and gland. 6, operculum from inside. 7, fruit.

RATNAPURA DISTRICT: Ratnapura, Oct. 1959, *Jayaweera 41(3)* (AMES); Gilimale, Nov. 1963, *Jayaweera 2359* (PDA). GALLE DISTRICT: *s. loc.*, *Sohmer & Waas 10370* (PDA, US).

46. TAENIOPHYLLUM

Blume, Bijdr. 354. 1825.

Small leafless epiphytes; stems short, non-pseudobulbous; roots flattened or terete, appressed to the bark of the host; scape of the inflorescence short, slender, rachis slowly elongating, bearing flowers in succession one or two at a time; bracts alternate and 2-ranked or facing all ways; flowers small, spicate; sepals and petals free or united at the base in a tube; lip simple or 3-lobed, spurred, the apex with or without a slender spine-like appendage; spur rounded, conic, cylindric or club-shaped; column short; anther with short or long beak; pollinia 4, equal or unequal, not joined in two pairs, sessile or attached by short or long stipes to a gland.

About 170 species, Ceylon and Northern India through Malaysia to Japan, Tahiti and Australia, Java and New Guinea.

KEY TO THE SPECIES

1 Flower 1.2 mm long; peduncle 0.6–1.2 cm long; bracts distichous.........**1. T. alwisii**
1 Flower 3.3 mm long; peduncle 2 cm long; bracts not distichous........**2. T. gilimalense**

1. Taeniophyllum alwisii Lindl., J. Linn. Soc. Bot. 3: 42. 1859; Trimen, Handb. Fl. Ceylon 4: 203. 1898.—**Fig. 125.**

Minute epiphyte without an apparent stem or leaves, pseudobulbs absent; roots green, fleshy, tortuous, 1.5–2.8 cm long, 1 mm diameter; seed germinating into a thallus-like structure lying at first vertical to and later flat on the bark of the tree and resembling a leaf; thallus small, less than 2 cm long, very narrow, acute at both ends; roots produced later from its base. Flowers minute, whitish-green, in very slender, erect, few-flowered spikes; peduncle 4.5 mm long. Floral bracts 0.55×0.8 mm, triangular-ovate, rounded, persistent; sepals, petals and lip connate into a 6-toothed perianth. At their free ends, dorsal sepal 0.76×0.6 mm, triangular-ovate, obtuse, 1-veined, lateral sepals 0.83×0.63 mm, lanceolate-ovate, obtuse, 1-veined; petals 0.7×0.56 mm, ovate, subacute, 1-veined; lip 1.16×0.91 mm, lanceolate-ovate with free margins, apex acute, recurved into a barb like a harpoon, cymbiform, 3-veined, with base produced into a rounded sac 0.9×0.7 mm; sepals and petals fused to the brim of this sac; column very short, 0.33 mm high, cup-shaped, rostellum divided into two spathulate arms in front, each measuring 0.41 mm in length. Anther terminal, depressed, sub-4-loculed, 0.45 mm long and as

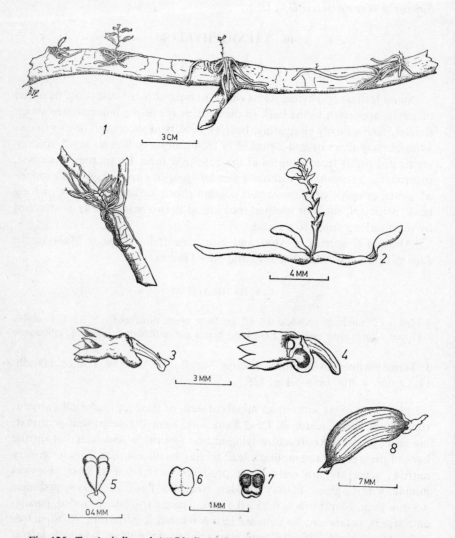

Fig. 125. *Taeniophyllum alwisii* Lindl. 1, plants with inflorescences and fruits growing on the bark of host plant. 2, inflorescence with roots. 3, flower from side. 4,
flower from side with part of perianth removed showing column, anther and spur.
5, pollinia with gland. 6, operculum from front. 7, operculum from inside. 8, fruit.

broad; pollinia 4, sessile on a broad gland, pyriform, 0.25 × 0.15 mm in super-posed pairs. Ovary 1.3 mm long. Fruit a sausage-shaped capsule 5–10 mm long.

D i s t r. Endemic. Rare, on branches of trees and shrubs both in the sub-montane or mid-country tropical wet evergreen forests and the subtropical montane forests from 457 to 1829 m alt. Nuwara Eliya, Mahacoodagala, Hantane, Hunnasgiriya, Botanic Gardens Peradeniya, Hakgala, etc. The sun-light that filters through to the plants is about 15 per cent of normal sunlight.

E c o l. Flowers all the year round. Some of its many host plants are *Calophyllum burmanni* Wight, *Memecylon* sp., *Symplocos* sp., *Eurya japonica* Thunb., *Pygeum wightianum* Bl. ex Walp., *Eugenia* sp., *Syzygium* sp., *Saprosma* sp., *Elaegnus latifolia* L., *Litsea cauliflora* Stapf., *Murraya paniculata* (L.) Jack, *Grevillea robusta* Cunn. and *Eriobotrya japonica* Lindl.

I l l u s t r. Reichb., f. Xenia Orchidacea 2: pl. 116, figs. 1, 11 & 1–3, 1874; PDA, drawing from *C.P. 3195*.

N o t e. There are no specimens of this species at Herb. Kew nor at Oakes Ames Orchid Herbarium. The species was discovered by Mr. H. de Alwis, draftsman of the Bot. Gardens.

S p e c i m e n s   E x a m i n e d. ANURADHAPURA DISTRICT: Riti-gala, Mar. 1905, *Willis s.n.* (PDA), May 1974, *Jayasuriya 1696* (PDA, US). KANDY DISTRICT: Peradeniya, Bot. Gard., *s. coll. C.P. 3195* (PDA), Nov. 1889, *s. coll. s.n.* (PDA), Mar. 1954, *Jayaweera 1113* (PDA). RATNAPURA DISTRICT: Kokkawita, Dec. 1893, *s. coll. s.n.* (PDA).

2. Taeniophyllum gilimalense Jayaweera, Bot. Mus. Leafl. 20 (4): 114–116. 1963.—Fig. 126.

Minute, non-pseudobulbous epiphyte without stems and leaves. Roots flattened, fleshy, dark green and tortuous, 2.5–4 cm × 3 mm. Leaves reduced to minute transparent scales. Flowers minute, greenish-yellow, 3.3 mm long in 2- or 3-flowered racemes, flowers opening one at a time. Peduncle jointed, slightly bent at the joint, 2 cm long, with a single, sterile bract. Floral bracts minute, lanceolate, acute. Sepals, petals and lip connate at the base only; dorsal sepal 1.9 × 0.56 mm, linear-oblong, acuminate, subacute, or rounded, 1-veined; lateral sepals 2.4 × 0.64 mm, lanceolate, rounded, 1-veined; petals 1.3 mm long, 0.7 mm broad, ovate, rounded, 1-veined, lip 2.1 × 0.7 mm; cymbiform, subulate, acute, 1-veined, base produced into a rounded, saccate spur, 0.5 × 0.54 mm; column very short, globular, broad, with two projecting arms in front. Anther terminal, depressed, 4-loculed, 0.26 × 0.34 mm; pollinia 4, pyriform, sessile on a broad gland; large pollinia 0.26 × 0.14 mm, slightly curved, and the smaller ones 0.1 × 0.06 mm. Fruit a sausage-shaped capsule, 4 × 1.3 mm.

D i s t r. Endemic. Very rare, on trees by streams in the tropical wet ever-green forests. Gilimale, etc., at about 152 m alt.

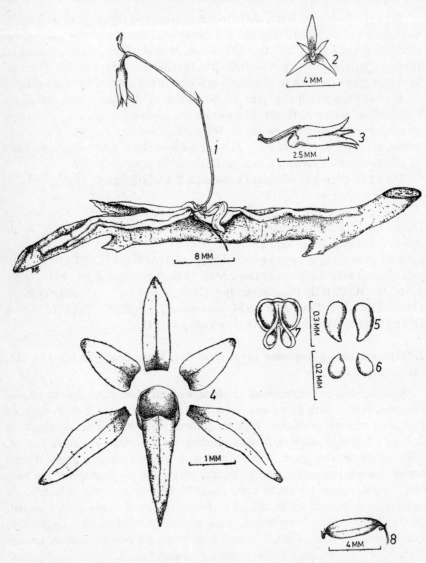

Fig. 126. *Taeniophyllum gilimalense* Jayaweera. 1, plant with inflorescence on twig of host plant. 2, flower from front spread out. 3, flower from side. 4, sepals, petals and lip spread out from front. 5, large pollinia. 6, smaller pollinia. 7, operculum from inside. 8, fruit.

E c o l. Flowers July.

I l l u s t r. Mus. Bot. Leafl. 20/4): pl. 19. 1963.

N o t e. Differs from *T. alwisii* in the size of the plant, longer and broader roots, larger flowers, 1-veined sepals and petals and smaller fruits. Only one collection was made from Gilimale; not observed since. Appears to be related to both *Taeniophyllum inconspicuum* Schltr. and *T. capillare* J.J. Sm. from Celebes but differs from both in the ovate, rotund petals. *T. inconspicuum* has a longer spur while *T. capillare* is a larger plant bearing bigger flowers than this species.

S p e c i m e n s   E x a m i n e d. RATNAPURA DISTRICT: Ratnapura (Gilimale), Jul. 1960, *Jayaweera 2182* (PDA, holotype).

47. PHREATIA

Lindl., Gen. et Sp. Orch. Pl. 63. 1830.

Epiphytes with 2- or 3-leaved pseudobulbous stems or stems without pseudobulbs containing many leaves; leaves distichous, narrow, jointed on the equitant sheaths, coriaceous or fleshy; peduncle terminal; flowers minute in spiciform racemes, rather one-sided; sepals subequal, connivent, lateral sepals adnate to the foot of the column; column-foot well developed with a distinct saccate mentum; petals shorter than sepals; lip inserted on the foot of the column, very small; column short, broad, base produced into a foot; anther terminal, 2-chambered; pollinia 8, microscopic, globosely pyriform, waxy, united by a narrow caudicle to a gland on the rostellum.

About 250 species in India, Ceylon, Malaya, Formosa extending southwards to Java, Sumatra, Borneo, Celebes, New Guinea, Fiji and the Philippine Islands.

Phreatia elegans Lindl., Gen. et Sp. Orch. 63. 1830; Trimen, Handb. Fl. Ceylon 4: 207. 1898.—**Fig. 127.**

Thelasis elegans Blume, Ann. Mus. Bot. Lugduno Batavum 2: 187. 1856.
Phreatis elegans Alston in Trimen, Handb. Fl. Ceylon 6: 278. 1931.

Epiphyte with very short, densely tufted, subpseudobulbous stems and stout fascicled root fibres. Leaves distichous, equitant, 5–10 cm long, sessile on their thin sheaths, linear, coriaceous, obtuse, narrowed at base, 1-veined. Flowers white, minute, in terminal, spiciform many-flowered racemes 5–7.5 cm long; peduncle longer than the leaf, erect; pedicel very short. Floral bracts ovate-oblong or obovate-oblong, acuminate, 1-veined, closely sheathing the curved ovary; sepals 1.2–2 mm long, broadly triangular, acute, 1-veined, dorsal smaller, laterals gibbous at the saccate base and adnate to the foot of the column; petals shorter than the lateral sepals, broadly ovate or ovate; mentum rounded; lip very small, nearly orbicular, clawed, inserted on the

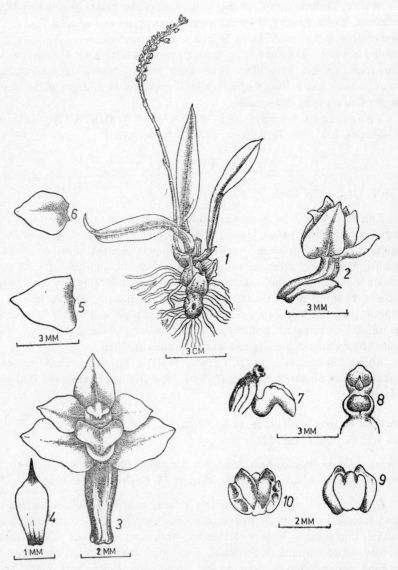

Fig. 127. *Phreatia elegans* Lindl., redrawn from a drawing in PDA. 1, plant with inflorescence. 2, flower from side. 3, flower from front. 4, bract. 5, sepal. 6, petal. 7, lip, column and ovary from side. 8, column from front. 9, anther from front. 10, operculum opened out from front.

foot of the column, obscurely 3-nerved; column very short truncate, with a minute rostellum, base produced into a foot. Anther terminal, membranous, 2-loculed; pollinia 8, very minute, globosely pyriform, cohering by a viscus.

D i s t r. Very rare, on trees in the submontane or mid-country tropical wet evergreen forests up to 762 m alt. Peradeniya, Maskeliya, etc., not collected since 1925. Also in the Khasia Hills and Sikkim Himalayas in India.

E c o l. Flowers January, August.

I l l u s t r. King & Pantling, Ann. R. Bot. Gard. (Calcutta) 8: pl. 333. 1898; PDA, drawing.

N o t e. Herb. Lindley contains Macrae's type collection from Ceylon. The genus is related to *Octarrhena* and *Thelasis* in the dorsal position of the anther in the column, the cellular tissue of the flowers and habit. This species is the only representative in India and Ceylon while other members of this genus are solely confined to Java.

S p e c i m e n s   E x a m i n e d. CEYLON: KANDY DISTRICT: Peradeniya, 1829, *Macrae 38* (K, holotype); Maskeliya, Mariacotta Estate, Jan. 1925, *S.B. Stedman s.n.* (PDA). LOCALITY UNKNOWN: *s. coll. C.P. 3186* (PDA). INDIA: Khasia Hills: *Hooker & Thomson 93* (K). Sikkim Himalaya: Aug. 1899, *Pantling 295* (AMES).

48. OCTARRHENA

Thw., Enum. Pl. Zeyl. 305. 1864.

Tufted epiphytes; roots fibrous; stems leafy towards the apex; leaves distichous, terete or laterally flattened, jointed on their equitant sheaths; peduncle axillary; flowers minute, secund on spiciform racemes; sepals and petals spreading, petals smaller; lip sessile at the base of the column, concave, fleshy, unlobed; column very short, broadly triangular with a deep stigmatic pit at the base; foot absent; anther dorsal, erect, 2-chambered; pollinia 8, microscopic, globosely pyriform, waxy, pendulous by a linear caudicle from a gland attached to the minute rostellum at the top of the column.

About 11 species extending from Ceylon, Malaysia to Sumatra, Borneo, Celebes, New Guinea and the Philippine Islands.

Octarrhena parvula Thw., Enum. Pl. Zeyl. 305. 1861; Trimen, Handb. Fl. Ceylon 4: 208. 1898.—**Fig. 128.**

Phreatia parvula Benth. ex Hook. f., Fl. Br. Ind. 5: 811. 1890.

Small, tufted, epiphytic herb with fibrous roots; stems simple, non-pseudobulbous, 3–8 cm long, stout, curved; bases ensheathed in remnants of old and dried-up leaf-sheaths. Leaves 1–2.5 × 0.25–0.3 cm, linear-oblong, fleshy, distichous, laterally compressed, coriaceous, acute, jointed on their petiolar sheaths and slightly curved. Flowers small, 2.7 mm broad, pale yellowish-green in

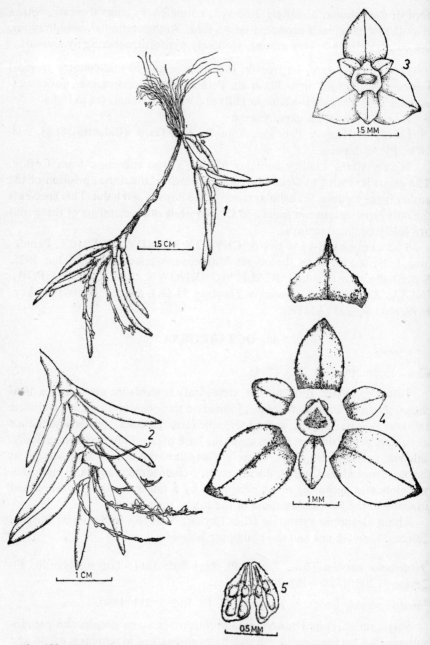

Fig. 128. *Octarrhena parvula* Thw. 1, plant with young inflorescences and fibrous roots. 2, apical portion of a plant with inflorescences bearing open flowers. 3, flower from front. 4, bract, sepals, petals, lip and column spread out from front. 5, anther showing pollinia and caudicles.

spiciform, axillary racemes 2–2.5 cm long and curved; peduncle 0.3–0.7 cm long with 1–3 fleshy sterile bracts. Floral bracts fleshy, green, 1.8×2 mm, broadly ovate, mucronate, suberose, 1-veined, sheathing the short ovary; dorsal sepal 1.7×1.2 mm, oblong-ovate, acute or subacute, 1-veined; lateral sepals 1.6×1.4 mm, obliquely oblong-ovate, obtuse or subacute, 1-veined; petals 0.7×0.56 mm, oblong-ovate, rounded at apex, 1-veined; lip 1×0.6 mm, oblong-lanceolate, concave, sessile at the base of the column; column 0.6 mm high and as broad, triangular with a deep transversely oval stigmatic pit at its base; foot absent. Anther dorsal, erect, 2-loculed; pollinia 8, waxy in 4 pairs, two pairs to each loculus attached to a gland at the top of the rostellum by long caudicles; anterior pollinium of each pair slightly smaller and more spherical than its posterior one, 0.16×0.14 mm; the larger one 0.24×0.16 mm. Ovary with pedicel 1.6 mm long.

Distr. Common, on the upper branches of trees in the submontane or mid-country tropical wet evergreen forests extending to the subtropical montane forests up to 2134 m alt. Rangala, Hakgala, Hantane, Matale, Maturata, Dimbula, Horton, Plains, etc. Also in British North Borneo.

Ecol. Flowers May, August–January. *Calophyllum trapezifolium* Thw. is one of its many host plants. Other epiphytes growing in association with it besides mosses and lichens are *Eria bicolor* Lindl., *Adrorhizon purpurascens* Hook. f., *Podochilus malabaricus* Wight, *Bulbophyllum* sp., *Hymenophyllum* sp., *Pleopeltis* sp., *Vittaria elongata* Sw., etc.

Illustr. PDA, drawing from *C.P. 3072*.

Note. This species is allied to *O. nana* Schlech. from Malay Peninsula and Java, and *O. amesiana* Schlech. from the Philippine Islands. There seems to be hardly any appreciable difference among these three species.

Specimens Examined. CEYLON: KANDY DISTRICT: Corbet's Gap, Sept. 1889, *s. coll. s.n.* (PDA), *Jayaweera 2384* (PDA), Sept. 1959, *Jayaweera 40* (AMES); Dolosbage, *Mrs. Fernando s.n.* (PDA). NUWARA ELIYA DISTRICT: Nuwara Eliya, Nov. 1960, *Jayaweera 2035* (PDA); Horton Plains, Sept. 1890, *s. coll. s.n.* (PDA); Pattipola, May 1906, *A.M. Silva s.n.* (PDA). BRITISH NORTH BORNEO: Mt. Kinabalu, *Clemens 34398* (AMES), at 4500 ft, inner petals purple, *Clemens 34402* (AMES).

49. CRYPTOSTYLIS

R. Br., Prod. 317. 1810.

Terrestrial herbs with short vertical rhizome, thick spreading roots, a few petioled, ovate, membranous leaves from ground level and erect slender stem terminating in a loose-flowered raceme; sepals and petals narrow, spreading, sepals longer than petals; lip superior, erect, unlobed, widest near the base, tapering to the apex, inserted at the base of the column, entire, embracing the column; base strongly concave; column very short with lateral auricles; foot absent; anther dorsal, erect, 2-chambered; pollinia 4, powdery, sessile on a small gland, pendulous from the rostellum; stigma prominent, fleshy.

About 10 species in North India, Ceylon and extending to Australia and Fiji Islands through Malaya, Java, Sumatra, etc.

Cryptostylis arachnites Blume, Orch. Archip. Ind. 133, pl. 45, f. 2. 1858–1859; Trimen, Handb. Fl. Ceylon 4: 209. 1898.—**Fig. 129.**

Zosterostylis arachnites Blume, Bijdr. 419, pl. 32. 1825.
Zosterostylis zeylanica Lindl., Gen. et Sp. Orch. 446. 1840.
Zosterostylis walkerae Wight, Ic. Pl. Ind. Or. 5 (1): 20, pl. 1748. 1851.

Terrestrial herb with a thick rootstock and long, stout, roots with numerous root hairs giving a tomentose appearance. Leaves petioled, 1–3 to a plant, 5–9 × 2.2–3.8 cm, oval-lanceolate, narrowed at both ends, bright green, glabrous and shining with 3 principal veins and many transverse venules; petioles 3–5.5 cm long, chocolate-brown in colour, surrounded at the base by brown, papery sheaths. Flowers green with a reddish-pink lip spotted dark red, 3 cm broad, in long-peduncled racemes 13 cm long; peduncle stout, 20.5 cm long, reddish-brown, base covered with imbricating, brown sheaths and higher up with two fleshy, sterile bracts. Floral bracts 1.3 × 0.5 cm, ovate, acuminate, acute, 5-veined; dorsal sepal 1.4 cm × 2.9 mm, linear-ovate, acuminate, acute, 3-veined; lateral sepals 1.4–1.5 cm × 3.1 mm, linear, ovate, acuminate, acute, 3-veined; petals 0.8–0.9 cm × 1.6 mm, linear or linear-lanceolate, acute, 3-veined; lip superior, 1.5 cm × 6.5 mm oblong, curvaceous, velutinous, acute, margins recurved, cordate, base embracing the minute column; column 3.6 mm high, 2 mm broad, conical, with a broad, acute, notched rostellum. Anther dorsal, 2-loculed, 3.4 × 1.8 mm; pollinia 2, sessile, linear, club-shaped, granular, on a small gland in the rostellum; pollinia 2.5 × 0.8 mm, bifid lengthwise. Ovary with pedicel 1.3 cm long.

D i s t r. Rare, under the shade of trees in the submontane or mid-country tropical wet evergreen forests. Rangala (Corbet's Gap), Nuwara Eliya (Westward Ho), Hatton (Duke's Nose), etc. Also in India, Malaya, Java, Tahiti and the Philippine Islands.

E c o l. Flowers February, March, July, September, October. Associated with *Bambusa* sp., *Exacum axillare* Thw., *Hedyotis* sp., *Calophyllum calaba* L., *Agrostistachys* sp., *Lasianthus* sp., *Sonerila ceylanica* Wight & Arn., *Memecylon* sp., *Gordonia ceylanica* Wight, *Cyperus* sp., etc.

I l l u s t r. Blume, Tabellen en Pl. Jav. Orch. pl. 32. 1825; Hook, Bot. Mag. 89, pl. 5381. 1863; PDA, drawing.

S p e c i m e n s E x a m i n e d. CEYLON: KANDY DISTRICT: Rangala, Sept. 1888, *s. coll. s.n.* (PDA), Mar. 1961, *Jayaweera 1995* (PDA); Gartmore, July 1924, *J.M. de Silva s.n.* (PDA). NUWARA ELIYA DISTRICT:

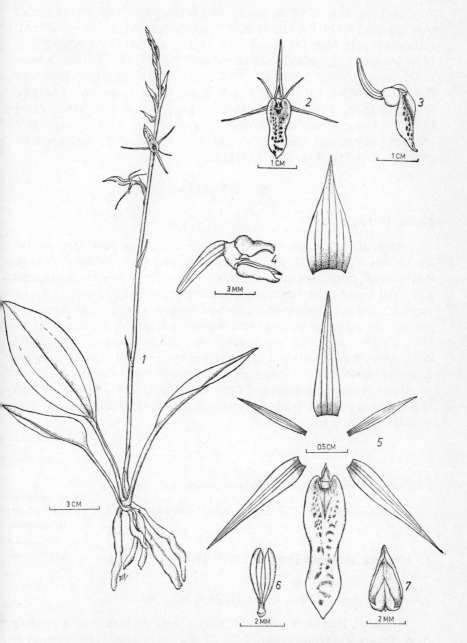

Fig. 129. *Cryptostylis arachnites* Blume. 1, plant with inflorescence. 2, flower, from front. 3, ovary and lip from side, column hidden by base of lip. 4, anther on column from side, operculum slightly parted. 5, bract, sepals, petals, lip and column spread out from front. 6, pollinia with gland. 7, operculum from front.

Westward Ho, May 1959, *Jayaweera 1981* (PDA), May 1959, *Jayaweera 42* (AMES). RATNAPURA DISTRICT: Palabaddala, 1892, *s. coll. s.n.* (PDA); Karawita Kande, Mar. 1881, *s. coll. s.n.* (PDA). LOCALITY UNKNOWN: 1829, *Macrae 13* (K); *Walker 177* (K); *s. coll. C.P. 383* (K). INDIA: Khasia Hills, Herb. *Griffith 5319* (K). JAVA: *Brink 5056* (AMES), *Lobb 196* (K). PHILIPPINE ISLANDS: Luzon, Rizal Prov., *Loher 1470* (AMES); Sorsogon Prov., *Elmer 15842* (AMES); Laguna Prov., *Taguibao 42502* (AMES). Leyte: *Wenzel 384* (AMES). Negros: *Curran & Foxworthy 13617* (AMES). Mindanao: *Elmer 11845* (AMES). Polillo: *C.B. Robinson 9097* (AMES). TAHITI: *Wilkes s.n.* (AMES).

50. HETAERIA

Blume, Fl. Java 84. 1858.

Terrestrial leafy herbs; stems erect from a creeping base, leafy below; leaves relatively broad, usually asymmetric, petioled above the sheathing base; flowers small, glandular-pubescent, in laxly many-flowered spikes; upper sepal and petals form a hood; lateral sepals enclosing the saccate base of the lip; lip superior, concave, shallow and narrowed towards the tip, base containing papillae and glands of various kinds, margins adnate to the sides of the column; column short with two parallel wing-like appendages on the front; anther short, dorsal; pollinia 2, each attached by a caudicle to a gland; stigmas 2, convex, sometimes close together; rostellum sometimes fairly long.

About 74 species in India and Ceylon, extending to Fiji Islands through Malaya, Java, Sumatra, Borneo, New Guinea and the Philippine Islands. Also in Brazil; one African.

KEY TO THE SPECIES

1 Leaves ovate, 3-veined; petals narrowly spathulate, lip with few calli on veins within....
....**1. H. gardneri**
1 Leaves oblong lanceolate, 5- or more-veined; lip with a few, soft spines towards the base
....**2. H. elongata**

1. Hetaeria gardneri (Thw.) Trimen, Handb. Fl. Ceylon 4: 209. 1898 —Fig. 130.

Rhamphidia gardneri Thw., Enum. Pl. Zeyl. 313. 1861.

Terrestrial, leafy herb with erect stems 30–42 cm high from a creeping base. Leaves few, rather distant, 5–8 × 2.7–4.2 cm, petiolate, oblong, ovate or oblique, acute, bright green, glabrous and shining above, paler beneath, 3-veined; petioles 3–3.5 cm long, dilating into short, reddish-brown, hyaline sheaths. Flowers brownish-white with distinct yellow lip, 3.4 mm broad, in

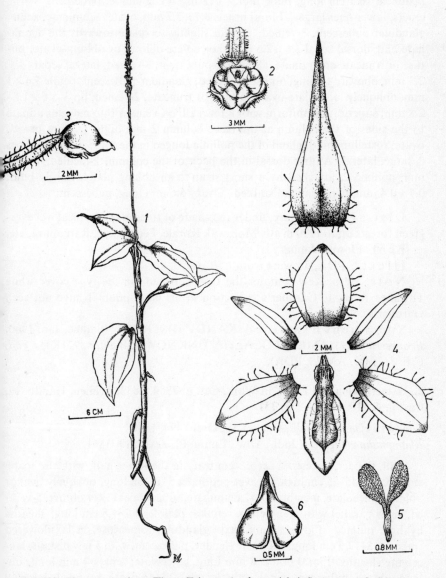

Fig. 130. *Hetaeria gardneri* (Thw.) Trimen. 1, plant with inflorescence. 2, flower from front. 3, ovary, lip and column from side. 4, bract, sepals, petals spread out from front, lip natural position from front showing the calli inside, column from front. 5, pollinia with straps and gland. 6, operculum from inside.

many-flowered, glandular-pubescent spikes measuring 26 cm in length; peduncle 16.5 cm long, puberulous, bearing 6 acuminate, pubescent, sterile bracts, lower ones larger. Floral bracts 8.7 × 2.7 mm, ovate, acuminate, acute, glandular-pubescent, 3-veined, margin slightly serrulate towards the acuminate end; dorsal sepal 3.6 × 2.6 mm, lanceolate-oblong or oblong-ovate, obtuse or truncate-emarginate, glandular-pubescent, 3-veined; lateral sepals 4 × 2.3 mm, obovate-oblong, obtuse, 3-veined, glandular-pubescent; petals 3.6 × 1 mm, obliquely lanceolate-ovate, obtuse or truncate, 2-veined; lip 3–3.6 × 1.8–2.8 mm, superior, cymbiform with a few calli on veins within margins adnate to the sides of the column at the base; column 2 mm high, 1.2 mm broad, ovate; rostellum bifid, gland of the pollinia lodged in the foɪk; stigmatic lobes 2, large, lateral. Anther dorsal in the back of the column, 2-loculed, 1 × 0.8 mm; pollinia 2, attached by a short strap to an oblong gland, faintly bifid, 0.7 × 0.4 mm, pyriform and stalked. Ovary 5.6 mm long, pubescent.

D i s t r. Endemic. Rare, under the shade of trees in the tropical wet evergreen forests up to 1220 m alt. Morawak Korale, Peradeniya, Ratnapura, etc.
E c o l. Flowers January.
I l l u s t r. PDA, drawing from *C.P. 3425.*
N o t e. Herb. Kew contains the *C.P.* collection in the type cover while Thwaites refers to Gardner's collection in his description. I have not seen Gardner's collection.
S p e c i m e n s E x a m i n e d. KANDY DISTRICT: Nilambe, Jan. 1960, *Jayaweera 43 (1)* (AMES). LOCALITY UNKNOWN: *Walker 297* (K); *s. coll. C.P. 3425* (K, AMES, PDA).

2. Hetaeria elongata Lindl. in Wall., Cat. n. 7384. 1832; Trimen, Handb. Fl. Ceylon 4: 210. 1898.—**Fig. 131.**

Goodyera elongata Lindl., Gen. et Sp. Orch. 494. 1840.
Rhamphidia elongata (Lindl.) Thw., Enum. Pl. Zeyl. 313. 1861.

Tall, slender, terrestrial herb; stem leafy in the lower half, with the scape and raceme 45–75 cm high. Leaves petiolate, 5–10 cm long, obliquely oval or oblong-lanceolate, membranous, acuminate, subacute or lower obtuse, 5-veined, veins parallel with many cross venules; petioles 1.2–1.8 cm long, sheaths hyaline, inflated. Flowers pink, laxly glandular-tomentose, in lax-flowered spikes, 7.5–12.5 cm long; peduncle slender, pubescent, with a few distant, lanceolate sheaths. Floral bracts 6 mm long, lanceolate; sepals 4 mm long, oblong, obtuse, pubescent; petals subfalcately oblong-ovate, rounded, inserted on the sides of the column; lip superior, membranous, cymbiform, acute, 5-veined; veins with soft spines at the base, lateral lobes short; column very short, stigmatic lobes lateral, rostellar arms subulate. Anther dorsal, ovate-cordate, 2-loculed; pollinia 2, subglobose, each attached by a slender caudicle to a small oblong gland.

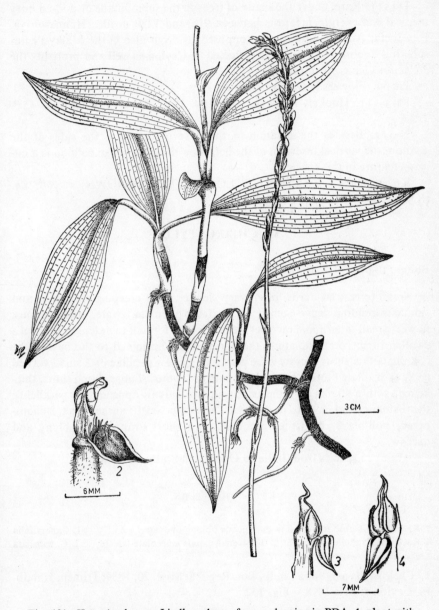

Fig. 131. *Hetaeria elongata* Lindl., redrawn from a drawing in PDA. 1, plant with inflorescence. 2, flower with sepals removed, side view showing petals, column and lip with soft spines at base. 3, lateral view of column with operculum drawn back. 4, front view of column with operculum drawn back.

D i s t r. Rare, under the shade of trees in the submontane or mid-country tropical wet evergreen forests between 915 and 1220 m alt. Hunnasgiriya, Hewaheta, Ambagamuwa, etc. Supposed to occur also in the Malay Peninsula, but doubtful as Finlayson collected in Ceylon as well and probably the collections have got mixed up.

E c o l. Flowers November–January.

I l l u s t r. Hooker, Ic. Pl. 22: pl. 2190. 1890; PDA, drawing from *C.P. 2739*.

N o t e. Besides the advation of the base of the lip to the sides of the column, the vertical insertion of the petals on the sides of the column is a curious feature in this species.

S p e c i m e n s E x a m i n e d. LOCALITY UNKNOWN: *s. coll. s.n.* (K); *s. coll. C.P. 2739* (PDA).

51. CHEIROSTYLIS

Blume, Bijdr. 413. t. 16. 1825.

Small terrestrial herbs, often very slender, with creeping rhizomes, and simple ascending leafy stems; leaves few, petiolate, ovate, membranous; flowers small in terminal racemes; sepals joined for half their length to form a swollen tube; petals adnate to the dorsal sepal; lip joined to the base of the column with a short saccate base containing a few papillae or 2 small forked calli, apex dilated into a bilobed, crenate or toothed limb; column short, thickened, with a stigma on either side and two narrow appendages, parallel to the rostellum and close to it; rostellum at length 2-cleft; anther erect, 2-chambered; pollinia 2, bipartite, granular, on a short strap, gland oblong and narrow.

About 15 species from India to Queensland, also in Africa.

KEY TO THE SPECIES

1 Racemes puberulous, 8–10 flowered; petals oblong-obovate............**1. C. parvifolia**
1 Racemes glandular-pubescent, 2–3-flowered; petals lanceolate-falcate....**2. C. flabellata**

1. Cheirostylis parvifolia Lindl., Bot. Reg. 25: Misc. 20, 1839; Trimen, Handb. Fl. Ceylon 4: 211. 1898.—**Fig. 132.**

Small terrestrial herb; whole plant 7.5–15 cm high on a non-pseudobulbous, prostrate stem; internodes short, green, tumid, the upper internodes enclosed in hyaline sheaths, lower ones bearing fibrous roots. Leaves 3–6, rather distant, 1.2–2.4 cm long, ovate or ovate-lanceolate, membranous, acuminate, dark greenish-brown above, glabrous; veins obscure; petioles 6 mm long,

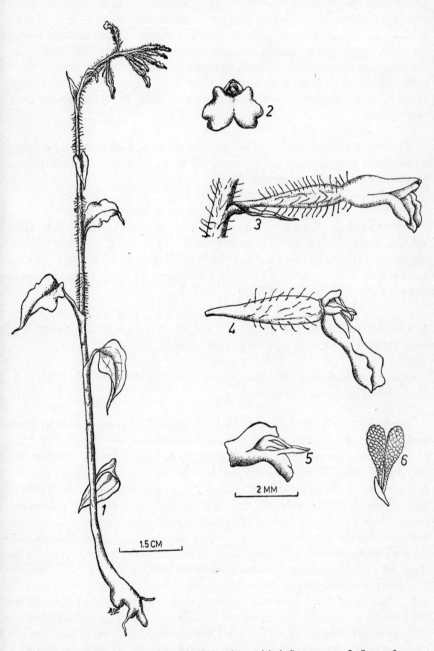

Fig. 132. *Cheirostylis parvifolia* Lindl. 1, plant with inflorescence. 2, flower from front. 3, flower from side showing fused sepals. 4, ovary, lip and column from side. 5, column from side. 6, pollinia with gland.

sheaths hyaline, inflated. Flowers minute, pinkish-white, in terminal, elongate, puberulous, 8–10-flowered racemes. Floral bracts about as long as pedicels; sepals 2–3 mm long, glabrous, pink, connate to the middle, dorsal broadest, ovate, obtuse; petals oblong-obovate, obtuse, white; lip longer than the sepals, subquadrate, 6–8-lobed, base subsaccate, enclosing 2 small, forked calli; column with 2 parallel appendages in front; rostellum at length bifid, arms subulate. Anther dorsal, 2-loculed; pollinia 2, pyriform, sessile on a short gland.

D i s t r. Rare, in the shade of trees in the submontane or mid-country tropical wet evergreen forests between 610 and 1220 m alt. Ambagamuwa, Hantane, etc. Also in Bombay in India.

E c o l. Flowers January, February.

I l l u s t r. PDA, two drawings of which one is from *C.P. 3071*.

S p e c i m e n s   E x a m i n e d. CEYLON: ANURADHAPURA DISTRICT: Ritigala, Jan. 1973, *Jayasuriya 1201* (PDA, US), May 1974, *Jayasuriya 1695* (PDA, US). LOCALITY UNKNOWN: *M.N. Beckett 226* (K); *Loddiges s.n.* (K); *s. coll. C.P. 3071* (K—holotype, PDA). INDIA: Bombay: Sawantwadi, Ambole, Nov. 1929, *T.R. Bell* (K).

2. **Cheirostylis flabellata** Wight, Ic. Pl. Ind. Or. 5 (1): 16, pl. 1727. 1851: Trimen, Handb. Fl. Ceylon 4: 211. 1898.—**Fig. 133.**

Goodyera flabellata A. Rich., Ann. Sc. Nat. Bot. 11. 15: 89. pl. 12. 1841.
Monochilus flabellatus Wight, ibid.

Terrestrial herb 2.5–9 cm high with a simple, stout stem swollen at internodes, creeping at first, later erect; internodes 0.9–1.17 cm long, lower internodes with fibrous roots. Leaves petiolate, 2–4, spreading, 0.9–1.5 × 0.7–1.2 cm, ovate, acute, 3-veined, connected by transverse venules, green, rugose; petioles 0.8–1.1 cm long, somewhat broad, pink, sheathing the stem. Flowers white, 1 cm long, 0.6 cm broad, in long peduncled, terminal, 2- or 3-flowered racemes; peduncle, bracts and sepals glandular-pubescent; peduncle 8 cm long with 2 or 3 distant, lanceolate, pink, sterile bracts. Floral bracts 3.8–6 × 1.7–2.8 mm, ovate, acuminate, acute, 1-veined; sepals fused half way up; dorsal sepal 3.4 × 2.5 mm, ovate, subacute, 1-veined; lateral sepals 3.1 × 1.2 mm, oblong, obtuse or rounded, 1-veined and faintly crenulate; petals 3.2–3.4 × 1.16 mm, lanceolate-falcate, truncate, 1-veined, closely appressed to the dorsal sepal forming a concave hood over the rostrum; lip 6.6 mm long, attached to the base of the column, cymbiform, bilobed, 3-veined, saccate at the base but not protruding, with two calli within; lobes spreading, trifid, main vein supplying the lip dividing into 3 venules, the lateral ones dividing again into two each, terminating in the forks; column 2.4 mm high, 1.8 mm broad, rostellum

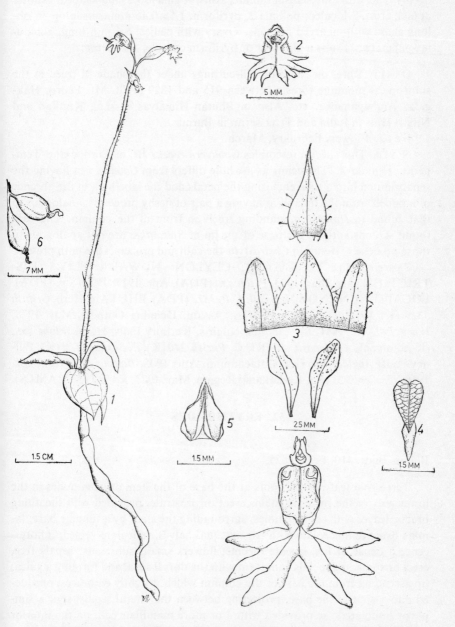

Fig. 133. *Cheirostylis flabellata* Wight. 1, plant with inflorescence. 2, flower from front. 3, bract, sepals, petals and lip spread out from front, column from inside. 4, pollinia with gland. 5, operculum from inside. 6, fruits.

deeply bifid with long, subspathulate, arms; stigma lobes club-shaped. Anther dorsal, erect, 2-loculed; pollinia 2, pyriform, 1.5×0.46 mm, sessile on an oblong gland with incurved margins. Ovary with pedicel 6.4 mm long, glandular-pubescent. Fruits a globular or pyriform capsule, 5×3.5 mm.

D i s t r. Rare, on roadside hill-cuttings under the shade of trees in the subtropical montane forests between 915 and 1829 m alt. Mt. Pedro, Hakgala, Ambagamuwa, etc. Also in Bhutan Himalyas, Assam, Konkan and Nilgiri Hills in India and Tenasserim in Burma.

E c o l. Flowers February, March.

N o t e. This species resembles *Goodyera repens* Br. of Europe and Temperate Himalaya. The genus as a whole differs from *Goodyera* in having the sepals united into a tube enclosing the petals and the labellum, in the absence of a pouch from the lip and in having a pair of fleshy processes, analogous to that found in *Habenaria*, standing freely in front of the column. The calli found so constantly at the base of the lip of *Spiranthes* are not analogous to those processes. Hence in *Cheirostylis* the calli and processes are both present.

S p e c i m e n s   E x a m i n e d. CEYLON: NUWARA ELIYA DISTRICT: Hakgala, Mar. 1923, *Petch s.n.* (PDA), Apr. 1917, *Petch s.n.* (PDA). LOCALITY UNKNOWN: *s. coll. C.P. 3377* (PDA). BHUTAN: Herb. *Griffith 5329* (K), *Griffith s.n.* (K). INDIA: Assam, Denning Outpost, Mar. 1928, *Ward 7902* (K, AMES). Madras: Nilgiris, Kartairy Falls, Herb. *Wight s.n.*, (K-holotype), *A. Richard s.n.* (K), *C. Parish 340* (K), *E. Barnes 1120* (K); Pulney Hills, *Anglade 976* (K); Ootacamund, Apr. 1905, *Bourne 4778* (K); Apr. 1910, *Fischer 3928* (K). Kodaikanal Region, Mar. 1927, *Koelz 11272* (AMES).

52. ERYTHRODES

Blume, Bijdr. 410. t. 72. 1825.

Terrestrial leafy herbs; roots at the base of the stem or from nodes in the lower part of the rhizome; stems erect or prostrate, provided with sheathing bracts; leaves with short petioles, surrounding the stem by a tubular base; lamina ovate to lanceolate with two unequal halves, reticulate-veined; inflorescence a dense or lax, spicate raceme; flowers small, subsessile; sepals free, erect or spreading; petals connivent with the dorsal sepal and forming a galea; lip ascending from the base of the column which it lightly embraces, produced into a spur at the base, projecting between the lateral sepals; spur a simple or bifurcated sac provided with 4 or more mamillate calli on the interior wall near the base; column short with a bifid rostellum; anther dorsal, 2-chambered; pollinia 2, clavate, granular, bipartite, attached to a small gland.

A complex genus of about 93 species distributed in the mild temperate regions and in the tropics and subtropics of both hemispheres.

Erythrodes humilis J.J. Smith, Bull. Dep. Agric. Indes Neerl. 13: 11. 1907.
—Fig. 134.

Physurus blumei Lindl. in Wall., Cat. n. 7397. 1832; Trimen, Handb. Fl. Ceylon 4: 212. 1898.

Physurus humilis Blume, Orch. Archip. Ind. 96, pl. 27, f. 2. 1858–1859.

Terrestrial herb with a stout, erect, leafy, glabrous stem 10–20 cm long, arising from a creeping rootstock. Leaves scattered, petioled, sheathing at the base, 4–9 × 2.3–4 cm, obliquely ovate, acute, 3–5-veined; petiole 2–3 cm long with a sheath 0.5–1 cm long. Flowers white, 1.5 cm long, 1 cm broad, in long, terminal, many-flowered, pubescent spikes measuring 12–16 cm in length; peduncle pubescent, 17–21 cm long, greenish at lower part, bearing a reduced leaf at the base and 4–7 pubescent, finely acuminate, sterile bracts. Floral bracts 7.6 × 2.6 mm, ovate, acuminate, acute, glandular-pubescent, 1-veined; dorsal sepal 3.8–4.8 × 1.4–2.1 mm, oblong, subacute, glandular-pubescent, 1-veined; lateral sepals 5 × 2.6 mm, obovate-oblong, subacute, glandular-pubescent and 1-veined; petals 4.4 × 2 mm, obovate or spathulate, acute and twisted at apex, 1-veined, closely appressed to the dorsal sepal and together with it forming a concave hood over the rostrum; lip 6.2 × 4.4 mm, base forming a bifurcated spur, fusing with the foot of the column to form a sac; lateral lobes of lip fleshy, brownish and infolded; midlobe white, bifid or emarginate; column together with the long, erect, bifid rostellum 2.6 mm long, 1.2 mm broad. Anther dorsal, long acuminate, 2-loculed, 2.2 × 0.8 mm; pollinia 2, clavate, 2.1 × 3.6 mm, granular, bipartite attached to the rostellum by a small gland. Ovary 1 cm long and pubescent. Fruit a cigar-shaped capsule, 1.3 × 0.4 cm.

D i s t r. Rather rare, under the shade of trees in the tropical wet evergreen forests extending to the mid-country from 305 to 915 m alt. Ratnapura, Ambagamuwa, Hantane, Peradeniya, etc. Also in Sylhet in Bangladesh, Java and Borneo.

E c o l. Flowers January–March, December.

I l l u s t r. Blume, Orch. Archip. Ind. pl. 27, fig 2. 1858–9; PDA, drawing from *C.P. 598.*

N o t e. Herb. Lindley contains the collection *Wallich 7397* from Sylhet under the synonym *Physurus blumei* Lindl.

S p e c i m e n s E x a m i n e d. CEYLON: KANDY DISTRICT: Peradeniya, Jan. 1894, *s. coll. s.n.* (PDA); Ambagamuwa, Apr. 1960, *Jayaweera 2043* (PDA), Mar. 1960, *Jayaweera 45* (AMES); Adam's Peak, Oct. 1960, *Jayaweera 2046* (PDA). RATNAPURA DISTRICT: Ratnapura, Dec. 1960, *Jayaweera 2044* (PDA); Gilimale, Sept. 1960, *Jayaweera 2045* (PDA). LOCALITY UNKNOWN: 1829, *Macrae 59* (K); *s. coll. C.P. 598* (K, PDA). INDIA: Maharashtra: Bombay, Herb. *Dalzell s.n.* (K). BANGLADESH: Sylhet: *Wallich 7397* (K). BRITISH NORTH BORNEO: Mt. Kinabalu, Mar. 1933, *Carr 3771* (AMES).

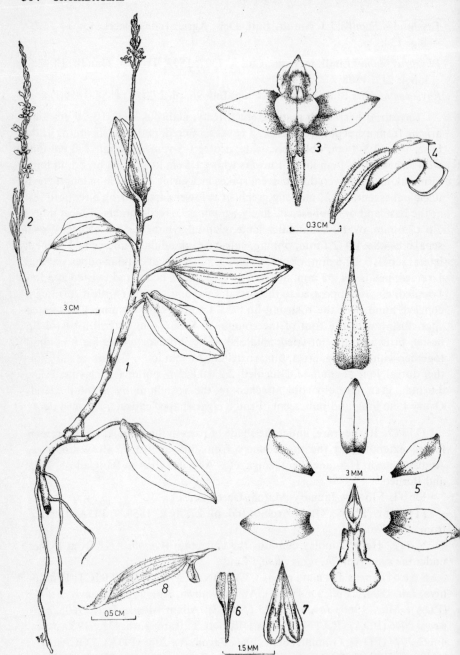

Fig. 134. *Erythrodes humilis* J.J. Smith. 1, plant with inflorescence. 2, inflorescence.
3, flower from front. 4, lip and column from side, column partially hidden by lateral
lobes of lip. 5, bract, sepals, petals and column spread out from front, lip in natural
position. 6, pollinia. 7, operculum from front. 8, fruit.

53. ANOECTOCHILUS

Blume, Bijdr. 8: 411. t. 15. 1825.

Terrestrial leafy herbs; stems creeping below; leaves stalked, membranous; flowers few, fairly large, in a glandular-pubescent terminal spike; dorsal sepal forming a hood with the petals; lip attached to the base of the column, either with a projecting spur or with a saccate base enclosed by the sepals or protruded beyond; cavity of spur or sac with two large unstalked glands; middle part of the lip narrowed to a channelled claw with a toothed or fringed flange on either side, apex widened to a transverse, 2-lobed blade; column short with two wings in front; rostellum short, at length bifid; stigmas 2, on either side of the base of the rostellum; anther dorsal on the column, 2-chambered; pollinia 2, clavate or pyriform, lamellate, narrowed into a single caudicle and attached by a gland to the rostellum.

About 40 species distributed in India, Ceylon extending to Japan and southwards to Malaysia and the Pacific Islands.

Anoectochilus setaceus Blume, Bijdr. 412. 1825.—**Fig. 135.**

Anoectochilus regalis Blume, Orch. Archip. Ind. 46. 1858; Trimen, Handb. Fl. Ceylon 4: 213. 1898.
Chrysobaphus roxburghii Wall., Tent. Fl. Nep. 37, pl. 27. 1826.
Anoectochilus setaceus var. *inornatus* Hook., Bot. Mag. 86: pl. 5208. 1860.

Small, terrestrial, leafy herb with a creeping stem 15–25 cm long, the terminal end erect and above ground. Leaves 3–5, spreading, 2.5–4 × 1.7–2.5 cm, ovate, acute, glabrous, dark velvety-green above with orange reticulations, paler beneath, petioles sheathing the stem. Flowers white, 1.8 cm broad, in a glandular-pubescent, terminal spike; peduncle 6–8 cm long, glandular-pubescent with 2 or 3 lanceolate, coloured, sterile bracts. Floral bracts 0.9–1.1 cm × 3.5–4 mm, lanceolate-ovate, acuminately acute, glandular-pubescent, 1-veined; sepals glandular-pubescent and 1-veined; dorsal sepal 9 × 4.5 mm, oblong-ovate, acuminate, acute; lateral sepals 1 cm × 3.5 mm, obliquely obovate-oblong, acute, bases appressed on the spur and cohering slightly; petals 1 cm × 3 mm, falcate-oblong, acute, 2-veined, appressed on the dorsal sepal and together with it forming a concave hood over the column; lip 1.1 cm long, attached to the base of the column, spurred, clawed, margins of the claw crinate with 8 long flexuous, filiform lobes on each side; midlobe 2-winged; wings quadrate; spur 8 × 2.5 mm, inflated, base notched or bifid with two fimbriated calli inside; column 6 mm high, 2.7 mm broad, obconical with two parallel lamellae in front and lateral stigmatic lobes; rostellum 2.6 × 1.6 mm, acuminate, not bifid. Anther dorsal on the column, 2-loculed, 4.8 × 2.4 mm; pollinia 2, clavate, lamellate and narrowing to a single caudicle, attached to the rostellum by a small gland. Ovary 1.2 cm long, glandular-pubescent.

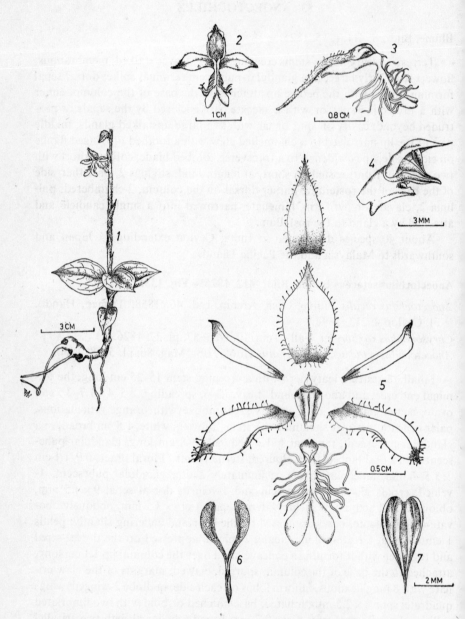

Fig. 135. *Anoectochilus setaceus* Blume. 1, plant with inflorescence. 2, flower from front. 3, lip, column and spur from side. 4, column with the operculum open to show position of pollinia. 5, bract, sepals, petals, lip and column spread out from front. 6, pollinia with caudicles and gland, enlarged. 7, operculum from inside.

D i s t r. Rather common, under shade of trees among fallen leaves in the tropical wet evergreen forests extending to the subtropical montane forests between 305 and 1829 m alt. Ambagamuwa, Nuwara Eliya, Ratnapura, Adam's Peak, Ritigala, Nilambe, Hantane, etc.

E c o l. Flowers January, May–September, December. It grows in diffused sunlight of very low intensities, humidity of over 80 per cent and temperatures below 80°F. It is always found in association with *Zeuxine regia* Trimen, both of which are used medicinally.

V e r n. Wana-raja (S).

I l l u s t r. Hook., Bot. Mag. 70: pl. 4123. 1844; Lindl., Bot. Reg. 23: pl. 2010. 1837; Blume, Orch. Archip. Ind. pl. 17b. 1858–9; PDA, drawing from *C.P. 384.*

S p e c i m e n s E x a m i n e d. CEYLON: ANURADHAPURA DIST-RICT: Ritigala, Mar. 1905, *Willis s.n.* (PDA), Jan. 1973, *Jayasuriya 1045* (PDA, US), Sept. 1975, *Jayasuriya, Premadasa & Foster 2275* (PDA, US), Jan. 1973, *Jayasuriya 2319* (PDA, US). MATALE DISTRICT: Kalupahana, Jul. 1973, *Jayasuriya & Subramaniam 1219* (PDA, US). KANDY DISTRICT: Hantane, *Champion s.n.* (AMES); Peradeniya, Bot. Gard., cultd., Jan. 1957, *Jayaweera 280* (PDA); Ambagamuwa, Jan. 1960, *Jayaweera 1971* (PDA); Dolosbage, Sept. 1885, *s. coll. s.n.* (PDA); Walankande, Dec. 1893, *s. coll. s.n.* (PDA); Hunnasgiriya, Apr. 1960. *Jayaweera 46* (AMES). RATNAPURA DIS-TRICT; Sinharaja Forest, Nov. 1963, *Jayaweera 2375* (PDA). GALLE DIS-TRICT: Hiniduma, Sept. 1969, *Cramer 2693* (PDA). MATARA DISTRICT: Deniyaya—Rakwana Rd., Apr. 1974, *Sumithraarachchi & Waas 328* (PDA, US). LOCALITY UNKNOWN: *Macrae 1* (K); *Champion s.n.* (K); *s. coll. C.P. 384* (K). BRITISH NORTH BORNEO: Mt. Kinabalu, *Carr 3084* (AMES).

54. GOODYERA

R. Br. in Aiton, Hort. Kew. ed. 2. 5: 197. 1813.

Terrestrial leafy herbs; stems erect from a creeping base, leaves petioled; flowers small, in often twisted spikes; dorsal sepal forming a hood with the petals, lateral sepals covering the sac of the lip by their bases; lip erect, sessile on the base of the column, hollow or saccate, glandular or with bristly hairs inside, narrowed to an acute tip which is sometimes reflexed, not lobed; column short without appendages at base; rostellum long and deeply cleft; stigma not divided, large, on front of the column; anther dorsal; pollinia 2, pyriform or clavate, granular with or without a strap and a small gland.

About 159 species distributed in all the warmer parts of the world except Africa.

1 Lip with short recurved tip; spikes 7.5–15 cm long; petals spathulate; column very short with broadly pyriform pollinia...**1. G. procera**
1 Lip with long revolute tail; spikes 30 cm long; petals dimidiate-lanceolate, falcate; column long, slender and arched with clavate pollinia.................**2. G. fumata**

1. Goodyera procera (Ker-Gawl.) Hook., Exot. Fl. 1: pl. 39. 1823; Trimen, Handb. Fl. Ceylon 4: 214. 1898.—**Fig. 136.**

Neottia procera Ker-Gawl., Bot. Reg. 8: pl. 639. 1822.
Cionisacus lanceolatus Breda, Gen. Sp. Orch. Asclep. 1. 1828.
Goodyera carnea A. Rich., Ann. Sc. Nat. Bot. 11, 15: 80. 1841.
Cordylestylis foliosa Falconer, J. Bot. (Hook.) 4: 75. 1842.
Leucostachys procera Hoffmannsegg, Preisverz Orch. 26. 1842.

Terrestrial, leafy herb with a tall, erect stem 27–39 cm long arising from a prostrate, rooting base; roots long and vermiform. Leaves 12–18 × 2–4 cm, lanceolate, acuminate, midrib stout, veins ascending obliquely; petioles stout, 3–4 cm long, dilated into broad, open sheaths. Flowers greenish-white, fragrant, 8 mm long, 3.2 mm across in stout, terminal, racemose spikes measuring 5–7 cm in length; peduncle stout with many large, foliaceous, sterile bracts. Floral bracts 4.6–7.4 × 2.1–2.5 mm, ovate-lanceolate, acuminate, irregularly serrate, glandular-pilose, 1-veined; dorsal sepal 3.6 × 1.8 mm, lanceolate-oblong, obtuse, 1-veined with a faint lateral vein on either side; lateral sepals 3.1 × 2.1 mm, lanceolate-oblong, obtuse, 3-veined; petals 3.2 × 1.5 mm, obliquely dimidiate-spathulate, obtuse, margin suberose; lip brownish-white, 2.4 × 3.4 mm when spread out, cymbiform with margins infolded, glandular hairs of two kinds within and 2 calli; column 2 mm high, 1.1 mm broad, rostellum bifid. Anther dorsal, operculate, beaked, 2-loculed, 0.9 × 0.7 mm; pollinia 2, broadly club-shaped, granular, sessile on an oblong gland; each pollinium 1 × 0.2 mm, bipartite. Ovary with pedicel 5.2 mm long.

D i s t r. Rather rare, on moist banks and hill-cuttings along with grasses above 762 m alt. Dolosbage, Madulkelle, Norton Bridge, etc. Also in the tropical Himalayas, Khasia Hills, Sikkim, Malabar Ghats and Nilgiri Hills in India, Nepal, Burma, Malaya, Tibet, China, Formosa, Java, Borneo and the Loo Choo Islands.

E c o l. Flowers January, June, September.

I l l u s t r. Wight, Ic. Pl. Ind. Or. 5: pl. 1729. 1851; King & Pantling, Ann. R. Bot. Gard. (Calcutta) 8: pl. 377. 1898; PDA, drawing from *C.P. 597.*

N o t e. This species resembles *Goodyera repens* R. Br. but for the presence of glandular hairs and two calli in the lip. Herb. Lindley contains the collections *Wallich 7393* from Nepal, *Perrottet 1107* from Nilgiris, *Macrae 33* from Ceylon and four other collections from China, Assam and Loo Choo Island.

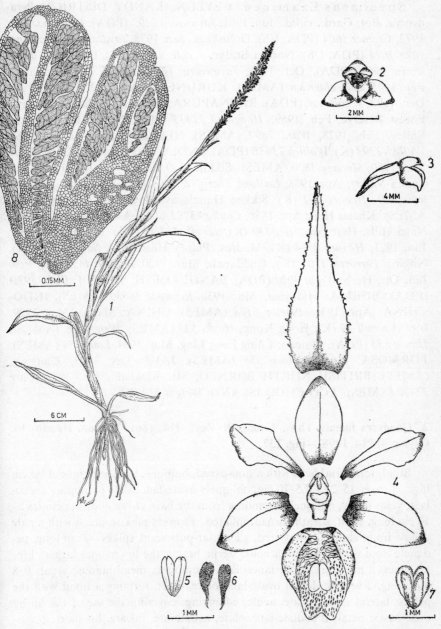

Fig. 136. *Goodyera procera* (Ker-Gawl.) Hook. 1, plant with inflorescence. 2, flower from front. 3, lip and column from side. 4, bract, sepals, petals, lip and column spread out from front, enlarged. 5, young pollinia. 6, mature pollinia. 7, operculum from front. 8, transverse section of young anther (camera lucida drawing).

Specimens Examined. CEYLON: KANDY DISTRICT: Peradeniya, Bot. Gard., cultd., Jun. 1961, *Jayaweera 2197* (PDA); Hantane, Feb. 1972, *Cramer 3604* (PDA, US); Dolosbage, Jan. 1973, *Jayasuriya & Dassanayake 1014* (PDA, US); Norton Bridge, *s. coll. s.n.* (PDA), Dec. 1960, *Jayaweera 1994* (PDA), Oct. 1956, *Jayaweera 47 (1)* (AMES); Ginigathena, Feb. 1905, *Schlechter s.n.* (AMES). KURUNEGALA DISTRICT: Pannala, Dec. 1893, *s. coll. s.n.* (PDA). RATNAPURA DISTRICT: Bambarabotuwa Forest Reserve, Feb. 1969, *Hoogland 11433* (PDA, US). TIBET: Oikang Valley, Feb. 1928, *Ward 7894* (AMES). NEPAL: *Wallich s.n.* (AMES), *Wallich 7393* (K), *Wallich 7393B* (PDA). INDIA: Uttar Pradesh: Dehra Dun, May 1950, *Mooney 3800* (AMES). Sikkim, *J.D. Hooker s.n.* (AMES, PDA); Teesta Valley, Apr. 1938, *Ludlow, Sheriff & Taylor 4001* (AMES); Hot Valleys, *J.D. Hooker 291* (K). Sikkim Himalayas: May 1899, *Pantling 67* (K, AMES). Khasia Hills: Apr. 1886, *Clarke 43322A* (K). Assam: *Simons* (PDA); Naga Hills, Herb. *Griffith 5330* (K), *s. coll. 133/420* (K). Madhya Pradesh: Jun. 1921, *Haynes 3564* (K). Madras: Pulney Hills, 1914, *Sauliere 707* (K); Nilgiris, *Perrottet 1107* (K); Cuddapah, Mar. 1920, *Fischer 4633* (K). Pen. Ind. Or., Herb. *Wight 3020* (PDA). BANGLADESH: Sylhet, *Wallich 7393A* (PDA). BURMA: Mytkyina, Mar 1938. *Kermode 16630* (AMES). INDO-CHINA: Apr. 1936, *Petelot 5178* (AMES). CHINA: Macao: May 1929, *G.H. Vachell 79* (K); Hong Kong, *Hook. 533* (AMES), *Wright s.n.* (AMES), *Hance 533* (PDA). Hainan: Ching Fung Ling, Mar. 1934, *Lau 3484* (AMES). FORMOSA: 1864, *Oldham 558* (AMES). JAVA: Oct. 1923, *Kant s.n.* (AMES). BRITISH NORTH BORNEO: Mt. Kinabalu, Jan. 1933, *Carr 27470* (AMES). LOO CHOO ISLAND: *Wright 339* (K).

2. Goodyera fumata Thw., Enum. Pl. Zeyl. 314. 1861; Trimen, Handb. Fl. Ceylon 4: 214. 1898.—**Fig. 137.**

Stout, terrestrial herb with a non-pseudobulbous, leafy stem about 90 cm high. Leaves 15–25 × 7.5–10 cm, obliquely ovate-lanceolate or elliptic-lanceolate, veins many, obliquely ascending from the base of the midrib; petioles 5–10 cm long, stout, sheaths broad, inflated. Flowers pinkish-green with a pale yellow lip in stout, lax-flowered, glandular-pubescent spikes 30 cm long; peduncle stout with large, foliaceous, sterile bracts, the lower ones larger. Floral bracts 8 mm long, ovate-lanceolate, acuminate, membranous; sepals 6–8 mm long, 3-veined; dorsal ovate-lanceolate, erect, forming a hood with the petals; lateral sepals ovate, acute, conniving, covering the sac of the lip by their bases; petals dimidiate-lanceolate, acuminate, falcate, lip short, rhomboidly orbicular, concave, sessile on the base of the column, strongly many-veined, suddenly contracted into a revolute, acuminate, ligulate tail, glandular within; column long, slender, arched, apex dilated, conical; rostellum

2.1 CM

7 MM

Fig. 137. *Goodyera fumata* Thw., redrawn from a drawing in PDA. 1, part of a plant and inflorescence. 2, flower from side. 3, column from above. 4, column from above, with operculum opened out showing the pollinia.

elongate, erect, entire or 2-toothed. Anther dorsal, ovate, 2-loculed; pollinia 2, clavate, sessile on a small, oblong gland.

D i s t r. Locality in Ceylon not exactly known, though Thwaites' specimens are labelled "Ambagamuwa". I have not come across it in the locality cited. Also in Sikkim Himalayas, Burma, Siam and China.

E c o l. Flowers December.

I l l u s t r. King & Pantling, Ann. R. Bot. Gard. (Calcutta) 8: pl. 377. 1891; Herb. Perad., drawing from *C.P. 3668.*

N o t e. The column is incorrectly described by Hooker in Flora of British India.

S p e c i m e n s E x a m i n e d. CEYLON: LOCALITY UNKNOWN: *Walker s.n.* (K); *s. coll. C.P. 3668* (K-holotype, PDA); Feb. 1929, *Alston s.n.* (PDA). INDIA: Runghee, Mar. 1897, *Pantling 467* (K). Madras: Tinnevelly, Feb. 1948, *E. Bowden* (K). BURMA: West Kengtung, Apr. 1911, *W.A. Robertson 306* (K). THAILAND: Doi Chiengdao, Mar. 1950, *Garrett 1297* (AMES). INDO-CHINA: Siam Khong, Mar. 1936, *Lau 25779* (AMES).

55. SPIRANTHES

Rich., Mem. Mus. Paris 4: 50. 1818.

Terrestrial leafy herbs; roots usually fleshy, cylindric or tuberous, rarely fibrous; leaves narrow, basal or fugaceous, bases sheathing or petioled; flowers small, only slightly opened in spirally arranged, glandular-pubescent spikes; dorsal sepal forming a hood with the petals; lateral sepals more or less decurrent on ovary to form basally a sac or spur-like mentum; lip concave or saccate at the base containing appendages, not protruded beyond the bases of the lateral sepals, simple or 3-lobed; column short, terete, with or without a foot but with a convex stigma in front; anther dorsal, erect, 2-chambered; pollinia 2, deeply bipartite, powdery-granular, narrowly obovoid, with their filaments coherent to a narrow viscid gland on the rostellum terminating the column.

This is a polymorphic genus of about 300 species distributed throughout the temperate and tropical regions of both worlds except in Africa.

Spiranthes sinensis (Pers.) Ames, Orch. 2: 53. 1908 Alston in Trimen, Handb. Fl. Ceylon 6: 279. 1931.—**Fig. 138.**

Neottia sinensis Pers., Syn. Pl. 2: 511. 1807.
Neottia australis R. Br., Prod. Fl. Nov. Holland. 319. 1810.
Neottia flexuosa Smith in Rees, Cyclop. 24: n. 9. 1813.
Neottia parviflora Smith, ibid. n. 10.
Neottia amoena Bieb., Fl. Taur. Cauc. 3: 606. 1819.

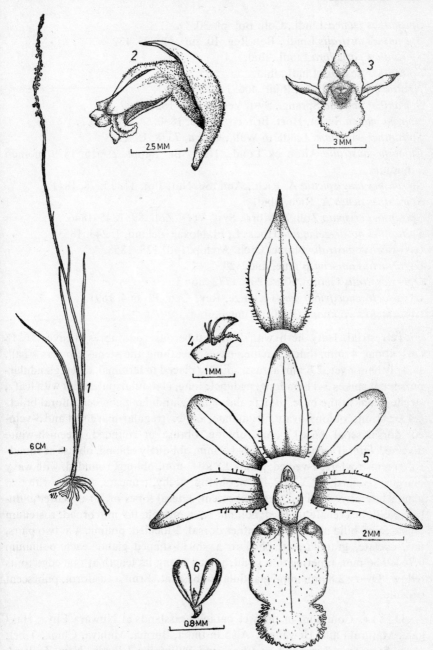

Fig. 138. *Spiranthes sinensis* (Pers.) Ames. 1, plant with inflorescence. 2, flower and
bract from side. 3, flower from front, lateral sepals spread out. 4, column from side
showing anther. 5, bract, sepals, petals, lip and column spread out from front. 6,
pollinia with gland.

Spiranthes pudica Lindl., Coll. Bot. pl. 30. 1821.
Spiranthes australis Lindl., Bot. Reg. 10: sub. pl. 823. 1824.
Spiranthes parviflora Lindl., ibid.
Spiranthes flexuosa Lindl., ibid.
Neottia crispata Blume, Bijdr. 406. 1825.
Spiranthes amoena Spreng., Syst. Veg. 3: 708. 1826.
Neottia pudica Sweet, Hort. Brit. ed. 2. 485. 1830.
Spiranthes wightiana Lindl. in Wall., Cat. n. 7378. 1832.
Calanthe australis Aiton ex Loud., Hort. Br. Suppl. 2: 615. 1839, nomen
nudum.
Spiranthes longispicata A. Rich., Ann. Sc. Nat. Bot. 11. 15: 78. 1841.
Spiranthes densa A. Rich., ibid.
Spiranthes crispata Zoll. & Morr., Syst. Verz. Zoll. 89. 1845–1846.
Spiranthes novae-zelandiae Hook. f., Fl. Novae Zeland. 1: 243. 1853.
Gyrostachys australis Blume, Orch. Archip. Ind. 128. 1858.
Gyrostachys amoena Blume, ibid. 129.
Ophrys spiralis Georgi, Reise 232. 1772, non L.
Gyrostachys novifriburgensis Kuntze, Rev. Gen. Pl. 664. 1891.
Gyrostachys wightiana (Wall.) Kuntze, ibid.

Terrestrial, leafy herb with fleshy, tuberous root fibres. Leaves 16–18
cm×about 4 mm, linear, acute, bases sheathing the stem. Flowers small,
sharply bent over, 2.8 mm across, spirally placed in terminal, erect, glandular-
pubescent spikes 3–11 cm long; peduncle long, glandular-pubescent with leafy,
sterile bracts at the base. Bracts and sepals glandular-pubescent; floral bracts
4.4 × 2.4 mm, oblong-ovate, acuminate, acute, irregular-margined and 3-vein-
ed; dorsal sepal 3.6 × 1.6 mm, oblong, obtuse or rounded, greenish-white
3-veined; lateral sepals 3–3.4 × 1.2–1.4 mm, obliquely oblong, obtuse or rounded, greenish-white, 2-veined; petals 2.8 × 1.3 mm, oblong, rounded, with wavy
margin, 1-veined; lip 3.2 × 2.4 mm, oblong, fleshy, truncate, saccate, with two
glands laterally, 3-veined; disc pubescent; lateral lobes of lip obscure, undulate, midlobe crenate-toothed; column 1.2 mm high, 0.9 mm broad, rostellum
crenate and bifid at the apex. Anther dorsal, 2-loculed; pollinia 4 in two pairs,
flat, clavate, granular, attached to a shield-shaped gland; each pollinium
0.76 × 0.36 mm, tapering to a point, joined along its length at one edge to its
fellow. Ovary 2.8 mm long, glandular-pubescent. Fruit a fusiform, pubescent
capsule.

D i s t r. Common, in the wet patana grasslands at Nuwara Eliya, Hak-
gala, Maturata and Hewaheta. Also in India, Burma, Malaya, China, Tibet,
Java, Sumatra, Borneo, Loo Choo and Philippine Islands, New Zealand,
Australia and Eastern Siberia.

E c o l. Flowers almost throughout the year. Other orchids found in this
area growing in association with it are *Ipsea speciosa* Lindl. and *Satyrium*

nepalense D. Don. Other plants associated with these are *Chrysopogon zeylanicus* Thw., *Ischaemum commutatum* Hack., *Anaphalis brevifolia* DC., *Pollinia phaeothrix* Hack., *Cyperus globosus* Allion, *Wahlenbergia gracilis* A. DC., *Justicia procumbens* Linn., *Emilia javanica* C.B. Rob., *Pteridium aquilinum* Kuhn., *Osbeckia cupularis* D. Don., *Osbeckia* sp., *Rhododendron zeylanicum* Booth (small tree) and *Acacia melanoxylon* Br. (small tree).

I l l u s t r. Blume, Orch. Archip. Ind. 1: pl. 37, fig. 3 & pl. 38, figs. A & D. 1858; Wight, Ic. Pl. Ind. Or. 5: pl. 1724. 1851; Griffith, Ic. Pl. Asiat. 3: pl. 348. 1851; King & Pantling, Ann. R. Bot. Gard. (Calcutta) 8: pl. 369. 1898; PDA, two drawings one of which is from *C.P. 550.*

N o t e. Herb. Lindley contains 17 collections from India to Tasmania. Large-flowered and small-flowered varieties occur in the same locality. The colour of the flower is either white or pink. Lindley and Sprengel describe the species under two synonyms based on Royle's collections. The white-flowered form was placed by Lindley under *Spiranthes parviflora* Lindl. and the pink-flowered form under *Spiranthes amoena* Spreng. by Sprengel.

S p e c i m e n s E x a m i n e d. CEYLON: KANDY DISTRICT: Hantane, May 1924, *J.M. Silva s.n.* (PDA); Pussellawa, Ambagahakotuwa, Feb. 1973, *Cramer 4058* (PDA, US). NUWARA ELIYA DISTRICT: Hewaheta, Nov. 1963, *Jayaweera 2353* (PDA); Nuwara Eliya, Sept. 1959, *Jayaweera 49* (AMES); Horton Plains, Jan. 1906, *Willis s.n.* (PDA), Oct. 1970, *Cramer 3257* (PDA, US); Pattipola, Sept. 1969, *van Beusekom s.n.* (PDA, US); Sita Eliya, Oct. 1906, *Willis s.n.* (PDA); Pidurutalagala, Oct. 1974, *Davidse & Sumithraarachchi 7997* (PDA, US), Aug. 1970, *Cramer 3131* (PDA, US), Oct. 1974, *Davidse & Sumithraarachchi 7998* (PDA, US); Hakgala, Feb. 1906, *A.M. Silva s.n.* (PDA). BADULLA DISTRICT: Namunukula, Mar. 1907, *J.M. Silva s.n.* (PDA). INDIA: Kashmir: Shigar, *Stewart 20548* (AMES). Khasia Hills, *Griffith s.n.* (K), *Lobb s.n.* (K), *J.D. Hooker & T. Thomson s.n.* (PDA). Sikkim: *J.D. Hooker 327* (K), *King s.n.* (PDA), *J.D. Hooker s.n.* (PDA). North-west Himalayas: *T. Thomson 326* (K); Aug. 1899, *Ramsukh 22999* (AMES). Malabar: *Stocks s.n.* (AMES); Malabar, Konkan etc., *Stocks, Law* etc. *s.n.* (PDA). Coonoor: Apr. 1883, *Gamble 11380* (K). Mysore: Canara, *Dalzell 40* (K). Kodaikanal Region: Pulneys, May 1897, *Bourne 35* (K). Madras: Jan. 1940, *Barnes 1164* (AMES); Nilgiris: *Vine 252* (K, AMES), *Perrottet 865* (K), *A. Richard* (K); High Wavy Mts., May 1909, *Blatter & Hallberg 26528* (K). East India Co., Herb. *Falconer s.n.* (PDA). NEPAL: Aug. 1954, *Stainton, Sykes & William 3895* (AMES), *Wallich 7377* (PDA). BHUTAN: *Griffith 19* (K). BURMA: Myitkyina, Jul. 1938, *Naw Mu Pa 17424* (AMES); North Burma: Valley of Nmai Hka, 1940, *Kingdon Ward 481* (AMES). MALAYA: *Ridley s.n.* (AMES). U.S.S.R.: East Siberia: Vladivostok & vicinity, Oct. 1919, *Topping 2418* (AMES). CHINA: Tibet: Aug. 1924, *Kingdon Ward 6073* (AMES). North Manchuria: *Skvortzov s.n.* (AMES); Kiangyin, Jun. 1922, *Allison 117* (AMES). Tonking: *Bon s.n.* (AMES). Kwangtung:

Lin Fa Shan, Mar. 1932, *Metcalf 17006* (AMES). Hong Kong: *Wright 526* (AMES). KOREA: Port Chusan, 1959, *C. Wilford s.n.* (K). LOO CHOO ISLANDS: *C. Wright 325* (K), *Wright 337* (K), *Wright 335* (AMES). FORMOSA: Mar. 1921, *Shimada s.n.* (AMES). SUMATRA: *Schiffner 1826* (AMES). BRITISH NORTH BORNEO: Mt. Kinabalu, Feb. 1932, *Clemens 28528* (AMES). JAPAN: Komae, Jan. 1957, *Suzuki 1164* (AMES); Nagasaki, *Oldham 849* (PDA). PHILIPPINE ISLANDS: Luzon: Bontoc, Jul. 1914, *Vanoverbergh 565* (AMES), Benquet, Oct. 1904, *Elmer 6623* (AMES). AUSTRALIA: New South Wales: Melbourne, Hume River, Herb. *Ames s.n.* (AMES); Port Jackson, *Cunningham 9* (K). TASMANIA: *Archer s.n.* (K). NEW ZEALAND: *J.D. Hooker 203* (K); Lake Tangongi-Kaitaia, 1920, *Mathews s.n.* (AMES).

56. ZEUXINE

Lindl., Coll. Bot. App. 1825.

Terrestrial leafy herbs; stems creeping below; leaves sessile on a broad sheath or petiolate, often membranous; flowers small, few or many in a terminal spike, hardly opening; upper sepal and petals forming a hood; lateral sepals enclosing the base of the lip; lip sessile with a saccate base but not protruded beyond the lateral sepals; the sac containing 2 glands inside, more or less contracted in the middle, dilated at apex into a small entire or wing-like terminal lobe; column short with or without appendages on the front; rostellum large, deeply divided; stigmas 2 on either side of the column; anther dorsal on the column, 2-chambered, membranous; pollinia 2, pyriform, granular, attached by a gland to the rostellum, with or without a caudicle.

About 30 species distributed in Africa extending through India, Ceylon to Malaysia and Samoa.

KEY TO THE SPECIES

1 Leaves cauline, sessile, erect, linear-lanceolate....................**1. Z. strateumatica**
1 Leaves towards the base of the stem, ovate, oblong-ovate, or ovate-lanceolate
  2 Midlobe of lip coarsely toothed................................**2. Z. longilabris**
  2 Midlobe of lip entire
    3 Sepals 3-veined; lip cymbiform with 2 stout, linear calli.................**3. Z. regia**
    3 Sepals and petals 1-veined; lip saccate with 2 calli, midlobe bifid........**4. Z. flava**

1. Zeuxine strateumatica (L.) Schlecht., Fedde Repert. Beib. 1: 77. 1911; Alston in Trimen, Handb. Fl. Ceylon 6: 279. 1931.—**Fig. 139.**

Orchis strateumatica L., Sp. Pl. 943. 1753.
Pterygodium sulcatum Roxb., Hort., Beng. 63. 1814.
Spiranthes strateumatica Lindl., Bot. Reg. 10: sub. pl. 823. 1824.

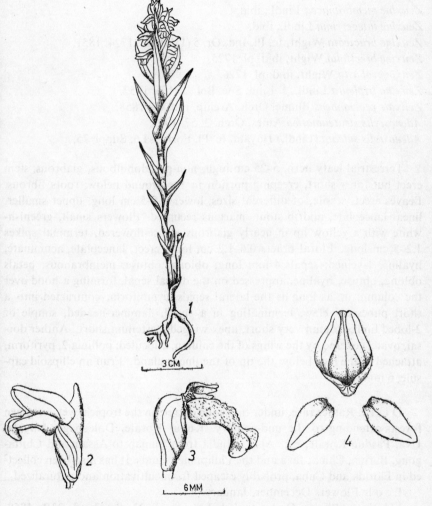

Fig. 139. *Zeuxine strateumatica* (L.) Schlecht. 1, plant with inflorescence. 2, bract and flower from side. 3, ovary, lip and column from side. 4, dorsal sepal with the two petals inside and lateral sepals spread out from front.

Adenostylis emarginata Blume, Bijdr. 414, pl. 17. 1825.
Adenostylis integerrima Blume, ibid.
Tripleura pallida Lindl. in Wall., Cat. n. 7391. 1832.
Zeuxine emarginata Lindl., Gen. et Sp. Orch. 485. 1840.
Zeuxine sulcata Lindl., ibid.; Trimen, Handb. Fl. Ceylon 4: 215. 1898.
Zeuxine membranacea Lindl., ibid.
Zeuxine integerrima Lindl., ibid.
Zeuxine bracteata Wight, Ic. Pl. Ind. Or. 5 (1): 16, pl. 1724. 1851.
Zeuxine brevifolia Wight, ibid. pl. 1725.
Zeuxine robusta Wight, ibid. pl. 1726.
Zeuxine tripleura Lindl., J. Linn. Soc. Bot. 1: 186. 1857.
Zeuxine procumbens Blume, Orch. Archip. Ind. 68. 1858.
Adenostylis strateumatica Ames, Orch. 2: 57. 1908.
Adenostylis sulcata (Lindl.) Hayata, Ic. Pl. Formosa 6: Suppl. 75.

Terrestrial leafy herb, 5–25 cm high, non-pseudobulbous, glabrous; stem erect but for a short, creeping portion in the ground below; roots fibrous. Leaves erect, sessile, of different sizes, lower 2.5–5 cm long, upper smaller, linear lanceolate, midrib stout, margins recurved. Flowers small, greenish-white with a yellow lip in nearly glabrous, dense-flowered, terminal spikes 1.2–5 cm long. Floral bracts 0.6–1.2 cm long, erect, lanceolate, acuminate, hyaline, 1-veined; sepals 4 mm long, oblong, obtuse, membranous; petals oblong, obtuse, hyaline, appressed on the dorsal sepal, forming a hood over the column; lip as long as the lateral sepals, cymbiform, contracted into a short pubescent claw, terminating in a small, hammer-headed, simple or 2-lobed limb; column very short, apex winged, rostellum short. Anther dorsal, ovate, covered by the wings of the column, 2-loculed; pollinia 2, pyriform, attached to the face below the tip of the linear gland. Fruit an ellipsoid capsule, 6 mm long.

D i s t r. Rather rare, under the shade of trees in the tropical wet evergreen forests extending to the mid-country. Kukul Korale, Dolosbage, Nilgala, Uva, Pasdun Korale, etc. Also in India from Punjab to Assam and Chittagong, Burma, China, Java and the Philippine Islands. It has also been collected in Florida and Cuba, probably escaped from cultivation and naturalized.

E c o l. Flowers December, January.

I l l u s t r. Blume, Orch. Archip. Ind. 1: pl. 22, fig. 3; pl. 23B. 1858; Wight, Ic. Pl. Ind. Orient. 5: pls. 1724 & 1726. 1851; King & Pantling, Ann. R. Bot. Gard. (Calcutta) 8: pl. 381. 1858; PDA, drawing from *C.P. 3017.*

N o t e. There seems to be some confusion in the collections in Herb. Lindley. It contains 9 collections from Ceylon, India and the Philippine Islands. Two specimens of the collection *Hooker 352* have been localised as from Ceylon and Sikkim and a third in Herb. Kew as from Chittagong. Collection *Champion 524* is annotated as from Hong Kong whereas it should have been from Ceylon. This species has a very wide distribution. Morel's collection from France is probably a specimen found among others imported from elsewhere.

S p e c i m e n s E x a m i n e d. CEYLON: BADULLA DISTRICT: near Nilgala, Jan. 1888, *s. coll. s.n.* (PDA). LOCALITY UNKNOWN: *Gardner 352* (K), *Macrae 70* (K), *s. coll. C.P. 3017* (PDA). AMERICA: Florida: Ormond Trop. Gard., *Ames s.n.* (AMES), Kissimenee prairies north of Lake Okeechobee, *Johnson s.n.* (AMES), *Deam 58681* (AMES); Sanibal Island, Dec. 1953, *Cooley 2466* (AMES); Rock Springs, Jan. 1946, *Howard & Howard 8055* (AMES); Hernandoco, *Pease s.n.* (AMES); Jacksonville, 1943, *Diddell s.n.* (AMES). CUBA: Mabana, *Acuna* 19125 (AMES). FRANCE: probably imported with other specimens, Oct. 1960, *Morel s.n.* (AMES). PAKISTAN: Lahore, *Chaudhuri s.n.* (AMES), 1922, *Drummond 20652* (K). BHUTAN: *Griffith 16* (K). TIBET: Southern Tibet, Arbor Hills, *Ward 7840* (K, AMES). INDIA: North-west India: 1844, *Edgeworth 60* (K). Punjab: Dovera, *Stewart 1243* (AMES); Uttar Pradesh: Dehra Dun, 1898, *Gamble 26478* (K); Saharanpur, Feb. 1901, *Inayat s.n.* (AMES); Nainital, Feb. 1950, *D. Chatterjee s.n.* (K); Delhi, *H.H. Rich 976* (K); Jaunpur, Feb. 1942, *Mooney 2023* (K). Sikkim: Hot Valleys, *J.D. Hooker 352* (K). Assam: 1938, *Jenkins s.n.* (AMES, PDA). Madras: Coimbatore, *Fischer 1767* (K). BANGLADESH: Sylhet, *Wallich 7391B* (K), *Wallich 7391* (K), *Wallich 7392* (K). BURMA: Chittagong, *J.D. Hooker & T. Thomson 352* (K). INDO-CHINA: *Petelot 5638* (AMES). CHINA: Yunnan: Mar. 1883, *Delavay 384* (AMES). Kwangtung: Canton, Feb. 1929, *Wang 1837* (AMES); Hong Kong, *Wilford s.n.* (AMES). Hainan: 1936, *Lau 25524* (AMES). PHILIPPINE ISLANDS: *Cumings s.n.* (K). Mindanao: Lake Lanao, *Clemens s.n.* (AMES); 1906, *Clemens 679a* (AMES).

2. Zeuxine longilabris (Lindl.) Trimen, Cat. 90. 1885; Handb. Fl. Ceylon 4: 216. 1898.—**Fig. 140.**

Monochilus longilabre Lindl., Gen. et Sp. Orch. 487. 1840.
Monochilus affine Wight, Ic. Pl. Ind. Or. 5 (1): 16, pl. 1728. 1851, not of Lindl.

Terrestrial, leafy herb with non-pseudobulbous stem, whole plant 15–25 cm high, very slender, ascending from a creeping, rooting base. Leaves few, distant, shortly petioled, 2.5–3.7 cm long, ovate or ovate-oblong, acute, with rounded base, 7-veined, glabrous, petiolar sheaths short, hyaline, inflated. Flowers large, greenish with a white lip in glandular-pubescent, lax-flowered spikes measuring 5–7.5 cm in length; peduncle very slender, pubescent, with distant, narrowly lanceolate sheaths. Floral bracts as long as the ovary, narrowly lanceolate; sepals 6 mm long, oblong, obtuse, pubescent; petals oblong, obtuse, glabrous, appressed to the dorsal sepal, forming a hood over the column; lip twice as long as the lateral sepals, saccate at base with 2 spurs within, dilating into a deeply 2-lobed, obovate, cuneate midlobe, lobes separated by a narrow acute sinus, margins coarsely toothed. Anther dorsal, long-beaked, 2-loculed; pollinia 2, pyriform, adnate for about 2/3 of their length to a linear strap, gland small.

Distr. Rare, under the shade of trees in the submontane or mid-country tropical wet evergreen forests up to 1220 m alt. Maturata, Laggala, etc. It also occurs in Assam, lower parts of Bengal, Western Ghats, South Konkan and Kerala in India and in Burma.

Ecol. Flowers May, September.

Illustr. PDA, 2 drawings from *C.P. 2377.*

Note. This species differs from the others in that the midlobe of the lip is coarsely toothed.

Specimens Examined. CEYLON: MATALE DISTRICT: Laggala, May 1884, *s. coll. s.n.* (PDA). LOCALITY UNKNOWN: *s. coll. C.P. 2377* (K, PDA). INDIA: Malabar, Konkan, etc., *Stocks s.n.* (AMES), Herb. *Stocks 13* (K). Madras. Coimbatore, Feb. 1907, *Fischer 1429* (K); Madurai, High Wavy Mts. May 1917, *Blatter & Hallberg 26530* (K); Chingleput Dist., Feb. 1937, *Barnes 1843* (K). Kerala: Quilon, Courtallam, Herb. *Wight 1030* (K).

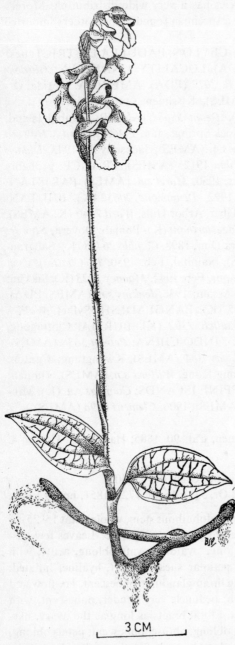

3 CM

Fig. 140. *Zeuxine longilabris* (Lindl.) Trimen. Plant with inflorescence.

3. Zeuxine regia (Lindl.) Tri-

men, Cat. 90. 1885; Handb. Fl. Ceylon 4: 216. 1898.—**Fig. 141.**

Monochilus regium Lindl., Gen. et Sp. Orch. 487. 1840.

Terrestrial leafy herb with a creeping stem rooting at nodes and rising above to 7–12 cm in height. Leaves few, 4–6 to a plant, 3.5–6.5 × 1.3–2.1 cm, rather distant, lower leaves smaller, oblanceolate, or ovate-lanceolate, acute, reddish-brown with a silvery grey band in the middle on the upper surface running from base to apex, paler beneath; petioles short, membranous, sheathing the stem at the base. Flowers small, greenish-white, in terminal, long-peduncled, glandular-pubescent spikes; peduncle 8–16 cm long, glandular-pubescent with 3 or 4 sterile bracts, the lowest leaf-like. Floral bracts 4.6 × 2.6 mm, broadly ovate, acuminate, 1-veined, glandular-pubescent; sepals glandular-pubescent; dorsal sepal 3.5 mm long, 2.4 mm broad, ovate, acuminate, subacute, 3-veined; lateral sepals 3.7 × 1.5 mm, oblong, subacute, 3-veined; petals 3.5 × 1.34 mm, dimidiate-ovate, rounded or subacute, 2- or 3-veined, the larger vein towards the straight edge of the margin, appressed on the dorsal sepal forming a hood over the column; lip 3.2 × 2.3 mm, subquadrate, cymbiform, lateral lobes folding in and enclosing 2 stout, linear, recurved calli; column 1.7 mm high, 1.2 mm broad, ovate, acuminate, deeply bifid; stigmatic lobes along the margin. Anther dorsal, 2-loculed, 1 × 0.74 mm; pollinia 2, obovoid or pyriform, sessile on a linear strap; gland small, shield-shaped, 0.8 × 0.3 mm; pollinia 0.9 × 0.36 mm. Ovary 6 mm long, glandular-pubescent. Fruit a small, fusiform capsule, 7.5 × 3 mm.

D i s t r. Endemic. Rather common, under the shade of trees in the sub-montane or mid-country tropical wet evergreen forests among fallen leaves in association with *Anoectochilus setaceus*. Ritigala, Kurunegala (Dolukande), Muruthalawa, Galaha (Nilambe), Hantane, Rangala (Corbet's Gap), Amba-gamuwa, Adam's Peak, Nuwara Eliya (Westward-Ho), Ratnapura (Karawita Kande), etc.

E c o l. Flowers December, January.

U s e s. It is used medicinally.

V e r n. Iru-raja (S).

I l l u s t r. PDA, drawing.

N o t e. Herb. Lindley contains the type collection. Bentham (Hook. Ic. Pl. pl. 2174) and Hooker (Fl. Br. Ind.) mention that the leaves of this plant are dark green and the former figures the petals oblong. The leaves on the other hand are reddish-brown with a silver grey band in the middle on the upper surface and the petals are dimidiate-ovate.

S p e c i m e n s E x a m i n e d. MATALE DISTRICT: Kalupahana forest, Jul. 1973, *Jayasuriya 1207* (PDA, US). KANDY DISTRICT: Hantane, Aug. 1905, *Schlechter s.n.* (AMES); Peradeniya, Bot. Gard. cultd., Feb. 1929, *J.M. de Silva s.n.* (PDA), Jan. 1957, *Jayaweera 279* (PDA); Pitakande, Kalugam-

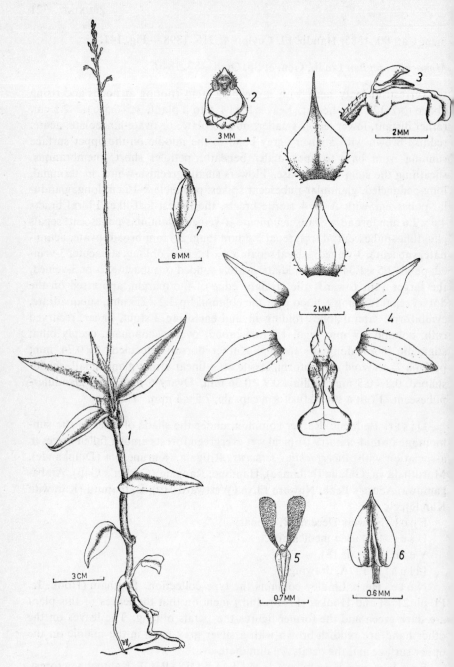

Fig. 141. *Zeuxine regia* (Lindl.) Trimen. 1, plant with inflorescence. 2, flower from front. 3, lip and column from side with the operculum slightly open. 4, bract, sepals, petals and column spread out from front, lip in natural position. 5, pollinia with strap and gland. 6, operculum from inside. 7, fruit.

mana, Feb. 1927, *J.M. de Silva s.n.* (PDA); Tanilla, Walaukande, Dec. 1893, *s. coll. s.n.* (PDA); Hunnasgiriya, Jan. 1961, *Jayaweera 2062* (PDA); Ambagamuwa, Jan. 1960, *Jayaweera 48 (3)* (AMES). LOCALITY UNKNOWN: 1829, *Macrae 63* (K-holotype), *Walker s.n.* (K), *s. coll. C.P. 2643* (PDA), *M.N. Beckett 1198* (K).

4. Zeuxine flava (Wall.) Trimen, Cat. 90. 1885; Handb. Fl. Ceylon 4: 217. 1898.—**Fig. 142.**

Etaera flava Lindl. in Wall., Cat. n. 7380 A.B. 1832.
Monochilus flavum Wall. ex Lindl., Gen. et Sp. Orch. 487. 1840.

Terrestrial, leafy, prostrate herb with a non-pseudobulbous, creeping, reddish stem about 25 cm long. Leaves 2 or 3, petiolate, 4–4.5 × 2.1–2.4 cm, oblong-ovate, acute or obtuse, minutely rugose, 5-veined, main vein depressed and conspicuously whitish-green on a background of dark green; petioles short, attaching to nodes below by obliquely truncate, hyaline, reddish-brown sheaths about 1.5 cm long. Flowers white with a pink sac, 4 mm broad, in many-flowered, terminal spikes measuring 9 cm in length; peduncle 11 cm long, hairy with 3 sterile bracts, the lowest foliaceous. Floral bracts 5.1 × 2.4 mm, ovate, acuminate, acute, pubescent, 1-veined; dorsal sepal 3.8 × 2.4 mm, ovate, rounded at apex, 1-veined, hairy; lateral sepals 3.3 × 2 mm, lanceolate-ovate, obtuse, 1-veined, also hairy; petals 3.3 × 1.6 mm, dimidiate-oblong, obtuse, 1-veined; lip 3.8 mm long, sessile, base saccate, enclosing two calli; claw expanded into two oblong-quadrate, divaricate, 3-veined wings; column 1.4 mm high and as broad, globular, narrowed at base into a neck; stigmatic lobes two, marginal; rostellum bipartite with erect segments. Anther dorsal, 2-loculed, 1.2 × 0.9 mm; pollinia 2, obovoid-pyriform, 1.2 × 0.3 mm, shortly stipitate on an oblong gland lodged in the fork of the rostellum. Ovary 5.8 mm long, pubescent with multicellular hairs.

D i s t r. Rare, under the shade of trees in the submontane or mid-country tropical wet evergreen forests between 305 and 915 m alt. Hunnasgiriya, Dolosbage, Ambagamuwa, etc. Also in Assam and Naga Hills in India. Nepal, Burma, Java, Borneo and Fiji Islands.

E c o l. Flowers February, March, April.

I l l u s t r. Hook. f., Ic. Pl. 22: pl. 2176. 1894; King & Pantling, Ann. R. Bot. Gard. (Calcutta) 8: pl. 386. 1898; PDA, drawing from *C.P. 3120*.

N o t e. Lindley mentions that "The flowers are yellow in a one-sided spike from 3–4 inches long"; the Ceylon specimens bear white flowers which are variable in the form of the lip.

S p e c i m e n s E x a m i n e d. CEYLON: KANDY DISTRICT: Hantane, Feb. 1905, *Schlechter s.n.* (AMES); Pitakande, Feb. 1927, *J.M. de Silva s.n.* (PDA); Hunnasgiriya, May 1964, *Jayaweera 2465* (PDA), Apr. 1960, *Jaya-*

324   ORCHIDACEAE

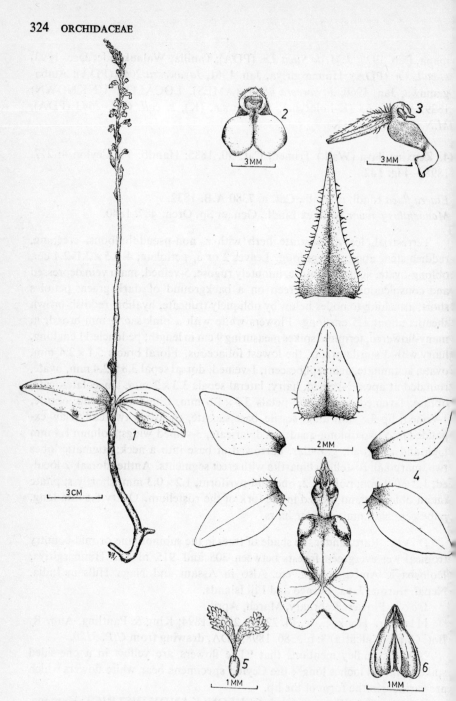

Fig. 142. *Zeuxine flava* (Wall.) Trimen. 1, plant with inflorescence. 2, flower from front. 3, lip and column from side. 4, bract, sepals, petals, lip and column spread out from front. 5, pollinia with gland. 6, operculum from inside.

weera 48 (*4*) (AMES). RATNAPURA DISTRICT: Maudella, Feb. 1969, *Hoogland 11429* (PDA). LOCALITY UNKNOWN: *s. coll. C.P. 3120* (PDA). NEPAL: *Wallich 7380* (K). Sikkim: Mongpoo, Mar. 1891, *Pantling 109* (K). INDIA: Assam: Naga Hills, 1886, *Prain 11* (K). BURMA: Chin States: Kanpetlet, Apr. 1839, *Dickason 8448* (K, AMES). FIJI ISLANDS: Viti Leou, Oct. 1942, *Greenwood 956* (AMES).

57. CORYMBORKIS

Thouars, Orch. Iles Afr. tt. 37, 38. 1822.

Tall, erect, leafy, terrestrial herbs; roots fibrous; leaves broad, plaited, sessile or petiolate, base sheathing; flowers large in axillary panicles; sepals and petals long and narrow, approximate below, widened towards the tip; lip erect from the base, inserted at the base of the column, linear, channelled, tip dilated and recurved; column long, slender, straight, terete, clavate at the tip, terminating in 2 erect lobes or auricles, rostellum at length bifid, erect, acute; anther dorsal, erect, acuminate, 2-chambered, chambers contiguous; pollinia 2, long, clavate, granular, grooved, affixed to a subulate stipe, with a peltate gland, descending behind the rostellum; capsule linear, subterete, crowned with the column and remains of the persistent perianth.

About 30 species distributed in Africa extending through India, Ceylon, Malaya to Australia and southwards to Celebes and New Guinea. Also in tropical America.

Corymborkis veratrifolia (Reinwardt) Blume, Orch. Archip. Ind. 125, pl. 42E. 1858–1859; Alston in Trimen, Handb. Fl. Ceylon 6: 279. 1931.—**Fig. 143.**

Hysteria veratrifolia Reinwardt ex Blume, Cat. Gewassen Buitenz. 99. 1823, nomen.

Rhynchanthera paniculata Blume, Bijdr. pl. 78. 1826.

Macrostylis disticha Breda, Kuhl et. Hasselt. Orch. pl. 2, f. 1. 1828.

Corymborchis assamica Blume, Orch. Archip. Ind. 126, pl. 43, f. 2. A & B. 1858–1859.

Corymbis disticha Lindl., Fol. Orch. 1. 1859, in part.

Corymbis veratrifolia Reichb. f., Flora 48: 184. 1865, nomen.

Tall terrestrial leafy herb with a non-pseudobulbous stem and fibrous roots; stem 1.2 m high, thick, leafy throughout. Leaves 30–45 × 7.5–10 cm, oval or ovate-lanceolate, caudate-acuminate, veins many and strong, sheaths strongly ribbed. Flowers greenish-white, 2.5–3 cm long, sessile, erect, in axillary panicles which are 10–15 cm long and as broad; sepals and petals subsimilar, narrowly oblanceolate, at first cohering in a tube with spreading tips; lip lanceolate, acuminate, inserted at the base of the column, channelled, tip

Fig. 143. *Corymborkis veratrifolia* (Reinw.) Blume, redrawn from King & Pantling, Ann. R. Bot. Gard. (Calcutta) 8: pl. 354. 1898. 1, an entire plant reduced in size. 2, part of plant with inflorescences, with an entire leaf on background. 3, flower side view. 4, bract, ovary, column and lip, side view. 5, lip. 6, upper part of the column, front view. 7, side view of upper part of the column showing stigma and anther. 8, pollinia enlarged.

dilated and recurved; column 6 mm high, erect, terete, tip clavate, 2-lobed or auricled; rostellum at length bifid; stigma erect, transverse, saccate. Anther terminal, narrow, erect, acuminate, 2-loculed; pollinia long, clavate, granular, peltately attached by a subulate caudicle to a gland. Fruit a sessile, fusiform capsule, 3.7 cm long.

D i s t r. Very rare, in ravines under the shade of trees at higher altitudes of the tropical wet evergreen forests. Maturata, Four Korales, etc. I have not come across this species in a live state. Also in Sikkim Himalayas, Assam, Andaman Is., and Malabar in India, Chittagong in Bangladesh, Burma, Malaya, Thailand, Java, Sumatra, Borneo, Fiji, Samoan and the Philippine Islands. Towards the West it extends as far as the west coast of Africa.

E c o l. Flowers October.

I l l u s t r. Blume, Orch. Archip. Ind. pl. 42E. 1858–59; King & Pantling, Ann. R. Bot. Gard. (Calcutta) 8: pl. 354. 1898.

S p e c i m e n s E x a m i n e d. CEYLON: RATNAPURA DISTRICT: Four Korales, Oct. 1882, *s. coll. s.n.* (PDA). NUWARA ELIYA DISTRICT: Mathurata, *s. coll. C.P. 3206* (PDA). AFRICA: *M. Perville 142* (K); Fernando Po: *Barber 1478* (K). INDIA: Sikkim: *J.D. Hooker s.n.* (K); Hot Valleys, *J.D. Hooker 58* (K); Valley of Teesta, Aug. 1899, *Pantling 475* (K, AMES). Assam: *Griffith s.n.* (K), *Masters s.n.* (PDA). Andhra Pradesh: Cuddapah, 1881, *Beddome s.n.* (K), Herb. *Wight 927* (K). BANGLADESH: Chittagong: *J.D. Hooker & T. Thomson s.n.* (K). Shan States: Jan. 1922, *Rock 1945* (AMES). THAILAND: Doi Chiendao, Jul. 1955, *Garrett 1417* (AMES). MALAYA: Singapore, 1890, *Ridley 2037* (AMES). SUMATRA: *Banghan 712* (AMES). JAVA: *Blume s.n.* (AMES). BRITISH NORTH BORNEO: Mt. Kinabalu, Nov. 1915, *Clemens 123* (AMES). PHILIPPINE ISLANDS: *Cumming s.n.* (K). SOLOMON ISLANDS: Rennell Island: Jan. 1933, *Stewart s.n.* (AMES). FIJI ISLANDS: 1890, *Seemann 603* (AMES). TONGA ISLANDS: Eua Island, Mar. 1953, *Yuncker 15467* (AMES). TANNA ISLAND: 1928, *Kajewski 146* (AMES).

58. TROPIDIA

Lindl. in Wall., Cat. No. 7386. 1831.

Tall, leafy, terrestrial herbs; rootstocks woody with rigid root fibres; stems simple or branched; leaves plicate, strongly veined, bases sheathing; flowers in short and dense unbranched terminal spikes or paniculate racemes of numerous small resupinate flowers; bracts strongly veined and persistent; dorsal sepal free, lateral sepals connate at base forming a mentum with the base of the lip; lip superior, sessile on the base of the column with a broad, shortly spurred or saccate base; column short, stout, rostellum at length bifid; stigma anticous; anther dorsal, erect, pollinia chambers contiguous; pollinia 2, calvate granular, 2-cleft, pendulous by a slender caudicle from a small gland on the tip of the rostellum.

About 35 species spreading from Ceylon to Fiji Islands with two species in tropical America.

KEY TO THE SPECIES

1 Leaves narrowly linear-lanceolate, 3–5-veined . . . .**1. T. thwaitesii**
1 Leaves ovate or ovate-lanceolate, 5–7-veined . . . .**2. T. bambusifolia**

1. Tropidia thwaitesii Hook. f., Fl. Br. Ind. 6: 93. 1890; Trimen, Handb. Fl. Ceylon 4: 219. 1898.—**Fig. 144.**

Tropidia curculigoides Lindl., Gen. et Sp. Orch. 497. 1840, in part.

Terrestrial leafy, grass-like herb with a woody rootstock and wiry, stout root fibres; stem 15–30 cm long, slender, clothed with leaf sheaths except at the base. Leaves suberect, 7.5–13.5 × 0.5–1.1 cm, linear-lanceolate, acuminate, membranous, 3–5-veined with many slender intermediate venules; bases sheathing; sheaths long and strongly ribbed. Flowers yellowish-green, 6 mm broad, in subcapitate many-flowered spikes; peduncle 0.6–2.5 cm long with many circular, erect, strongly nerved, sterile bracts. Floral bracts 8.5 × 2.5 mm, subulate from a broadly dilated base, 3-veined, glabrous but with a few scattered hairs inside; dorsal sepal 6.5 × 2.3 mm, oblanceolate, acuminate, 3-veined, lateral veins branching at base giving a 5-veined appearance, lateral sepals 8 × 3 mm, ovate or lanceolate-oblong, acuminate, 3- or 5- veined, lateral veins branching at base, bases connate with lip in a saccate mentum; petals 5.5 × 2 mm, falcate-ovate, acuminate, 3-veined; lip sessile at the base of the column, 7 × 3 mm, saccate with a thick intramarginal ridge, undulate, 3-veined, acute or subacute, constricted and recurved at the apical end; column short, stout, 4.5 mm long, 2 mm broad, rostellum bifid, stigma anticous. Anther dorsal, erect, linear-oblong, 2 × 0.75 mm, apiculate; pollinia 2, clavate, 1.7 × 0.4 mm, granular, 2-cleft; caudicle short and slender, gland small; ovary 7.5 mm long, glabrous.

D i s t r. Endemic. Rare, under the shade of trees extending from the dry zone to the submontane or mid-country tropical wet evergreen forests up to 610 m alt. Kandy (Udawattekelle), Muruthalawa, Minneriya, Polonnaruwa, Bintanne, Four Korales, etc.

E c o l. Flowers March, July, November.

I l l u s t r. PDA, drawing from *C.P. 3565.*

N o t e. Herb. Lindley contains three collections, two of which are from India and the third *Macrae 58* from Ceylon. Macrae's collection seems to be the true *Tropidia thwaitesii* while the Indian specimens namely *Wallich 7386* and Griffith's collections may belong to the Indian *T. curculigoides* Lindl. It

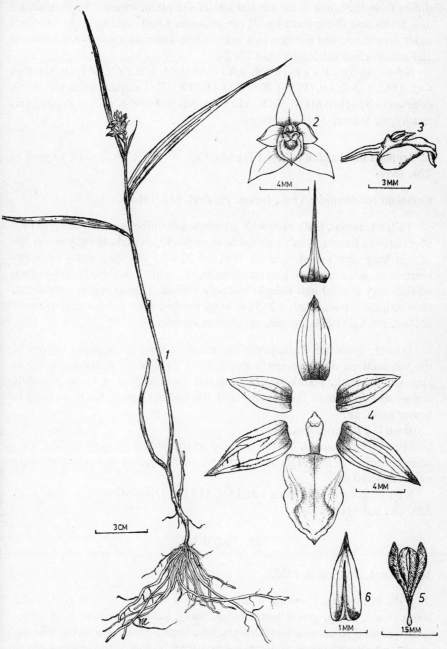

Fig. 144. *Tropidia thwaitesii* Hook. f. 1, plant with inflorescence. 2, flower from front.
3, lip and column from side. 4, bract, sepals, petals, lip and column spread out from
front. 5, pollinia with gland. 6, operculum from inside.

differs from the latter in the smaller size of the plant, smaller 3-veined sepals and petals and the saccate lip. *T. curculigoides* Lindl. on the other hand has much larger 5-veined leaves which are caudate-acuminate and 5-veined sepals and petals which are longer than the lip.

Specimens Examined. RATNAPURA DISTRICT: Four Korales, Oct. 1882, *s. coll. s.n.* (PDA). KANDY DISTRICT: Udawattekelle, Oct. 1960, *Jayaweera 51 (1)* (AMES). LOCALITY UNKNOWN: *s. coll. C.P. 3565* (K, lectotype), *Macrae 58* (K, syntype).

2. **Tropidia bambusifolia** (Thw.) Trimen, Cat. 90. 1885; Handb. Fl. Ceylon 4: 220. 1898.

Cnemidia bambusifolia Thw., Enum. Pl. Zeyl. 314. 1861.

Tall, terrestrial, leafy herb with a non-pseudobulbous stem and rigid root fibres arising from a woody rootstock; stem 60–90 cm high, lower portion 30–35 cm long and naked. Leaves few, 10–22 × 2.5–6.8 cm, ovate or ovate-lanceolate, acuminate or caudate-acuminate, with acute base, 5–7-veined, veinlets very slender and sheaths strongly ribbed. Flower spikes very short, terminal, stout-peduncled, 1.2–5 cm long, clothed with imbricating, ovate or oblong, strongly ribbed, green, coriaceous sheaths.

Distr. Endemic. Rare, under the shade of trees in the moist regions of the submontane or mid-country tropical wet evergreen forests up to 915 m alt. Adam's Peak, Katukande, Lininigala, Hewesse, etc. I have not come across this species in the jungles and the material available is wanting in flower and fruit.

Ecol. Flowers June, July.

Note. This species is closely allied to the Indian *T. curculigoides* from which it differs in the larger size of the plant, 5–7-veined leaves and strongly peduncled spikes.

Specimens Examined. LOCALITY UNKNOWN: *s. coll. C.P. 3207* (K, holotype, PDA).

59. VANILLA

Mill., Gard. Dict. ed. 6. 1752.

Tall, branching, climbing plants bearing a leaf and root at each node; stems terete, fleshy, green; leaves large, fleshy, sessile or subsessile or sometimes reduced to small scales; flowers few, large, in short axillary inflorescences; sepals and petals about equal and free; lip joined to the sides of the column, embracing it and gradually dilating into an entire or 3-lobed limb with hairy appendages inside; column elongate, curved, footless; anther terminal, incumbent on the front of the column over a broad rostellum; pollinia free, granulose, without strap or gland; stigma transverse, situated under the rostellum; fruit long, fleshy, cylindric, often not opening; seeds not winged.

About 70 species distributed throughout the tropics of both worlds.

KEY TO THE SPECIES

1 Leaves absent or arrested; petals spathulately obovate, disc of the lip with 2 pubescent ridges from the base to beyond the middle; fruit linear, 12.5–15 cm long............ ....**1. V. walkerae**

1 Leaves fleshy, oval or linear-oblong; petals oblong-lanceolate, disc of lip with a broad hirsute band from the upper third to the tip and a hemispheric tuft of papillae at the base; fruit linear-oblong, 10 cm long..................................**2. V. moonii**

1. Vanilla walkerae Wight, Ic. Pl. Ind. Or. 3 (3): 1 pl. 932. 1845; Trimen, Handb. Fl. Ceylon 4: 220. 1898.—**Fig. 145.**

Scandent, non-pseudobulbous, apparently leafless epiphyte, climbing by means of aerial roots; stems thick, terete, ash-green, branching, deeply channelled. Leaves arrested, 1.2–3.7 cm long, lanceolate, acuminate, not noticeable at first sight. Flowers large, white, 6.8 cm broad, in very stout, many-flowered racemes about 13–15 cm long. Floral bracts 8 × 5 mm, broadly ovate, subacute, 5–7-veined; sepals 4.5 × 1.6–1.7 cm, broadly oblanceolate, subacute, 13–15-veined; petals as long as sepals, 2.8 cm broad, spathulately obovate, 15-veined, margins thin and wavy; lip erect, 3.7–4.3 × 2.4 cm, obovate-oblong, undulate, crenate, inserted at the base of the column, embracing and fusing with it by a convolute claw and dilating into a trumpet-shaped limb with recurved margins, lateral lobes absent, apex triangular, acute; disc with 2 broad, papillate ridges from the base to beyond the middle; column long, narrow, 1.7 cm long, 2.5 mm broad. Anther terminal, incumbent, mitriform, 2-loculed, 2.5 mm long; pollinia 4, free without straps or glands, 1.7 × 0.7 mm. Ovary with pedicel 4.1 cm long. Fruit a very slender capsule, 12.5–15 cm long.

D i s t r. Common, scrambling in open rocky patches in the tropical mixed evergreen forests below 305 m alt. Wariapola, Dambulla, Nalanda, etc. Also in South India.

E c o l. Flowers March–June. Other orchids growing along with it are *Vanda spathulata* Spreng. and *Eulophia epidendrea* C. E. C. Fischer.

I l l u s t r. Wight, Ic. Pl. Ind. Or. 3: pl. 932. 1845; PDA, drawing from *C.P. 3964.*

N o t e. Herb. Lindley contains Champion's collection from Ceylon. It is quite probable that *Vanilla wightiana* Lindl. and *V. parishii* Reich. are the same species as *V. walkerae*, as all of them are leafless but the two former contain hairy discs.

S p e c i m e n s E x a m i n e d. CEYLON: MATALE DISTRICT: Dam-

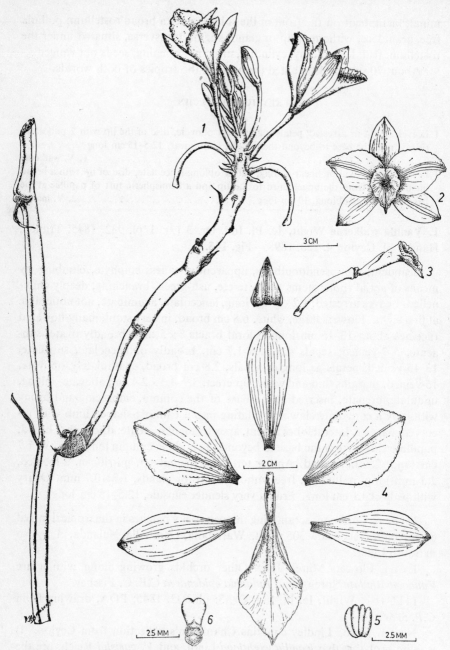

Fig. 145. *Vanilla walkerae* Wight. 1, terminal portion of a stem with inflorescence. 2, flower from front. 3, lip from side with the column hidden between its folds. 4, bract, sepals, petals, lip and column spread out from front. 5, pollinia. 6, operculum from front.

GASTRODIA 333

bulla, Sept. 1959, *Jayaweera 52 (1)* (AMES). GALLE DISTRICT: Galle, *Champion s.n.* (K). LOCALITY UNKNOWN: *s. coll. C.P. 2964* (K, PDA). INDIA: Madras: Coimbatore, Apr. 1906, *Fischer 1011* (K). Kerala: Quilon, Herb. *Wight s.n.* (K).

2. Vanilla moonii Thw., Enum. Pl. Zeyl. 312. 1861; Trimen, Handb. Fl. Ceylon 4: 221. 1898.—**Fig. 146.**

Scandent epiphyte with non-pseudobulbous, terete, flexuous, deeply channelled stems, climbing by means of aerial roots. Leaves subsessile, 12.5–17.5 cm long, ovate or linear-oblong, obtusely acuminate, fleshy and many-veined. Flowers large, buff-coloured with a yellow lip, in crowded, stout-peduncled racemes. Floral bracts short, ovate, subacute; sepals and petals about 2.5 cm long, oblong-lanceolate, subacute, spreading from an erect base; lip entire, 1.6 cm long, erect, inserted at the base of the column and embracing it by a convolute claw and expanding into a trumpet-shaped limb with recurved undulate margins; disc with a broad hirsute band from the upper third to the tip and a hemispheric tuft of papillae at the base; column long, slender. Anther terminal, incumbent, mitriform, 2-loculed; pollinia 4, sausage-shaped, free, without straps or glands. Ovary with pedicel 1.2–3.7 cm long. Fruit a linear-oblong capsule 10 cm long.

D i s t r. Endemic. Rare, in the tropical wet evergreen forests up to an alt. of about 610 m. Kalutara, Galle, Heneratgoda, Hunnasgiriya, Negombo, Kurunegala, etc.

E c o l. Flowers April, August, September.

I l l u s t r. Trimen, Handb. Fl. Ceylon pl. 91. 1898; PDA, two drawings one of which is from *C.P. 3204.*

N o t e. This species resembles *V. planifolia* very closely but is much smaller in all parts. The fruits too are much shorter but stouter. Herb. Lindley contains Champion's collection from Ceylon.

S p e c i m e n s   E x a m i n e d. GALLE DISTRICT: Galle, *Champion s.n.* (K). LOCALITY UNKNOWN: *Gardner 1869* (K); *s. coll. C.P. 3204* (K-holotype, PDA); Aug. 1926, *J.M. de Silva s.n.* (PDA).

60. GASTRODIA

R. Br., Prod. 330. 1810.

Terrestrial leafless saprophytes; rhizomes horizontal, tuberous, of many internodes; stem erect, each bearing a terminal inflorescence; petals and sepals joined together into a 5-lobed tube, cleft in front between the lateral sepals; lip joined to the end of the column-foot; spur absent; column long, narrow, sides narrowly winged towards the top, base produced into a short or long

Fig. 146. *Vanilla moonii* Thw., redrawn from a drawing in PDA. 1, portion of the plant with clusters of flowers. 2, longitudinal section of flower showing the inside lip and parts separated.

foot; stigma prominent at the base of the column; anther terminal, erect, 2-chambered; pollinia 2, pyriform, of large granules, without strap or gland; fruit erect, sometimes on an elongated pedicel.

About 15 species distributed from India to Japan and southwards through Malaysia to Australia and New Zealand.

Gastrodia zeylanica Schlechter in Fedde Repert. 3: 77. 1906; Alston in Trimen, Handb. Fl. Ceylon 6: 279. 1931.—**Fig. 147.**

Gastrodia javanica Thw., Enum. Pl. Zeyl. 311. 1861, non Lindl.; Trimen, Handb. Fl. Ceylon 4: 221. 1898.

Terrestrial, leafless, brown coloured, saprophytic herb with a tuberous

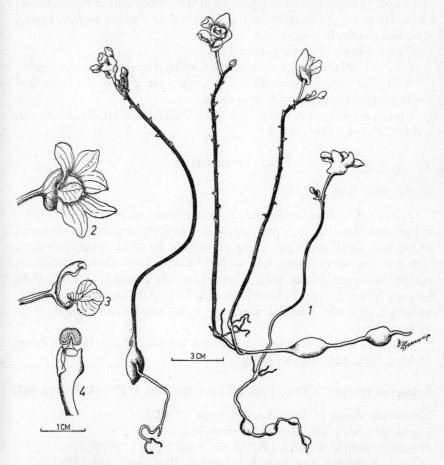

Fig. 147. *Gastrodia zeylanica* Schlechter, redrawn from a drawing in **PDA.** 1, plants with inflorescences and tuberous rootstocks. 2, flower from front, two-thirds view. 3, ovary, lip, column and foot from side. 4, column from side with operculum opened.

rootstock and tubuliferous rootlets; stem 7.5–15 cm long, erect, naked or with a few empty sheaths. Flowers about 1.2 cm broad, white in colour, slightly tinged with violet, in lax, terminal racemes about as long as the stem, elongating much during flowering. Floral bracts small, orbicular; sepals connate with petals in a ventricose, 5-lobed tube, cleft in front; lip shorter than petals, broadly oblong, articulate with the foot of the column, base with a large bifid callus; spur absent; column long, narrow, sides winged, base produced into a foot; stigma prominent, anticous. Anther terminal, erect, 2-loculed; pollinia 2, pyriform, free, coarsely granular without strap or gland. Ovary with pedicel 1.2–1.6 cm long.

D i s t r. Endemic. Very rare, in moist conditions under the shade of trees in a carpet of fallen and decaying leaves of the tropical wet evergreen forests below 610 m alt. Ambagamuwa, Hiniduma Kande, Pasdun Korale, Eratne, Karawita Kande, Balangoda, etc.

E c o l. Flowers February–April.

I l l u s t r. PDA, three drawings one of which is from the type specimen.

N o t e. Schlechter separated this as a new species from the Javan *Gastrodia javanica* Lindl. to which it is related.

S p e c i m e n E x a m i n e d. GALLE DISTRICT: Hiniduma Kande, *s. coll. C.P. 3463* (PDA, holotype).

61. EPIPOGIUM

IR. Br., Prod. 330, 331. 1810.

Terrestrial, leafless saprophytes; rhizomes tuberous, of many short internodes; stems simple, erect, sheathed, fleshy, bearing terminal, few-flowered, ax racemes; sepals and petals subequal, narrow; lip wide, spurred, concave, with minutely warty ridges; spur short, obtuse; column short, strongly incurved, thickened at the apex, stigma prominent, broad, at base of the column, 2-lobed; anther horizontal, tumid, dorsally thickened, 2-chambered; pollinia 2, pyriform, bifid, granular, each with a slender curved caudicle but without gland.

About 14 species distributed in Europe, tropical Africa, India, Ceylon, Malaya, Java, Australia and Japan.

Epipogium roseum (D. Don) Lindl., J. Linn. Soc. Bot. 1: 177. 1857.—**Fig. 148.**

Limodorum roseum D. Don, Prod. Fl. Nepal 30. 1825.
Ceratopsis rosea Lindl., Gen. et Sp. Orch. 384. 1840.
Podanthera pallida Wight, Ic. Pl. Ind. Or. 5 (1): 22, pl. 1759. 1851.
Galera rosea Blume, Ann. Mus. Bot. Lugduno Batavum 2: 188. 1856.
Epipogium nutans Lindl., J. Linn. Soc. Bot. 1: 177. 1857; Trimen, Handb. Fl.
    Ceylon 4: 222. 1898.

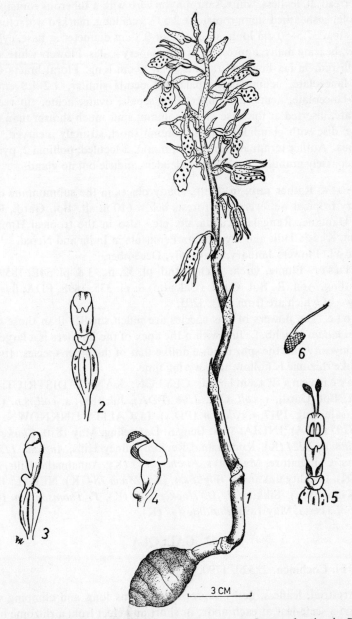

Fig. 148. *Epipogium roseum* (D. Don) Lindl., redrawn from a drawing in PDA.
1, plant with tuberous rootstock and inflorescence. 2, ovary and column from front.
3, same from side. 4, column from behind showing opening of operculum and pollinia. 5, column from front with operculum opened out and pollinia. 6, pollinium
with caudicle (2–6, enlarged).

Terrestrial, leafless, white, saprophytic herb with a tuberous rootstock and a simple, ensheathed stem; rootstock 2.5–7.5 cm long, marked with closely set scars; stem 37.5–50 cm long, stout, about 0.8 cm diameter at base, cylindric, hollow, bearing many, appressed, broad, papery scales. Flowers white, speckled with red, in lax-flowered racemes 7.5–20 cm long. Floral bracts 0.6 cm long, lanceolate, acuminate; sepals and petals similar, 1.2–1.8 cm long, linear-lanceolate, acute; lip longer than sepals, ovate, acute, tip recurved, serrulate, inserted at the base of the column; spur much shorter than the lip, obtuse; disc with glandular ridges; column short, strongly incurved, stigma anticous. Anther terminal, horizontal, tumid, 2-loculed; pollinia 2, pyriform, bifid, coarsely granular, each with a slender caudicle but no gland.

D i s t r. Rather rare, in damp, shady places in the submontane or mid-country tropical wet evergreen forests below 610 m alt. Bot. Gard., Peradeniya, Hantane, Rangala, Kundasale, etc. Also in the tropical Himalayas, Sikkim, Khasia Hills and the Deccan Peninsula in India and Nepal.

E c o l. Flowers January, May–July, December.

I l l u s t r. Blume, Orch. Archip. Ind. pl. 52, fig. 3 & pl. 54E. 1859; King & Pantling, Ann. R. Bot. Gard. (Calcutta) 8: pl. 335. 1898; PDA, five drawings two of which are from *C.P. 3205*.

N o t e. The flowers of this species are much smaller than those of *Epipogium nutans* Reichb. f. Just within the apex of the lip there is a large papillose convexity and the spur is quite unlike that of the other species. Its short, stem-like rhizome is hollow at flowering time.

S p e c i m e n s E x a m i n e d. CEYLON: KANDY DISTRICT: Peradeniya, Bot. Gard., *s. coll. C.P. 3208* (PDA), Jul. 1887, *s. coll. s.n.* (PDA); Kundasale, Aug. 1917, *s. coll. s.n.* (PDA). LOCALITY UNKNOWN: *s. coll. C.P. 3205* (PDA). INDIA: West Bengal: Darjeeling, May 1870, *Clarke 11794* (K), *Gamble 8224* (K). Kodaikanal Region: Pulney Hills, *Anglade 1173* (K). Madras: Coimbatore, May 1911, *Fischer 2745* (K); Annaimalai Hills, *Barber 5497* (K). Locality unknown: *Wight s.n.* (K), *Mann 784* (K). NEPAL: *Wallich s.n.* (K-holotype). Sikkim: *J. D. Hooker 348* (K), *T. Thomson s.n.* (PDA); Valley of Teesta, May 1891, *Pantling 147* (K).

62. GALEOLA

Lour., Fl. Cochinch. 2: 520. 1790.

Terrestrial, leafless, fleshy saprophytes; stems long and climbing with a root and a scale-leaf at each node, or short and erect from a rhizome bearing fleshy roots; inflorescence a terminal panicle or raceme, or lateral in axils of upper scale-leaves of climbing stems; sepals and petals about equal, free; lip sessile, base of lip surrounding the column, the blade concave, entire or 3-lobed with longitudinal ridges; spur absent, disc bearded; column short, incurved, dilated above with membranous wings; anther terminal, conical, 2-chambered; pollinia 2, cleft, granular, without caudicles or gland; fruit a fleshy indehiscent berry or a long dry capsule.

About 33 species distributed in India, Ceylon, Malaya, Thailand, Cochin, China extending to Formosa and Japan and southwards to New Guinea and the Philippine Islands.

Galeola javanica (Blume) Benth. & Hook. f., Gen. Pl. 3: 590. 1883; Trimen, Handb. Fl. Ceylon 4: 223. 1898.—**Fig. 149.**

Cyrtosia javanica Blume, Bijdr. 396, pl. 6. 1825.

Leafless, fleshy, erect saprophyte with scale-like leaves and many stems; roots clavate or cylindric, fascicled fibres 2.5–5 cm long; stems 10–15 cm high,

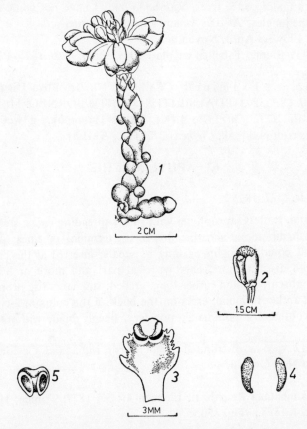

Fig. 149. *Galeola javanica* (Blume) Benth. & Hook., redrawn from a drawing in PDA. 1, plant with scales and inflorescence. 2, column and lip from side. 3, column from front. 4, pollinia. 5, operculum from front.

simple or sparingly branched, glabrous, shining below and papillose above, turning dull red-purple with age; scales alternate, ovate, of the same colour as the stem. Flowers pale green with a yellow column, 1.2 cm across, nodding in terminal loosely spicate racemes; sepals and petals subsimilar, oblong, erect, connivent, acute, membranous; lip sessile, adnate to the base of the column, embracing it by the base, shorter and broader than the sepals, semi-rotund, concave; disc thickened, bearded and ribbed; spur absent; column short, incurved, base thickened, gibbous above, dilated, fornicate with 2 short, lateral, rounded, erose wings; rostellum short. Anther terminal, conical, 2-loculed; pollinia 2, oblong, powdery without caudicle or gland. Fruit a sausage-shaped, terete, pendulous berry about 5 cm long.

D i s t r. Very rare, under the shade of trees in the submontane or mid-country tropical wet evergreen forests between 610 and 915 m alt. Pasbage, Pundaluoya under coffee trees, Ramboda, etc. I have not come across this species in the jungles. Also in Assam, Java and Borneo.

E c o l. Flowers April, November.

I l l u s t r. Blume, Tabellen en Platen Jav. Orch. pl. 6. 1825; PDA, drawing from *C.P. 3202.*

S p e c i m e n s E x a m i n e d. CEYLON: Nuwara Eliya District, Ramboda, *s. coll. C.P. 3203* (PDA). BRITISH NORTH BORNEO: Mt. Kinabalu, at 4000 ft alt., *C.E. Carr 3199A* (K); Dallas-Tinompok, in wet ravine at 4500 ft alt., fruit pod pink, *Clemens 27024* (K, AMES).

63. APHYLLORCHIS

Blume, Bijdr. t. 77. 1825.

Terrestrial, leafless saprophytes with thick, spreading roots; stems simple, erect with membranous sheaths; flowers in terminal racemes; sepals and petals about equal, free; lip as long as sepals, inserted at the base of the column, with distinct short, narrow, basal part and more or less 3-lobed blade; spur absent; column rather long, arched; stigmatic disc prominent below the tip; anther terminal, erect on the back of the column, 2-chambered, chambers contiguous; pollinia 2, powdery, deeply bifid, without strap or gland.

About 12 species distributed from North India and Ceylon through Malaysia to New Guinea.

Aphyllorchis montana Reichb. f., Linnaea 41: 57. 1877; Trimen, Handb. Fl. Ceylon 4: 224. 1898.—**Fig. 150.**

Apaturia montana Thw., Enum. Pl. Zeyl. 301. 1861, non Lindl.

Pale, leafless, glabrous, saprophytic herb with a fleshy rootstock; stem

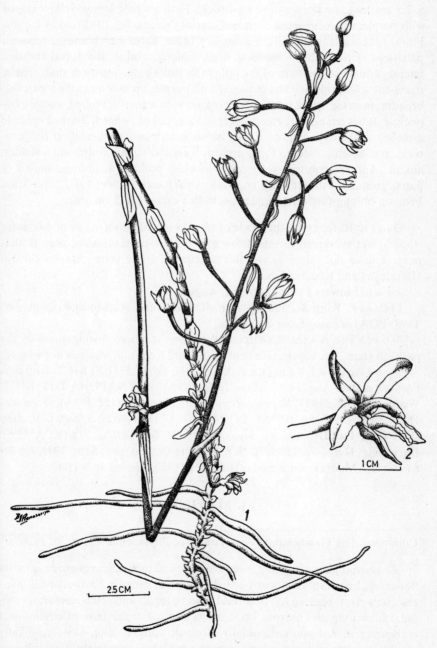

Fig. 150. *Aphyllorchis montana* Reichb. f., redrawn from a drawing in PDA.
1, plant with inflorescence. 2, flower from side, three-quarters front view.

60–90 cm high, purplish, naked, base clothed in oblong scales; roots vermiform, 5–7.5 cm long, as thick as the rootstock. Flowers pale lemon-yellow tinged with purple, in lax-flowered, terminal racemes measuring 10–20 cm in length. Floral bracts linear-lanceolate, acute or obtuse, pale, membranous, reflexed, persistent; sepals 1.2–1.6 cm long, linear-oblong, obtuse, the dorsal arching, laterals adnate to the base of the lip; petals subfalcate, narrower than sepals, straw-coloured, tips and backs tinged with purple; lip as long as the sepals but broader, inserted at the base of the column with a small, 2-lobed, saccate hypochile; lobes triangular, erect; a large ovate, naked, veined, 2-lobed epichile attached to the hypochile by a narrow neck with two small calli at the juncture; spur absent; column long, arched, truncate, stigma anticous, rostellum absent. Anther terminal, suberect, 2-loculed; pollinia 4, oblong, united in pairs, granular without strap or gland. Ovary with pedicel 1.6–2.5 cm long. Fruit an oblong-fusiform, slender-pedicelled capsule, 2.5 cm long.

D i s t r. Rare, under the shade of trees in the submontane or mid-country tropical wet evergreen forests below 610 m alt. Ambagamuwa, near Ratnapura. I have not come across this species in a live state. Also in Sikkim Himalayas and Khasia Hills.

E c o l. Flowers February, April, August.

I l l u s t r. King & Pantling, Ann. R. Bot. Gard. (Calcutta) 8 (4): pl. 349. 1898; PDA, drawing from *C.P. 3189*.

N o t e. This is a leafless terrestrial saprophytic herb distinguished by the purplish stem, free sepals, non spurred lip and a column which is not winged.

S p e c i m e n s E x a m i n e d. CEYLON: GALLE DISTRICT: Kottawa, Forest Reserve, Aug. 1929, *Alston 1372* (PDA). RATNAPURA DISTRICT: Weddagala, June 1972, *Hepper, Maxwell and Fernando 4551* (PDA); Sinharaja, Dec. 1895, *s. coll. s.n.* (PDA). LOCALITY UNKNOWN: *s. coll. C.P. 3189* (K, PDA). INDIA: Sikkim: Sivoke, Aug. 1898, *Pantling 344* (K, AMES). Darjeeling, Herb. *Griffith 5360* (K). Mysore: Cadamanay, Sept. 1905, *Barber 6116* (K). Madras: Annaimalai Hills Aug. 1920, *Fischer 4479* (K).

64. NERVILIA

Commerson ex Gaudichaud, Voy. Uranie & Physicienne 421. t. 35. 1826.

Terrestrial plants growing from underground tubers, leaves produced after flowering; leaves solitary, short or long-petioled, broadly heart-shaped; inflorescences erect, bearing 1, 2 or several flowers; sepals and petals similar, spreading, rather long and narrow; lip inferior, inserted at the base of column and embracing it, not spurred, usually 3-lobed; column long, slender, slightly clavate at apex without wings; anther terminal, imperfectly 2-chambered; pollinia 2, granular, divided, without caudicle or gland.

About 40 species distributed from Africa to India and China and through Malaya to Australia.

Nervilia juliana (Roxb.) Schlechter, Bot. Jahrb. Syst. 45: 402. 1911.—**Fig. 151.**

Pogonia juliana Wall., Cat. n. 7399. 1832: Trimen, Handb. Fl. Ceylon 4: 225. 1898.
Epipactis juliana Roxb., Fl. Ind. 3: 453. 1832.
Pogonia plicata Lindl. Gen. et Sp. Orch. 415 1835.

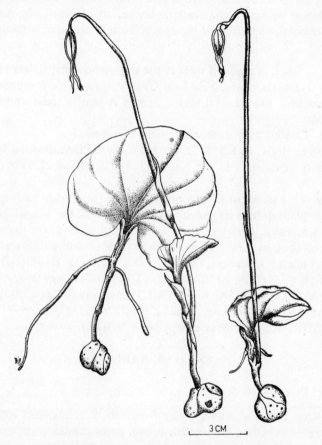

Fig. 151. *Nervilia juliana* (Roxb.) Schlt., redrawn from a drawing in PDA.
Plants with tuberous rootstock, leaves and fruits.

Terrestrial, tuberous, 1-leaved herb, tubers globose, white, 1.2–2.5 cm diameter; stem 5–7.5 cm high, erect, producing a few vermiform roots from above the tuber, a solitary leaf-bud and a long flowering scape. Leaves solitary, developed after flowering, short-petioled, broadly ovate, cordate, about

5 cm across, membranous, plicate, 5–7 veins radiating from the top of the petiole, green or purplish beneath; petiole with a few sheaths at the base. Flowers solitary, 2.5 cm broad, green with a pale pink lip mottled with red, and white lateral lobes, borne at the summit of a scape 12.5–15 cm long, with several convolute sheaths, the uppermost being the longest; pedicel short. Floral bracts shorter than the ovary; sepals and petals subequal, narrowly lanceolate, acuminate and purplish green in colour; lip inferior, inserted at the base of the column, longer than sepals, spurred at the base; lateral lobes of lip small, oblong, toothed, terminal lobe oval from a narrow base; disc pubescent between lobes; column high, slender, clavate, stigma anticous. Anther terminal, horizontal, imperfectly 2-loculed; pollinia 2, granular, without caudicle or gland.

Distr. Rare, in shade of trees in the dry mid-country. Near Haragama and Uma Oya in Dumbara, Nilgala in Uva Province. I have not come across this species in a live state. It also occurs in Assam in India and Sylhet in Bangladesh.

Ecol. Flowers May–June, September–October.

Illustr. Hook. f., Ic. Pl. 22: pl. 2194. 1892; PDA, drawing from *C.P. 3841*. Henry Teuscher, Am. Or. Soc. Bull. 47 (1): 21 and 22, 1978 (under *N. plicata*).

Note. This seems to be a doubtful species for Ceylon as the leaves of the Ceylon plant differ very much from the leaves of the Bengal plant. The collections at Herb. Peradeniya are lacking in flowers where the leaves are present, and the only flowering specimen available is without leaves.

Specimens Examined. CEYLON: KANDY DISTRICT: Dumbara, *s. coll. C.P. 3841* (PDA). BADULLA DISTRICT: Uma Oya, *s. coll. C.P. 3841* (PDA). MONERAGALA DISTRICT: Moneragala, Sept. 1911, *Vaughan s.n.* (PDA). INDIA: Durrang, Khaling Duar, May 1883, *Mann 78/1884* (K). BANGLADESH: Sylhet May 1868, *Clarke 7120* (K).

65. HABENARIA

Willd., Sp. Pl. 4: 44. 1805.

Terrestrial herbs, usually growing from tubers; stems erect with few or many leaves; leaves thin, not plaited, broad, bases sheathing and not jointed; flowers small or large, in terminal inflorescences; sepals unequal, free; petals simple or deeply bilobed, together with the dorsal sepal forming a hood; lip continuous with the column, produced at the base into a short or much elongated spur; limb spreading or pendulous, undivided or trilobed, side lobes sometimes pectinate or fimbriate; column short, footless; anther not operculate but lateral and confluent with the very short column; pollinia 2, granular, with short or long caudicles enclosed in short or long, often prominent tubes on the margins of the side lobes of the rostellum; rostellum trilobed, the middle lobe situated between the anther-chambers, side lobes much longer, acting as carriers for the caudicles of the pollinia; staminodes lateral; stigma bilobed, more or less extended into clavate and papillose processes.

Over 500 species widely distributed throughout the tropical and subtropical regions.

KEY TO THE SPECIES

1 Petals bifid or bipartite
  2 Sepals 5-veined; petals broader than sepals, bifid, margins tomentose; lip trifurcate, segments subulate; spur as long as the ovary..........................**1. H. barbata**
  2 Sepals 3-veined
    3 Petals bifid, upper lobe half as long as the lower lobe, glabrous, lip 5 mm long, 3-lobed; spur narrowly clavate, shorter than the ovary.............**2. H. acuminata**
    3 Petals bipartite
      4 Spur shorter than the ovary; lip longer than sepals, 3-partite, segments filiform subequal...**3. H. macrostachya**
      4 Spur as long as or longer than the ovary
        5 Lower segment of petal shorter; tubers oblong; spur 1.2 cm long................
        ....**4. H. dolichostachya**
        5 Lower segment of petal longer, tubers globose; spur 2 cm long, clavate..........
        ....**5. H. dichopetala**
1 Petals entire
  6 Lateral lobes of lip broad, midlobe narrow
    7 Lip puberulous, twice as long as sepals, 3-lobed, midlobe not bifid; petals linear lanceolate; spur as long as the ovary..........................**6. H. plantaginea**
    7 Lip glabrous, clawed, mid-lobe bifid, petals linear-pandurate; spur longer than the ovary..**7. H. crinifera**
  6 Lateral lobes of lip very narrow
    8 Floral bracts 1-veined
      9 Spur 6.5–7.2 cm long, sepals 9.4–10 mm long; petals linear-oblong; lip 3-cleft more than half way...**8. H. pterocarpa**
      9 Spur 1.3 cm long; sepals 2.2–3 mm long; petals obovate; lip 3-lobed..............
      ....**9. H. viridiflora**
    8 Floral bracts 3-veined; petals linear, 1-veined; lip 3-lobed, lateral lobes erose, midlobe subulate, denticulate; spur cylindric, as long as the ovary..................
    ....**10. H. rhynchocarpa**

1. Habenaria barbata Wight in Wall., Cat. n. 7034. 1832; Trimen Handb. Fl. Ceylon 4: 226. 1898.—**Fig. 152.**

Habenaria virens (Lindl.) Abeywick., Ceylon J. Sci. Biol. Sci. 2 (2): 151. 1959. *Ate virens* Lindl. Gen. et Sp. Orch. 327.1835.

Terrestrial, leafy herb with a stout stem 25–30 cm tall, leafing above the middle, sheathed below, bearing oblong or pyriform tubers and fleshy root fibres. Leaves 7.5–12.5 cm long, erect, lanceolate, acuminate, 5–7 veined, bases sheathing. Flowers 1.8 cm broad, yellowish-green with a pale yellowish-

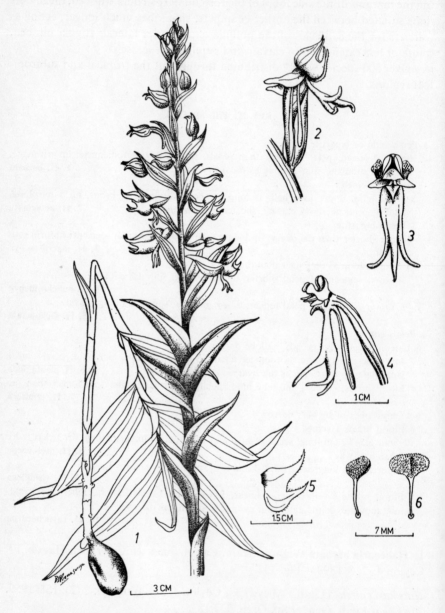

Fig. 152. *Habenaria barbata* Wight, redrawn from a drawing in PDA. 1, plant with tuberous rootstock and an inflorescence. 2, flower from side. 3, lip and column from front. 4, lip, column and spur from side. 5, petal. 6, pollinium from side and front showing the caudicle and gland.

brown lip, in lax-flowered, terminal racemes. Floral bracts large, as long as the flowers, lanceolate, acuminate, sheathing the ovary; sepals subequal, ovate-acuminate, 5-veined, glabrous or puberulous; dorsal horizontal, concave; laterals spreading or reflexed, narrowly falcate, oblong; petals much broader than sepals, bifid, upper lobe much the longest, tips filiform, lower broader acuminate, sinus rounded, margins tomentose; lip longer than sepals, linear, trifurcate at the end, scaberulous, segments subulate, spur as long as the ovary, mouth with a long, recurved ligule; column very short, base continuous with the lip; stigmatic processes long-spreading. Anther lateral, adnate to the column, 2-loculed, loculi parallel, upcurved; pollinia 2, clavate, caudicles long, glands small; staminodes short, stout, capitate. Fruit a linear-oblong capsule, 1.8 cm long.

D i s t r. Very rare, in moist conditions under shade of trees in the submontane or mid-country tropical wet evergreen forests at about 1220 m alt. Maturata, Hakgala, etc. I have not seen this species in a live state. Also in Kerala, South India.

E c o l. Flowers December, January.

I l l u s t r. Wight, Ic. Pl. Ind. Or. 3: pl. 928. 1843–45; PDA, drawing from *C.P. 3200.*

N o t e. Herb. Lindley contains Wallich's collection. Lindley placed this species under the genus *Ate* owing to the presence of a "curious, horny, channelled, recurved tooth, arising from the anterior edge of the orifice of the spur, and curved down upon the lip". He believed this to be a good generic character which distinguished it from *Habenaria.*

This species is distinguished by the bifid petals with tomentose margins, 5-veined sepals and elongate tubes of anther cells.

S p e c i m e n s   E x a m i n e d. CEYLON: NUWARA ELIYA DISTRICT: Mathurata, *s. coll. C.P. 3200* (PDA); Uda Pussellawa, Dec. 1946, *Sylva s.n.* (PDA). BADULLA DISTRICT: Nilgala, Jan. 1888, *s. coll. s.n.* (PDA). LOCALITY UNKNOWN: *Walker 205* (K). INDIA: Madras: Chingleput, Oct. 1930, *Barnes 1867* (K); Pulney Hills, Dec. 1898, *Bourne 1295* (K); Nilgiris, *G. Thomson s.n.* (K); Iriyamallay, Herb. *Wight 3011* (K). Kerala: Travancore, Nov. 1867, *E. Johnson 928* (K). LOCALITY UNKNOWN: *Wallich 7034* (K), *Wight s.n.* (K, AMES), Herb. *Wight 2084* (K).

2. Habenaria acuminata (Thw.) Trimen, Cat. 91. 1885; Trimen, Handb. Fl. Ceylon 4: 227. 1898.—**Fig. 153.**

Ate acuminata Thw., Enum. Pl. Zeyl. 309. 1861.

Terrestrial, leafy herb with undivided, oblong tubers and fleshy root fibres. Stem with the raceme 30–47 cm long, leafy from about 5 cm upwards, internodes ensheathed by leaf bases. Leaves erect, 4–9 × 0.8–1.2 cm, lanceolate,

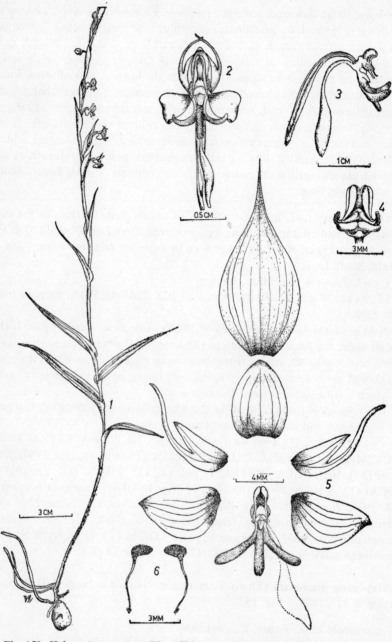

Fig. 153. *Habenaria acuminata* (Thw.) Trimen. 1, plant with tuber and inflorescence.
2, flower from front. 3, lip, column, ovary and spur from side. 4, column from inside showing stigmas. 5, bract, sepals, petals, lip and column spread out from front,
spur (dotted outline). 6, pollinia with caudicles and glands.

setaceously acuminate, acute, indistinctly 5–7 veined, bases sheathing. Flowers green with yellowish-green petals and purple lip, 1.5 cm broad when spread out, in elongated terminal racemes; peduncle as long as the raceme with about two leafy, sterile, acuminate bracts. Floral bracts leafy, 2.4 × 1.1 cm, broadly lanceolate-ovate, acuminate, acute, initially 3–5-veined but soon branching to give a 9-veined appearance; dorsal sepal 6 × 4 mm, oblong-ovate, obtuse, 3-veined, lateral veins branching; lateral sepals 7 × 4 mm, broadly and obliquely ovate, obtuse, 3-veined, the lateral veins branching giving a 5–7-veined appearance; petals 7 × 2 mm, bilobed, lobes variable in length and breadth, the upper lobe lanceolate, about half as long as the lower linear lobe, incurved, 2-veined; lip 5 mm or more × 2 mm, inserted at the base of the column, broadly 3-lobed, fleshy, lobes variable in length, slate-brown, obtuse; spur 1.7 cm long, narrowly clavate, mouth provided with a ligule; column 3.4 mm high, 3 mm broad, with a small, triangular rostellum and two viscid, sausage-shaped stigmas. Anther lateral, adnate to the column, 2-loculed, loculi divergent; pollinia 2, granular, golf club-shaped, stalked, 1.3–1.6 × 0.6 mm, each with a long slender caudicle 2.2–2.4 mm long, attached to a minute gland; staminodes short and fleshy, arising from the sides of the column and protruding above as granular masses. Ovary with pedicel 2 cm long.

D i s t r. Endemic. Rather common, on the slopes and hill cuttings among grass and other weeds at an alt. between 915 and 1524 m. Norton Bridge, Dimbula, Hantane, Ramboda, Galagama, top of Doluwa Kande, etc.

E c o l. Flowers October–December. Other terrestrial orchids found along with it are *Peristylus brevilobus* Thw., *Liparis odorata* (Willd.) Lindl., *Malaxis versicolor* Abeywick. and *Spathoglottis plicata* Bl. (escape) in association with the following herbs: *Blechnum occidentale* L., *Schizoloma ensifolium* (Sw.) J. Sm., *Nephrolepis cordifolia* (L.) Pr., *Gleichenia* sp., *Emilia javanica* C. Rob., *Ageratum conyzoides* Linn., *Osbeckia aspera* (L.) Bl., *Centella asiatica* (L.) Urb., *Panicum* sp., *Ischaemum* sp., *Pogonatherum crinitum* (Thunb.) Kunth., *Lobelia* sp., *Stachytarpheta urticifolia* Sims., *Mimosa pudica* L., *Bidens chinensis* Willd., *Lycopodium cernum* L., *Hedyotis* sp., *Cyperus* sp., etc.

I l l u s t r. PDA, 2 drawings from *C.P. 514.*

N o t e. This species bears a considerable resemblance to *Habenaria heyneana* Lindl. and *Habenaria latilabris* Hook. f. but differs from both in the bilobed petals and long caudicles of the pollinia.

S p e c i m e n s E x a m i n e d. KURUNEGALA DISTRICT: Doluwa Kande, Dec. 1883, *s. coll. s.n.* (PDA). KANDY DISTRICT: Rangala, Aug. 1926, *Alston 470* (PDA); Pusellawa, Nov. 1931, *Simpson 8765* (PDA); Watawala, Oct. 1959, *Jayaweera 58 (2)* (AMES); Madugoda, *Jayasuriya, Dassanayake & Balasubramaniam 490* (PDA, US). LOCALITY UNKNOWN: *Walker 124* (K), *Willis s.n.* (AMES), *s. coll. C.P. 514* (K, holotype, PDA, AMES).

3. Habenaria macrostachya Lindl., Gen. et Sp. Orch. 307. 1835; Trimen, Handb. Fl. Ceylon 4: 227. 1898.—**Fig. 154.**

Terrestrial, leafy herb with fleshy, radical, root fibres, stems 45–90 cm tall, leafy about the middle, closely ensheathed below it. Leaves 12.5–17.5 × 10–12.5 cm, oval, obovate or oblanceolate, acute, many-veined with cross venules, narrowed at the base into a broad petiole 2.5–7.5 cm long. Flowers whitish-green with a purple-brown lip in laxly many-flowered terminal racemes 15–25 cm long; rachis stout, channelled. Floral bracts narrowly lanceolate, as long as the narrow decurved ovary, 2.5–3 cm long; sepals 1.8 cm long, ovate-lanceolate, finely acuminate, dorsal erect, laterals deflexed under the lip; petals as long as the sepals, bipartite, erect, segments subequal or the lower shorter, filiform, sinus acute; lip longer than the sepals, 2.5 cm long, 3-partite, segments subequal, filiform, laterals spreading with recurved tips, terminal straight; spur shorter than the ovary, very slender, thickened downwards, mouth with ligula; column very short, base continuous with the lip, stigmatic processes long, slender, adnate to the mouth of the spur. Anther lateral, adnate to the column, 2-loculed, loculi parallel; pollinia 2, pyriform, glands minute.

D i s t r. Rather common, under the shade of trees at higher altitudes of the tropical wet evergreen forests extending to the mid-country. Hantane, Peradeniya, Dolosbage, near Kegalle, East Matale, Bintenne, Bibile, etc. Also in the Annaimalai Hills in India.

E c o l. Flowers October–January.

I l l u s t r. PDA, drawing.

N o t e. Herb. Lindley contains Macrae's type collection. I have not seen any collections from Kerala. Hooker f. says that "the spur is stoutest in the Kerala specimen".

S p e c i m e n s E x a m i n e d. POLONNARUWA DISTRICT: Feb. 1926; *J.M. de Silva s.n.* (PDA). AMPARAI DISTRICT: Gunner's Quoin, *Cramer 3645* (PDA). KEGALLE DISTRICT: Kegalle, Nov. 1886, *W.F. s.n.* (PDA). MONERAGALA DISTRICT: Bibile, Jan. 1888, *s. coll. s.n.* (PDA); Lower Bintenne, Jan. 1886, *H. Nevill s.n.* (PDA). LOCALITY UNKNOWN: *Macrae 51* (K-holotype), *Macrae s.n.* (K), *s. coll. C.P. 3197* (K, PDA).

4. Habenaria dolichostachya Thw., Enum. Pl. Zeyl. 309. 1861; Trimen, Handb. Fl. Ceylon 4: 228. 1898.—**Fig. 155.**

Terrestrial, leafy herb with an oblong tuber and fleshy root-fibres clothed with matted root hairs; stem 60–90 cm tall, slender, leafless below. Leaves rather distant, 5–7.5 cm long, oblong-lanceolate, acuminate, many-veined, base amplexicaul. Flowers green, subsessile, about 8 mm broad, in laxly many-flowered, channelled, stout racemes measuring 20–30 cm in length.

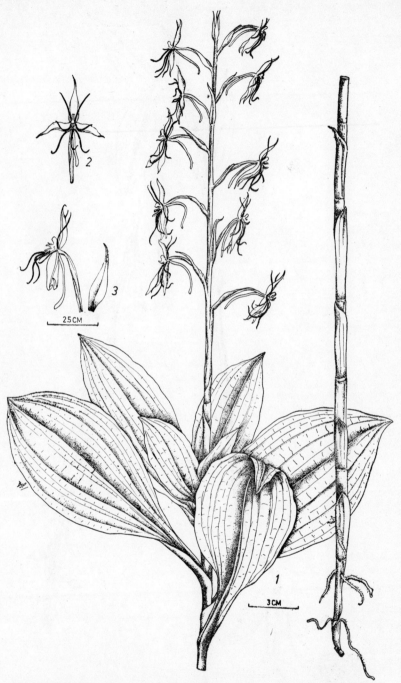

2.5 CM

1

3 CM

Fig. 154. *Habenaria macrostachya* Lindl., redrawn from a drawing in PDA.
1, lower part of stem and upper part with leaves and inflorescence. 2, flower
from front. 3, bract and flower from side.

3CM

Fig. 155. *Habenaria dolichostachya* Thw., redrawn from a drawing in PDA.
Plant with hairy tubers and root fibres and inflorescence.

Floral bracts as long as the flower, ovate-lanceolate, acuminate; dorsal sepal orbicular-ovate, concave, mucronate, 3-veined; lateral sepals 6 mm long, ovate or ovate-lanceolate, acute, spreading, also 3-veined; petals erect, bipartite, segments filiform or subulate, lower shorter, sinus rounded; lip longer than sepals, tripartite, segments filiform, 1.2 cm long, middle longest, laterals spreading; spur slender, nearly as long as the ovary, mouth with a short ligula; column short, continuous with the lip; rostellum short, triangular; stigmatic processes clavate, curved round the mouth of the spur. Anther lateral, broad, 2-loculed, loculi parallel, tubes long, upcurved; pollinia 2, clavate, caudicles slender, glands small. Ovary 1.2 cm long, slender and decurved.

D i s t r. Endemic. Rare, under the shade of trees in the subtropical montane forests. Ramboda, Bogawantalawa, Hakgala, Pidurutalagala, etc. I have not seen this species in a live state.

E c o l. Flowers October–December.

I l l u s t r. PDA, 2 drawings.

N o t e. This species is allied to *Habenaria digitata* Lindl. from North India but the plants are larger, leaves amplexicaul and racemes and flowers smaller.

S p e c i m e n s E x a m i n e d. POLONNARUWA DISTRICT: Polonnaruwa, *Jayasuriya 681* (PDA, US). NUWARA ELIYA DISTRICT: Pidurutalagala, Jul. 1923, *J.M. de Silva s.n.* (PDA). LOCALITY UNKNOWN: *s. coll. C.P. 3199* (K-holotype, PDA).

5. Habenaria dichopetala Thw., Enum. Pl. Zeyl. 309. 1861; Trimen, Handb. Fl. Ceylon 4: 228. 1898.—**Fig. 156.**

Terrestrial, leafy herb with a globose tuber 2 cm diameter and fleshy root-fibres matted with root hairs; stem 17–20 cm tall, leafy about the middle. Leaves 2.5–10 × 1.7–2.6 cm, very shortly petioled, ovate or ovate-lanceolate, acute, many-veined, dark green. Flowers white with a white lip, 2.2 cm broad, in laxly many-flowered terminal racemes; peduncle long with 2 or more foliaceous, sterile bracts. Floral bracts 2.1 × 0.7 cm, ovate-lanceolate, acuminate, 3-veined; dorsal sepal 7 × 4 mm, erect, broadly ovate, subacute or obtuse, hooded, 3-veined; lateral sepals 8 × 4 mm, obliquely ovate, acute, 3-veined; petals bipartite; segments unequal, linear, 1- or 2-veined, upper shorter, 6–7 mm long, lower 14.8–17 mm long, sinus rounded; lip tripartite to the base, lateral segments 18 mm long, median segment 12 × 1 mm, segments narrowly linear, tips of the lateral segments revolute; spur 2 cm long, slender, pendulous, incurved, clavate towards the subacute tip, mouth minute; column short, continuous with the lip; rostellum short, stigmatic processes large, clavate, glandular. Anther lateral, adnate to the column, 2-loculed; loculi parallel, distant; tubes short, ascending; pollinia 2, 1 × 0.5 mm, clavate, with long caudicles; glands small; staminodes pulvinate. Ovary with pedicel 2 cm long.

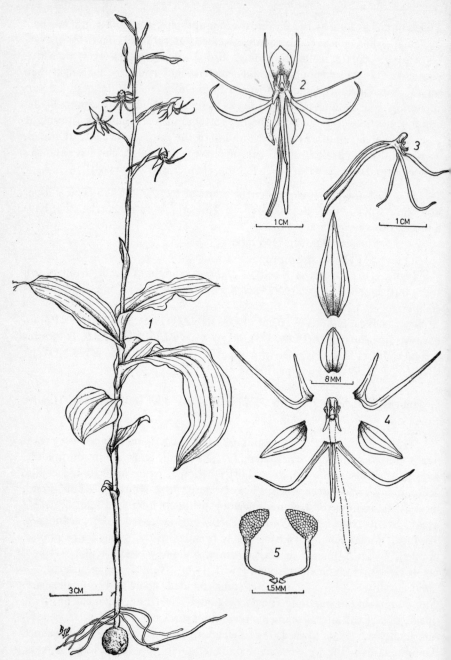

Fig. 156. *Habenaria dichopetala* Thw. 1, plant with tuber and inflorescence. 2, flower from front. 3, lip, column and spur from side. 4, bract, sepals, petals, lip and column spread out from front, spur (dotted outline). 5, pollinia with straps and glands.

D i s t r. Endemic. Rather rare; under the shade of trees in the tropical dry mixed evergreen forests in the dry zone. Anuradhapura, Bintenne, Bibile, Nilgala, etc.

E c o l. Flowers November, December and January.

I l l u s t r. PDA, drawing from *C.P. 3564.*

N o t e. Herb. Lindley contains Thwaites' type collection which differs somewhat from the description given by him in that its leaves are linear-oblong, erect, sheathing the stem all the way up and the median segment of the lip the shortest. The specimens collected from Anuradhapura are smaller with larger white flowers, lower segments of the bipartite petals longer than the upper segments and the lateral segments of the lip longer than the median segment.

S p e c i m e n s   E x a m i n e d. ANURADHAPURA DISTRICT: Anuradhapura along Jaffna Road, Nov. 1960, *Jayaweera 1999* (PDA), Nov. 1960, *Jayaweera 58 (5)* (AMES). MONERAGALA DISTRICT: Bintenne, *s. coll. C.P. 3564* (K-holotype, PDA).

6. Habenaria plantaginea Lindley, Gen. et Sp. Orch. 323. 1853; Trimen, Handb. Fl. Ceylon 4: 229. 1898.—**Fig. 157.**

Gymnadenia plantaginea Lindl. in Wall., Cat. n. 7053. 1832.
Orchis tenuis Rottler ex Wall., Cat. sub. n. 7053. 1832.
Orchis platyphyllos Roxb., Fl. Ind. 3: 450. 1832.

Terrestrial, scapigerous herb with a very short stem, oblong tubers and fleshy radical fibres. Leaves 3.5–7 cm long, radical, horizontal, narrowly oval or oblong, acute, spreading, membranous, narrowed at the base into a short sheath; veins many, slender. Scape slender, 20–30 cm long with many, distant, open, lanceolate, acuminate sheaths 1.2–2.5 cm long. Flowers white, 1.6 cm broad, in lax-flowered spikes 10–15 cm long. Floral bracts subulate-lanceolate, much shorter than the ovary; sepals subequal, 4 mm long, 3-veined, acute, dorsal ovate-oblong, laterals falcately oblong; petals linear-lanceolate; lip more than twice as long as the sepals, flabelliform from a narrow claw, puberulous, 3-lobed, lobes subacute, entire or toothed, lateral half ovate, midlobe as long, narrowly linear; spur 2.5–3.7 cm long, very slender, pendulous; column short; rostellum broad, triangular; stigmatic processes prominent, clavate; base of the column continuous with the lip. Anther lateral, adnate to the column, 2-loculed; loculi divergent below; tubes; rather, short, upcurved; pollinia 2, pyriform; caudicles broad, inserted on a concave, lanceolate gland dividing longitudinally; staminodes on the sides of the anther, pulvinate. Ovary 1.6–2.3 cm long, slender and beaked. Fruit 1.6 cm long, turgidly fusiform, curved; beak short, slender.

D i s t r. Common, under the shade of trees in the tropical dry mixed evergreen forests in the dry zone. It also occurs in the tropical Himalayas,

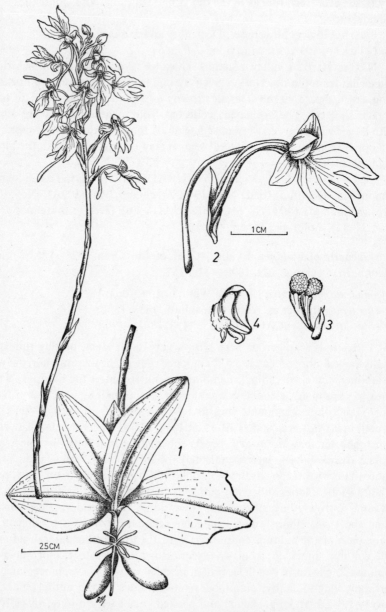

Fig. 157. *Habenaria plantaginea* Lindl. 1, plant with tubers, radical leaves and inflorescence. 2, bract and flower from side with long spur. 3, pollinia with broad caudicles and gland. 4, column from side, enlarged.

Sikkim, Bihar and in the Deccan Peninsula from Konkan southwards in India, and in Burma.

E c o l. Flowers March, April, June.

I l l u s t r. Wight, Ic. Pl. Ind. Or. 5: pl. 1710. 1851; PDA, two drawings of which one is from *C.P. 2374*.

N o t e. Herb. Lindley contains Wallich's collection from Madras and Thwaites' collection from Ceylon. Hooker says "in this species the caudicles of the pollinia are at first inserted in the hollow of a single concave 2-lipped or incurved gland of a lanceolate form, which afterwards splits longitudinally each pollinia carrying away one half". The late cohesion of the glands of the pollinia is unique.

S p e c i m e n s E x a m i n e d. CEYLON: VAVUNIYA DISTRICT: Vavuniya, *Davidse & Sumithraarachchi 9061* (PDA). ANURADHAPURA DISTRICT: Ritigala, *Jayasuriya & Sumithraarachchi 1610*, (PDA); *Gould 73627* (PDA). MATALE DISTRICT: Dambulla, *Cramer 3547* (PDA). POLONNARUWA DISTRICT: Polonnaruwa, Jan. 1927, *Lady Cecil 4* (K). TRINCOMALEE DISTRICT: Trincomalee, Hot Springs, *s. coll. 25* (K). BADULLA DISTRICT: Fort Macdonald, Mar. 1906, *Willis s.n.* (PDA). MONERAGALA DISTRICT: Bibile, Ikiriyankumbura, Jun. 1901, *s. coll. s.n.* (PDA); Bintenne, Apr. 1923, *J.M. Silva s.n.* (PDA). HAMBANTOTA DISTRICT: Ruhuna National Park, *Fosberg, Mueller-Dombois, Wirawan, Cooray & Balakrishnan 51090* (PDA), *Comanor 636* (PDA). INDIA: Uttar Pradesh: Dehra Dun, Oct. 1901, *Mackinon's Collector 25417* (AMES); Dec. 1900, *Mackinon's Collector 24174* (K). Sikkim: *J.D. Hooker s.n.* (K). Madhya Pradesh: Chota Nagpur, Oct. 1875, *J.J. Wood 148* (K). Orissa: Dhenkanal, Sept. 1939, *Mooney 1115* (K); Sambalpur, Bastar State, Oct. 1940, *Mooney 1421* (K); Hindol State, Sept. 1937, *Mooney 559* (K). Maharashtra: Bombay, 1898, *Dalzell s.n.* (K). Andhra Pradesh: Godavari, Nov. 1902, *Barber 4989* (K). Mysore: *Wight s.n.* (K). Kerala: Travancore, Herb. *Rottlerianum s.n.* (K). Madras: Kallar-Nilgiri, Oct. 1889, *Gamble 21452* (K); Rampa Dist., Sept. 1920, *Narayanswami 326* (K). Iryamallay, Herb. *Wight 3005* (K, AMES). Pen. Ind. Or., Herb. *Wight 3003* (AMES). Tinnevelly, *Wallich 7053* (K). BURMA: Chin Hills, Oct. 1928, *L. Daun 87* (K).

7. Habenaria crinifera Lindley, Gen. et Sp. Orch. 323. 1835; Trimen, Handb. Fl. Ceylon 4: 229. 1898.—**Fig. 158.**

Habenaria schizochilus J. Graham, Cat. Pl. Bombay 252. 1839.
Synmeria schizochilus J. Graham, ibid. (last unnumbered page).

Terrestrial, leafy herb with large, ovoid tubers and fleshy root-fibres; stem leafy, 5–15 cm long. Leaves 7.15 × 1.5–3.2 cm, linear-oblong-lanceolate, spreading, acute or acuminately acute, bases sheathing the stem, many-veined. Flowers white, 1.5 cm broad, in few-flowered terminal racemes; pedunc

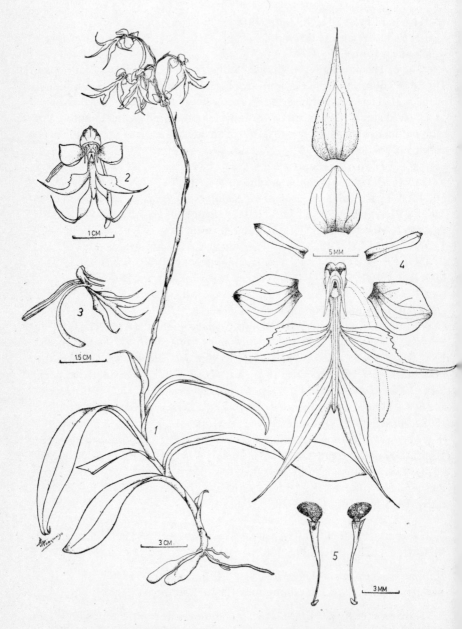

Fig. 158. *Habenaria crinifera* Lindl. 1, plant with tubers and inflorescence. 2, flower from front. 3, lip, column and spur from side. 4, bract, sepals, petals, lip and column spread out from front, spur (dotted outline). 5, pollinia with caudicles and glands.

18–29 cm long with 10–11 leafy, sterile bracts. Floral bracts 1.5 × 0.45 cm, ovate, acuminate, terminating in a long capillary point, serrulate, 3-veined, the lateral veins joining the midvein about 2/3 way up; dorsal sepal orbicular-ovate or oblong-ovate, 7 × 6 mm, obtuse, 3-veined; lateral sepals 8 × 6 mm, obliquely obovate, the lower margin conspicuously distended, obtuse, 3-veined; petals 7 × 1.5 mm, linear-pandurate, trifid-mucronate, 1-veined; lip the most conspicuous part of the flower, 2.2 cm long, clawed 3-lobed, 3-veined; lateral lobes cuneiform, curved outwards, outer margin dentate as if half has been bitten off, inner margin entire and produced into a slender curved tail, a branch from the lateral veins supplying them; midlobe cleft in 2, lobules lanceolate, acuminate, as long as the lateral lobes, undulate on the outer margin, entire within with a triangular wedge in between them; spur 2.7 cm long, slender, flat, strongly outcurved with its mouth at the base of the column; column 6 mm high, 2.5 mm broad, with two tusk-like clavate stigmatic processes adnate to the mouth of the spur. Anther lateral, 2-loculed; loculi parallel; tubes long, straight; pollinia 2, oblong, 2.2 × 1.4 mm, with slender caudicles 5.2 mm long, winged on one side, enclosed in thin, transparent, flat, conical sheaths adhering to them posteriorly and connected to small glands. Ovary with pedicel 2.3 cm long.

D i s t r. Rather rare, in the shade of trees in the tropical dry mixed evergreen forests as well as in the mid-country jungles up to 915 m alt. Ritigala, Hewaheta, Hantane, Galagama, Ratnapura, etc. Also in India from Konkan southwards as far as Kerala and in Bhutan.

E c o l. Flowers February, September, November.

I l l u s t r. Wight, Ic. Pl. Ind. Or. 3: pl. 926. 1843–5; PDA, drawing from *C.P. 207.*

N o t e. Herb. Lindley contains Macrae's type collection from Ceylon and Dalzell's collection from Konkan. The caudicles of the pollinia being winged on one side is a character also of *Habenaria longicalcarata* A. Rich.

S p e c i m e n s E x a m i n e d. CEYLON: KANDY DISTRICT: Peradeniya, Bot. Gard., cultd., Oct. 1960, *Jayaweera 2000* (PDA), Oct. 1960, *Jayaweera 58 (7)* (AMES). RATNAPURA DISTRICT: Karawita Kande, Sept. 1926, *J.M. Silva s.n.* (PDA). LOCALITY UNKNOWN: *Gardner 869* (K), *Walker 1801* (K), *Walker s.n.* (AMES), *Macrae 36* (K-holotype), *s. coll. C.P. 207* (K, AMES, PDA), *Simpson 10007* (PDA). BHUTAN: Jul. 1884, *Saunder's Collector s.n.* (K). INDIA. Maharashtra: Ramghat, *Richie 1401* (AMES); *Dalzell 5* (K); Malabar, Konkan etc., *Stocks, Law,* etc. *s.n.* (K, AMES, PDA); Kerala: Quilon, Courtallam, Herb. *Wight s.n.* (K). Mysore: Canara, Sept. 1903, *Barber 6118* (K). Pen. Ind. Or., Herb. *Wight 3006* (K, AMES).

8. Habenaria pterocarpa Thw., Enum. Pl. Zeyl. 309. 1861; Trimen, Handb. Fl. Ceylon 4: 230. 1898.—**Fig. 159.**

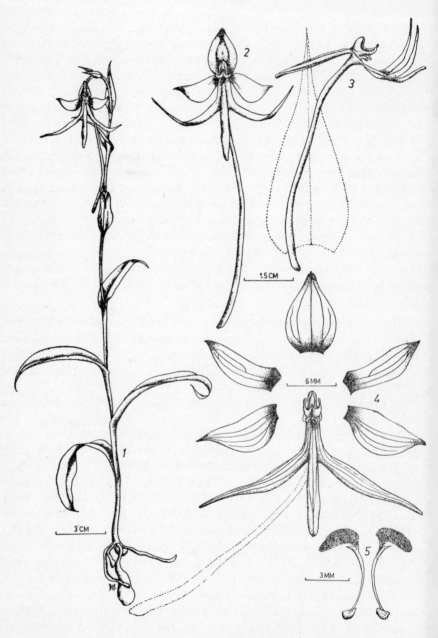

Fig. 159. *Habenaria pterocarpa* Thw. 1, plant with tubers and inflorescence. 2, flower from front. 3, lip, column and spur from side. 4, bract (dotted line), sepals, petals, lip and column spread out from front, spur (dotted line). 5, pollinia with caudicles and glands.

Terrestrial, leafy herb with clavate tubers and tuberous root fibres; stem 15-45 cm tall, stout and leafy throughout. Leaves 6-25 cm long, oblong or linear-lanceolate, acuminate, sheathing, many-veined; leaves gradually becoming smaller, ascending the peduncle of the terminal raceme as sterile bracts. Flowers white with a green spur, 3-3.5 cm broad across the spreading sepals, in 1-10-flowered racemes. Floral bracts 2.4 × 1 cm, ovate-lanceolate, finely acuminate, 1-veined; dorsal sepal erect, 9.4-10 × 6 mm, ovate-oblong, acute or apiculate, hooded, 3-veined, the lateral veins branching; lateral sepals 10 × 4 mm, obliquely oblong-lanceolate, falcate, acuminate, spreading or deflexed, 3-veined, the lower lateral vein branching; petals 10 × 3 mm, linear-oblong, falcate, forming a hood with the dorsal sepal; lip 2.5 cm long, 3-cleft more than half way, lateral lobes subulate-lanceolate, recurved or ascending, longer than the subulate midlobe; spur 6.5-7.2 cm long, narrowly clavate, mouth with a tooth; column short, blunt, continued with the lip, stigmatic processes elongate, clavate. Anther lateral, 2-loculed; loculi divaricate below; tubes as long as the cells; pollinia 2, golf-club-shaped, 2.6 × 1 mm, pyriform; caudicles narrowly winged or sheathed on one side; glands very small. Ovary with pedicel 2.4 cm long.

D i s t r. Endemic, rare under the shade of trees both in the submontane or mid-country tropical wet evergreen forests up to 220 m alt. and in the dry mixed evergreen forests of the dry zone. Kandy, Ramboda, Dolosbage, Dambulla, etc.

E c o l. Flowers October, November.

I l l u s t r. PDA, drawing from *C. P. 3201.*

N o t e. The type cover at Kew contains 3 collections from different localities bearing the same Thwaites' number *C.P. 3201.* The collection from Ramboda is considered as the holotype. This species too contains winged caudicles as in *Habenaria longicalcarata* A. Rich from Western Ghats in India.

S p e c i m e n s E x a m i n e d. NUWARA ELIYA DISTRICT: Ramboda, *s. coll. C.P. 3201* (K-holotype, AMES PDA); Nov. 1963, *Jayaweera 2361* (PDA), Nov. 1960, *Jayaweera 2004* (PDA); Oct. 1960, *Jayaweera 58 (8)* (AMES). KANDY DISTRICT: Madugoda, *Jayasuriya, Moldenke & Sumithraarachchi 1422* (PDA), *Jayasuriya, Dassanayake & Balasubramaniam 489* (PDA). KEGALLE DISTRICT: Dolosbage, Nov. 1963, *Jayaweera 2354* (PDA).

9. Habenaria viridiflora (Sw.) Lindl., Gen. et Sp. Orch. 319. 1840; Trimen, Handb. Fl. Ceylon 4: 231. 1898.—**Fig. 160.**

Orchis viridiflora Swartz, Kongl. Vetensk. Acad. Handl. 21: 206. 1800.
Habenaria graminea A. Rich., Ann. Sc. Nat. Bot. 11. 15: 72. 1841, not of Lindl. & Spreng.
Habenaria tenuis Griff., Calcutta J. Nat. Hist. 4: 379, pl. 20. 1844.

362 ORCHIDACEAE

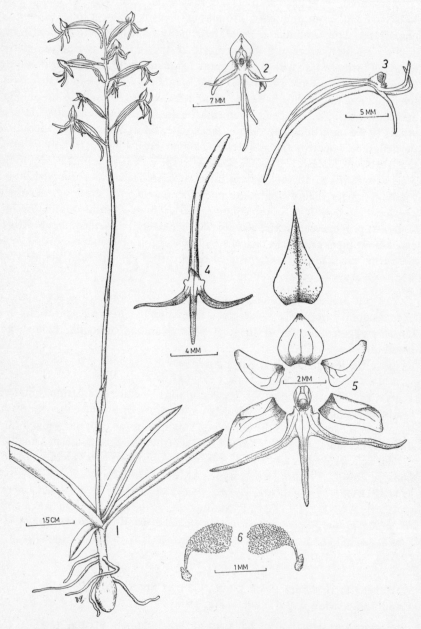

Fig. 160. *Habenaria viridiflora* (Sw.) Lindl. 1, plant with tuber and inflorescence.
2, flower from front. 3, lip, column and spur from side. 4, lip and spur from front.
5, bract, sepals, petals, lip and column spread out from front. 6, pollinia with
caudicles and glands.

Terrestrial, leafy herb with a short, radical leaved stem and ovoid or oblong tubers 2–2.5 cm long, with fleshy root-fibres. Leaves about 5 × 0.9 cm, lanceolate, acute, coriaceous, veins obscure but the midrib prominent on the under surface, bases sheathing the stem. Flowers small, 5 mm across, yellowish-green, spreading in many-flowered racemes; peduncle 9.5–11 cm long with 3 or 4 minute, lanceolate, sterile bracts, the lower ones larger. Floral bracts 4.1–4.4 × 2–2.2 mm, ovate, finely acuminate-acute, 1-veined; dorsal sepal 2.2 mm long and as broad, orbicular-ovate, truncate, 3-veined; lateral sepals 3 × 2 mm, obliquely ovate, obtuse, 3-veined, the outer edge folding over or reflexed forming a flap; petals 2.4 × 1.4 mm, obliquely triangular-obovate, truncate with one main vein giving off two lateral branches; petals along with the dorsal sepals forming a hood over the column; lip 3-lobed, the trunk quadrate, 5-veined; lateral lobes subulate, recurved, 4.8 mm long, 2-veined; midlobe shorter and straight, 1-veined with two branches from the adjoining veins; spur 1.3 cm long, longer than the ovary and parallel to it, slightly broader at the end; column minute; stigmatic processes long and clavate, projecting beyond the mouth of the spur. Anther lateral, 2-loculed, tubes short, upcurved; pollinia 2, pyriform, 0.8 × 0.6 mm; caudicles short and glands small. Ovary with pedicel 1.1 cm long. Fruit an erect, fusiform ribbed capsule.

D i s t r. Common, both in the wet and dry zones of the low country, rarely extending to the montane zone, commonly in rice fields. Dambulla rock, wedged in crevices under the shade of shrubs along with grasses. Ambagamuwa, Pidurutalagala, etc. Also in India in the lower Bengal area and the Deccan Peninsula.

E c o l. Flowers December–February.

I l l u s t r. Griff., Ic. Pl. Asiat. 3: pl. 342. 1851; Wight, Ic. Pl. Ind. Or. 5: pl. 1705. 1851.

N o t e. Herb. Lindley contains Gardner's collection probably from Ceylon. It is closely allied to *Habenaria khasiana* Hook. f. from which it differs in the broader leaves, shorter dorsal sepal and beaked ovary.

S p e c i m e n s   E x a m i n e d. CEYLON: MATALE DISTRICT: Dambulla, Dec. 1881, *s. coll. s.n.* (PDA). LOCALITY UNKNOWN: *Gardner 3985* (K), *Gardner 3991* (K), *s. coll. C.P. 2372* (K, PDA), Jul. 1932, *Simpson 9862* (PDA). INDIA: Assam: *Jenkins s.n.* (PDA). West Bengal: Serampore, *Griffith s.n.* (K); Sept. 1868, *Clarke 7740* (K). Maharashtra: Malabar, Konkan, etc., *Stocks, Law,* etc. *s.n.* (K, AMES, PDA); Bombay, *Dalzell s.n.* (K); S. Malabar, Sept. 1920, *Fischer 4493* (K). Mysore: Canara, 1837, *Hohenacker 140* (K, AMES). Madras: *Bourne 2953* (K); Chingleput, Dec. 1886, *Lawson s.n.* (K). Kodaikanal Region: Pulney Hills, Nov. 1933, *Venkataraman Ayyar s.n.* (K). Pen. Ind. Or., Herb. *Wight 2088* (K).

10. Habenaria rhynchocarpa (Thw.) Trimen, Cat. 91. 1885, Trimen, Handb. Fl. Ceylon 4: 230. 1898.—**Fig. 161.**

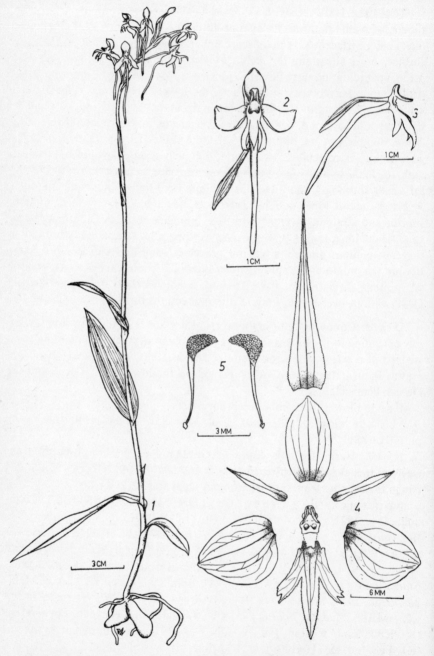

Fig. 161. *Habenaria rhynchocarpa* (Thw.) Trimen. 1, plant with tubers and inflorescence. 2, flower from front. 3, lip, column ovary and spur from side. 4, bract, sepals, petals, lip and column spread out from front. 5, pollinia with caudicles and glands.

Habenaria stenopetala Lindl., Gen. et Sp. Orch. 324. 1838.
Platanthera rhynchocarpa Thw., Enum. Pl. Zeyl. 310. 1861.

Terrestrial, leafy herb with large, clavate tubers and fleshy, radical roots; stem 30–60 cm tall. Leaves sessile, 5–15 × 0.6–1.6 cm, lanceolate or oblong-lanceolate, acute or acuminate, sheathing, many-veined. Flowers white with the end of the spur green, 1.5 cm across in densely flowered, terminal spikes measuring 5–7.5 cm in the length; peduncle about 12 cm long with three or more sterile bracts. Floral bracts 1.4–2.1 × 0.25–0.42 cm, narrowly lanceolate, finely acuminate, denticulate, 3-veined; dorsal sepal 8.5–9 × 4.6–5 mm, oblong-cymbiform, bluntly acute, denticulate, 3-veined; lateral sepals 9.2–10 × 5.5–7 mm, obliquely and broadly ovate or orbicular, subacute, deflexed, 3-veined, finely denticulate; petals 7–7.6 × 1 mm, acute, finely denticulate, 1-veined, forming a hood with the dorsal sepal; lip 10.5 × 5.2–7 mm, the lateral lobes lanceolate and divergent, 3-veined, lateral veins branching at the bases and higher up, supplying the lateral lobes, denticulate; midlobe subulate or lanceolate, spur 2.5–3.2 cm long, cylindric, compressed laterally, obtuse, mouth spiny with a large tooth; column short, rostellum minute, stigmatic processes elongate, incurved, adnate to the mouth of the spur, base continuous with the lip. Anther lateral, adnate to the column, 2-loculed, loculi divaricate below; tubes nearly straight; pollinia 2, clavate, granular, 1.7–1.9 × 1 mm; caudicles long; glands small. Ovary 2.3 cm long.

D i s t r. Endemic. Rare, on hill cuttings along roadsides among grass in the mid-country between 610 and 1220 m alt. Ettampitiya in Uva Province, Galagama, Belihulu Oya, Lunugala, Uma Oya, etc.

E c o l. Flowers November, December, January and February.
I l l u s t r. PDA, drawing from *C.P. 3658.*
N o t e. Herb. Lindley contains Thwaites' (type) and Macrae's collections from Ceylon and 3 other collections from India, the last probably belonging to *Habenaria stenopetala* Lindl.
S p e c i m e n s E x a m i n e d. KANDY DISTRICT: Madugoda, *Jayasuriya, Dassanayake & Balasubramaniam 494* (PDA, US). RATNAPURA DISTRICT: Belihulu Oya, Feb. 1882, *s. coll. s.n.* (PDA). BADULLA DISTRICT: Lunugala, Jan. 1888, *s. coll. s.n.* (PDA); Ettampitiya, Dec. 1960, *Jayaweera 58 (9)* (AMES). LOCALITY UNKNOWN: *Macrae 57* (K), *s. coll. C.P. 3058* (K-holotype, PDA), Mar. 1904, *Willis s.n.* (AMES), *Alston C34* (PDA).

66. PERISTYLUS

Blume, Bijdr. 404: t. 30. 1825.

Terrestrial herbs usually growing from tubers; stems erect with few or many leaves; leaves broad, thin, not plaited and not jointed at the base;

flowers small or large in terminal inflorescences; sepals and petals free, sub-equal; lip continuous with the column, produced at the base into a short or very short spur; limb erect or spreading, entire or trilobed; column short, footless; anther not operculate, lateral and confluent with the short column; pollinia 2, granular, with short caudicles and exserted naked glands; anther tubes absent or very short; staminodes lateral and auriculate; stigma sessile, convex, united to the base of the lip and to the auricles of the column; rostellum subulate or tooth-like, situated between the pollinia chambers, rather obscure.

About 60 species, distributed in the north temperate regions, and the tropics of Asia and Africa including Java, Sumatra, Borneo, Celebes, Japan and the Philippine Islands.

KEY TO THE SPECIES

1 Sepals 1-veined, petals 1- or 2-veined
  2 Lip nearly entire; spur minute, globose
    3 Lip longer than sepals, subflabelliform, faintly trifid; petals oblong, connivent with the sepals at their bases; anther tubes absent..........................**1. P. brevilobus**
    3 Lip shorter than sepals, broadly obovate, shortly 3-lobed; petals broad, obliquely orbicular; anther tubes shortly recurved.......................**2. P. plantagineus**
  2 Lip 3-lobed or 3-partite
    4 Spur clavate, bifid at base..**3. P. aristatus**
    4 Spur globose
      5 Spur sessile
        6 Bract 16–17 mm long; sepals and petals membranous; lip clawed, dilating into a 3-partite, flat, membranous limb.................................**4. P. trimeni**
        6 Bract 6–8 mm long; sepals and petals thick and fleshy; lip cuneate, 5-cleft to about the middle..**5. P. spiralis**
      5 Spur stipitate..**6. P. gardneri**
1 Sepals and petals 3-veined...**7. P. cubitalis**

1. Peristylus brevilobus Thw., Enum. Pl. Zeyl. 311. 1861.—Fig. 162.

Habenaria breviloba Trimen, Cat. 91. 1885; Trimen, Handb. Fl. Ceylon 4: 232. 1898.

Terrestrial, leafy herb with a slender stem bearing one or two oblong tubers at the base and tuberous vermiform roots; stem with the spike 25–45 cm long. Leaves 5–7.5 × 0.8–1.8 cm, basal and apical leaves smaller, oblong-lanceolate, acuminate; bases sheathing; veins slender. Flowers white, in long-peduncled, terminal, dense-flowered spikes; peduncle 10–15 cm or more long with 3 or 4 sterile bracts, the lowest being a small foliage leaf; flower-bearing portion of the spike 2.5–3 cm long. Floral bracts 9–10 × 2.8–3 mm, lanceolate-ovate, membranous, finely acuminate, 1-veined; dorsal sepal 7 × 2.5 mm, oblong-ovate, obtuse or rounded, 1-veined; lateral sepals 6 × 1.6 mm, linear-oblong or lanceolate, obtuse, 1-veined; petals 6.5 × 2 mm, oblong, 1-veined,

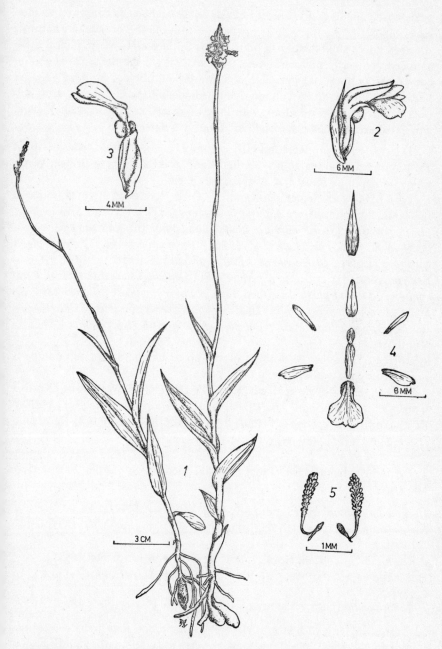

Fig. 162. *Peristylus brevilobus* Thw. 1, plants with tubers and inflorescences. 2, flower and bract from side. 3, ovary, lip, column and spur from side. 4, bract, sepals, petals, lip and column with ovary spread out from front. 5, pollinia with caudicles and glands.

veins branching laterally, apex rounded; petals and sepals connivent at their bases; lip 7 × 4.5 mm, sessile at the base of the column, broadening towards the apex into a subflabelliform limb, faintly 3-lobed and veined; lateral lobes rounded, crenulate; midlobe minute, triangular; spur a minute, inflated and incurved sac; column 1.5 mm high, 0.8 mm broad, oblong, rounded. Anther lateral, confluent with the column, 2-loculed; loculi parallel; tubes absent; pollinia 2, clavate, 0.96 mm long with long caudicles, each with a small gland concealed behind the bifid rostellum. Ovary 6.5 mm long.

D i s t r. Endemic. Rare, on hill cuttings in the open at altitudes of about 1524 m or below along with other herbs and grasses. Norton Bridge, Watawala, Ratnapura, Dolosbage, Ambagamuwa, etc.

E c o l. Flowers September–October. Other terrestrial orchids found in the same environment are *Habenaria acuminata* (Thw.) Trim., *Spathoglottis plicata* Bl. and *Liparis odorata* Lindl. along with the following species of herbs: *Schizoloma ensifolium* (Sw.) J. Sm.; *Blechnum orientale* L.; *Nephrolepis cordifolia* (L.) Pr., *Gleichenia* sp., *Emilia javanica* (Burm. f.) C. Rob., *Ageratum conyzoides* L., *Osbeckia aspera* (L.) Bl., *Centella asiatica* (L.) Urb., *Panicum* sp., *Stachytarpheta urticifolia* Sims., *Mimosa pudica* L., *Bidens chinensis* Willd., *Lycopodium cernum* L., *Hedyotis* sp., *Cyperus* sp., *Utricularia coerulea* L., *Ischaemum ciliare* Retz., *Lobelia* sp., *Pogonatherum crinitum* (Thunb.) Kunth., etc.

N o t e. Thwaites' description of the lip as having a minute midlobe is confirmed by the author.

S p e c i m e n s E x a m i n e d. KANDY DISTRICT: Watawala, Carolina Bank, Oct. 1948, *Tunnard s.n.* (PDA), Sept. 1959, *Jayaweera 58 (11)* (AMES); Rambukpitiya, *Jayasuriya 972* (PDA). RATNAPURA DISTRICT: Ratnapura *s. coll. C.P. 3493* (K-holotype, PDA).

2. Peristylus plantagineus (Lindl.) Lindl., Gen. et Sp. Orch. 300. 1835.— Fig. 163.

Herminium plantagineum Lindl., Bot. Reg. 18: sub. t. 1499. 1832.
Habenaria goodyeroides Hook., Companion Bot. Mag. pl. 3397. 1835, not of Lindl.
Peristylus elatus Dalzell, Hook. J. Bot. Kew Gard. Misc. 3: 344. 1851.
Habenaria wightii Trimen, Cat. 91. 1885; Trimen, Handb. Fl. Ceylon 4: 232. 1898.
Habenaria elata (Dalz.) Alston in Trimen, Handb. Fl. Ceylon 6: 280. 1931.

Terrestrial herb with large, cylindric-oblong tubers and fleshy root fibres; stem with the spike 30–60 cm long, robust, leafy about the middle, lower portion ensheathed loosely by long, narrowly lanceolate sheaths. Leaves 12.5–17.5 × 6.2–7.5 cm, oblong-lanceolate, acuminate or acute, wavy, strongly veined beneath, base subamplexicaul, sheaths tight. Flowers greenish with

Fig. 163. *Peristylus plantagineus* (Lindl.) Lindl. redrawn from a drawing in PDA.
1, lower portion of stem with tuber and upper part of plant with inflorescence.
2, bract and flower from side. 3, flower from front with globular spur below lip.
4, column from front showing position of the pollinia and staminodes. 5, pollinium
with caudicle and gland, enlarged.

white petals and lip, 4 mm broad, in dense-flowered spikes 10–20 cm long. Floral bracts 8 mm long, longer than the flower, erect, very narrowly lanceolate, acuminate; sepals connivent, obtuse, 1-veined, dorsal sepal 6 mm long, broadly ovate, laterals longer, oblong, apiculate below the tip; petals very broad, obliquely orbicular, nerves branched, tips recurved; lip about as long as the sepals, broadly ovate, shortly 3-lobed, lobes obtuse, contracted beyond the very broad, concave base; spur very small, globose; column short, base continuous into the lip; rostellum short, acute, stigmatic processes short and stout. Anther lateral, 2-loculed; loculi parallel; tubes short, recurved; pollinia 2, clavate; caudicles short; glands; small; staminodes large. Ovary 6–8 mm long and erect.

D i s t r. Very rare, first collected by Macrae in Ceylon and not collected since. Its exact locality is not known. It also occurs in Kerala and Konkan districts in India.

I l l u s t r. Wight, Ic. Pl. Ind. Or. 3: pl. 921. 1843–45.

N o t e. This species is allied to *Habenaria goodyeroides* Don from which it differs in the smaller leaves and flowers and the very small globose spur.

S p e c i m e n s   E x a m i n e d. CEYLON: LOCALITY UNKNOWN: *Macrae s.n.* (K, holotype). INDIA: Maharashtra: Bombay, *Dalzell s.n.* (K); Ramghat, *Richie 1396* (K); Malabar, *Stocks s.n.* (AMES). Mysore: North Canara, Aug. 1885, *Talbot 543* (K); Mysore & Canara, *Law s.n.* (K). Kerala: Travancore, *Rama Rao s.n.* (K): Mar. 1920, *Fischer 4476* (K).

3. Peristylus aristatus Lindl., Gen. et Sp. Orch. 300. 1835.—**Fig. 164.**

Habenaria aristata Trimen, Cat. 91. 1885, in part; Trimen, Handb. Fl. Ceylon 4: 233. 1898.

Slender, terrestrial herb with a rosette of leaves at the summit of the stem, 15–30 cm tall; roots tuberous and root-fibres fleshy. Leaves 2–5 × 0.8–2.2 cm, ovate-lanceolate, acuminate, acute, membranous, 5-veined, base and petiole sheathing the stem. Lamina much reduced or absent in the lower leaves. Flowers pale green, in long, slender, terminal, lax-flowered spikes measuring 7–12 cm in length; peduncle about the same length, slender, erect, with a few, sterile, bracteolar sheaths. Floral bracts 4.8 × 2.8 mm, ovate, acuminate, acute, 1-veined; dorsal sepal 2.6 × 1.6 mm, oblong-ovate or lanceolate, rounded or obtuse, 1-veined; lateral sepals obliquely obovate-lanceolate, obtuse or rounded, 1-veined; petals 3 × 1.7 mm, obliquely ovate, obtuse, 1-veined, appressed to the dorsal sepal and concave forming a hood over the column; lip variable in length, clawed, 3-lobed, lateral lobes about 3.6 × 0.5 mm, filiform and falcately incurved; midlobe shorter and broader, 2.4 × 1.2 mm; tongue-like, rounded; spur clavate, bifid at base; column 1 mm high, 1.2 mm broad; rostellum erect and bifid with the glands of the pollinia in the fork. Anther

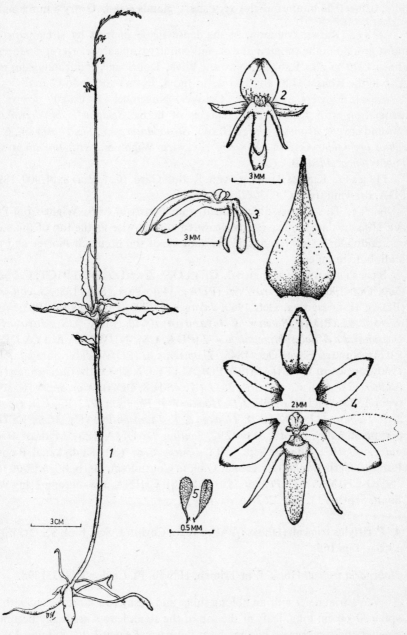

Fig. 164. *Peristylus aristatus* Lindl. 1, plant with tubers and inflorescence. 2, flower from front. 3, lip, column, ovary and spur from side. 4, bract, sepals, lip and column spread out from front, spur (dotted outline). 5, pollinia with caudicles and glands.

lateral, 2-loculed, loculi parallel; tubes absent; pollinia 2, clavate or pyriform, bifid, 0.36 × 0.24 mm; caudicles very short; glands small. Ovary 8 mm long.

D i s t r. Rather common, in the dense shade of trees by streams or on moist ground in the submontane or mid-country tropical wet evergreen forests above 1220 m alt. Rangala, Nuwara Eliya, Dolosbage, Pidurutalagala, etc. Also in the Khasia Hills and Kerala in India, Burma and Indo-China.

E c o l. Flowers September, October, November. It usually grows in association with the following species of herbs: *Selaginella brachystachys* (ground cover), *Alsophila glabra* Hook., *Strobilanthes* sp., *Scutellaria* sp., *Curculigo orchioides* Gaertn., *Sonerila ceylanica* Wight & Arn., *Impatiens* sp., *Phaius tancarvilleae* Bl., etc.

I l l u s t r. King & Pantling, Ann. R. Bot. Gard. (Calcutta) 8: pl. 409. 1898; PDA, drawing from *C.P. 3081.*

N o t e. This species differs much from *Peristylus exilis* Wight from Pulney Hills in that the leaves are crowded rosette-wise at the top of the stem and undulate; lateral lobules of the midlobe of the lip much shorter and the midlobule broader.

S p e c i m e n s E x a m i n e d. CEYLON: KANDY DISTRICT: Corbet's Gap, Oct. 1960, *Jayaweera 1996* (PDA); Dolosbage, Sep. 1885, *s. coll. s.n.* (PDA); Hunnasgiriya, Oct. 1960, *Jayaweera 1997* (PDA), Nov. 1963, *Jaya-weera 2385* (PDA), *Sohmer & Jayasuriya 10640* (PDA, US), *Jayasuriya, Dassanayake & Balasubramaniam 497* (PDA, US). NUWARA ELIYA DISTRICT: Nuwara Eliya, Oct. 1845, *Thomson s.n.* (PDA); Pidurutalagala, Jul. 1960, *Jayaweera 58 (13)* (AMES). LOCALITY UNKNOWN: *Gardner 880* (K), *Walker 1272* (K), *s. coll. C.P. 3081* (K, AMES, PDA), *Macrae 56* (K-holotype). INDIA: Khasia Hills: *J.D. Hooker & T. Thomson 1912* (K), *J.D. Hooker & T. Thomson 1753* (K), *J.D. Hooker & T. Thomson 296* (K), *Mann s.n.* (K). Sikkim Himalaya: Gorb, May 1897, *Pantling 176* (K, AMES). Madras: *Meebold 12971* (K); Nilgiris, Sept. 1913, *Bourne 6183* (K). Kodaikanal Region: Pulneys, Herb. *Wight* (K). Kerala: Quilon, Courtallam, Herb. *Wight 3000* (K). INDO-CHINA: 1933, *Petelot 5653* (AMES). CHINA: Kwangtung Tsing Wan Shan, Sept. 1933, *Lau 2207* (AMES).

4. Peristylus trimenii (Hook. f.) Abeywick., Ceylon J. Sci., Biol. Sci. 2 (2): 151. 1959.—**Fig. 165.**

Habenaria trimeni Hook. f. in Trimen, Handb. Fl. Ceylon 4: 233. 1898.

Terrestrial herb with an oblong tuber and fleshy root-fibres; stem with the spike 30–60 cm long, leafy at the top of the stem, leaves gradually becoming smaller and represented by sheaths at the base. Leaves 7–12 cm long, 2.8–3.2 cm broad, oval acute with 5 conspicuous veins, bases sheathing. Flowers white, 1.3 cm across, secund, in dense spikes measuring 5–17 cm in length;

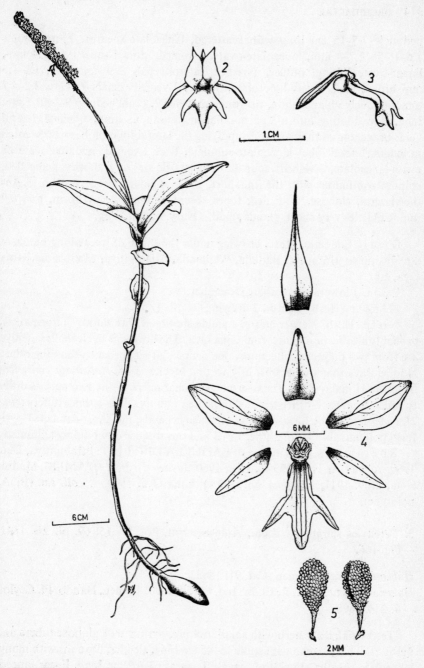

Fig. 165. *Peristylus trimenii* (Hook. f.) Abeywick. 1, plant with tuber and inflorescence. 2, flower from front. 3, lip, column, ovary and spur from side, three-quarters
view. 4, bract, sepals, petals and lip spread out from front, column from inside. 5,
pollinia with caudicles and glands.

peduncle 7.5–15 cm long with scattered, lanceolate sheaths. Floral bracts 1.6–1.75 × 2.7–3 mm, lanceolate-ovate, 1-veined; dorsal sepal 8.5 × 2.4 mm, linear-ovate-oblong, obtuse, 1-veined; lateral sepals 8–9 mm long, 1.2–1.5 mm broad, linear-ovate-lanceolate, obtuse, 1-veined; petals 9.5–11 × 3.2–4.7 mm, obliquely oblanceolate, tip rounded, veins 2, branched; lip 9.7–10.5 mm long, claw dilating into a 3-partite, flat, membranous limb, 3-veined, lateral veins branching at the base and supplying the lateral lobes, lobes nearly equal in length; lateral lobes lanceolate-subulate, 1- or 2-veined; midlobe ovate or ovate-lanceolate, 3-veined; spur globose, sessile or very shortly pedicelled; column continuous with the lip, short, wide; stigmatic processes short. Anther lateral, globose, 2-loculed; tubes absent; pollinia 2, pyriform, 1.6 × 0.9 mm; caudicles very short; glands small. Ovary 9.5 mm long.

D i s t r. Endemic. Rare, growing under the shade of trees along banks of streams up to 915 m alt. Badulla, Welimada, Ettampitiya, Madulsima, Uma Oya, etc.

E c o l. Flowers November, December.

I l l u s t r. Herb. Perad., 2 drawings.

N o t e. Herb. Kew contains a single specimen without any information, probably a collection made from Uma Oya. The drawings in Herb. Peradeniya are from two different collections, one a much larger specimen than the other. Hooker says that the nearest ally to this species is his *Habenaria constricta* from the Himalaya and Tenasserim. The characters of the two species differ so much from each other that I doubt their affinity. This species differs from *H. constricta* in the linear-oblong sepals and petals, the short-caudicled pyriform pollinia, absence of anther tubes and the absence of a bifid rostellum.

S p e c i m e n s E x a m i n e d. BADULLA DISTRICT: Ettampitiya, Dec. 1960, *Jayaweera 1998* (PDA), Dec. 1960, *Jayaweera 58 (14)* (AMES); Madulsima, Nov. 1911, *Vaughan s.n.* (PDA); Uma Oya, 1879, *s. coll. s.n.* (PDA, holotype).

5. Peristylus spiralis A. Rich., Ann. Sc. Nat. Bot. 11. 15: 69. pl. 2B. 1841. —Fig. 166.

Habenaria spiralis Trimen, Cat. 91. 1885.

Habenaria torta Hook. f., Fl. Br. Ind. 6: 159. 1890; Trimen, Handb. Fl. Ceylon 4: 234. 1898.

Terrestrial, leafy herb with small, oblong, pyriform or globose tubers and fleshy root fibres; stem with spike 15–45 cm long, slender, flexuous with many, lanceolate sheaths above the leaves. Leaves 2.5–6.2 cm long, linear-lanceolate, obtuse, acute or acuminate, upper leaves merging into the sheaths on the stem, 5–7-veined, bases sheathing. Flowers greenish-white, secund, variable in size, in slender, lax-flowered, spirally twisted spikes measuring 5–25 cm in

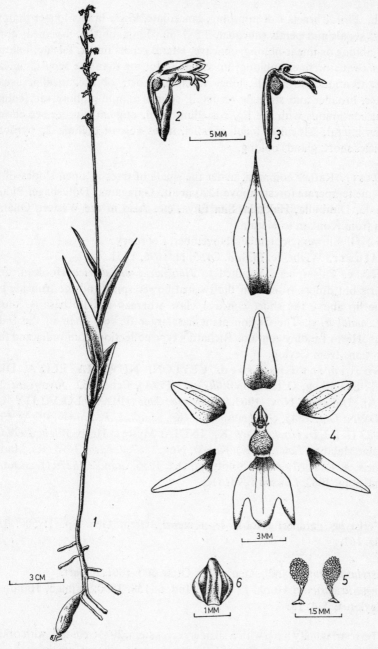

Fig. 166. *Peristylus spiralis* A. Rich. 1, plant with tuber and inflorescence. 2, flower
with bract from side, 3, ovary, spur, column and lip from side. 4, bract, sepals,
petals, lip and column spread out from front. 5, pollinia with caudicles and glands.
6, front portion of the rostrum where the pollinia are embedded.

length. Floral bracts 6–8 mm long, lanceolate, lower bracts longer than the ovary; sepals and petals subequal, 2.5–3 mm long, obtuse, 1-veined; dorsal, sepal oblong or linear-oblong, concave; lateral sepals linear, falcate, reflexed; petals ovate or linear-oblong; lip variable, longer than the sepals, cuneate, 3-cleft to about the middle, lobes variable, short, obtuse, median usually shorter, broader and strongly recurved; spur a minute globose sac; column short, continuous with the lip, rostellum trifid, stigmatic processes clavate. Anther lateral, 2-loculed, loculi parallel, tubes absent; pollinia 2, pyriform; caudicles short; glands oblong.

Distr. Rather common, under the shade of trees in open slopes of the montane temperate forests above 1220 m alt. Galagama, Dolosbage, Pidurutalagala, Dimbulla, Hakgala, Sita Eliya, etc. Also in the Western Ghats in India from Konkan to Kerala.

Ecol. Flowers September–November, February.

Illustr. Wight, Ic. Pl. Ind. Or. 5: pl. 1696, 1851.

Note. This species is allied to *Habenaria malabarica* Hook. f. from Nilgiris but differs from it in the twisted flower spike and the truncate base of the lip above the short concave claw whereas the lip base is 3-lobed in *H. malabarica*. The Ceylon plant has larger flowers than in the Indian forms. Herb. Lindley contains Richard's type collection from India and three collections from Ceylon.

Specimens Examined. CEYLON: NUWARA ELIYA DISTRICT: Sita Eliya, Oct. 1906, *Willis s.n.* (PDA), Feb. 1962, *Jayaweera 2003* (PDA); Hakgala, Nov. 1963, *Jayaweera 2366* (PDA). LOCALITY UNKNOWN: Oct. 1845, *G. Thomson s.n.* (K), *s. coll. C.P. 226* (K, PDA), *Gardner 883* (K), *J.D. Hooker 269* (K). INDIA: Mysore: Herb. *Wight 2999* (K). Kerala: Malabar, *Law s.n.* (K); Kerala, Nov. 1867, *Johnson 1696* (K). Madras: Nilgiris, *A. Richard s.n.* (K, holotype); Oct, 1886, *Gamble 18279* (K); Ootacamund, Sept. 1883, *Lawson 12941* (K).

6. Peristylus gardneri (Hook. f.) Kraenzl., Orch. Gen. Sp. 1: 506. 1898. —Fig. 167.

Peristylus aristatus Lindl., Gen. et Sp. Orch. 300. 1861, in part.
Habenaria gardneri Hook. f., Fl. Br. Ind. 6: 158. 1890; Trimen, Handb. Fl. Ceylon 4: 234. 1898.

Terrestrial leafy herb with a slender, erect stem, 20–56 cm tall, with oblong, tuberous roots, and root fibres. Leaves ash-green, distant on the stem, 4.5–9.5 × 1–2.5 cm, lanceolate, acuminate, acute, 5–7-veined with conspicuous transverse venules, margins undulate, bases sheathing the stem. Flowers green, 1 cm across in laxly many-flowered, terminal racemes measuring

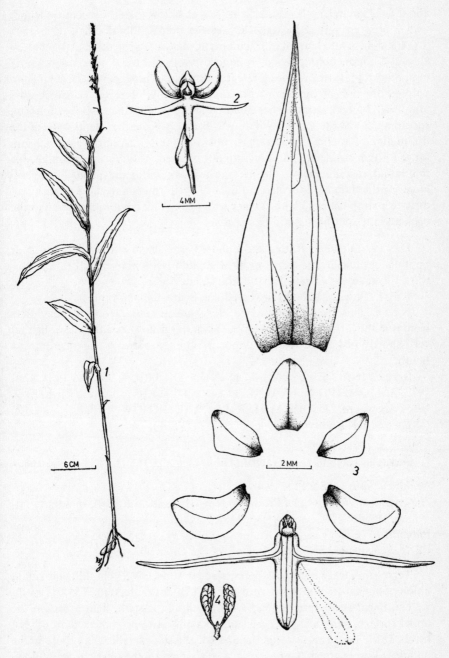

Fig. 167. *Peristylus gardneri* (Hook. f.) Kraenzl. 1, plant with tuber and inflorescence. 2, flower from front. 3, bract, sepals, petals, lip and column spread out
from front, spur (dotted outline). 4, pollinia with caudicles and gland, enlarged.

about 8–22 cm in length; peduncle as long as or less than the raceme in length with 3 progressively reducing, leafy, sterile bracts. Floral bracts 12.8–15 × 3.8–4.8 mm, ovate-lanceolate, acuminate, acute, 3-veined; dorsal sepal 3–3.2 × 2–2.1 mm, oblong-ovate, rounded, 1-veined; lateral sepals 4–4.4 × 1.8 mm, obovate-falcate or oblong-falcate, obtuse, 1-veined; petals 2.8 × 1.7 mm, oblong, one-half of the lamina protruded laterally, obtuse, 1-veined; lip 4.2 mm long, 3-lobed; lateral lobes about twice as long as the midlobe, filiform, spreading, 2-veined, veins originating as branches from the lateral veins of the lip; midlobe 2.8 mm long, straight, oblong, obtuse, 3-veined; spur 8.2 mm long, 1.8 mm diameter, globose, stipitate, curved; column 1.3 mm high, 0.8 mm broad; rostellum erect, plicate, toothed, concealing the glands of the pollinia. Anther lateral, 2-loculed; pollinia 2, pyriform, connected by short caudicle to a strap-shaped gland. Ovary with pedicel 1.2 cm long, grooved at the back and the spur fitting into this groove.

D i s t r. Endemic. Rather rare, under dense shade of trees by streams or on moist ground in the subtropical montane forests above 1220 m alt. Nuwara Eliya, Adam's Peak, Horton Plains, etc.

E c o l. Flowers February, May, June, September–November.

N o t e. This species is allied to *Habenaria aristata* Hook. f. but differs from it in the large robust habit of the plant, large flowers with thicker lip and very shortly pedicelled fruit. I doubt its affinity to *Habenaria stenostachya* Benth.

S p e c i m e n s E x a m i n e d. KANDY DISTRICT: Adam's Peak Oct. 1927, *Alston 943* (PDA). NUWARA ELIYA DISTRICT: Nuwara Eliya, Nov. 1963, *Jayaweera 2365* (PDA). LOCALITY UNKNOWN: *Walker s.n.* (K), *Gardner 881* (K-holotype), *s. coll. C.P. 2373* (PDA).

7. Peristylus cubitalis (L.) Kraenzl., Orch. Gen. Sp. 1: 502. 1898.—**Fig. 168.**

Orchis cubitalis L., Sp. Pl. 2: 940. 1753.
Habenaria cubitalis R. Br., Prod. Fl. Nov. Holland 312. 1810, in adnot; Trimen, Handb. Fl. Ceylon 4: 235. 1898.
Platanthera cubitalis Lindl., Gen. et Sp. Orch. 292. 1835.
Coeloglossum brevifolium Lindl., Gen. et Sp. Orch. 302. 1835.

Terrestrial, leafy herb with erect, slender stem, 30–53 cm tall, and small, oblong, root tubers and fleshy root-fibers. Leaves sessile, thin, 3.5–13.5 × 0.7–1.3 cm, linear-lanceolate, acute, bases sheathing the stem, light green on the upper surface, paler ash-green beneath, 3 veins more prominent than others; leaves at the base and towards the apex of the stem smaller than those in the middle. Flowers green, 3 mm broad, sharply bent on the ovary in many-flowered, slender, terminal spikes measuring 11–23 cm in length; peduncle 13–16 cm long with 4–7 sterile, foliaceous bracts. Floral bracts 7–10 × 2.5 mm,

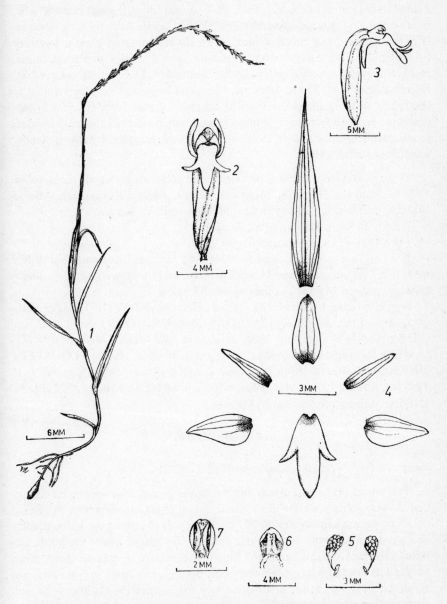

Fig. 168. *Peristylus cubitalis* (L.) Kraenzl. 1, plant with tuber and inflorescence. 2, flower from front with prominent ovary. 3, ovary, lip, column and spur from side. 4, bract, sepals, petals and lip spread out from front. 5, pollinia with caudicles and glands. 6, column from front. 7, column from front showing pollinia sacs.

ovate-lanceolate, acuminate, acute, 5–7-veined; dorsal sepal 3.5×2 mm, ovate-oblong, obtuse, concave, 3-veined; lateral sepals 2.7 × 1.3 mm, obliquely ovate, rounded and concave; petals 2.8 × 1.4 mm, oblong, obtuse, 3-veined; lip fleshy, 2.2 × 1.2 mm, 3-lobed, spreading; lateral lobes 1 mm long, linear, recurved, sometimes reduced to stubs; midlobe 1.3 × 0.9 mm, tongue-like, rounded; spur 2 × 0.7 mm, cylindric, blunt and bent, and running parallel to the ovary with 3 calli at the mouth; column 1.2 mm high, 0.8 mm broad; rostellum erect and truncate. Anther lateral, adnate to the column, 2-loculed, loculi parallel, tubes absent; pollinia 2, pyriform, attached by short, slender caudicles to small glands.

D i s t r. Rather common, on banks and hill-cuttings at altitudes below 1372 m. Rangala, Hewessa, Morawak Korale, Pasdun Korale, etc. Also in Malabar and Khasia Hills in India and Tenasserim in Burma.

E c o l. Flowers March, April, August.

I l l u s t r. PDA, 2 drawings from *C.P. 3202.*

N o t e. This species is allied to *Habenaria stenostachya* Benth. but differs from it in that the plants and leaves are larger and the flowers smaller. Herb. Lindley contains Macrae's collection from Ceylon.

S p e c i m e n s E x a m i n e d. CEYLON: KANDY DISTRICT: Rangala, Apr. 1932, *Simpson 9425* (PDA); Dolosbage, Oct. 1925, *s. coll. s.n.* (PDA); Norton Bridge, Aug. 1954, *Jayaweera 2002* (PDA), *Jayaweera 58 (17)* (AMES); Moragalakande, Mar. 1928, *Alston 1656* (PDA). LOCALITY UNKNOWN: *Macrae 10* (K), *Gardner 882* (K), *Walker 293* (K), *s. coll. C.P. 3202* (K, AMES, PDA), Mar. 1904, *Willis s.n.* (AMES), *Cramer 3077* (PDA). INDIA: Malabar, *Stocks s.n.* (AMES).

67. DISPERIS

Swartz, Kongl. Vetensk. Acad. Nya Handl. 21: 214. 1800.

Terrestrial herbs with ovoid tubers; leaves one to few, sessile, membranous; flowers solitary or few in racemes; dorsal sepal cohering with the broad petals to form a hemispheric hood, lateral sepals spreading or deflexed, each saccate dorsally; petals semilunate, deflexed; lip placed under the hood, adnate to the face of the column and long-clawed above it; column short, erect, very stout; rostellum large, membranous, bilobed, produced in front into two rigid, cartilaginous arms, holding at their extremities the glands of the pollinia; anther dorsal, oblong, 2-chambered; pollinia 2, pollen granules in a double row on the margins of the flattened caudicles which curl up in a spiral on removal; stigma bilobed, lobes situated on either side of the adnate claw of the lip.

About 90 species distributed in tropical South Africa, India, Ceylon, Thailand, Java, New Guinea, Australia and the Philippine Islands.

Disperis zeylanica Trimen, J. Bot. 23: 245. 1885; Trimen, Handb. Fl. Ceylon 4: 236. 1898.—**Fig. 169.**

Disperis tripetaloides Lindl., Gen. et Sp. Orch. 371. 1839, in part.

Terrestrial herb with a tuberous stem, the aerial parts brownish-red, 9.5–25 cm long, with 2 leaf-sheaths and 1–3 amplexicaul leaves. Leaves sessile, 1.4 × 0.9 cm, ovate, acute, cordate at base, 5-veined. Flowers pale pink, 1–1.2 cm broad, 2-lipped, in terminal subcorymbose racemes; peduncle stout, about 3 cm long, with a foliaceous sterile bract at the end. Floral bracts large, foliaceous 1 × 0.7 cm, ovate, acute, 5-veined; dorsal sepal 8 × 1.9 mm, linear-lanceolate, 3-veined, apex obliquely truncate; lateral sepals 9 × 5 mm, obliquely falcate with a linear depression in the centre, subacute, faintly connate at base forming the lower lip; petals 9 × 4.5 mm, of the same shape as lateral sepals, subacute, 3-veined, strongly appressed to the dorsal sepal and concave to form a hood over the labellum and the column; lip 4.3 × 5.8 mm, stiffly erect, resembling a ship's anchor, confluent with the column at the base and rising above, simulating the top of the column, bifid with two long, linear, recurved arms with minute yellow papillae; column short, truncate, with a 2-lipped deflexed appendage at the base. Anther dorsal, 2-loculed; pollinia 2, pinnate, each consisting of 25 biseriate pollinules, rachis long; caudicles long, recurved, terminating in small naked glands; pollinules oblong, 0.44 × 0.14 mm; hyaline membrane in front quadrate, 2.6 mm broad, erect, concave with two linear, twisted processes produced basilaterally.

D i s t r. Rather common under the shade of trees in the submontane or mid-country tropical wet evergreen forests between 915 and 1524 m alt. Hantane, Ritigala, Rangala, Matale, Hunnasgiriya, etc. Also in the Eastern Ghats in India.

E c o l. Flowers April, May, September.

I l l u s t r. Wight, Ic. Pl. Ind. Or. 3: pl. 930. 1843–45; PDA, two drawings one of which is from *C.P. 2363.*

N o t e. Earlier descriptions of this species have been based on dry specimens or imperfect drawings. The present account is from freshly gathered material. In Herb. Kew there is a sheet on which Thawaites' and Walker's collections from Ceylon are mounted along with *Hohenacker 1572* from Ootacamund and annotated *Disperis neilgherensis* Wight by Fischer. It appears to me that the Indian species is a form of *D. zeylanica* though it is larger than the Ceylon form and the petals are cuspidately acuminate.

S p e c i m e n s   E x a m i n e d. CEYLON: ANURADHAPURA DIST-RICT: Ritigala, Jul. 1889, *s. coll. s.n.* (PDA), Aug. 1972, *Jayasurya, Wheeler & Cramer 830* (PDA, US), Aug. 1972, *Jayasuriya, Premadasa & Foster 2274* (PDA, US). KANDY DISTRICT: Hantane, May 1924, *J.M. de Silva s.n.* (PDA), Aug. 1960, *Jayaweera 1985* (PDA), *s. coll. s.n.* (PDA); Corbet's Gap,

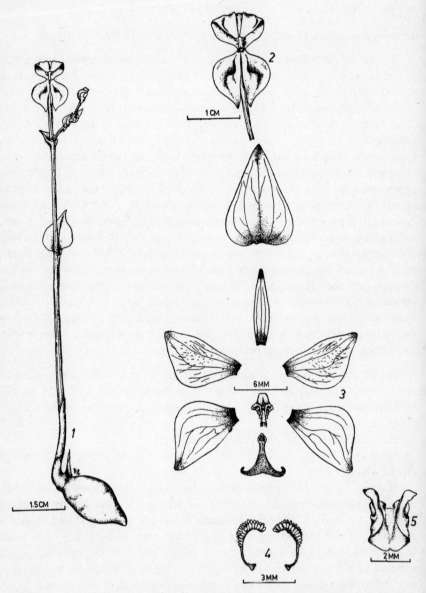

Fig. 169. *Disperis zeylanica* Trimen. 1, plant with tuber and inflorescence. 2, flower from front. 3, bract, sepals, petals, lip and column spread out from front. 4, pollinia with caudicles and glands. 5, hyaline membrane in front of the anther.

Jun. 1960, *Jayaweera 1984* (PDA), Aug. 1960, *Jayaweera 59* (AMES); Kobonilla Hill Sept. 1888, *s. coll. s.n.* (PDA). INDIA: Malabar, Konkan, etc., Herb.
Stocks s.n. (K); Bababoodun Hills, *Law s.n.* (K). Madras: Nilgiris, *Bourne
6152* (K), Sept. 1908, *Bourne 5252* (K), *Gamble 15313* (K), Oct. 1883, *Gamble
16965* (K); Pulneys, *1897 Bourne 332* (K); Coimbatore, May 1911, *Fischer
2761* (K). Pen. Ind. Or., Herb. *Wight 3108* (K).

68. SATYRIUM

Swartz, Kongl. Vetensk. Akad. Nya Handl. 21: 214. 1800.

Terrestrial herbs with tubers and erect leafy stems; leaves sheathing, few
and basal or more numerous and cauline, decreasing upwards into the bracts;
flowers spicate, resupinate; ovary not twisted; sepals and petals subequal,
spreading or deflexed; lip superior, sessile at the base of the column, erect,
hooded, base more or less united to the lateral sepals, produced behind into a
pair of descending spurs; column erect under the lip, short or long, divided at
the apex into 2 lobes, the upper convex, bearing the pulvinate stigma on its
anterior surface, the lower anticous and forming the rostellum; anther short,
hanging under the rostellum, chambers nearly parallel, tubes short; pollinia
2, granular, clavate, bipartite, each with a slender caudicle and gland.

About 170 species distributed mostly in tropical South Africa with a few
species in India, Ceylon, China and Java.

Satyrium nepalense D. Don, Prod. Fl. Nepal 26. 1825; Trimen, Handb. Fl.
Ceylon 4: 237. 1898.—**Fig. 170.**

Satyrium wightianum Lindl., Gen. et Sp. Orch. 340. 1838.
Satyrium ciliatum Lindl., ibid. 341.
Satyrium perrottetianum A. Rich., Ann. Sc. Nat. Bot. 11. 15: 76, pl. 53. 1841.
Satyrium albiflorum A. Rich., ibid.
Satyrium pallidum A. Rich., ibid. 77.

Terrestrial, leafy, erect herb with oblong tubers and fleshy root-fibres.
Stem short, ensheathed by leaf-bases. Leaves 2 or 3, fleshy 10–25 × 5–10 cm,
elliptic or ovate-lanceolate, acute, base broad and sheathing, strongly ribbed
beneath, 5–7-veined. Flowers not rotated, pink or rarely white, 1 cm broad,
in terminal spikes measuring 7–9 cm in length; peduncle stout, about 14 cm
long with 3 or 4 lanceolate, foliaceous, sterile bracts. Floral bracts 1.3–1.6 ×
0.7 cm, oblong-lanceolate or lanceolate, acuminate, acute, erect when young,
later recurved; dorsal sepal 7 × 2 mm, oblong-lanceolate, obtuse, recurved,
ciliolate, 3-veined; lateral sepals obovate-oblong, 6 × 3.5 mm, obtuse, ciliolate,
3-veined; petals 6 × 2 mm, oblanceolate, obtuse, ciliolate, 3-veined; lip superior, sessile, attached to the base of the column and enclosing it, 6 × 4 mm,
margins recurved, concave, strongly keeled at the back, with two parallel

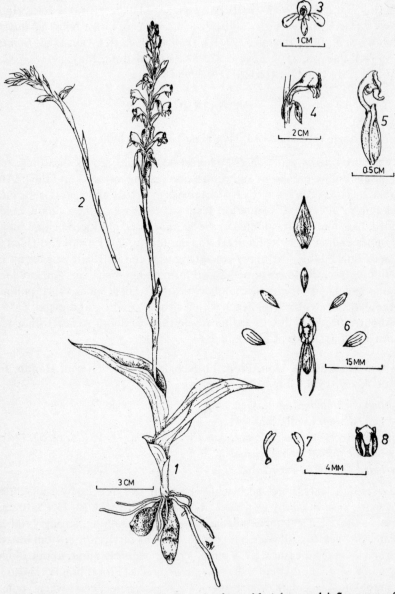

Fig. 170. *Satyrium nepalense* D. Don. 1, plant with tubers and inflorescence. 2, young inflorescence showing bracts. 3, flower from front. 4, flower from side showing prominent, globular lip, bract and one of its spurs. 5, ovary and column from side. 6, bract, sepals, petals spread out from front; ovary, column and spurs from front. 7, pollinia with caudicles and glands. 8, column from front showing pollinia sacs.

spurs extending beyond the ovary; each spur 1.6 cm long, pinkish white, tip tinged green; column 6 mm high, cylindrical, curved, 0.8 mm diameter, expanding at the apex to a broad stigma, projecting upwards above the anther, anticous. Anther lateral, subparallel, 2-loculed; pollinia 2, club-shaped, bilobed, granular, 1.9 × 0.56 mm, connected by short slender caudicles to large glands. Ovary 8 mm long, strongly ribbed. Fruit an erect, fusiform capsule.

D i s t r. Common, in the wet patana lands among grass above 1220 m alt. Adam's Peak, Hakgala, Nuwara Eliya, etc. It also occurs in India along the Kashmir range, Khasia Hills and the mountain ranges from Konkan to Kerala, upper Burma and China.

E c o l. Flowers, September, October, November, December, January.

I l l u s t r. Wight, Ic. Pl. Ind. Or. 3: pl. 929. 1843–45; King & Pantling, Ann. R. Bot. Gard. (Calcutta) 8: pl. 444. 1898; Hook. f., Bot. Mag. 108: pl. 6625. 1882; PDA, drawing from *C.P. 227*.

N o t e. This is a very variable species with sweet-scented dark pink to white flowers. The Burmese specimens have orbicular leaves at the very base of the stem. The tubers are used medicinally in India.

S p e c i m e n s   E x a m i n e d. CEYLON: KANDY DISTRICT: Madulkelle, Oct. 1887, *s. coll. s.n.* (PDA); Adam's Peak, Nov. 1927, *F.W. de Silva 46* (PDA), Aug. 1959, *Jayaweera 2181* (PDA), Oct. 1959, *Jayaweera 60* (AMES); Maskeliya, Adam's Peak, Dec. 1975, *Bernardi 15928* (PDA), Oct. 1975, *Sohmer & Sumithraarachchi 9918* (PDA), Sept. 1969, *van Beusekom 1544* (PDA), Nov. 1974, *Davidse & Sumithraarachchi 8629* (PDA), Oct. 1969, *Reitz 30004* (PDA), Dec. 1975, *Bernardi 15770* (PDA). BADULLA DISTRICT: Ohiya to Farr Inn, Nov. 1973, *Sohmer, Jayasuriya & Eliezer 8576* (PDA). NUWARA ELIYA DISTRICT: Nuwara Eliya, Westward-Ho, Nov. 1963, *Jayaweera 2362* (PDA), Nov. 1960, *Jayaweera 2058* (PDA), Dec. 1960, *Jayaweera 2059* (PDA); Horton Plains, Sept. 1890, *s. coll. s.n.* (PDA), Oct. 1974, *Davidse 7608* (PDA), Aug. 1970, *Cramer 3137* (PDA), Sept. 1969, *van Beusekom 1458* (PDA), Dec. 1970, *Theobold* and *Krahulie 2749* (PDA); Nuwara Eliya, Dec. 1971, *Davidse 8898* (PDA); between Hakgala and Nuwara Eliya, *Read & Desautels 2283* (PDA), Sept. 1969, *Read & Desautels 2261* (PDA); Diyagama Estate, Oct. 1975, *Sohmer & Sumithraarachchi 10032* (PDA); Moon Plains; Oct. 1970, *Cramer 3244* (PDA); Bopathalawa, Mar. 1906, *Willis s.n.* (PDA). LOCALITY UNKNOWN: *s. coll. C.P. 227* (AMES, PDA), *s. coll. C.P. 522* (K), *Macrae s.n.* (K), *Gardner 299* (K), *Walker 192* (K). TIBET: E. Tibet, *J.A. Soulier 67* (K), *Goondu 447* (PDA). INDIA: Himachal Pradesh: N.W. Himalayas, Jul. 1938, *Stewart 16682A* (AMES); Jaunsar, Sept. 1898, *Gamble 27283* (K), Herb. *Griffith s.n.* (PDA). Himalayan Border: *T. Thomson s.n.* (AMES); W Himalaya, Almora, Jul. 1900, *Duthie s.n.* (K). Punjab: 1888, *Drummond 23188* (K). Yembathang, *Wigram 104* (K). Khasia Hills, *J.D. Hooker & T. Thomson s.n.* (AMES, PDA). Sikkim, *J.D. Hooker s.n.* (AMES), *Clarke 24993* (K), *T. Thomson s.n.* (PDA); Sikkim Himalaya, *King's Collector s.n.* (PDA); Singalelak Range, *Pantling 464* (K, AMES, PDA); Bijan, 1888, *King's Collector s.n.* (PDA); Malabar, Konkan etc., *Stocks, Law*, etc. *s.n.* (PDA). Mysore: Herb. *Wight 2995* (K). Kerala: Travancore, Sept. 1894, *Bourdillon 354* (K). Madras: Nilgiris, Oct. 1883, *Gamble 12959* (K); Pular Rocks, Jul. 1898, *Bourne 1872* (K); Herb. *Wight 3023* (K); Kodaikanal Region, *Barber 7243* (K); Billigiriran Hills, *Barnes 568* (AMES); Annaimalai Hills, *Barber 4031* (K). Assam: Naga Hills, Sept. 1935, *Bor 6277* (K). Pen. Ind. Or., Herb. *Wight 2995* (AMES), Herb. *Bannerji 1268* (AMES), Herb. *Griffith 5302* (K), East India Co., Herb. *Falconer 1050* (PDA). NEPAL: 1889, *Wallich s.n.* (AMES), *Wallich 7025A* (PDA). BURMA: South Shan States, Oct. 1911, *Robertson 439* (K). CHINA: Yunnan: 1904, *Ducloux 2865* (AMES).

BIGNONIACEAE

(by William L. Theobald*)

Juss., Gen. Pl. 137. 1789.

Trees, shrubs, or lianas, very rarely herbs. Leaves usually opposite, rarely alternate, usually palmately or pinnately-compound, terminal leaflet sometimes tendril-like; stipules absent. Inflorescence usually a terminal raceme or panicle, sometimes axillary, solitary or dichasial, occasionally cauliflorous. Bracts and bractlets usually present. Flowers hermaphroditic often irregular, usually large and showy. Calyx 5-merous, usually campanulate or spathaceous, sometimes 5-lobed, toothed, or 2-lipped. Corolla 5-merous, gamopetalous, campanulate, funnelform, or tubular, often ventricose and oblique, usually 2-lipped; lobes imbricate. Stamens usually 4, rarely 2 or 5 (*Oroxylum*), inserted on corolla tube; anthers connivent in pairs or free, bilocular; locules often divergent; staminodium usually present. Disk usually present, usually annular or cupular, often enlarged and conspicuous. Ovary superior, bilocular with axile placentation, occasionally with false septa, and then appearing 4-locular, rarely unilocular with 2 parietal placentae; style simple; stigma 2-lipped. Fruit usually a capsule, septicidally or loculicidally dehiscent, rarely fleshy and indehiscent. Seeds numerous, large, usually winged; wings membranous or corky.

A family of 120 genera and 650 species with a large number of small or monotypic genera. It is primarily tropical and especially abundant in northern South America where many are climbers and an important feature of the forests. Only two genera (*Campsis* and *Catalpa*) occur both in the New and Old World. Ceylon representatives of the family include one species each of *Oroxylum*, *Dolichandrone*, *Stereospermum*, and *Spathodea*. The first three are apparently native, while *Spathodea campanulata*, a native of Africa, has become widely naturalized on the island. All are known from the moist lowlands of the Southwest, especially near the coast. However, *Oroxylum* and *Stereospermum* are also reported from areas surrounding Kandy in the Central Province. *Spathodea* is widespread along the coast and in the montane regions of Wet Zone up to elevations of approximately 1200 m.

Numerous members of the family are cultivated on the island including

*Pacific Tropical Botanical Garden, Hawaii.

Bignonia, Tecomaria, Jacaranda, and *Tabebuia. Millingtonia hortensis* L.f. and *Stereospermum suaveolens* DC., have been reported by Thwaites and Trimen as being commonly planted on the island, with the latter often seen near Buddhist Temples. Worthington (Ceylon Trees, p. 340. 1959) has noted *Markhamia platycalyx* as introduced by himself in 1928 and now naturalized.

None of the taxa are endemic and all are widespread in adjacent regions, including India, Southeast Asia, and Indonesia. For an excellent discussion of the taxonomy, geographic distribution and possible origins of these and other taxa, see C.G.G.J. van Steenis, Malayan Bignoniaceae, their taxonomy, origin and geographic distribution, Rec. Trav. Bot. Neerl. 24: 787–1049. 1927.

KEY TO THE GENERA

1 Leaves 2–3 pinnate; stamens 5; capsule broadly-linear, greater than 7 cm broad, septicidally 2-valved..**1. Oroxylum**
1 Leaves simply pinnate; stamens 4; capsule oblong or narrowly-linear, less than 3 cm broad, loculicidally 2-vlaved
  2 Calyx spathaceous; corolla; white or orange-red, greater than 7 cm long; capsule oblong or narrowly-linear, greater than 1.7 cm broad; seeds flattened membranous or corky-winged
    3 Corolla white, opening at night, tubular portion greatly exceeding the calyx, capsule linear, seeds, corky-winged.................................**2. Dolichandrone**
    3 Corolla orange-red, open during day, tubular portion included within calyx; capsule oblong, seeds membranous winged..............................**3. Spathodea**
  2 Calyx campanulate; corolla pinkish or yellowish, flecked and striped reddish-purple, less than 3 cm long; capsule narrowly-linear, less than 6 mm broad, seeds 3-angled, membranous-winged..**4. Stereospermum**

1. OROXYLUM

Vent., Decne., Gen. Nov. 8. 1808.

Calosanthes Blume, Bijdr. 760. 1826.

Trees. Leaves opposite, large, 2–3 pinnate. Inflorescence a large, compact, terminal raceme on an elongated peduncle, usually extending obliquely well above the foliage; bracts present; flowers large, longer than 9 cm (in ours). Calyx large, coriaceous, oblong-campanulate, truncated or shallowly lobed. Corolla thick and fleshy, campanulate-ventricose; lobes 5, crisped and crumpled, upper 3 lobes subequal, lower 2 slightly smaller, partially fused at base. Stamens 5, equally inserted near base of tube, not or only slightly exerted at throat; filaments in 2 unequal pairs and 5th shorter; anthers glabrous, bilocular; locules oblong, parallel or slightly divergent. Disk large, cushion-like, not surrounding the base of the ovary. Ovary linear-oblong, bilocular; style slender; stigma 2-lipped, lips flattened. Fruit a large capsule, broadly linear, over

50 cm long, greater than 7 cm broad, tapering at both ends, septicidally 2-valved; valves woody, compressed parallel to the septum; septum flat. Seeds numerous, thin, discoid, surrounded by a broad, membranous wing, except at base.

A genus of one or two species known from South China and India south-eastward to the Philippines and parts of Indonesia.

Oroxylum indicum (L.) Vent., Dec. Gen. Nov. 8. 1808; Trimen, Handb. Fl. Ceylon 3 : 281. 1895.—**Fig. 1: A1–A3.**

Bigonia indica L., Sp. Pl. 625. 1753.
Spathodea indica Pers., Syn. Pl. 2: 173. 1806.
Calosanthes indica Blume, Bijdr. 761. 1826.

Usually small trees, often irregularly branched near top, 5–8 m high, sometimes up to 13 m; bark thick, yellowish-gray with numerous, large, corky lenticels. Leaves deltoid-ovate in outline, 9–13 dm long, 5–8 dm broad; ultimate divisions ovate-elliptical, 4–16 cm long, 3–9 cm broad, base variable, obtuse to cordate or oblique, margin entire, apex caudate-acuminate, minutely lepidote, appearing glabrous, sometimes pubescent along veins, paler beneath; petiole and rachis stout, cylindrical, base and joints of rachis distinctly swollen, articulate, corky lenticels prominent. Inflorescence on very stout, branch-like peduncle, persistent, 35 cm or more long; pedicels stout, 3–7 cm long, articulate at base, glabrous; bracts fused to pedicel at base. Calyx blackish-purple, glabrous, 3–4.5 cm long, 1.5–2.5 cm broad. Corolla opening in evening; tube 5–7 cm long, c. 3 cm broad at throat, deep maroon to reddish-purple without, creamy-yellow with a diffuse dull pink within; glandular within; lobes much crumpled in bud, obovate in outline, 4–6 cm long, 3–4.5 cm broad, usually with 2 deep longitudinal grooves without, crisped and sparsely toothed at margins, color similar to tube but usually paler, surface papillose, glandular, and minutely pubescent. Filaments glandular, densely tomentose at point of insertion, longest pair c. 5 cm long, 2nd pair c. 4 cm long, solitary stamen c. 3 cm long; anthers 8–10 mm long, locules parallel or slightly divergent. Disc shallowly 5-lobed, 12–15 mm in diameter, 4–5 mm high. Ovary c. 17 mm long, style c. 5 cm long; stigma c. 7 mm long, c. 5 mm broad. Capsule flat, 50–75 cm long, 7–9 cm broad, tapering at both ends, acute; valves semiwoody, thin, median and 2 larger marginal ridges evident externally. Seeds c. 2 cm in diameter, winged margin 1.5–2 cm broad.

D i s t r. In the moist low country below 700 m and inland to Weragamtota along the Mahaweli Ganga. It is a conspicuous tree due to the very large leaves, the persistent, long, broad capsules, and the long inflorescence extending well above the foliage. It is probably more widespread than indicated by known collections, and Trimen has reported it as common. Also found from India east to Southeast Asia, Indonesia and the Philippines.

Fig. 1. *Oroxylum indicum* Vent. A-1, Flower, × .75. A-2, Mature fruit, × .5. A-3, Seed, × .1. *Dolicandrone spathacea* K. Sch. B-1, Flower, × .75. B-2, Mature fruit, × .5. B-3, Seeds, × 1.25. *Spathodea campanulata* P. Beauv. C-1, Flower, × .75. C-2, Mature fruit, × .5. C-3, Seed, × 1. *Stereospermum personatum* Chatterjee. D-1, Flower, × 1. D-2, Mature fruit, × .5. D-3 Seeds, × 1.4.

E c o l. Trimen has noted it to be a weedy little tree, and those observed in the present study do appear to be growing readily in disturbed areas along roadsides. The flowers open at night and give off a somewhat fetid odor. This combined with the thick, fleshy petals, and an inflorescence that extends well beyond the leaves point to possible bat-pollination. Flowering June–September.

V e r n. Totila (S).

I l l u s t r. Wight, Ic. Pl. Ind. Or. 4: t. 1337–38. 1848 (*Calosanthes indica*). N o t e. Van Steenis (Rec. Trav. Bot. Neerl. 24: 819. 1927) has noted that Miquel described a new araliaceous taxon from Ceylon, *Arthrophyllum zeylanicum* n. sp. ?, which he based on sterile material and which is in all probability *Oroxylum indicum*. The same is also true for *A. reticulatum* Blume ex Miq. from Java.

S p e c i m e n s   E x a m i n e d. COLOMBO DISTRICT: south edge of road near small bridge, Tarakuliya, on road around southern edge of Negombo Lagoon, *Theobald & Grupe 2376* (A, K, L, NY, PDA, UC, US). KANDY DISTRICT: river bank in jungle, Mahaweli Ganga near Weragamtota, *Simpson 8463* (BM); growing in Royal Botanic Garden, Peradeniya, *Theobald & Grupe 2390* (A, BO, E, K, L, LE, PDA, SING, UC, US); Royal Botanic Garden, Peradeniya, *Trimen s.n.* (PDA). LOCALITY UNKNOWN: *Gardner s.n.* (K).

2. DOLICHANDRONE

(Fenzl.) Seem., Ann. Mag. Nat. Hist. Ser. 3, 10 : 31. 1862, nom. cons.

Pongelia Raf., Sylva Tell. 78. 1838.
Dolichandra Sect. B. *Dolichandrone* Fenzl, Denkschr. Baier. Bot. Ges. Regensburg 3 : 113, 265. 1841.

Trees. Leaves opposite (in ours), simply pinnate. Inflorescence a terminal, few-flowered raceme or panicle; flowers large, longer than 10 cm (in ours). Calyx spathaceous, curved, cauducous. Corolla opening towards evening, lower portion of corolla tube very long, cylindrical, much exceeding the calyx, upper portion inflated and funnel-shaped; lobes 5, subequal, rounded, crisped. Stamens 4, didynamous, equally inserted at base of swollen portion of tube; anthers very large, bilocular, locules divergent, glabrous; staminodium small. Disk large, annular, cushion-like. Ovary linear-oblong, bilocular with 2 false septa, appearing 4-locular; style slender; stigma 2-lipped, lips flattened. Fruit a capsule, linear, curved, subcylindrical or compressed contrary to the septum in transection, loculicidally 2-valved; valves perpendicular to the septum, flat or convex, septum flat. Seeds numerous, corky or membranous winged.

A genus of about 9 species known from tropical East Africa and Madagascar east through India and Southeast Asia to Indonesia, North Australia and New Caledonia.

Dolichandrone spathacea (L.f.) K. Schum., Fl. Kais. Wilh. Land. 123. 1889; Alston in Trimen, Handb. Fl. Ceylon 6: 220. 1931.—**Fig. 1: B1–B3.**

Bignonia spathacea L.f., Suppl. Pl. 283. 1781.
Spathodea longiflora Vent., Choix. 40. 1807.
Spathodea rheedii Wall., Cat. no. 6516. 1832.
Dolichandrone rheedii Seem., J. Bot. 8: 380. 1870; Trimen, Handb. Fl. Ceylon 3: 282. 1895.

Trees, often branching from near base, up to c. 15 m high. Leaves odd-pinnate, obovate-oblong to elliptical in outline; leaflets 5–9, ovate-lanceolate, 6–17 cm long; 3–6 cm broad, base acute to rounded or oblique, margin entire, apex acuminate-caudate, glabrous, paler beneath, shortly petiolate; petiole and rachis cylindrical, channelled above, joints of rachis not swollen, articulate. Inflorescence 2–8 flowered, peduncles stout, less than 1 cm long; pedicels stout, 1–3 cm long; bracts not evident. Calyx spathaceous, glabrous, 2.5–5 cm long, c. 1 cm broad when closed, hooked at tip. Corolla white, fragrant; cylindrical portion of tube c. 7–10 cm long, 4–6 mm broad, funnelform portion c. 2.5 cm long, 1.5–2.5 cm broad, lobes rounded, 2–3 cm long, c. 2–3 cm broad, much crisped and crenate on margins. Filaments glabrous; anthers c. 7 mm long. Disk c. 5 mm in diameter, c. 2 mm high, not surrounding base of ovary. Stigma c. 4 mm long, 3–4 mm broad. Capsules of variable lengths, 25–50 cm long, 1.7–2.5 cm broad; valves thin, semiwoody, bluntly pointed, smooth or obscurely ribbed; septum and false septa woody; seed scars evident. Seeds corky-winged, oblong in outline, 11–15 mm long, 6–9 mm broad, including wing.

Distr. Mainly found in mangrove swamps and tidal marshes of the moist low country of the south-west from Negombo south to Galle. This is the most widespread species in the genus, being found primarily in coastal areas from India east through Southeast Asia and Indonesia to New Caledonia and the Solomon Islands.

Ecol. The trees begin flowering at a very young age and are often shrub-like in appearance. They are found in nearly pure stands along the edge of lagoons or scattered near the inner edge of mangrove swamps. The corky-winged seeds appear to be an adaptation for water-dispersal. The flowers open at sunset and fall off early the next morning. They are very fragrant and are said to be moth-pollinated. Flowering May–July.

Vern. Diya-danga (S).

Illustr. Wight, Ic. Pl. Ind. Or. 4: t. 1339. 1848 (*Spathodia rheedii*).

Specimens Examined. COLOMBO DISTRICT: scattered along

inner edge of mangrove swamp on outer, upper peninsula west of Negombo, *Theobald & Grupe 2373* (A, BO, E, K, L, NY, PDA, UC, US); Negombo estuary, *Simpson 7914* (BM, PDA). GALLE DISTRICT: along edge of lagoon and scattered among mangroves just south of Bentota, *Theobald & Grupe 2388* (A, BM, E, K, L, LE, NY, PDA, SING, UC, US). KALUTARA DISTRICT: Paiyagala, Kalutara, *Trimen s.n.* (PDA).

3. SPATHODEA

P. Beauv. Fl. Oware. 1: 46. 1805.

Trees. Leaves opposite, simply pinnate. Inflorescence a dense, terminal raceme, peduncles usually not greatly exceeding the leaves; flowers large, showy, longer than 8 cm. Calyx large, spathaceous, recurved. Corolla orange-red; basal portion short, cylindrical, enclosed within calyx; upper portion abruptly much widened, broadly ventricose-campanulate, erect; lobes 5, subequal, erect. Stamens 4, subequal, unequally inserted near base of swollen portion of tube, not exserted; filaments glabrous; anthers large, bilocular, locules divergent, glabrous; staminodium small. Disk annular, shallowly lobed, surrounding base of ovary. Ovary ovate-oblong, bilocular, pubescent, papillose; style slender, glabrous; stigma 2-lipped, lips flattened. Fruit a capsule, lanceolate-oblong, flattened parallel to the septum, loculicidally 2-valved; valves perpendicular to the septum, boat-shaped, woody, often remaining attached together at apex and base; septum flat. Seeds numerous, membranous-winged.

A genus of 2 species native to tropical Africa. Our species has been much planted and now is widespread throughout India, Ceylon and other parts of the New and Old World Tropics.

Spathodea campanulata. Beauv., Fl. Oware 1: 47, t. 27. 1805; Trimen, Handb. Fl. Ceylon 3: 282. 1895.—**Fig. 1: C1–C2.**

Large trees at maturity, branching widely at top; bark smooth, light brownish-gray. Leaves odd-pinnate, obovate to oblong in outline; leaflets 13–19, elliptical-oblong to obovate, 5–9 cm long, 3–4.5 cm broad, base rounded, margin entire, apex acuminate, glabrous above, paler beneath, veins puberulent below, shortly petiolate; petiole and rachis sparsely pubescent, cylindrical, channelled above, joints of rachis indistinct, not articulate. Inflorescence on a stout peduncle, pedicels 3–4 cm long, articulate at base, glabrous; bract at base of pedicel oblong-lanceolate, c. 2 cm long; bractlets 2, oblong-lanceolate, 7–10 mm long; near apex of pedicel. Calyx golden-brown, velutinous, glabrous within, 5–6 cm long, 2–2.5 cm broad when enfolding corolla. Corolla tube 7.5–9 cm long, 5–6 cm broad, bright reddish-orange without; tube yellowish-orange within, red spots and stripes prominent within, glandular; cylindrical portion 1.5–2 cm long, c. 9 mm broad; inflated portion 6–7 cm long, 5–6 cm broad; lobes deltoid, 3–4.5 cm long, 3–4 cm broad, bright reddish-orange without, orange within, narrow yellow margin evident on all lobes. Filaments 4–6 cm long, glabrous; anthers; c. 8 mm long. Style c. 6 cm long; stigma ovate-lanceolate, c. 5 mm long, 2.5 mm broad. Disk 8 mm in diameter, 4 mm high. Capsule brownish-black, 15–23 cm long, 3–5 cm broad. Seeds winged all around, 1.7–2.4 cm broad, including hyaline wing.

D i s t r. Not native. An introduced species which has now become very widespread in the moist lowlands and the montane region, from sea level up to elevations of 1200 m or possibly higher. Widespread in New and Old World Tropics.

E c o l. Trimen reported that he had known it to fruit only once in Kandy, but today there is abundant evidence for its fruiting in many localities. The bright orange-red flowers form a conspicuous part of the landscape during the monsoon season. Flowering June–September.

I l l u s t r. Bot. Mag. t. 5091. 1859.

S p e c i m e n s E x a m i n e d. COLOMBO DISTRICT: along roadside south of Negombo, near Kadolkele area, *Theobald & Grupe 2374* (US). KANDY DISTRICT: scattered in Oodewella tea plantation below summit of Hantane Mt. No. 1, *Theobald & Grupe 2342* (BM, NY, PDA, US); along edge of road, 3 miles south of Peradeniya on road to Gampola, *Theobald & Grupe 2364* (K, L, PDA, UC, US). NUWARA ELIYA DISTRICT: scattered in tea plantation along edge of road approx. 1 mile north of Talawakelle on road to Dimbulla, *Theobald & Grupe 2310* (A, PDA, US).

4. STEREOSPERMUM

Cham., Linnaea 7: 720. 1832.

Trees. Leaves opposite, simply pinnate. Inflorescence paniculate, lax, many-flowered, terminal, or sometimes lateral; bracts present; flowers small, less than 3 cm long (in ours). Calyx small, campanulate, 3–5 lobed. Corolla campanulate to tubular-ventricose, geniculate; lobes 5, upper 2 partially connate, lower 3 distinct, margins crisped. Stamens 4, subequal, equally inserted near base of tube; anthers free, bilocular; locules divergent, glabrous. Disc cupular, surrounding base of ovary. Ovary linear-oblong, bilocular; septum thickened; style slender; stigma 2-lipped, lips flattened. Fruit a capsule, linear, twisted and curved, terete to quadrangular in transection, loculicidally 2-valved, valves thin, perpendicular to the septum; septum thickened, subterete, corky, notched. Seeds with a deep, transverse furrow across centre, embedded in notches of septum, trigonous, membranous-winged at each end.

A genus of about 24 species extending from tropical Africa eastward through India and Ceylon to Southeast Asia and Indonesia.

Stereospermum personatum (Hassk.). Chatterjee, Bull. Bot. Soc. Bengal 2: 70. 1948.—Fig. 1: D1–D3.

Dipterosperma personatum Hassk., Flora 25, pt. 2. Beibl. 28. 1842.
Stereospermum chelonioides Auct. et DC., Prod. 9: 210. 1845, p.p. tantum; Trimen, Handb. Fl. Ceylon 3: 283. 1895.
Stereospermum tetragonum DC., Prod. 9: 210. 1845; Alston in Trimen, Handb. Fl. Ceylon 6: 221. 1931.

Usually large trees with numerous spreading branches, up to 25 m high; bark thick, rough, grayish-yellow. Leaves odd-pinnate; broadly obovate to obovate-oblong in outline; leaflets 5–9, elliptical-oblong, 3–11 cm long, 2.5–5 cm broad, base acute, obtuse, or oblique, margin entire, apex narrowly caudate, glabrous, petiolate; petiole and rachis cylindrical, channelled above, petiole base and joints of rachis distinct, slightly swollen, articulate, sparsely lenticellate. Inflorescence on short peduncles, 1–7 cm long; pedicels slender, glabrous, articulated at base, bracts minute, caducous. Calyx yellowish-purple, 5–8 mm long, c. 5 mm broad, lobes obtuse, glabrous. Corolla tube 15–18 mm long, 6–8 mm broad, basal portion narrow, cylindrical, c. 5 mm long, 3 mm broad; upper portion campanulate-ventricose, abruptly inflated and sharply geniculate, nearly perpendicular to calyx tube, 10–13 mm long, 6–8 mm broad at throat, dull pink to yellow without, with numerous, deep reddish-purple flecks and stripes, sparsely to moderately pubescent, 2 pubescent ridges evident on lower surface within; upper 2 lobes partially fused laterally, reflexed, c. 8 mm long, lower 3 distinct, c. 7–10 mm long, 6–8 mm broad, each with 2 prominent ridges. Filaments glandular-pubescent at point of insertion, c. 8 mm long; anthers c. 1.5 mm long. Disk 1.5 mm broad, 0.8 mm high. Style c. 10 mm long; stigma c. 1 mm long, 1 mm broad. Capsules of very variable lengths, curved or spirally twisted, up to c. 50 cm long, c. 5 mm broad; valves thin, often with thickened ridges at the angles; septum c. 4 mm thick, notches c. 3 mm deep. Seeds 4 mm long, 4 mm wide, 3 mm high; wings c. 6 mm long.

D i s t r. Trimen reports the species as common along the coast and extending up to 650 m in the moist low country. Worthington (Ceylon Trees, p. 343. 1959) has reported it from Bibile (Uva Province) in the Dry Zone on east side of the island. It is also known from India east through Southeast Asia to Malaysia and possibly Borneo.

E c o l. Flowering May–August.

V e r n. Lunu-madala, Dunu-madala (S); Padri (T).

I l l u s t r. Wight, Ic. Pl. Ind. Or. 4: t. 1341. 1848 (*Stereospermum chelonioides*).

S p e c i m e n s E x a m i n e d. KANDY DISTRICT: Poilakanda estate, Kadugannawa, *Worthington 1113* (BM); Andiatenne, Kadugannawa, *Worth-*

ington 324 (BM); Udawela village, Andiatenne, *Worthington 342* (BM); growing at Royal Botanic Gardens, Peradeniya, *Theobald & Grupe 2394* (A, BM, BO, E, K, L, LE, NY, PDA, SING, UC, US); *de Silva s.n.* (PDA). KEGALLE DISTRICT: roadside, Kegalle, *Worthington 148* (BM). KURUNEGALA DISTRICT: Kurunegala, *Gardner s.n.*, part of *C.P. 1959* (PDA). LOCALITY UNKNOWN: *Gardner 597* (K); *s. coll. s.n.*, part of *C.P. 1959* (BM, K).

LEMNACEAE

(by F.N. Hepper*)

Nomenclatural type: *Lemna* L.

Aquatic herbs, floating or submerged and freely drifting, very reduced in structure to a flat or curved thallus or suborbicular, often minute, stems and leaves undifferentiated. Vascular tissue minimal. Roots present or absent, often solitary, suspended in the water, devoid of root hairs, occasionally sheathed at point of insertion, tip covered by a cap. Vegetative reproduction usual with daughter thallus budding from a lateral pocket, often remaining attached to parent; resting buds (turions) sometimes produced in adverse conditions. Flowering erratic; flowers monoecious; developing in a pouch or pit, enclosed by a spathe or spathe absent. Staminate flowers 1–2; anthers 2-thecous. Pistillate flower solitary; style short; stigma concave; ovules 1–6. Seeds ellipsoid, usually ribbed; endosperm scanty or none.

Cosmopolitan in still fresh-water, with most species in the warmer countries.

These duck-weeds are seldom collected in flower and often overlooked, especially the submerged species, although none of the latter have yet been recorded from Sri Lanka. They are best preserved in spirit to aid identification. Since the plants are greatly reduced to a thallus or frond, much discussion has taken place as to its nature, whether the thallus represents a stem or a leaf, or both. The family has affinity with Araceae and especially *Pistia*, on account of the spathaceous flowers and similar roots.

KEY TO THE GENERA

```
1 Roots present
  2 Root solitary on each thallus...........................................1. Lemna
  2 Roots numerous arising from a swelling.............................2. Spirodela
1 Roots absent, thallus minute.........................................3. Wolffia
```

1. LEMNA

L., Sp. Pl. 970. 1753; Hegelmaier, Lemnac. Monogr. 134. 1868; Trimen, Handb. Fl. Ceylon 4: 366. 1898; Daubs, Monogr. Lemnac. 16. 1965. Type species of genus: *L. trisulca* L.

*Royal Botanical Gardens, Kew.

Aquatics, submerged or more usually floating in great numbers, individual thalli more or less cohering. Thalli oblong or ovate, ± asymmetrical, thin or spongy. Daughter thallus budding from lateral pocket. Root solitary, devoid of hairs, shortly sheathed near point of insertion, sheath simple or laterally winged; apex of root sheathed by a conspicuous root-cap, tip acute or obtuse. Flowering erratic; floral pocket lateral with spathe enclosing 2-staminate and 1-pistillate flower. Fruit 1 (–6)-seeded. Seeds usually longitudinally ribbed.

KEY TO THE SPECIES

1 Thallus thin; root sheathed and winged at point of insertion, root-cap conspicuously acute..**1. L. perpusilla**
1 Thallus thick and spongy with large cells; root sheath not winged; root-cap obtuse..
....**2. L. gibba**

1. Lemna perpusilla Torrey, Fl. New York 2: 245. 1843; Hegelmaier, Lemnac. Monogr. 139, t. 6/19, 20, t. 7/18, 19, 1868; Daubs, Monogr. Lemnac. 25, t. 9. 1965; Hepper, Fl. Trop. E. Afr. Lemnac. 4, f. 1., 4A-B. 1973. Type: U.S.A., *Torrey s.n.*—Fig. 1A.

Lemna paucicostata Engelm. in Gray, Man. Bot. ed 5, 681.1867; Hegelmaier, Lemnac. Monogr. 139, t. 8. 1868; Trimen, Handb. Fl. Ceylon 4: 366. 1898. Type not specified.

Thallus free-floating, pale green, ovate to oblong, variable in size, 1.5–4 mm long, 0.7–2.5 mm wide, asymmetrical, upper surface with or without an apical papilla and 1 or more along the midline, obscurely 3-nerved. Daughter thallus very shortly stipitate, several individuals adhering closely. Root solitary, sheath winged below the thallus; root-cap acute. Flowering cavity lateral; spathe open. Staminate flowers 2; anthers 2-thecous. Pistillate flower 1; style concave. Fruit ribbed, 1-seeded.

D i s t r. Widespread in the tropics and subtropics forming extensive floating mats on the still pools usually rich in nitrogen, such as cattle-watering places and muddy outlets from tanks, actively propagating vegetatively during wet season, flowering time uncertain.

V e r n. Diyapanshi (S).

N o t e. There are many synonyms for this species which varies considerably in size and appearance throughout its wide distribution. The undetermined specimen referred to in a note by Trimen (Handb. Fl. Ceylon 4: 366. 1898) as '*L. minor*, from Tissor Wewa, Kelvin Grove, Feb. 1883 (W. F.)' must be the Ferguson specimen in PDA labelled 'Tissa Wewa, July 1883', but the data discrepancy is irreconcilable.

S p e c i m e n s E x a m i n e d. ANURADHAPURA DISTRICT: Tissa Wewa, *Ferguson s.n.* July 1883 (PDA); Anuradhapura, *Trimen*, Jan. 1890

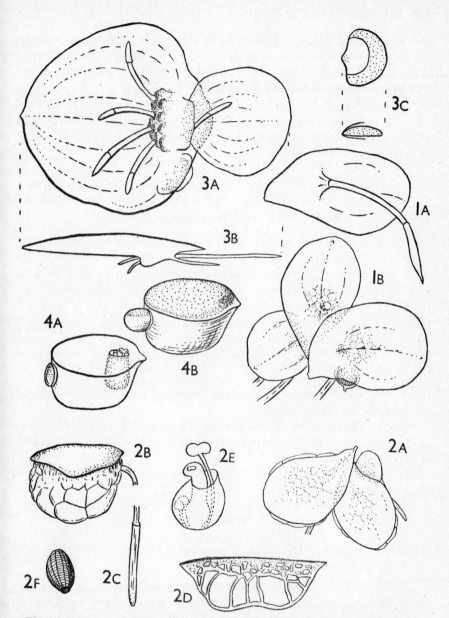

Fig. 1. Lemnaceae. 1, *Lemna perpusilla*. 1A, view of undersurface, × 8. 1B, thalli, one with fruit, × 8. 2, *Lemna gibba*. 2A, sterile thalli, × 8. 2B, lateral view, × 10. 2C, root cap, × 10. 2D, transverse section, × 18. 2E, flower, × c. 27. 2F, seeds, × c. 12.3, *Spirodela polyrhiza*. 3A, undersurface of budding thallus, × 8. 3B, transverse-section, × 8. 3C, resting-bud, × 6. 4, *Wolffia arrhiza*. 4A, fertile thallus, × 20. 4B, sterile thallus budding, × 20. (1A, B, from *Richards 20226*; 2A-D, from *Richards 23320*. 2E, F, after Daubs (1965). 3A-C, after *Brenan 4995*. 4A, B, from *Hall 3037*. Drawn by F.N. Hepper).

(PDA), *Hepper & Jayasuriya 4656* (K, L, PDA, US); Madatugama to Keki-rawa, *Hepper & Jayasuriya 4612* (K, PDA, US). MANNAR DISTRICT: Murunkam, *Hepper & Jayasuriya 4645* (K, PDA, US). VAVUNIYA DIS-TRICT: Cheddikulam, *Hepper & Jayasuriya 4637* (K, PDA, US). HAMBAN-TOTA DISTRICT: Tissamaharama, *Hepper & de Silva 4748* (K, L, PDA, PRE, US); Bundala, *Hepper & de Silva 4752* (K, PDA, US). COLOMBO DISTRICT: Colombo, Madampitiya, old quarry, *W. Ferguson s.n.* 8 Oct. 1880 (PDA).

2. Lemna gibba L., Sp. Pl. 970. 1753; Alston in Trimen, Handb. Fl. Ceylon 6: 298. 1931; Daubs, Monogr. Lemnac. 17, t. 8. 1965; Hepper in Fl. Trop. E. Afr. Lemnac. 2, f. 1, 2A–F. 1973. Type: Europe, unspecified.

Thallus free-floating, surface broadly ovate; yellow-green, asymmetrical slightly convex, 3–5 (–6) mm long, 2–4 (–5) mm wide, almost hemispherical below and spongy with large inflated hyaline cells and airspaces (even in flat form the large cells are evident). Daughter thalli budding laterally, 2 or 3 remaining attached with very short stipes. Root solitary; sheath unwinged; root-cap 5 mm long, tip obtuse (rarely acute). Floral cavity lateral. Spathe enclosing 2–1-staminate flowers and 1-pistillate. Fruits narrowly winged above, 1–2 seeded. Seeds ribbed and transversely striate. Chromosome number $2n = 64$.

D i s t r. Cosmopolitan, although in the topics only at higher altitudes, occurring on the surface of pools.

N o t e. The specimen cited is presumably the one referred to by Trimen in his note (Handb. Fl. Ceylon 4: 366. 1898) as 'St. Sebastian Quay, Colombo, Jan. 1885 (W.F.).

S p e c i m e n   E x a m i n e d. COLOMBO DISTRICT: St. Sebastian Quarry, Colombo, *W. Ferguson s.n.* July 1885 (PDA).

2. SPIRODELA

Schleid. in Linnaea 13: 391. 1839; Hegelmaier, Lemnac. Monogr. 147. 1868. Type species: *S. polyrhiza* (L.) Schleid.

Floating aquatics, thallus discoid to oblong, 3–10 mm long, 1.2–8 mm wide. Daughter thallus budding from lateral slit, remaining attached to parent by slender stipe, several individuals often connected. Roots 2-numer-ous, from swollen portion beneath thallus; root-cap acute. Turions (resting buds) produced in adverse conditions. Flowers rarely produced, unisexual; spathe enclosing 2–3 male and 1 hermaphrodite flower in lateral slit pouch; male flowers each with 1 stamen; pistillate flower bearing 1–4 ovules.

Cosmopolitan genus with five species, easily recognised by the presence of several roots.

Spirodela polyrhiza (L.) Schleid. in Linnaea 13: 392. 1839; Hegelmaier, Lemnac. Monogr. 73, 151, t. 13/10–16, t. 14, 15. 1868; Alston in Trimen, Handb. Fl. Ceylon 6: 298. 1931; Maheshwari in Nature 181: 1745. 1958; Daubs, Monogr. Lemnac. 10, t. 3. 1965; Hepper, Fl. Trop. E. Afr. Lemnac. 5, f. 2, 1A–C. 1973.

Lemna polyrhiza L., Sp. Pl. 970, 1753; Thwaites, Enum. Pl. Zeyl. 331. 1864; Trimen, Handb. Fl. Ceylon 4: 367. 1898; Abeywick. in Ceylon J. Sci., Biol. Sci. 2: 140. 1959. Type: Europe, not specified.

Free floating aquatics. Thallus orbicular-ovate, 1–3 mm long almost as wide, rather thick, with 5–11 conspicuous nerves sometimes tinged pink above, normally purple beneath. Daughter thallus budding from near point of root insertion in a slit in the parent thallus, bearing at its base a small lobe which is supposed to be a basal leaf. Roots 5–15, arising from greatly thickened part of the thallus; root-cap acute. Flowers seldom produced, surrounded by a small open spathe in a lateral slit-pouch with 1-pistillate flower and 2–3-staminate flowers each consisting of a single stamen. Fruit slightly wing-margined. Seeds 1–2. Chromosome number 2n=40.

D i s t r. Cosmopolitan species floating on still water, actively propagating vegetatively during the rainy season.

S p e c i m e n s   E x a m i n e d. PUTTALAM DISTRICT: Puttalam, *Trimen*, Aug. 1883 (PDA). KANDY DISTRICT: Kandy, *Hepper 4794* (K). HAMBANTOTA DISTRICT: Tissamaharama, *Ferguson*, 19 Dec. 1882 (PDA); *Hepper & de Silva 4742* (K, L, PDA, PRE, US). BADULLA DISTRICT: Horabora wewa Tank, *Gardner s.n.* (PDA); *Simpson 9928* (BM, PDA); Mapagala, between Mahiyangana and Bibile, *Hepper & de Silva 4712* (K, L, PDA, PRE, US). RATNAPURA DISTRICT: Kahawatta, *Hepper, Maxwell & C. Fernando 4559* (K, L, PDA, PRE, US).

3. WOLFFIA

Horkel ex Schleid. in Linnaea 13: 389. 1839: Hegelmaier, Lemnac. Monogr. 121. 1868; Trimen, Handb. Fl. Ceylon 4: 367. 1898. Type of the genus: *W. michelii* Schleid. (lectotype)—Den Hartog in Taxon 18 (5): 591–595. 1969.

Minute free floating aquatics. Thallus almost ellipsoid, about 1 mm in diameter, flattened on the upper surface at water-level. Daughter thallus produced in a circular lateral pit, soon separating from parent. Roots absent. Flowers in a pit on the upper surface on the median line, 1-staminate, 1-pistillate; spathe absent.

Cosmopolitan genus with two or three species, lacking roots or appendages.

Wolffia arrhiza (L.) Horkel ex. Wimmer in Fl. Schles., ed. 3: 140. 1857; Hegelmaier, Lemnac. Monogr. 124, t. 2, figs. 6–17, t. 3/1–12. 1868; Daubs, Monogr. Lemnac. 48, t. 18. 1965; Hepper, Fl. Trop. E. Afr. Lemnac. 8, f. 2, 4 A-B. 1973.

Lemna arrhiza L., Mant. 294. 1771. Type: Europe (Italy, France) *Du Chesne s.n.*

Minute aquatic 1–1.5 mm long, rather less in breadth than depth, upper surface flattened and dark green, paler elsewhere. Flowers opening on to surface from simple median pit. Stamen solitary, with filament 0.5 mm long. Style short; stigma concave. Fruit ellipsoid, 0.7 mm long, erect.

D i s t r. Widespread in the warmer parts of the world but infrequent or not occurring in the cooler regions.

S p e c i m e n s   E x a m i n e d. ANURADHAPURA DISTRICT: Anuradhapura, ? *Trimen*, Jan. 1890 (PDA); Anuradhapura, ancient palace on east side, *Hepper & Jayasuriya 4657* (K, L, PDA, PRE, US). MATALE DISTRICT: Pelbendiyawa, near Dambulla, *Hepper & Jayasuriya 4667.* (K, L, PDA, US). COLOMBO DISTRICT: old quarry near Madampitiya, *Ferguson*, 8 Oct. 1880 (PDA).

N o t e. Alston in Trimen, Handb. Fl. Ceylon 6: 298. 1931 adds *W. microscopica* Kurz. on the basis of a report by Petch "pond near the (old) Post Office and 'well' near Ruanvella Dagoba, Anuradhapura". He saw no specimens and commented that the species "is only known from Griffiths' figure of a Bengal specimen". It is now well known in India having been used for embryological and cytological studies by Maheshwari, but its occurrence in Ceylon has not been confirmed, although I looked for it in the places mentioned above.

MYRTACEAE

(by P.S. Ashton*)

Tanniniferous evergreen trees or shrubs, as a rule (in Sri Lanka) hardly buttressed, with cymose branching generally forming a more or less crooked trunk and rounded crown with sinuous branches; bark smooth or frequently thinly scaly, white, grey, yellowish or most often pale rusty brown (unless exposed); occasionally fibrous, dark. Leaves opposite, alternate or whorled, estipulate, lamina simple and ± pellucid punctate with the nerves curving and anastomosing distally into a more or less prominent intramarginal nerve (excl. *Eugenia uniflora*). Twigs frequently quadrangular. Inflorescences various; flowers actinomorphic, hermaphrodite, greenish white, cream or pink; calyx tube adnate to the inferior ovary, with –5 epigynous lobes; petals –5, free or connate into a lid (calyptra) in bud, caducous; stamens many, epigynous around the perimeter of the ovary disc, free or ± connate at base, with long slender filaments and small 2-celled white or yellow anthers; ovary inferior, 2-celled with 1-many axile ovules; style simple, columnar. Fruit a drupe or capsule; seed without endosperm; cotyledons small or absent.

Pantropical, and warm temperate especially in Mediterranean climates. Eight genera in Sri Lanka, of which five are exotic.

The fruit of some species of exotic *Syzygium* have long been cultivated; their name, jambu, is as widespread as their cultivation—from Sri Lanka to Indonesia. The American genus *Psidium*, the pera or guava, has been introduced for the same purpose. The flower buds of *Syzygium aromaticum* provide the cloves of commerce and were much cultivated in the last century, especially in the intermediate zone north of Kandy. Other exotic myrtaceous spice trees that have been introduced to Peradeniya but have never been widely cultivated in Sri Lanka are *Pimenta officinalis* Lindl., the Allspice tree; *P. acris* Kostel. var. *citrifolia* (Kostel.) the Scented Allspice, and *P. acris*, the Bay Berry of South American origin (reference: Macmillan, H.F., Tropical Planting and Gardening, London, 1935, pp. 318–319). The type species of the family, the Mediterranean Myrtle, *Myrtus communis* L., was once tried in Kandy as an ornamental but appears not to have survived. *Eucalyptus* was originally introduced as an ornamental tree in tea estates,

*The Arnold Arboretum, Harvard University, U.S.A.

404 MYRTACEAE

though latterly some species have become important fast growing hardwood plantation trees especially in the hills.

Though a few species of *Eugenia* extend east of the Indian Peninsula, *Eugenia* in the strict sense is a South American genus represented in Asia particularly well in Sri Lanka, where the majority of species are confined to the wet zone; one mountain species extends south to Mauritius and Reunion. This distribution at once suggests a Gondwana origin, and the abundance of Myrtaceae in the mountain forests of Sri Lanka, in the complete absence of *Fagaceae*, may give us a glimpse of what the moist forests of the Indian Gondwana plate were like before it collided with Laurasia.

The large genera of Myrtaceae are taxonomically difficult, the mountain species in particular tending to be fragmented into frequently vicarious forms; sometimes closely similar varieties may grow together in close proximity, especially on the exceptionally wet ridges of the Peak Sanctuary, and one suspects that apomixis may occur. In the accounts of *Eugenia* and *Syzygium* presented here species have been defined by qualitative characters or marked discontinuities in more than a single quantitative character. This had led to reduction of several species based on one or a few collections from adjacent localities.

KEY TO NATIVE AND WIDELY PLANTED GENERA

1 Leaves opposite or whorled
  2 Leaves opposite, nerves more or less distinctly raised beneath; fruit baccate, indehiscent
    3 Embryo horse-shoe shaped or coiled, cotyledons not concealing the hypocotyl; testa hard; petals conspicuous; leaf nervation generally depressed above
      4 Ovary cells with false partitions; shrub with grey-brown woolly leaf undersurface and round twig...1. **Rhodomyrtus**
      4 Ovary cells without false partitions; small cultivated tree with glabrous or sparsely pubescent leaves and ± sharply angled twigs.......................2. **Psidium**
    3 Embryo ± globose or ellipsoid, cotyledons ± concealing the hypocotyl; testa membranous, cartilaginous or cheesy; petals often inconspicuous and frequently falling at anthesis; leaf nervation generally not depressed above
      5 Young shoots pubescent, or if not then flowers axillary, solitary or in clusters, with more or less persistent bracts.....................................3. **Eugenia**
      5 Young shoots glabrous; flowers in terminal or axillary paniculate cymes; bracts minute, fugacous..4. **Syzygium**
  2 Nervation more or less obscure and unraised beneath; fruit capsular
    6 Leaves mostly in whorls of 4; fruit coalescing into a head..............5. **Syncarpia**
    6 Leaves opposite; fruit free.......................................6. **Angophora**
1 Leaves of mature trees spiral; fruit capsular
  7 Petals fused into a calyptra (lid) over the bud; stamens free..........7. **Eucalyptus**
  7 Petals free; stamens united into 5 bundles.........................8. **Tristania**

1. RHODOMYRTUS

(DC.) Reichb., Nom. 117. 1841.

Shrubs with terete twigs; lamina with depressed nervation above and prominent greyish velutinate tomentum beneath. Perianth 5-merous; ovary 3-celled, each with two axile rows of many ovules each in turn isolated by false septa. Fruit a fleshy berry. Embryo coiled or horse-shoe shaped, cotyledons not hiding the radicle.

About 20 species, all but one of which confined in Australasia.

Rhodomyrtus tomentosa (Ait.) Hassk., Flora 1842, 2: 35. 1842; Wight, Spicel. Neilgh. 1: 60. 1845; Bedd., Fl. Sylv. 16: t. 14. 1842; Duthie in Hook. f., Fl. Br. Ind. 2: 469. 1878; Trimen, Handb. Fl. Ceylon 2: 166. 1894; Merr., J. Arn. Arb. 19: 196. 1938.

Myrtus tomentosa Ait., Hort. Kew. 1, 2: 159. 1789; Wight & Arn., Prod.1: 328. 1836.

Rhodomyrtus parviflora Alston in Trimen, Handb. Fl. Ceylon 6: 111. 1931.

Young parts densely greyish ocherous velutinate, ± caducous on lamina upper surface, elsewhere persistent; petals sparsely so within, densely outside; stamens glabrous. Twig stout, terete, much branched, becoming orange-brown, thinly flaky. Lamina 2–8 cm × 1.4–4 cm, elliptic or sometimes obovate, coriaceous, drying dark purple above, ocherous beneath with dark grey-brown nervation, with cuneate base, acute mucronate apex and subrevolute margin; 5- nerved, the outermost pair obscure; tertiary nerves between the outer two pairs subscalariform, between the inner and the midrib subreticulate; nervation prominently elevated beneath, depressed above; petiole 3–8 mm long. Flowers large, axillary, solitary or –3 in a –1.5 cm long pedunculate cyme; bracts 3–8 mm long, linear, paired; pedicel –3 cm long (Kandy specimens) or flowers subsessile; calyx tube c. 6 mm diam., subglobose, with 4–5, –3 mm long and broad, rotundate obtuse segments; petals –12 mm long, 8 mm broad, elliptic, obtuse, pink, darker on the outer surface; stamens –8 mm long, many, with crimson filaments and yellow anthers. Fruit –1 cm diam., globose, crowned with the persistent calyx segments in a c. 8 mm diam. ring; seeds imbedded in purple pulp.

D i s t r. Sri Lanka and Peninsular India to Fukien and southeastwards to Australia. Confined to open places in the mountains above 1500 m in Sri Lanka, and common there. Elsewhere common also in scrub on coasts and sandy degraded soils.

S p e c i m e n s   E x a m i n e d. KANDY DISTRICT: Lake, Kandy, *s. coll. s.n.*, 25.10.1901 (PDA); Royal Botanic Gardens, *J.M.S. s.n.*, 25.2.1917 (PDA). NUWARA ELIYA DISTRICT: Nuwara Eliya & Maturata *s. coll.*

C.P. 1591, (PDA); Hakgala, *A.M.S. s.n.*, 4.4.1906 (PDA), *A.D.A. s.n.*, March 1920 (PDA), *Ashton 2291* (PDA, US); Horton Plains, *N.M.S. s.n.*, 20.5.1911 (PDA), *I.C.W. s.n.*, 25.1.1906 (PDA), *Mueller-Dombois & Comanor 67070852* (PDA, US), *Mueller-Dombois & Cooray 68011309* (PDA, US), *Ashton 2296* (PDA, US). BADULLA DISTRICT: Namunukulakande, *J.M.S. s.n.*, 29.4.1907 (PDA), *s. coll., s.n.*, 29.4.1924 (PDA). LOCALITY UNKNOWN: *Walker s.n.* (PDA).

N o t e. I follow Merrill's interpretation of the Ceylon plant rather than that of Alston, finding no consistent difference between it and the mainland species. It is commonplace elsewhere in the Asian humid tropics to find species with a mountain-top and sandy soil lowland, or coastal, distribution.

2. PSIDIUM

L., Gen. Pl. 615, 17. 1772; Fosberg, Ceylon J. Sci., Biol. Sci. 9. 2: 58–60. 1971.

Untidy slender small trees or shrubs with drooping branches. Leaves opposite, lamina with prominent intramarginal nerve; twigs ± sharply 4-angled. Flowers 1–3-axillary, large; calyx deeply divided into 2–3 prominent ± imbricate lobes above the ovary; petals large and broad; ovary generally 4–5-locular, with many multiseriate ovules. Fruit a fleshy or hard berry with many hard seeds; embryo horse-shoe shaped, the radicle not concealed by the small cotyledons.

About 140 spp., native to the American tropics but several have been planted widely as ornamentals and fruit trees, and some have escaped as ruderals in scrubland and river beds.

The present account is largely based on Fosberg's review. In it he indicated that, besides the few species described here, *P. friedrichsthalianum* (Berg) Ndz. and *P. polycarpa* Lam. have been planted in the botanic gardens, Peradeniya.

KEY TO THE MAIN CULTIVATED SPECIES

1 Lamina prominently nerved and pubescent beneath, nerves depressed above
  2 Twig sharply angled or winged; tomentum short, appressed; fruit exceeding 3 cm diam when ripe...**1. P. guajava**
  2 Twig not sharply angled; tomentum loosely velutinate, not appressed; fruit at most 2 cm diam...**2. P. guineense**
1 Lamina nervation not prominent beneath, ± elevated above; parts glabrescent
  3 Lamina obovate, apex hardly or not acuminate.................**3. P. cattleyanum**
  3 Lamina broadly elliptic, prominently acuminate.................**4. P. montana**

1. Psidium guajava L., Sp. Pl. 470. 1753; Duthie in Hook. f., Fl. Br. Ind. 2: 468. 1878; Trimen, Handb. Fl. Ceylon 2: 167. 1894 (Sphalm. *guayava*)

Alston in Trimen, Handb. Fl. Ceylon 6: 111. 1931; Fosberg, Ceylon. J. Sci., Biol. Sci. 9, 2: 60. 1971.

Psidium pyriferum L., Sp. Pl. ed. 2. 672. 1762.

A small tree or shrub with prominently scroll-marked, overall smooth, grey and rust-brown bark and bright yellow-green crown with hanging leaves and twigs. Young parts and lamina nervation beneath sparsely appressed grey-brown puberulent. Lamina 4–10 × 2.5–6 cm, oblong-lanceolate to elliptic, with broadly cuneate base and obtuse or subacute apex; nerves 7–15 pairs (variable), prominent beneath, narrowly depressed above as also the subreticulate tertiary nerves; petiole 2–7 mm long, short. Flower 3 cm diam. Fruit –4 cm diam., ± pear-shaped, hard.

D i s t r. Widespread in cultivation, including throughout Sri Lanka.

S p e c i m e n s E x a m i n e d. KANDY DISTRICT: Anniewatte, Kandy, *Fosberg 51808* (PDA, US); Peradeniya, University campus, *Cooray 69122601R* (PDA, US). MATALE DISTRICT: Lagalla, *Balakrishnan & Dassanayake NBK 1149* (PDA); between Balana & Alagalla, *Comanor 1198* (PDA, US). DISTRICT UNKNOWN: Iryagama, *de Silva s.n.*, 19.7.28 (PDA). LOCALITY UNKNOWN: *s. coll., s.n.* (PDA).

2. Psidium guineense Sw., Prod. Veg. Ind. Occ. 77. 1788; Fosberg, Ceylon J. Sci., Biol. Sci. 9, 2: 60. 1971.

P. molle Bertol., Nove. Comment. Acad. Sci. Inst. Bonon. 4: 422, t. 24. 1840.

Resembling *P. guajava* but twigs hardly or not angled; lamina elliptic, narrowly cuneate at the base, ± sparsely velutinate beneath; flowers –1.8 cm diam.; fruit –2 cm diam., depressed globose.

D i s t r. Not commonly cultivated, apparently always in the wet zone in Sri Lanka.

S p e c i m e n s E x a m i n e d. KANDY DISTRICT: Peradeniya, University Campus, *Mueller-Dombois & Cooray 67103101* (PDA, US), *67111318* (PDA, US), *69122602* (PDA, US), *Comanor 1180* (PDA, US); Royal Botanic Gardens, *s. coll., s.n.* 1887 (PDA). BADULLA DISTRICT: between Palugama and Boralanda, *Fosberg & Mueller-Dombois 50117* (PDA, US).

3. Psidium cattleyanum Sabine, Trans. Hort. Soc. London 4: 317, t. 11. 1821; Fosberg, Ceylon J. Sci., Biol. Sci., 9, 2: 60. 1971.

Psidium littorale Raddi, Opusc. Sci. 4: 254, t. 7. 1820; Merr., J. Arn. Arb. 19: 198. 1938.
Psidium variabile Berg. in Mart., Fl. Bras. 14. 1: 400. 1857.

Resembling *P. guajava* but parts glabrous. Lamina –8 cm wide, broadly obovate; base narrowly cuneate; apex obtuse to shortly acuminate; nerves ascending, slender but elevated on both surfaces; midrib applanate above; fruit depressed globose, fleshy, sweet.

D i s t r. Known in Sri Lanka only from the specimens cited.

S p e c i m e n s E x a m i n e d. KANDY DISTRICT: Royal Botanic Gardens, *s. coll. s.n.*, Dec. 1887 (PDA); Peradeniya, University Campus, *Fosberg 51809* (PDA, US). BADULLA DISTRICT: Thotulaggala estate, east of Haputale, *Fosberg 51849* (PDA, US).

N o t e. Merrill considered Raddi's name to antedate Sabine's, but Fosberg does not follow this view.

4. Psidium montana Sw., Prod. Veg. Ind. Occ. 77. 1788; Fosberg, Ceylon J. Sci., Biol. Sci. 9, 2: 60. 1971.

Differing from *P. cattleyanum* in its broadly elliptic and prominently acuminate lamina.

D i s t r. Apparently scatsered in cultivation through the Sri Lanka hill country.

S p e c i m e n s E x a m i n e d. KANDY DISTRICT: South garden, *s. coll. s.n.*, 9.8.1905; Peradeniya, University Campus, *Fosberg 51812* (PDA, US). BADULLA DISTRICT: Spring valley, Badulla, *Canfield s.n.*, 28.3.1950 (PDA).

3. EUGENIA

L., Sp. Pl. 1: 470. 1753; Trimen, Handb. Fl. Ceylon 2: 167. 1894 p.p.; Alston in Trimen, Handb. Fl. Ceylon 6: 109, 118. 1931; Niedz. in Pflanzenfam. 3, 7: 81. 1893; Schmid, Amer. J. Bot. 594: 423–436. 1972.

Jossinia Comm. ex DC., Prod. 3: 237. 1828; Merr., J. Arn. Arb. 31: 329–360. 1950; Philipp. J. Sci. 79: 356–360. 1950.

Trees, usually small, generally tomentose at least on innovations or inflorescences. Leaves opposite, with prominent intramarginal nerves (excl. *E. uniflora*). Flowers ± long-pedicelled, solitary or in clusters, mostly axillary, sometimes in racemes, flowering in centripetal sequence, with subpersistent bracteoles. Calyx ± obtuse at base, ± prominently persistently 4-merous; petals 4-merous, large; ovary 2–3-locular, loculi medial, each with many ovules. Embryo subglobose, cotyledons usually fused, concealing the hypocotyl; seedcoat smooth.

About 1000 species, pantropical but mainly in the Americas.

I follow Niedenzu, and latterly Schmid in considering the Asiatic species, which conform with the type of *Jossinia* (*J. continifolia* (Jacq.) DC. of the

Mascarenes, Sri Lanka and South India) in characters of the testa, as part of *Eugenia* L. In this I disagree with Merrill. I keep *Syzygium* separate though (see there). Nevertheless *E. uniflora* L., the only American species cultivated in Sri Lanka, differs from our native species in a number of respects.

KEY TO THE SPECIES

1 Lamina without distinct intramarginal nerve; calyx segments longer than broad, becoming reflexed at anthesis. Cultivated.................................**1. E. uniflora**
1 Lamina with distinct intramarginal nerve; calyx not as above
  2 Young shoots entirely glabrous
    3 Petiole exceeding 5 mm long, leaf base cuneate.......................**2. E. glabra**
    3 Petiole at most 2 mm long; leaf base cordate
      4 Lamina at least 9 × 3 cm; flowers −1 cm diam. at anthesis...........**3. E. amoena**
      4 Lamina at most 7 × 5.5 cm; flowers −5 mm diam. at anthesis........**4. E. rotundata**
  2 Young shoots at first densely puberulent
    5 Flowers c. 2 cm diam., large, cream-yellow, solitary; young parts densely silvery pubescent; shrub on mountain peaks................................**5. E. cotinifolia**
    5 Not as above
      6 Mountain shrubs with slender glabrescent twigs, small leaves, and slender glabrous peduncles
        7 Lamina spatulate to elliptic; twigs brown; flowers 1–3 axillary.....**6. E. mabaeoides**
        7 Lamina ovate-lanceolate to elliptic; twigs pale cream; flowers many-axillary in clusters...**7. E. thwaitesii**
      6 Lowland shrubs or trees with densely ± persistently pubescent twig endings and peduncles
        8 Lamina nervation very slender and hardly raised; intramarginal nerve c. 1 mm within margin and not looped; flowers in reduced terminal racemes. Small trees of dry and intermediate zones...............................**8. E. bracteata**
        8 Lamina nervation not as above; flowers in axillary clusters
          9 Lamina undersurface glabrous.............................**9. E. terpnophylla**
          9 Lamina undersurface at first pubescent, persisting at least on base of midrib
            10 Lamina nerves very slender and hardly elevated beneath.......**10. E. rufo–fulva**
            10 Lamina nerves distinctly elevated beneath
              11 Twig and petiole distinctive cream........................**11. E. rivulorum**
              11 Twig cream but petiole drying pubescent or black..............**12. E. fulva**

1. Eugenia uniflora L., Sp. Pl. 470. 1753 pp.; Urb., in Engl. Bot. Jahrb. 19: 620. 1895; Alston in Trimen, Handb. Fl. Ceylon 6: 119. 1931.

Myrtus brasiliana L., Sp. Pl. 471. 1752.
Plinia rubra L., Mant 2: 243. 1771.
Plinia pedunculata L. f., Suppl. 253. 1781.
Eugenia michelii Lam., Enc. 3: 203. 1789; Trimen, Handb. Fl. Ceylon 2: 188. 1894.
Stenocalyx michelii Berg, in Mart., Fl. Bras. 14, 1: 337, 628. 1857.

A small shrub. Bud puberulent, parts otherwise glabrous. Twigs terete,

slender, pale brown, much branched. Lamina 3.6–5 × 1.3–3 cm ovate, chartaceous, densely punctate and drying chocolate-brown beneath, with broadly
cuneate or obtuse base and bluntly subacuminate or obtuse apex; nerves c.
5 pairs, sinuate, arching and branching within the margin but not uniting to
form a distinct intramarginal nerve, slender but distinctly elevated beneath,
less so above, as also the reticulate tertiary nerves; midrib slender, elevated
beneath, drying black; petiole 2–3 mm long, short. Flowers –3-axillary, white,
on –2 cm long very slender peduncles; calyx –2 mm long and diam., funnel-
shaped with 4, –4 mm long, –2 mm broad, prominent oblong subacute lobes
becoming reflexed at anthesis; stamens –5 mm long. Fruit –2.5 cm diam.,
depressed-globose, prominently ribbed, succulent, crimson, with a small prominent apical ring of calyx segments.

D i s t r. A Brazilian species cultivated at middle altitudes in the wet zone
for its aromatic fruits, which are used for jellies and condiments.

V e r n. Goraka jambu (S); Brasilian cherry (E).

S p e c i m e n s E x a m i n e d. BADULLA DISTRICT: Ella, *Worthington
2935* (K). KANDY DISTRICT: Attabage, *Worthington 2818* (K); Royal
Botanic Gardens, *s. coll. s.n.* Sept. 1887 (PDA).

2. Eugenia glabra Alston in Trimen, Handb. Fl. Ceylon 6: 120. 1931.

Eugenia decora (non Salisb., non Wall.) Thw., Enum. Pl. Zeyl. 115. 1859;
   Trimen, Handb. Fl. Ceylon 2: 185. 1894.

A small tree with dark grey deeply but widely fissured bark. Vegetative
parts glabrous. Twigs terete, with long internodes. Lamina 10–21 × 4–7 cm,
narrowly ovate to elliptic, coriaceous, with narrowly or broadly cuneate base
and –2 cm long tapering to subcaudate acumen; main nerves c. 10–13 pairs,
slender but prominent beneath, distinctly elevated above, as also the shorter
intermediates and reticulate tertiaries; intramarginal nerve at 2–4 mm from
margin, prominently looped, with a slender second tier parallel to it just
within the margin; midrib stout and drying black beneath, broad and hardly
depressed above; petiole 5–15 mm long, stout. Flowers –3-axillary, subsessile; buds c. 3 mm diam., globose. Fruit c. 12 mm long, 18 mm diam., depressed globose, distinctly bulging with 2 seeds, the apex retaining a c. 8 mm
diam. ring bearing the recurved deltoid c. 2 mm long puberulent calyx segments.

D i s t r. Endemic. Rare, known only from the cited collections, from
lowland mixed rain forest.

S p e c i m e n s E x a m i n e d. GALLE DISTRICT: Galle, *s. coll. C.P.
3545* (PDA, K); Naunkitaela F.R., *Worthington 4142* (K).

N o t e. A little understood species from which more specimens are required; differing (when sterile) from *Syzygium makul* in the disposition and prominence of main and intramarginal nerves, and applanate leaf margin.

3. Eugenia amoena Thw., Enum. Pl. Zeyl. 114. 1859; Trimen, Handb. Fl. Ceylon 2: 186. 1894; Alston in id. 6: 119. 1931.

A small tree. Disc puberulent, parts otherwise glabrous. Twigs terete, straight, thinly flaking, red-brown. Lamina 9–15 × 3–6 cm, lanceolate, cordate, with attenuate-acuminate apices; nerves c. 12–15 pairs, with slender sinuate intermediates and reticulate tertiaries, distinctly elevated on both surfaces; intramarginal nerve very distinct, c. 1 mm within margin; midrib stoutly prominent beneath, as a channelled rib above; petiole c. 2 mm long, very short, stout. Flowers in terminal or subterminal axillary fascicles, on –3 cm long slender peduncles; bracts minute, linear; flowers –1 cm diam. at anthesis; calyx –3 mm long and diam., shallowly urceolate, with 4 (–5), –5 mm long, 4 mm broad ovate acute spreading segments; petals –8 × 4 mm, elliptic, acute; stamens –10 mm long, very many; filaments crisped; disc stoutly prominent, square. Fruit unknown.

D i s t r. Endemic. Rare; besides the cited collection Thwaites mentions Dolosbage, Alston Pasdun Korale and Ratnapura, but I have not seen confirmatory specimens.

S p e c i m e n s E x a m i n e d. GALLE & RATNAPURA DISTRICT: Hapugodde, Kukul Korale & Rakwana, *s. coll. C.P. 3439* (PDA, K).

N o t e. Clearly closely allied to *E. rotundata* of the intermediate zone which differs in having shorter leaves and smaller flowers.

4. Eugenia rotundata Trimen, Handb. Fl. Ceylon 2: 185. 1894.

Eugenia mooniana var. *B.* Thw., Enum. Pl. Zeyl. 114. 1859.
Eugenia amoena Thw. var. *rotundata* Trimen, Cat. 33. 1885.

–2 m tall densely leafy shrub with smooth pale greyish white bark. Parts glabrous but for the calyx. Twigs slender, terete, becoming cream-brown. Lamina (1.3–) 2–7 × (0.8–) 1–5.5 cm, ovate or lanceolate, coriaceous, rufous to chocolate-brown on drying; base subcordate, obtuse or broadly cuneate; apex ± broadly –1.5 cm long acuminate; nerves c. 10 pairs, very slender, hardly raised beneath, ± obscure above, with sinuate intermediates, ± obscure densely reticulate tertiaries and intramarginal nerve immediately or –1 mm within margin; midrib slender beneath, obscure and depressed above; petiole –2 mm long, very short. Flowers white, in terminal or axillary fascicles, on –5 mm long slender peduncles; buds –2 mm long and diam., small, subtended by small deltoid bracts; calyx c. 1 mm long and diam., cup-shaped, puberulent, with 4, c. 1 mm long and broad, ovate segments; petals c. 3 × 2 mm, elliptic, obtuse. Fruit –12 mm long, –10 mm diam., ellipsoid to globose, ripening bright red, with c. 2 mm diam. terminal ring of persisting calyx segments.

D i s t r. Endemic; local in the intermediate, and margins of the dry zone; on rocky summits to 700 m.

S p e c i m e n s E x a m i n e d: ANURADHAPURA DISTRICT: Riti-gala, *s. coll. s.n.*, 22.3.05 (PDA), 24.3.05 (PDA), *s.n.* July 1887 (PDA), *Bala-krishnan & Jayasuriya 1043* (PDA, US, K), *1092* (PDA, US, K), *1108* (PDA, US, K), *Worthington 244* (K), *Ashton 2322* (PDA, US). MONERAGALA DISTRICT: Ooma Oya, *s. coll. s.n.* 1880 (PDA). MATALE DISTRICT: Lagalla, *s. coll. s.n.* Sept. 1887 (PDA). KURUNEGALA DISTRICT: Doluwe Kande, *s. coll. s.n* 19.12.1883 (PDA). Arankelle, *Ashton 2320* (PDA, US). KANDY DISTRICT: Deltota, *s. coll. C.P. 2803* (PDA); Hunnasgiriya, *Davidse & Jayasuriya 8382* (PDA, US); Royal Botanic Garden, *s. coll. s.n.* 19.2.1919 (PDA). DISTRICT UNKNOWN: *Walker (Herb. Wight) 164* (K), *162* (K).

N o t e. The Deltota and Ooma Oya collections have somewhat larger leaves with more distinct nervation and are in this respect intermediate with *E. amoena* of the wet zone.

5. Eugenia cotinifolia Jacq., Obs. Bot. 3: 2. 1764; Alston in Trimen, Handb. Fl. Ceylon 6: 119. 1931.

Eugenia lucida (non Banks) Lam., Enc. 3: 205. 1791; Duthie in Hook. f., Fl. Br. Ind. 2: 501. 1879; Trimen, Handb. Fl. Ceylon 2: 180. 1894.
Eugenia elliptica Lam., l.c.
Jossinia cotinifolia DC., Prod. 3: 238. 1928.

ssp. **codyensis** (Munro ex Wight) Ashton, comb. nov.
Eugenia codyensis Munro ex Wight, Ill. 2: 13. 1850.
Eugenia hypoleuca Thw., in Beddome., For. Man. 112. 1874; Trimen, Cat. 33. nomen nudum.

'A much branched bush with rough silvery-grey bark' (Trimen). Inno-vations densely greyish caducous pubescent. Twigs terete, much branched, pale grey dappled, rapidly becoming stout. Lamina 3–6 × 2–5 cm, broadly elliptic to suborbicular, thickly coriaceous, concave, drying chocolate-brown beneath; margin prominently revolute; base broadly cuneate; apex retuse, obtuse, or subacute; nerves c. 8 pairs, very slender, ascending, hardly elevat-ed on either surface; intramarginal nerve c. 1 mm within margin, ± obscure; tertiary nerves obscure; midrib stoutly prominent beneath; petiole 5–10 mm long, stout. Flowers white to pale yellow, very large, solitary, axillary; pedi-cels –3.5 cm long, very slender; calyx –8 mm diam., –7 mm long, shallowly cup-shaped, puberulent, with 4, –7 mm long and broad, prominent seg-ments forming a –20 mm diam. ring; petals –15 × 10 mm, elliptic-spatulate, obtuse, very large; stamens c. 10 mm long. Fruit –2.5 cm diam., globose, ripening green flushed with crimson, with prominent c. 12 mm terminal rim bearing the persisting calyx segments.

D i s t r. Mauritius and Reunion (type subspecies), Ceylon, western Ghats. Locally common on rocky places on the exposed summits of the Knuckles Massif above 1500 m.

S p e c i m e n s E x a m i n e d. KANDY DISTRICT: Knuckles, *Ferguson s.n.* March 1887 (PDA); Rangalla hill, *Ferguson s.n.* Sept. 1888 (PDA); Kobonilla hill, Rangalla, *Ferguson s.n.* Sept. 1888 (PDA); Wattekelle, *s. coll. C.P. 3865* (PDA, K); Royal Botanic Gardens, *s. coll. s.n.* April 1887 (PDA), *s. coll. s.n.* May 1893 (PDA), *s. coll. s.n.* August 1894 (PDA).

N o t e. A beautiful shrub that should be introduced to gardens. The Mauritius and Reunion subspecies (the type) differs notably in that the flowers are subsessile, which is the main difference also between *E. codyensis* and the Sri Lanka species. I have no hesitation in uniting them therefore but retain the Indian and Sri Lanka populations as a separate subspecies.

ssp. **phyllyraeoides** stat. nov.

Eugenia phyllyraeoides Trimen, J. Bot. 23: 207. 1885; Handb. Fl. Ceylon 2: 183. 1894; Alston in id. 6: 119. 1931.

A shrub, differing as follows: Twigs very slender, ascending, ± persistently pubescent; lamina 11–30 × 4–7 mm broad, narrowly oblanceolate, subacuminate; petiole 2–4 mm long. (Flowers unknown). Fruit (young): pedicel not exceeding 1.5 cm long; fruit not exceeding 15 mm diam.

D i s t r. Endemic, known from a single collection.

S p e c i m e n E x a m i n e d. MATALE DISTRICT: Summit of Kalupahane Kande, Lagalla, *s. coll. s.n.* May 1884 (PDA, K).

N o t e. A form typical of particularly exposed (dry?) summits and recurring in other taxa. This subspecies most closely resembles the allied vicariant of the Western Ghats, *Eugenia rottleriana* W. & A.

A further very interesting collection, *Davidse & Sumithraarachchi 8639*, from a flat rocky outcrop with open vegetation at 1740 m on the Adam's Peak trail from the Moray Group Estates, is in some respects intermediate between the two Sri Lanka subspecies. The leaves are obovate, obtuse to subacuminate, but otherwise as in ssp. *codyensis*. The specimen is in flower; the petals are at most 5 mm wide, the pedicel –10 mm long.

6. Eugenia mabaeoides Wight, Ill. 2: 13. 1850; Trimen, Handb. Fl. Ceylon 2: 186. 1894.

ssp. **mabaeoides**

A shrub or small tree. Young shoots and calyx fugaceous pubescent. Twigs slender, terete, much branched. Lamina 12–40 × 6–25 mm, spatulate (if small) to elliptic (if large), coriaceous, drying dull rust to purplish brown and usually distinctly punctate beneath; margin subrevolute; base ± narrowly cuneate; apex obtuse to broadly subacuminate; nerves c. 7 pairs, ascending, slender, obscure or ± equally elevated on both surfaces; intramarginal nerve –2 mm within margin, usually clearly evident; tertiary nerves obscurely reticulate; midrib prominent towards base beneath, tapering; petiole 3–6 mm long. Flowers pale green (Trimen), 1–3-axillary; pedicels –8 mm long, very slender; calyx –2 mm long, –3 mm diam. including the 4 deltoid acute segments, shallowly cup-shaped; petals –3 × 2 mm, elliptic, concave; stamens c. 3 mm long. Fruit –12 mm long, –10 mm. diam., ellipsoid, crimson, succulent, with a c. 3 mm diam. apical ring of prominent persisting calyx segments.

D i s t r. Endemic; common in the mountains of the main massif between 1300 and 2500 m.

S p e c i m e n s E x a m i n e d. NUWARA ELIYA DISTRICT: Ohiya road, Horton Plains, *Fosberg 50115* (PDA, US, K); Hakgala, *A.M.S. s.n.* 4.10.06 (PDA); Maturata, Nuwara Eliya, Wattegodde, *s. coll. C.P. 1588* (PDA, K). KANDY DISTRICT: Palagala, Adam's Peak, *s. coll. C.P. 445* (PDA); Moray estate trail to Adam's Peak, *Davidse & Sumithraarachchi 8641* (PDA, US), *Ashton 2340* (PDA, US). Above Warriagala, Hantane, *s. coll. s.n.* Dec. 1889 (PDA). BADULLA DISTRICT: Top of Naminakuli, *J.M. Silva s.n.* 12.3.07 (PDA). LOCALITY UNKNOWN: *Scott 2362* (K), *Mackenzie s.n.* (K), *Wight s.n.* (K), *Walker, 1658* (K), *Gardner 303* (K), *s. coll. C.P. 452* (K), *s. coll. C.P. 2693* (K).

spp. **pedunculata** stat. nov.

Eugenia pedunculata Trimen, J. Bot. 27: 162. 1889; Handb. Fl. Ceylon 2: 187. 1894.
Eugenia aprica Trimen, Handb. Fl. Ceylon 2: 186. 1894.

Differing significantly only in the 2.5–5 × 1.7–4.5 cm broadly elliptic lamina.

D i s t r. Endemic to the summits of the Kunckles Massif.

S p e c i m e n s E x a m i n e d. KANDY DISTRICT: Summit of Rangala ridge, *s. coll. s.n.* 24.9.1888 (PDA), *s. coll. s.n.* Sept. 1888 (PDA, K); Rangala, *s. coll. s.n.* April 1886 (PDA); Knuckles, *s. coll. s.n.* April 1887 (PDA); Madukelle, Knuckles, *Worthington 1963* (K).

N o t e. The smallest leaved forms are mainly found at the highest elevations. Though the largest leaved specimens from the Knuckles Massif exceed these from elsewhere the smaller leaved specimens are identical throughout the range of the species; neither can the differences in leaf and fruit shape quoted by Trimen be substantiated.

7. Eugenia thwaitesii Duthie in Hook. f., Fl. Br. Ind. 2: 506. 1879; Trimen, Handb. Fl. Ceylon 2: 188. 1894; Alston in Trimen, Handb. Fl. Ceylon 6: 120. 1931.

Eugenia mooniana (non Gardn.) Wight, Ill. 2: 13. 1850; Thw., Enum. Fl. Zeyl. 114. 1859; Duthie in Hook. f., Fl. Br. Ind. 2: 505. 1879; Trimen, Handb. Fl. Ceylon 2: 187. 1894.

Eugenia concinna (non Phil.) Thw., Enum. Pl. Zeyl. 416. 1864; Duthie in Hook. f., Fl. Br. Ind. 2: 506. 1879.

A shrub or small tree. Twigs slender, much branched, becoming conspicuous cream. Buds caducous puberulent, parts otherwise glabrous. Lamina 1.8–14 × 0.5–6 cm, ovate-lanceolate to narrowly or broadly elliptic, very variable in size and shape, chartaceous or occasionally thinly coriaceous, drying pale grey-brown beneath; margin undulate, ± narrowly subrevolute; base narrowly or broadly cuneate; apex shortly or –2.5 cm long attenuate acuminate; main nerves c. 8–10 pairs, diverging or ascending, very slender but distinctly elevated beneath, evident above, with shorter less distinct intermediate and reticulate tertiary nerves; intramarginal nerve distinct, c. 1–2 mm within margin; midrib slender but prominent beneath, usually drying black; petiole 3–7 mm long, short, drying black. Flowers small, white, in lax terminal or axillary clusters, on –2.5 cm long very slender pedicels; calyx –2 × 2 mm, cup-shaped, with 4 oblong lobes forming an –5 mm diam. rotate circle; petals –5 × –3 mm, elliptic; stamens c. 5 mm long. Fruit –15 mm diam., depressed-globose to ovoid, pendulous, crimson, with a c. 2 mm diam. ± prominent apical ring of persistent sepals.

D i s t r. Western Ghats, Ceylon. Common throughout the wet zone hills below 1300 m, local in the intermediate zone in evergreen forest; on skeletal soils and rocky places, often in open conditions and spreading into patanas.

S p e c i m e n s E x a m i n e d. KANDY DISTRICT: Moray estate, Maskeliya, *Balakrishnan & Dassanayake 931* (PDA, US), *Ashton 2240* (PDA, US); Ambagamuwa, *s. coll. C.P. 2802* (PDA, K); Galle, *C.P. 3545* (PDA); Madamahanuwara, *s. coll. C.P. 365* (PDA, K); Hunnasgiriya, Ella Plains, Deltota, *s. coll. C.P. 11* (PDA, K); Hantane, *J.M.S. s.n.* 24.5.24 (PDA), *s. coll. C.P. 733* (K), *Gardner 304* (K); Nilambe, *Kostermans 2327* (PDA, US, K); Madugoda, *Maxwell & Jayasuriya 736* (PDA, US); Hunnasgiriya-Weragantota road, *Maxwell & Jayasuriya 727* (PDA, US); Kabonilla hill, Rangala, *s. coll. s.n.* Sept. 1888 (PDA); Royal Botanic Gardens, *s. coll. s.n.* (PDA). KURUNEGALA DISTRICT; Arankelle, Dunkande, *Ashton 2330* (PDA, US). MATALE DISTRICT: Dambulla rest house, *Kostermans 23554* (PDA, US, K); 4 miles East of Pallegama, *Davidse 7381* (PDA, US). NUWARA ELIYA DISTRICT: Hakgala nature reserve, *Ashton 2287* (PDA, US). LOCALITY UNKNOWN: *Walker s.n.* (K), *Ferguson s.n.* 'Colombo' (K).

N o t e. One of several montane species in Sri Lanka (see e.g. *Eugenia cotinifolia, E. mabaeoides*) exhibiting great variation in leaf size, the small-leafed forms being restricted to the higher altitudinal ranges; no discontinuity in the size range can be detected. Trimen wrongly associated this species with *E. phyllyraeoides*, considered by me as a subspecies of *E. cotinifolia* and differing from the present species both in the tomentum, lamina nervation and fruit. On the other hand I cannot distinguish any discontinuity in the range of leaf dimensions to maintain *E. thwaitesii* as a separate species from *E. mooniana* Wight, *C.P. 3802* (the type of the former) bearing leaves quite identical to some, for instance, on *C.P. 365* (type of the latter), and there being no other way to distinguish them. As Wight's name is antedated by that of Gardner which refers to a Brazilian plant, *E. thwaitesii* becomes the correct name for this widespread species.

8. Eugenia bracteata Roxb., Hort. Beng. 37. 1813, nomen nudum; Fl. Ind. 2: 490. 1832, desc.; Trimen, Handb. Fl. Ceylon 2: 182. 1894.

Eugenia ceylanica (non Willd.) Roxb., Fl. Ind. 2: 490. 1832; Moon, Cat. 38. 1824; Arn., Nova Acta Phys. Med. Acad. Caes. Leop. Carol. Nat. Cur. 18: 336. 1836.

Eugenia willdenowii (non DC.) Wight, Ic. Pl. Ind. Or. 545. 1843; Ill. 13. 1850; Thw., Enum. Pl. Zeyl. 114. 1859.

Eugenia roxburghii DC., Prod. 3: 238. 1828; Duthie in Hook. f., Fl. Br. Ind. 2: 502. 1879.

A much-branched shrub or small tree; bark smooth, pale grey-brown; crown irregular, dense, with ascending branches. Innovations fulvous pubescent, persistent on twigs, petioles, peduncles, calyx, outside of petals, bracts and staminal disc, subpersistent on midrib beneath. Twigs slender, terete, much branched. Lamina (2–) 4–8 × (0.9–) 1.5–3 cm, elliptic, smelling of cloves when bruised, drying rufous-brown (darker above), with narrowly subrevolute margin, cuneate base and obtuse, bluntly subacuminate or shallowly retuse apex; nerves c. 10 pairs, very slender, wavy, with about one short intermediate between each and with laxly reticulate obscure tertiary nerves, hardly elevated and ± obscure beneath, obscure above; intramarginal nerve c. 1 mm within margin; midrib slender but prominent beneath; petiole 6–9 mm long, short, slender. Flowers c. 12 mm diam. at anthesis, cream, showy, terminal or to 3-axillary, or –4 on a reduced cyme; borne on –14 mm long slender peduncles, subtended by small linear bracts; calyx –3 mm long, –2 mm diam., urceolate, segments 4 (–5), –3 mm diam., suborbicular, revolute, reflexed; petals c. 6 × 4 mm, elliptic; stamens –7 mm long, many, disc small, polygonate. Fruit –13 × 10 mm, pyriform to subglobose, green ripening through yellow to orange-red, with a c. 3 mm diam. apical ring of persistent sepals.

D i s t r. Peninsular India, Ceylon. Common, often abundant, in secondary vegetation, including fire-climax savanna, in the dry zone especially near the coast; locally frequent in the intermediate zone and occasionally in the coastal lowlands of the wet zone.

Specimens Examined. JAFFNA DISTRICT: Jaffna, *s. coll. C.P. 1586* (PDA, K), *C.P. 1590* (PDA, K), *Dyke s.n.* (K); RATNAPURA DISTRICT: Embilipitiya, *Balakrishnan & Jayasuriya 884* (PDA, US). BADULLA DISTRICT: Dunhinda falls, *Balakrishnan & Jayasuriya 858* (PDA, US, K). MATALE DISTRICT: Leloya, *Jayasuriya 328* (PDA, US); Erawalagala Kande, *Davidse & Sumithraarachchi 8105* (PDA, US); Nalanda 36¾ m., *Worthington 6697* (K). POLONNARUWA DISTRICT: Jamburawela, *Jayasuriya 325* (PDA, US); Polonnaruwa, *Hladik 1062* (PDA, US). ANURADHAPURA DISTRICT: Wilpattu N.P., *Wirawan, Cooray & Balakrishnan 1088* (PDA, US, K), *Wirawan, Balakrishnan, Cooray & Mueller-Dombois 69042811* (PDA, US, K). TRINCOMALEE DISTRICT: Palwakke, *Worthington 733* (K). KANDY DISTRICT: Madugoda, *Worthington 1571* (K); 9 miles west of Mahayangana, *Davidse 8435* (PDA, US). NUWARA ELIYA DISTRICT: Maturata road, *Ashton 2309* (PDA, US), *2310* (PDA, US). MONERAGALA DISTRICT: Udawalawe area, *Balakrishnan & Jayasuriya 892* (PDA, US, K). DISTRICT UNKNOWN: Eastern Province. *s. coll. s.n.* August 1885 (PDA). *s. coll. s.n.* Sept. 1888 (PDA).

9. Eugenia terpnophylla Thw., Enum. Pl. Zeyl. 114. 1859; Duthie in Hook. f., Fl. Br. Ind. 2: 503. 1879; Beddome, Ic. t. 283. 1874; Trimen, Handb. Fl. Ceylon 2: 181. 1894; Alston in Trimen, Handb. Fl. Ceylon 6: 119. 1931.

A moderate sized tree (Trimen). Innovations fulvous pubescent, caducous except on peduncles, calyx and disc. Twigs slender, pale brown, terete. Lamina 6–11 × 1.5–4.8 cm, elliptic-lanceolate, thinly chartaceous, drying pale brown; margin hardly or not revolute; base cuneate; acumen –2 cm long, prominent, slender; main nerves 8–9 pairs with few or no intermediates, slender but distinctly raised beneath, ± obscure above; intramarginal nerve obscurely 2-tiered, the inner (3–) 5–9 mm within the margin, prominently looped, as prominent as nerves beneath; tertiary nerves obscurely laxly reticulate; midrib very slender but prominent beneath; petiole 5–10 mm long, slender, drying black. Flowers greenish white (Trimen), on short bracteate peduncles in dense axillary clusters; bracts small, linear; pedicel –5 mm long, slender; calyx –3 mm long, –2 mm broad, small, campanulate, with 4 acute deltoid segments; petals c. 4 × 2 mm, narrowly elliptic-oblong, obtuse; stamens –6 mm long. Fruit (? young) c. 7 mm diam. ('rather over ¾ inches' in Trimen), globose, crowned with a c. 2 mm diam. ring bearing the persisting lorate reflexed calyx segments.

Distr. A rare endemic which, besides the type locality, is recorded from Ratnapura and Reigam Korale by Thwaites, and from Kitulgala by Alston, all in the wet lowlands; I have not seen confirmatory specimens.

Specimen Examined. KANDY DISTRICT: Ambagamuwa, *s. coll. C.P. 2623* (PDA, K).

N o t e. Apparently related to *Eugenia fulva*, but differing distinctly in the smaller chartaceous lamina, more slender twigs and fewer nerves.

10. Eugenia rufo-fulva Thw., Enum. Pl. Zeyl. 416. 1864; Duthie in Hook. f., Fl. Br. Ind. 2: 503. 1879; Trimen, Handb. Fl. Ceylon 2: 183. 1894.

Eugenia xanthocarpa Thw., l.c.; Duthie l.c. Trimen, id.: 182; Alston in Trimen, Handb. Fl. Ceylon 6: 119. 1931.

Medium-sized tree with pale patchily flaked bark. Innovations caducously, petiole and leaf undersurface (mature trees only), peduncle, outside of petals, calyx and disc persistently shortly evenly densely chocolate fulvous velutinate; lamina above ± subpersistently sparsely puberulent. Twigs slender, terete, becoming conspicuously pale cream. Lamina (4–) 5–12 × (1–) 1.5–3.5 cm, elliptic-lanceolate; lower surface ± concave; base attenuate-cuneate; apex with –3 cm long caudate acumen; nerves c. 10 pairs, very slender but slightly elevated beneath, ± obscure above, with short intermediates; intramarginal nerves not prominently looped, 1–2 mm within margin; midrib slender, elevated beneath, narrowly depressed above; petiole 7–12 mm long, slender, deeply channelled above. Flowers white, –2-axillary or terminal, on –3 mm long very slender peduncles, subtended by –10 mm long linear bracts; flower bud –4 × 3 mm, flower –8 mm diam. at anthesis; calyx urceolate at anthesis, segments 4–5, –3 mm, long, linear; petals –6 × 3 mm, elliptic, exceeding sepals; stamens –6 mm long; disc prominent, polygonal. Fruit –4 mm diam., subglobose, with 2–4 seeds, with calyx segments ± persisting in a c. 4 mm diam. ring.

D i s t r. A rare endemic known only from the cited collections.

Specimens Examined. COLOMBO & KEGALLE DISTRICTS: Bentota & Manamalwatte, *s. coll., C.P. 3834* (PDA, K); Nellowekande, Gattehatte (near Avissawella) & Reigam Korale, *s. coll., C.P. 3835* (PDA, K). KANDY DISTRICT: Peradeniya Botanic Gardens, *Ashton 2355* (PDA, US). LOCALITY UNKNOWN: *Walker 431* (K).

N o t e. Apparently a derivative of the widespread *Eugenia bracteata*. The specimens under *C.P. 3834* (type of *E. xanthocarpa*) lack the characteristic dense fulvous tomentum on the leaves and thus bear the same relation to this species as do those of the type of *E. floccifera* to *E. fulva*. The leaves of one of the collections under *C.P. 3835* are identical to those of one under *C.P. 3008*, *E. fulva*. The main difference between *E. rufo-fulva* and *E. fulva*, length and diameter of the peduncle, requires confirmation with further collections.

11. Eugenia rivulorum Thw., Enum. Pl. Zeyl. 115. 1859; Duthie in Hook. f., Fl. Br. Ind. 2: 504. 1879; Trimen, Handb. Fl. Ceylon 2: 184. 1894; Alston in

Trimen, Handb. Fl. Ceylon 6: 120. 1931.

Small understorey tree with distinctive pale cream smooth bark. Innovations densely rufous sericeous, subpersistent on petiole, calyx and disc. Twig stout, terete. Lamina 20–35 × 5–12 cm, lanceolate, chartaceous, drying matt pale chocolate-brown beneath; base obtuse or broadly cuneate, subequal, margin narrowly subrevolute; acumen –3 cm long, slender, attenuate; main nerves 12–15 pairs, distant, slender but prominent beneath; ± evident, elevated or shallowly obscurely depressed above as also the intramarginal nerves; intramarginal nerves looped, at c. 5–8 mm within margin; intermediates 1 (–3) between each nerve, more slender but also reaching intramarginal nerves; tertiary nerves remotely reticulate; petiole 5–10 mm long, short, stout, conspicuously rugulose white. Flowers subsessile, terminal to cauliflorous even to ground level; calyx c. 5 mm long, 7 mm diam., campanulate, with 4 prominent ovate obtuse segments; petals c. 8 mm long, c. 5 mm broad, elliptic, obtuse, pinkish violet; stamens c. 7 mm long, white. Fruit c. 1 cm diam., large, irregularly subglobose; pericarp thick, fleshy, dark brown, wrinkled (Trimen).

D i s t r. A rare endemic of lowland forests in the valleys of the western Sinharaja.

S p e c i m e n s E x a m i n e d. KALUTARA DISTRICT: Uguduwagoda, Hewesse, *Trimen s.n.* (PDA); Pelawatte Mukulana, *s. coll. s.n.* March 1887 (PDA). RATNAPURA DISTRICT: Sinharaja forest, *s. coll. C.P. 3440* (PDA, K).

N o t e. Of these collections the first two differ from the last in having relatively narrower lamina, more slender and less distinct main nerves with 3–5 intermediates, and a straight intramarginal nerve c. 1 mm from the margin. This variable species is allied to *Eugenia fulva* but the petiole easily distinguishes it.

12. Eugenia fulva Thw., Enum. Pl. Zeyl. 115. 1859; Duthie in Hook. f., Fl. Br. Ind. 2: 504. 1879; Trimen, Handb. Fl. Ceylon 2: 184. 1894.

Eugenia floccifera Thw., Enum. Pl. Zeyl. 115. 1859; Duthie in Hook. f., Fl. Br. Ind. 2: 504. 1879; Trimen, Handb. Fl. Ceylon 2: 183. 1894; Alston in Trimen, Handb. Fl. Ceylon 6: 120. 1931.

Eugenia insignis Thw., Enum. Pl. Zeyl. 416. 1864; Duthie in Hook. f., Fl. Br. Ind. 2: 185. 1879; Trimen, Handb. Fl. Ceylon 2: 185. 1894.

Eugenia haeckeliana Trimen, J. Bot. 23: 207. 1885; Handb. Fl. Ceylon 2: 181. 1894.

Shrub or small tree; bark becoming cracked and peeling. Twigs, flowers, fruit, peduncle, petiole and lamina beneath densely golden brown velutinate, longer, sparser and confined to innovations in young plants. Twigs stout, terete. Lamina (8–) 11–16 × (3–) 4.5–8.5 cm, elliptic-oblong to elliptic-lanceolate, coriaceous, with ± distinctly revolute margin, cordate, obtuse or cuneate base and acute –2 cm caudate (young trees) apex; inner nerves c. 8–10 pairs, distinctly elevated beneath, broadly elevated above and with a ± distinct median furrow at least towards the base; intramarginal nerve prominently looped, at 1–4 mm from margin; tertiary nerves laxly reticulate; midrib stout, prominent beneath; petiole 5–12 mm long, stout. Flowers pink, subtended by –15 mm long, –5 mm broad, prominent lanceolate bracts; peduncle 10 mm long, long or short; calyx c. 5 mm diam., urceolate, with a –12 mm diam. rotate ring of ovate segments; petals –8 mm long, suborbicular, exceeding calyx segments; stamens c. 10 mm long; staminal disc prominent, persistently pubescent, pentagonal. Fruit (young) 1 cm diam., globose.

Distr. Endemic and apparently rare in forest on the low hills of the southern and western wet zone to the coastline.

Specimens Examined. COLOMBO DISTRICT: Reigam Korale, *s. coll. C.P. 463* (PDA, K); Walpattu, Reigam Korale, *s. coll. C.P. 3677* (PDA, K). MATARA DISTRICT: Weligama, *Trimen s.n.* 25.12.1892 (PDA, K); Morawak Korale & Hellepelle *s. coll. C.P. 3008* p.p. (PDA, K).

Note. No recent collections have appeared which can be ascribed to the four names united here; the size of the flowers and young fruit, and the distinctive indumentum, prevent me on the evidence available from maintaining them as separate species. *C.P. 3677* (type of *E. insignis*) differs from Hellepelle specimens under *C.P. 3008* only in the sparser tomentum on the lamina undersurface and the ocherous rather than rufous young parts. The longer tomentum of *C.P. 463* (type of *E. floccifera*), also sparse on the lamina undersurface, would suggest that both these numbers were gathered from young trees. The long peduncles by which *E. haeckeliana* (type: *Trimen s.n.*) are distinguished are only found on one of the two flowering shoots present at Peradeniya herbarium while the broad caudate lamina is exactly matched by one of the several specimens numbered *C.P. 3008* (type of *E. fulva*). Three of the latter come close to *E. rufo-fulva* in lamina nervation, and more collections could well indicate that there is in fact no discontinuity in flower dimensions between these two species.

4. SYZYGIUM

R. Browne ex Gaertn., Fruct. 1: 166, t. 33. 1788; Alston in Trimen, Handb. Fl. Ceylon 6: 111. 1931; Merr., J. Arn. Arb. 19: 99. 1938; Merr. & Perry, Mem. Amer. Acad. Arts 18: 135–202. 1939; Schmid, Amer. J. Bot. 59, 4: 423–436. 1972.

Jambosa Comm. ex DC., Prod. 3: 286.1829.
Cleistocalyx Blume, Ann. Mus. Bot. Lugduno-Batavum 1: 84. 1849; Merr. & Perry, J. Arn. Arb. 18: 322–343. 1937.

Glabrous trees. Leaves opposite, with prominent intramarginal nerve. Flowers small or large, in terminal or axillary peniculate cymes, flowering in centrifugal sequence; bracteoles fugaceous. Flower calyx frequently prominently extended into a pseudopedicel at the base; calyx lobes and petals each 4–5; calyx lobes small or large, deciduous or persistent, obscure or distinct; corolla small; ovary 2–3-locular, loculi distal, each with many ovules. Embryo subglobose, cotyledons usually distinct, concealing the hypocotyl; seed-coat rough.

About 1000 species, African and Asian tropics.

Syzygium with *Eugenia* (which is the older name) forms parts of a vast array of more or less closely allied species found throughout the tropics. Within this array more or less distinct constellations can be recognised, a common phenomenon in large genera and one which leads to differing interpretations and hence much nomenclatural confusion. Through the latter part of the nineteenth century a broad generic definition dominated in Asiatic floras, with all species being considered as part of *Eugenia* whose type, *E. uniflora*, is Brazilian. Niedenzu (in Pflanzenfam, 3, 7: 81. 1893) reinstated *Syzygium* and also *Jambosa* but regarded the genus *Jossinia* Comm. ex DC., which contained Asian species more closely similar to *Eugenia* in the strict sense, as a synonym of the latter. Schmid, to whose paper readers should refer for the most recent review of the problem, has confirmed the validity of this general view by anatomical study, though reuniting *Jambosa* with *Syzygium*, and I follow his interpretation. Merrill, however, did not and recognised not only *Jossinia*, but several small segregates among S.E. Asian *Syzygium* as separate genera as well. All decisions at the generic level must essentially be arbitrary, and I follow Schmid's most recent interpretation not only as it is the most recent and informed, but because it conforms with the last revision of Sri Lanka species, by Alston—who nevertheless mistook the cultivated *Syzygium malaccense* for a *Eugenia*. My definition of *Eugenia* and *Syzygium* therefore draws on those gross morphological characters found most useful by Schmid.

KEY TO THE SPECIES

1 Calyx tube with a thickened staminal disc at the mouth; petals large, not at first caducous; fruit large; large trees with ± distinctly nerved large leaves and showy flowers
  2 Leaves subsessile, base cordate or obtuse
    3 Lamina thickly coriaceous, obtuse; flowers bright pink, calyx tube bugle-shaped; indigenous tree . . . . .1. S. aqueum
    3 Lamina chartaceous, typically acuminate; flowers white, calyx tube cup-shaped; cultivated exotic . . . . .2. S. samarangense
  2 Leaves prominently petiolate, lamina base cuneate
    4 Lamina thickly coriaceous and prominently revolute, elliptic or obovate, obtuse in mature tree

5 Lamina 3.5–6 × 1.2–2.5 cm; nerves c. 5 pairs......................**3. S. turbinatum**
5 Lamina 10–17 × 5.5–11 cm; nerves many...........................**4. S. firmum**
4 Lamina not thickly coriaceous or prominently revolute, elliptic or ovate, prominently acuminate
  6 Lamina lanceolate or narrowly elliptic, with at least 14 pairs of nerves; cultivated exotics
    7 Lamina with single-tiered intramarginal nerve; flowers white; cyme terminal.......
    ....**5. S. jambos**
    7 Lamina with 2-tiered intramarginal nerve; flowers pink; cyme axillary............
    ....**6. S. malaccensis**
  6 Lamina elliptic
    8 Lamina nerves 6–8 pairs, evident but frequently channelled above; flowers tinged pink, with prominent bugle-shaped calyx tube; inland rivers......**7. S. cylindricum**
    8 Lamina nerves c. 12 pairs, distinctly elevated above; flowers white with cup-shaped calyx tube; hill country.....................................**8. S. hemisphericum**
1 Calyx tube not as above; petals small, usually calyptrate and falling immediately at anthesis; leaves small, or large but generally without prominent nervation
  9 Calyx tube long, bugle-shaped; lamina drying grey-green with the midrib paler than the blade beneath
    10 Young twigs quadrangular; petioles at most 4 mm long, short
      11 Fruit –8 mm diam., subglobose, ripening distinct white; lamina lanceolate or linear, with cuneate base; dry and intermediate zones..................**9. S. zeylanicum**
      11 Fruit –18 mm long, –10 mm diam., urceolate; lamina broadly elliptic-ovate, with cordate or obtuse base; wet zone mountains....................**10. S. fergusoni**
    10 Young twigs terete; petioles at least 5 mm long
      12 Lamina thinly chartaceous, ovate-lanceolate to elliptic; cymes –1.5 cm long, mainly axillary; indigenous trees....................................**11. S. lanceolatum**
      12 Lamina coriaceous, oblanceolate to elliptic; cymes –4 cm long, mainly terminal or subterminal axillary; cultivated trees
        13 Lamina 7–12 × 3–5 cm, oblanceolate; petioles 1–2 cm long; calyx tube –15 mm long, 6 mm diam...**12. S. aromaticum**
        13 Lamina 4–10 × 1.8–4 cm, ± elliptic; petiole –8 mm long, calyx tube –5 mm long, 3 mm diam...**13. S. sp.**
  9 Calyx tube short, cup or funnel-shaped; midrib typically drying darker than lamina beneath
    14 Twigs at first sharply quadrangular, small leaved trees of hills and mountain forests
      15 Lamina small, elliptic to suborbicular, base obtuse or cordate; cymes terminal
        16 Lamina base obtuse or broadly cuneate, petiole short but slender, distinct.......
        ....**14. S. rotundifolium**
        16 Lamina subsessile, base cordate..........................**15. S. sclerophyllum**
      15 Lamina oblanceolate, elliptic or lanceolate, base cuneate
        17 Leaf at most 25 mm long, small, broadly obovate; cymes mostly axillary........
        ....**16. S. oliganthum**
        17 Leaf 2–7 cm long, oblanceolate to lanceolate; cymes terminal or subterminal axillary
          18 Leaf drying purplish brown, prominently acuminate, margin hardly or not revolute, nerves densely parallel.............................**17. S. rubicundum**
          18 Leaf drying olive or chocolate-brown, shortly bluntly acuminate or obtuse, main nerves relatively few, not as above
            19 Flowers –2 mm long and diam., very small, pinkish; fruit –7 mm diam........
            ....**18. S. spathulatum**

19 Flowers −4 mm long and diam., white; fruit −20 mm diam..........**19. S. umbrosum**
14 Twigs terete; leaves medium sized or large
20 Lamina oblong-elliptic or ovate-lanceolate, drying dark chocolate-brown, base cordate
21 Lamina large, at least 7 cm wide, with prominently revolute margin; fruit −2 cm
   diam..**20. S. cordifolium**
21 Lamina at most 5 cm wide, margin hardly revolute or applanate; fruit −1 cm
   diam..**21. S. neesianum**
20 Lamina base cuneate or, if cordate, than leaf suborbicular
22 Twigs conspicuous cream
23 Lamina drying chocolate-brown beneath, purplish above, with many slender nerves
24 Lamina 6.5–11 × 2.5–5 cm, elliptic, margin applanate; petiole slender; cymes
   mainly ramiflorous; dry zone.................................**22. S. cumini**
24 Lamina 9–17 × 4.5–7 cm, narrowly obovate to elliptic, margin ± revolute; petiole
   stout; cymes terminal or subterminal axillary; wet zone............**23. S. makul**
23 Lamina chartaceous, drying pale grey-green
25 Lamina elliptic-obovate, with 7–15 pairs of distant nerves narrowly depressed
   above; cymes mainly ramiflorous.........................**24. S. operculatum**
25 Lamina ovate-lanceolate, with many very slender densely parallel nerves slightly
   elevated on both surfaces; cymes terminal or subterminal axillary..**25. S. gardneri**
22 Twigs grey or brown
26 Lamina lanceolate, with −2 cm long prominent subcaudate acumen
27 Leaves and twigs pendent; nerves including tertiaries elevated above; flowers
   very small, calyx −2 mm long, −1 mm diam., in slender terminal or axillary to
   ramiflorous cymes...**26. S. micranthum**
27 Leaves and twigs ascending; nerves narrowly depressed above, tertiaries obscure;
   flower calyx −4 mm long, −2 mm diam.; cymes stout, terminal or subterminal
   axillary..**27. S. lewisii**
26 Lamina elliptic or obovate-oblanceolate; acumen if prominent broad, tapering
28 Lamina at most 1.7 times as long as broad, broadly obovate or suborbicular,
   thickly coriaceous, obtuse or subacute; tertiary nerves distinctly and ± equally
   elevated on both surfaces..................................**28. S. revolutum**
28 Lamina at least twice as long as broad, obovate-elliptic; tertiary nerves more
   prominent beneath than above
29 Lamina obtuse or (in young trees) bluntly subacuminate, dull beneath with the
   tertiaries forming a distinctly elevated reticulum.........**29. S. caryophyllatum**
29 Lamina shortly but prominently downcurved acuminate, lustrous beneath;
   tertiaries very slender, ± obscure..........................**30. S. assimile**

1. Syzygium aqueum (Burm. f.) Alston, Ann. R. Bot. Gard. Perad. 11: 204.
1929; in Trimen, Fl. Ceylon 6: 115. 1931.

Eugenia aquea Burm. f., Fl. Ind. 114. 1768; Hermann, Mus. Zeyl. 67. 1717;
  Burm., Thes. 125. 1747; Wight, Ic. Pl. Ind. Or. t. 216, 550. 1843; Duthie in
  Hook. f., Fl. Br. Ind. 2: 473. 1879.
Eugenia sylvestris (non Wight) Moon, Cat. 38. 1824.
Eugenia grandis Wight, Ill. 2: 17. 1850 p.p. excl. syn.
Jambosa aquea DC., Prod. 3: 288. 1828; Thw., Enum. Pl. Zeyl. 115. 1859.
Syzygium montanum Thw., Enum. Pl. Zeyl. 116. 1859 excl. syn.

A medium-sized tree, −20 m tall, −4 m girth, with short crooked ribbed trunk, tawny-brown flaky bark and dense dark irregularly oblong crown. Parts entirely glabrous. Twigs stout, much branched, pale rust-brown, at first bluntly quadrangular, quickly becoming ± terete. Young leaves brilliant crimson; lamina 4.5–23 × 1.5–11 cm, elliptic-oblong, coriaceous, drying dark-red-brown beneath; base ± broadly cuneate to narrowly subcordate; apex obtuse, subretuse or shortly broadly acuminate; main nerves c. 9 pairs, ± prominent beneath, distinctly elevated and ± channelled above, with shorter intermediates, frequently with more than one pair arising from near the lamina base; intramarginal nerve irregularly 2-tiered, the inner tier at 3–8 mm within the margin; tertiaries densely reticulate, distinctly elevated on both surfaces though more prominently so beneath; midrib stout, prominent beneath, elevated though channelled above; petiole 1–5 mm long, stout, drying black. Flowers –10, in short terminal or subterminal axillary cymes, subsessile or shortly pedicellate. Calyx tube 1.5–3 cm long, funnel-shaped; segments –6 mm long and broad, ovate, obtuse, becoming rotate, forming a – 1.5 cm diam. ring at anthesis; petals –12 × 8 mm, oblong, obtuse, concave, pale pinkish white; stamens –1.5 cm long, folded in bud, filaments brilliant pink, anthers white. Fruit –2 cm diam., globose, red, crowned with a prominently necked to 8 mm diam. persistent calyx ring.

D i s t r. Ceylon and from Bangladesh and Burma through western Malaysia. Common in S.W. Sri Lanka and often left after felling of forest in the tea estates, at all altitudes below 1500 m. Growing in *Shorea gardneri* mid-mountain forests in the wet zone, and evergreen sclerophyll forests in the intermediate zone; scattered in wet zone lowland forests. Occurring in the Kottawa arboretum.

S p e c i m e n s   E x a m i n e d. GALLE DISTRICT: Kottawa Arboretum, *Ashton 2271* (PDA, US). NUWARA ELIYA DISTRICT: Rikiligas Kande, *Worthington 5602* (K); Maturata road, *Ashton 2312* (PDA, US). KANDY DISTRICT: Kitulgala road, Laxapana, Maskeliya *Kostermans 24117* (PDA, US); Madugoda, *Worthington 1607* (K), *Alston 474* (PDA); Hantane, *J.M.S. s.n.* 24.5.24 (PDA), *Worthington 6500* (K); Arabodde, Kitulgala, Hantane & Hunnasgiriya, *s. coll. C.P. 418* (PDA, K); Royal Botanic Gardens, *s. coll. s.n.* 4.11.1923 (PDA), *s. coll. s.n.* June 1893 (PDA). MATARA DISTRICT: Anningkande, Deniyaya, *Worthington 6617* (K). RATNAPURA DISTRICT: Karawita Kande, *Ashton 2267* (PDA, US); Illumbe Kande, Rakwana, *Worthington 3644* (K); Balangoda estate jungles, *Worthington 764* (K); Balangoda-Bogawantalawa road, *Meijer 945* (PDA, US); Belihul Oya, *Frederick s.n.* July 1890 (PDA). MATALE DISTRICT; Kalupahana Kande, below Lagalla, *J.M.S. s.n.* Sept. 1887 (PDA, K). DISTRICT UNKNOWN: Allagalla, *Worthington 300* (K).

N o t e. The timber is hard and durable in up-country conditions.

Very variable in leaf and flower dimensions, those with the smallest size being collected towards the upper altitudinal limits.

S. *courtallense* (= *Eugenia courtallense* Gamble) is the barely distinguishable vicariant of Peninsular India and is cultivated in the Royal Botanic Gardens.

2. **Syzygium samarangense** (Bl.) Merr. & Perry, J. Arn. Arb. 19: 115. 1938.

Myrtus samarangensis Bl., Bijdr. 1084. 1826.
Jambosa samarangensis DC., Prod. 3: 286. 1828.
Eugenia javanica Lam., Enc. 3: 200. 1789; Duthie in Hook. f., Fl. Br. Ind. 2. 474. 1874 non *S. javanicum* Miq.

A small tree, –7 m tall, –80 cm girth, with smooth grey bark and dense crown. All parts glabrous. Twigs yellow-brown, terete. Lamina 8–14 × 4–8 cm, broadly elliptic, thinly coriaceous; base cordate; margin applanate, apex obtuse or shortly acuminate; nerves 8–16 pairs, very slender but sharply elevated beneath as also the few more slender intermediates, evident and ± distinctly channelled above; tertiary nerves laxly reticulate, barely evident on either surface; intramarginal nerve obscurely 2-tiered, the inner tier alone prominent, looped and c. 5–8 mm within margin; midrib slender but prominent beneath; petiole 1–2 mm long, short, hidden in the cordate leaf-base. Flowers white, in –6 cm long slender lax terminal or subterminal-axillary cymes; calyx –1 cm diam., subglobose, with –8 mm long funnel-shaped pedicel and 4, –4 mm long and broad, accrescent segments; petals –6 × 5 mm, elliptic, obtuse, cupped, caducous; stamens –6 mm long. Fruit c. 2 cm long and diam., obturbinate, ripening red, with c. 8 mm diam. terminal ring of persisting sepals.

D i s t r. Western Malaysia. Cultivated throughout South Asia including the wet zone lowlands of Ceylon below 1300 m.

V e r n. Pini jambu (S); Jambu ayer (Malay).

N o t e. The fruit is succulent and, though smaller than that of the jambu, *S. malaccense*, has a particularly delicious clove-scented taste.

S p e c i m e n s   E x a m i n e d. RATNAPURA DISTRICT: Karawita village, *Ashton 2266* (PDA, US); Adam's Peak trail above Carney estate, *Davidse & Sumithraarachchi 8745* (PDA, US). DISTRICT UNKNOWN: Elkaduwa village, *Worthington 6645* (K).

3. **Syzygium turbinatum** Alston in Trimen, Handb. Fl. Ceylon 6: 114. 1931.

Strongylocalyx hemisphericus (non Blume) Thw., Enum. Pl. Zeyl. 116. 1859 p.p.
Eugenia hemispherica (non Walp.) Trimen, Handb. Fl. Ceylon 2: 170. 1894 p.p.
Eugenia aquea (non Burm. f.) Trimen, Handb. Fl. Ceylon 2: 169. 1894 p.p.

A small tree, -10 m tall, -1 m girth; bark surface pale grey-brown, thinly flaky; crown dense, with up-pointing leaves. All parts glabrous. Twigs terete, red-brown, rugulose. Lamina 3.5–6 cm long, 1.2–2.5 cm broad, elliptic to narrowly obovate, coriaceous, with narrowly revolute margin; base cuneate, shortly decurrent; apex obtuse, subacute or rarely shortly bluntly acuminate; main nerves c. 5 pairs, ascending, very slender and hardly more elevated than the shorter intermediates and obliquely reticulate tertiaries beneath, evident above; intramarginal nerves obscurely 2-tiered, the inner tier c. 2–4 mm within margin and prominently looped; petiole (2–) 3–5 mm long, drying black. Cymes -4 cm long, short, stout, terminal or subterminal-axillary; pedicels c. 3 mm long; flowers -15 mm diam., large, cream; calyx tube c. 8 × 5 mm at anthesis, funnel-shaped, with 4 (–5), c. 2 mm long, 3 mm broad, orbicular segments; petals -6 × 5 mm, large, elliptic, concave; stamens -10 mm long, many. Fruit -15 mm diam., turbinate to subglobose, pink and white blotched, crowned by a -12 mm diam. prominent ring of persisting calyx segments.

D i s t r. Except for a single record from Nuwara Eliya, known only from the Knuckles region of Ceylon where it is rather frequent in montane forest between 1300–2000 m.

S p e c i m e n s   E x a m i n e d. KANDY DISTRICT: Elk plains, *C.P. 2450* p.p. (PDA); Corbet's Gap, *Worthington 3606* (K); Rangala, Knuckles, *Ashton 2304* (PDA, US), *2305* (PDA, US); 2 miles north of Hunnasgiriya, *Davidse 8438 A* (PDA, US). NUWARA ELIYA DISTRICT: Dimbulla, *s. coll. C.P. 418* (K).

(The remaining sheets of *C.P. 2450* belong to *Syzygium hemisphericum.*)

N o t e. A rather clearly defined species, allied most closely to *S. cylindricum* and *S. aqueum* but differing in both leaf and calyx shape. Worthington's collection has shorter petals and more diverging nervation, but the fruit are the same and I cannot place it elsewhere.

4. Syzygium firmum Thw., Enum. Pl. Zeyl. 417. 1864; Alston in Trimen, Handb. Fl. Ceylon 6: 114. 1931.

Eugenia grandis Wight, Ill. 2: 17. 1850 p.p. excl. syn.; Ic. Pl. Ind. Or. t. 614. 1843 nomen nudum; Duthie in Hook. f., Fl. Br. Ind. 2: 476. 1879; Trimen, Handb. Fl. Ceylon 2: 170. 1894.
Syzygium montanum Thw., Enum. Pl. Zeyl. 116. 1859 p.p. excl. syn.

A large tree, -25 m tall, -3 m girth, with pale orange-brown patchily thinly flaked fluted bole, spreading concave stout buttresses and dense oblong crown; inner bark distinctive purplish. All parts glabrous. Twigs stout, terete, pale cream brown, becoming minutely striated. Young leaves coppery-brown. Lamina 10–17 × 5.5–11 cm, broadly elliptic to obovate, thickly coriaceous, lustrous, drying tawny-brown beneath, purplish above, with prominently revolute margin, broadly cuneate base, and retuse, obtuse or (in young trees) acuminate apex; nerves many, with many ± shorter intermediates, very slender but distinctly and ± equally elevated on both surfaces as also the less prominently densely reticulate tertiaries and 2-tiered intramarginal nerves; intramarginal nerves ± looped, the inner c. 3–6 mm within the margin and the more prominent; midrib stoutly prominent beneath, broad and elevated with a median channel above; petiole 12–20 mm long, stout, drying black. Flowers pale cream-yellow, subsessile in threes at the endings of –10 cm long terminal or axillary stout remotely branched axillary cymes; calyx with –10 × 7 mm funnel-shaped tube and –14 mm diam. ring of 4–5 obtuse ovate segments; petals –6 × 5 mm, concave, caducous; stamens –2 cm long, many, spreading. Fruit –2 cm diam., subglobose, green, with –1 cm diam. prominent crown of persistent calyx segments.

D i s t r. Endemic; local in the lowland wet zone forests. Represented in the Kottawe arboretum.

V e r n. Waljambu (S).

S p e c i m e n s   E x a m i n e d. KANDY DISTRICT: Ambagamuwa, *s. coll. C.P. 2694* (PDA, K); Hillcrest, Kandy, *Worthington 7175* (K), *6885* (K); Royal Botanic Gardens, *Alston 811* (PDA), *812* (PDA). GALLE DISTRICT: Haycock, *J.M.S. s.n.* (PDA), *Cramer 2768* (PDA, US); Kottawe arboretum, *Worthington 6013* (K); Kanneliya forest, *Worthington 6025* (K), *Meijer 1021* (PDA, US), *Balakrishnan 272* (PDA, US, K). RATNAPURA DISTRICT: Gilimale forest, *Worthington 6455* (K), *6459* (K), *6489* (K), *6491* (K), *Meijer 487* (PDA, US, K), *Ashton 2253* (PDA, US), *2332* (PDA, US); Carney road, Gilimale, *Worthington 6492* (K), *6493* (K), *4452* (K); Rasagalla, Ratnapura, *Kostermans 24644* (PDA, US, K). LOCALITY UNKNOWN: *J.M.S. s.n. 11.2.19* (PDA).

N o t e. A very clearly defined and uniform species.

5. **Syzygium jambos** (L.) Alston in Trimen, Handb. Fl. Ceylon 6: 116. 1931.

Eugenia jambos L., Sp. Pl. 175, 470. 1753; Duthie in Hook. f., Fl. Br. Ind. 2: 474. 1878.
Myrtus jambos HBK., Nov. Gen. et Sp. 6: 144. 1823.
Jambosa vulgaris DC., Prod. 3.: 286. 1828.
Jambosa jambos Millsp., Publ. Field Columban Mus. Bot. Sér. 2: 80. 1900.

A small tree, –10 m tall, –50 cm girth, with diffuse branching; bark grey-brown, smooth. All parts glabrous. Twigs red-brown, terete, smooth. Lamina 9–20 × 1.5–4.5 cm, narrowly lanceolate, thinly coriaceous, semi-pendant; base cuneate; acumen to 3 cm long, slender; nerves c. 14–20 pairs, ascending, slender but distinctly elevated beneath, elevated above, as also the intramarginal nerve; with less prominent intermediates and densely reticulate tertiaries; intramarginal nerve c. 2–3 mm within margin; midrib slender but prominent beneath; petiole 5–6 mm long, drying black. Flower white, in 2 cm long short terminal singly branched cymes. Flower calyx –10 mm long, –8 mm diam., tapering into pedicel; segments 4, –10 × 7 mm, suborbicular; petals –1.5 cm diam., suborbicular, concave, caducous; stamens –3 cm long, very long, fluffy; style –4 cm long, prominently protruding. Fruit –2.5 × 2 cm, obturbinate, white, shortly stoutly pedicellate, prominently crowned by a c. 1.5 cm diam. ring of persisting sepals.

D i s t r. Western Malaysia. Cultivated in the wet zone lowlands of Ceylon and frequently occurring as an escape.

V e r n. Veli Jambu, Seenijambu (S); Rose apple (E).

N o t e. Cultivated for its succulent fruit.

S p e c i m e n s   E x a m i n e d. KANDY DISTRICT: Udawattekelle, *Meijer 13* (PDA, US); Poilakande, Kadugamuwa, *Worthington 1750* (K), 792 (K); Hillcrest, Kandy, *Worthington 6930* (K); Dunally, Galaha, *Worthington 2877* (K); Royal Botanic Gardens *Alston 817* (PDA), *s. coll. s.n.* Sept. 1887 (PDA). NUWARA ELIYA DISTRICT: Maturata road, *Ashton 2313* (PDA, US). RATNAPURA DISTRICT: Houpe estate, Kahawatte, *Ashton 2269* (PDA, US).

6. Syzygium malaccensis (L.) Merr. & Perry, J. Arn. Arb. 19: 215. 1938.

Eugenia malaccensis L., Sp. Pl. 470. 1753; Duthie in Hook. f., Fl. Br. Ind. 2: 471. 1878.

Eugenia macrophylla Lam., Enc. 3: 196. 1786.

Jambosa malaccensis DC., Prod. 3: 286. 1828.

Jambosa purpurascens DC., l.c. quoad syn. Roxb.

Eugenia purpurea Roxb., Fl. Ind. ed. 2, 2: 483. 1832.

Jambosa domestica Blume, Ann. Mus. Bot. Lugduno-Batavum 1: 91. 1849.

Calophyllus malaccensis Stokes, Bot. Mat. Med. 3: 72.

A medium-sized tree, –20 m tall, with smooth grey-brown lenticellate patchily flaked bark and dense oblong shiny-leaved crown. Twigs stout, pale brown, terete. Lamina 16–34 × 5–13 cm, elliptic, subcoriaceous; base narrowly cuneate; acumen to 2 cm long, slender, tapering; nerves c. 15 pairs, ascending, with a few short intermediates, slender but prominent beneath, elevated above as also the inner intramarginal nerve; intramarginal nerve 2-tiered, the outer ± obscure, the inner 2–6 mm within the margin; tertiary nerves slender but evident on both surfaces, subscalariform, perpendicular to midrib; midrib prominent beneath; petiole 8–15 mm long, stout, drying black. Flowers in –1 cm long short axillary cymes, bright peuce; calyx –15 × 8 mm, funnel-shaped with 4, –5 × 4 mm suborbicular rotate segments; petals to 10 × 8 mm, elliptic, obtuse, cupped; stamens –2 cm long. Fruit –4 × 3.5 cm, obturbinate, pale pinkish white, succulent, with c. 1.5 cm diam. terminal ring of persisting segments.

D i s t r. A west Malaysian species. Commonly cultivated in the wet zone lowlands; its brilliant peuce flowers are often to be seen along the roadside and are visited by bats. The seed is known to be polyembryonic.

V e r n. Peria-jambu (T); Jambu (S; Malay).

S p e c i m e n s E x a m i n e d. RATNAPURA DISTRICT: Gilimale, *Worthington 796* (K); Karawita, *Ashton 2268* (PDA, US). KANDY DISTRICT: Poilakande garden, Kadugannawa, *Worthington 704* (K); Royal Botanic Gardens, *s. coll. s.n.* April 1902 (PDA). LOCALITY UNKNOWN: Putupeurala estate, *Worthington 2520* (K); *Worthington 796* (K).

7. Syzygium cylindricum (Wight) Alston in Trimen, Handb. Fl. Ceylon 6: 115. 1931.

Eugenia cylindrica Wight, Ic. Pl. Ind. Or.: t. 527. 1840; Ill. 2: 14. 1850; Duthie in Hook. f., Fl. Br. Ind. 2: 479. 1879; Beddome Fl. Sylv. t. 201. 1859; Trimen, Handb. Fl. Ceylon 2: 171. 1894.
Jambosa cylindrica Thw., Enum. Fl. Zeyl. 115. 1859.

A shrub or small tree –10 m tall, –1 m girth, with smooth pale grey-brown bark; bole branching low, crown graceful, diffuse with pendant twigs. All parts glabrous. Twigs slender, terete, pale honey-brown. Lamina 6–15 × 2–5.5 cm, elliptic, thinly coriaceous, drying pale tawny-brown beneath; base cuneate, shortly decurrent; acumen –2 cm long, slender; nerves 6–8 pairs, few, ascending, slender but prominent beneath, evident or more frequently channelled above, arching round to form a prominent looped inner intramarginal nerve 4–6 mm from margin; outer intramarginal nerve less prominently elevated, c. 1 mm within margin, intermittently connected by side nerves to the inner; intermediate nerves few, short, slender; tertiaries remotely reticulate, distinctly elevated beneath, ± obscure above; midrib prominent beneath, drying pale; petiole 5–7 mm long, swollen towards base, drying black. Flowers large, pale pink, borne sparsely in –4 cm long slender lax terminal or axillary cymes; calyx white, bugle-shaped with –2 cm long slender tapering stem and –1 cm diam. shallow distal cup with 4 broad acute segments; petals –7 mm × 6 mm, ovate, acute; stamens –14 mm long, very long, conspicuous. Fruit –17 mm diam., globose, with –9 mm diam. prominent terminal rim.

D i s t r. Endemic. Locally frequent by fast running streams in the hills of the moist region below 1200 m. frequently left as relicts in tea estates.

S p e c i m e n s E x a m i n e d. BADULLA DISTRICT: Thotugalle estate above Haputale, *Kostermans 23231* (PDA, K). KANDY DISTRICT: Ambagamuwa, *s. coll. C.P. 601* (PDA, K); road down to Laksapana power station,

Worthington 5520 (K); Imboopitiya, Nawalapitiya, *Worthington 6637* (K).
KALUTARA DISTRICT: Dotalu Kande, Kukul Korale, *s. coll. s.n.* Sept.
1891 (PDA). KEGALLE DISTRICT: Levant estate, Yatiyantota, *Worthington 2115* (K). RATNAPURA DISTRICT: Illumbakanda, Rakwana, *Worthington 2634* (K); Morapitya road, Matugama, *Kostermans 24972* (PDA, US, K). DISTRICT UNKNOWN: Udabage estate, K.V., *Worthington 2094* (K). LOCALITY UNKNOWN: *Wight 1049* (K).

8. Syzygium hemisphericum (Walp.) Alston in Trimen, Handb. Fl. Ceylon 6: 115. 1931.

Jambosa hemispherica Walp., Rep. 2: 191. 1845.
Strongylocalyx hemisphericus Blume, Ann. Mus. Bot. Lugduno-Batavum 1: 90, 184. 1849; Thw., Enum. Pl. Zeyl. 116. 1859.
Eugenia hemispherica Wight, Ill. 2: 14. 1850; Ic. Pl. Ind. Or. t. 525. 1840; Duthie in Hook. f., Fl. Br. Ind. 2: 477. 1879; Beddome, Fl. Sylv. t. 203. 1869; Trimen, Handb. Fl. Ceylon 2: 170. 1894.

Medium sized tree; bark surface overall smooth, patchily flaked over small areas, pale brown; crown dense, oblong or hemispherical. All parts glabrous. Twigs stout, terete, rugulose, cream. Young leaves mauve. Lamina 5–11 × 2–6 cm, elliptic, thinly coriaceous, drying rufous brown and somewhat lustrous beneath; margin hardly revolute; base narrowly cuneate; acumen –1.5 cm long, slender; nerves c. 12 pairs, ascending, very slender but distinctly elevated on both surfaces as also the densely reticulate tertiaries and many short intermediates; intramarginal nerves 2-tiered, the inner 2–6 mm within margin, looped, the outer intermittent; midrib prominent beneath, drying pale; petiole 10–15 mm long, drying black. Cyme –9 cm long, terminal or axillary, rather stout, bearing many large white flowers; pedicel –15 mm long, slender; calyx with c. 6 mm long, c. 4 mm diam. shortly funnel-shaped tube and 4, –5 mm long and broad, prominent suborbicular cupped rotate sepals; petals –9 mm × 7 mm, suborbicular, concave; stamens many, –14 mm long. Fruit –1.5 cm diam., globose, crowned with a –8 mm diam. apical disc bearing the persistent calyx segments.

Distr. Southern India and Ceylon. Rare in Ceylon, at 500–1500 m in the southern and eastern margins of the main mountain block.

Specimens Examined. KANDY DISTRICT: Moray estate, Maskeliya, *Kostermans 24183* (PDA, US, K). *Ashton 2338* (PDA, US), *Davidse & Sumithraarachchi 8679* (PDA, US); Royal Botanic Gardens, *Worthington 3784* (K), *3569* (K), *3835* (K). KANDY & BADULLA DISTRICTS: Deltota, Ambagamuwa, Haputale-Galegama, *s. coll. C.P. 2450* (excl. sheet from Elk Plains) (PDA, K). MONERAGALA DISTRICT: Diyadenia falls, Wellawaya, *Worthington 5697* (K). KALUTARA DISTRICT: Kukul Korale *s. coll. C.P. 3438* (PDA, K).

N o t e. *C.P. 2540*, quoted under this species by Trimen, was later removed to *S. turbinatum*, but is a mixture and in part belongs here. The large flowers and fruits and short calyx tube readily isolate this distinctive species from others.

9. Syzygium zeylanicum DC., Prod. 3, 260. 1828; Gamble, Fl. Pres. Madras 479. 1919; Alston in Trimen, Handb. Fl. Ceylon 6: 115. 1931.

Myrtus zeylanica L., Sp. Pl. 472. 1753; Moon, Cat. 39. 1824.
Eugenia spicata Lam., Enc. 3: 201. 1789; Burm., Thes. 166. 1647: Hermann, Mus. Zeyl. 9. 1717; L., Fl. Zeyl. n. 182. 1747; Wight, Ic. Pl. Ind. Or. t. 73. 1840; Bedd., Fl. Sylv. t. 201. 1869; Trimen, Handb. Fl. Ceylon 2: 171. 1894.
Eugenia zeylanica Wight, Ill. 15. 1850; Duthie in Hook. f., Fl. Br. Ind. 2: 485. 1879.
Acmena zeylanica Thw., Enum. Pl. Zeyl. 118. 1859. var. *zeylanicum*.

Small tree, –10 m tall, –2 m girth, with pale grey-brown, bronze or green smooth or irregular cracked and flaky bark, dense broad rather flat crown with twisted branches and short crooked trunk. Young expanding leafy buds and calyx segments caducous brownish puberulent, parts otherwise glabrous. Twigs slender, much branched, pale brown, quadrangular at first, becoming terete (saplings excepted). Young leaves pale pink, flushes sporadic on different branches. Lamina 2.5–8 × 0.6–4 cm, variable, lanceolate, thinly coriaceous; base broadly or narrowly cuneate; apex attenuate acuminate; lower surface minutely pitted, drying purplish; nerves c. 12 pairs with shorter intermediates, very slender, ascending, obscure or very slightly elevated beneath as also the laxly reticulate tertiaries, narrowly depressed above; intramarginal nerve c. 1 mm within margin, rather straight, frequently obscure; petiole 1–4 mm, slender, short. Flowers shortly pedicellate, densely clustered in –4 cm long slender terminal or subterminal axillary racemes, white. Calyx tube –5 mm × 3 mm, funnel-shaped, glaucous, with 4 (–5) short obtuse or subacute ovate segments; petals small, concave, fugaceous; stamens –7 mm long, many, dense. Fruit –8 mm diam., broadly ellipsoid or subglobose, conspicuous milk-white on ripening, with c. 2 mm diam. crown of persisting segments.

D i s t r. Peninsular India, Western Malaysia and Ceylon. Locally common in the dry and intermediate zone and on rocky summits at the margins of the main massif, local also in the wet zone coastal plains. On sandy and skeletal soils near the coast and on rocky ridges, especially in evergreen sclerophyll forest, between 600–1000 (–2100) m inland.

V e r n. Yakul maran (S); Marung, Mariangi, Maranda (T).

S p e c i m e n s E x a m i n e d. BADULLA DISTRICT: Palugama, *s. coll.* *C.P. 380* (PDA, K). KANDY DISTRICT: Nawanagalla, Madugoda, *Worthington 1595* (K); Royal Botanic Gardens, *Worthington 6834* (K). KALU-

TARA DISTRICT: Badureliya, *Worthington 4617* (K). ANURADHAPURA DISTRICT: Ritigala, *Ashton 2323* (PDA, US), *Jayasuriya, Wheeler & Cramer 835* (K). RATNAPURA DISTRICT: Belihul Oya, *Worthington 444* (K); Aigburth estate, Rakwana, *Worthington 2162* (K), *2163* (K), *3717* (K); Balangoda-Kaltota, *Worthington 3301* (K); Rajawakanda, Ugalkaltota-Balangoda road, *Worthington 3763* (K); Haputale-Belihul Oya road, *Kostermans 23402* (K). BATTICALOA DISTRICT: Batticaloa, *s. coll. C.P. 56* p.p. (PDA, K). MONERAGALA DISTRICT: Bibile, *Worthington 4905* (K). NUWARA ELIYA DISTRICT: Hakgala, *Worthington 6760* (K), *Kostermans 24513* (PDA, US), *Ashton 2280* (PDA, US), *J.M.S. s.n.* 28.5.1911 (PDA), *Balakrishnan 1207* (PDA, US, K); Nuwara Eliya park, *Nock 835* (K). DISTRICT UNKNOWN: Weweltenna Plain South, *Jayasuriya 1331* (K); Haragama, *Alston 833* (PDA); Valaickena, East coast, Worthington *946* (K). LOCALITY UNKNOWN: *Walker 235* (K), *28* (PDA), *Worthington 282* (K), *s. coll. s.n.* 24.3.1905 (PDA), *Parlett s.n.* (K) *s. coll. C.P. 1579* (K).

N o t e. I have not seen the holotype of this species.

var. **lineare** (Wall.) Alston in Trimen, Handb. Fl. Ceylon 6: 115. 1931.

Syzygium lineare Wall., Cat. 3596. 1828; Gamble, Fl. Pres. Madras 479. 1919. *Eugenia linearis* Duthie in Hook. f., Fl. Br. Ind. 2: 846. 1879.

Diffuse crowned shrub with pendent branches. Lamina $3-9 \times 0.3-1$ cm, linear-lanceolate.

D i s t r. Throughout the species range; in Ceylon a rheophyte along intermediate and dry zone rivers.

S p e c i m e n s E x a m i n e d. MONERAGALA DISTRICT: Galagama and Uma Oya, *s. coll. C.P. 56.* p.p. (PDA); Banks of Walawe Ganga, Uda Walawe, *Balakrishnan & Jayasuriya 895* (PDA, US, K).

N o t e. This variety clearly represents a series of morphologically similar ecotypes of separate origins.

10. Syzygium fergusoni Gamble, Kew Bull. 52. 1920; Alston in Trimen, Handb. Fl. Ceylon 6: 115. 1931.

Eugenia fergusoni Trimen, Handb, Fl. Ceylon 2: 172. 1894. ssp. *fergusoni*.

ssp. **fergusoni**

A small tree with dense hemispherical crown bearing upturned leaves, mauve flushes of young leaves and overall smooth but locally cracked and flaked grey bark. All parts glabrous, twigs narrowly but distinctly 4-winged, much branched, with short internodes. Lamina $2-8 \times 1.8-5.4$ cm, broadly elliptic, ovate, thinly coriaceous and wrinkling on drying, matt on both surfaces, drying pale greenish grey; margin narrowly revolute; base obtuse or subcordate; apex acute or retuse; main nerves c. 8 pairs, wavy, not parallel, with a few short intermediates, hair-slender, distinctly elevated beneath and narrowly depressed above as also the yet more slender reticulate tertiaries; midrib slender but prominent beneath; petiole 1–2 mm long, very short, drying grey-green. Flowers pale pink or cream, in very short terminal or subterminal-axillary cymes; calyx –3.5 × 0.5 cm, bugle-shaped, sessile, with (4–) 5 shallow obtuse ± recurved segments; petals –5 × 4 mm, elliptic, calyptrate, fugaceous; stamens many, protruding –1.5 cm. Fruit –18 × 10 mm, urceolate, broadest at base, tapering, to 7 mm diam. with apical calyx rim.

D i s t r. Southern India, Ceylon. Confined in the latter to the Knuckles massif, where it is common above 1300 m.

V e r n. Wel Karabu (wild clove) (S).

S p e c i m e n s   E x a m i n e d. KANDY DISTRICT: Rangala, *s. coll. C.P. 160* (PDA), *N.B.K. 604* (PDA, US), *Ashton 2303* (PDA, US), *s. coll. s.n.* April 1886 (PDA); Kallebokke, Knuckles, *Ferguson s.n.*, April 1887 (PDA); Jungle above Kattoloya, Knuckles, *Worthington 1954* (K); Corbet's gap, *Worthington 5478* (K), *6420* (K); between Knuckles and Rilagala No. 2 peaks, east of Bambrella, *Davidse 8270* (PDA, US).

ssp. **minor** Trimen, Handb. Fl. Ceylon 2: 173. 1894.

Differing as follows: Leaf 1.4–3.5 cm long, 1.5–2.2 cm broad; base broadly cuneate; fruit to 11 mm long, to 9 mm diam., relatively broader.

S p e c i m e n   E x a m i n e d. KANDY DISTRICT: Adam's Peak *s. coll. C.P. 160* (PDA, K).

N o t e. A very distinctive species not easily confused with others.

11. Syzygium lanceolatum (Lam.) Wight & Arn., Prod. 2: 230. 1834; Alston in Trimen, Handb. Fl. Ceylon 6: 115. 1931.

Eugenia lanceolata Lam., Enc. 3: 200. 1789; Trimen, Handb. Fl. Ceylon 2: 172. 1894.
Eugenia wightiana Wight, Ic. Pl. Ind. Or. t. 529, 530. 1840 p.p.; Duthie in Hook. f., Fl. Br. Ind. 2: 285. 1879 p.p.

A small tree with smooth bark. Twigs slender, terete. Lamina 6–14 × 1.5–5.5 cm, ovate-lanceolate to elliptic, chartaceous, drying grey-green, with narrowly subrevolute margins, tapering cuneate base and –2.5 cm long slender acumen; nerves many, parallel, very slender and barely elevated beneath, ± obscure above as also the reticulate tertiaries; midrib slender but prominent beneath; petiole 5–8 mm long, rather short, slender, prominently channelled above. Flowers in short, –1.5 cm long, terminal or more often axillary to ramiflorous cymes; calyx –12 mm × 3 mm, funnel-shaped; segments short, broad; petals –3 mm long and broad, suborbicular; stamens

–6 mm long. Fruit (young) obturbinate, with prominent apical ring of persistent calyx segments.

Distr. Southern India, Ceylon. In Ceylon locally common, especially in damp valleys and by streams, in the wet and intermediate zones below 400 m.

Specimens Examined. VARIOUS DISTRICTS: Kurunegala, Ambagamuwa, Sinharaja and Matara, *s. coll. C.P. 2863* p.p. (PDA). KALUTARA DISTRICT: Moragala, *s. coll. s.n.* March 1887 (PDA). KEGALLE DISTRICT: Ginagathena-Kitulgala road 6/5, *Worthington, 3162* (K). KANDY DISTRICT: Ginagathena, *Worthington 2085* (K). DISTRICT UNKNOWN: Delgoda, *s. coll. s.n.* March 1887 (PDA).

The Pasdun Korale sheet under *C.P. 2863* does not belong here, as suggested already by Trimen.

12. Syzygium aromaticum (L.) Merr. & Perry., Mem. Amer. Acad. Arts 18: 196. 1939.

Caryophyllus aromaticus L., Sp. Pl. 515. 1753.
Eugenia carylophyllata Thunb., Diss. 1. 1788.
Myrtus caryophyllus Spreng., Syst. 2: 485. 1825, non *M. aromaticus* Salisb.
Eugenia aromatica (L.) Baill., Hist. Pl. 6: 311, 345. 1877 non Berg.
Jambosa caryophyllus (Spreng.) Niedz. in Pflanzenfam. 3, 7: 84. 1893, non
    Jambosa aromatica Miq.
Eugenia caryophyllus (Spreng.) Bullock & Harrison, Kew Bull. 52. 1958;
    Purseglove, Tropical Crops 2: 401. 1968.

A medium sized tree with smooth pale brown bark. All parts glabrous. Twigs terete, becoming pale grey-brown. Lamina 7–12 × 3–5 cm, oblanceolate, thinly coriaceous, lustrous, densely punctate beneath, drying pale grey-brown; base narrowly attenuate cuneate; apex shortly broadly acuminate; nerves many, parallel, obscure on both surfaces but sometimes evident above; intramarginal nerve c. 1 mm within margin; petiole 1–2 cm long, very long, slender. Cymes –4 cm long; calyx c. 15 × 6 mm, tubular, verruculose, with 4 hook-like involute ascending segments; petals –10 × 5 mm, elliptic, calyptrate.

Distr. Moluccas. A major spice crop in the intermediate zone north of Kandy. The flower buds are the cloves of commerce.

Vern. Karabu neti (S); Karambu (T), Clove (E).

Specimens Examined. KANDY DISTRICT: Royal Botanic Gardens, *s. coll. s. n.* 9.3.27 (PDA), *s.n.* 1901 (PDA), *s.n.* Feb. 1899 (PDA), *s.n.* Feb. 1883 (PDA), *S.O. de Silva s.n.* 5.10.29 (PDA), *C.F. Baker 108* (PDA).

Note. Purseglove gives an excellent account of the culture of cloves and its history under the name *Eugenia caryophyllus*.

13. Syzygium sp.

A very tall handsome tree with good girth; bark reddish in cracks, with green-grey scales (Worthington). Parts entirely glabrous. Twigs pale brown, terete. Lamina 3.5–7 (–12 in young trees) × 1.2–3 (–4.5) cm, elliptic, thinly coriaceous, with prominently punctate undersurface, drying sandy brown; base cuneate; apex –1.5 cm long, prominently attenuate-acuminate; margin narrowly shallowly revolute; nerves c. 12 pairs, very slender and barely elevated beneath, obscure above; tertiary nerves obscure; intramarginal nerve more or less concealed within margin; petiole –8 mm long, slender. Cymes –6 (–12) cm long, terminal or subterminal axillary, slender, many flowered; flower calyx shallowly saucer-shaped, hardly lobed, on a slender funnel-shaped receptacle; petals c. 2 mm long and broad, elliptic, calyptrate, fugaceous; stamens c. 3 mm long, short. Fruit –12 mm diam., globose, pale mauve, with c. 5 mm diam. hardly raised terminal ring.

D i s t r. A cultivated species in Ceylon, known only from the collections cited.

S p e c i m e n s   E x a m i n e d. RATNAPURA DISTRICT: Balangoda Estates Bungalow. *Childerstone & Worthington 6919* (K); NUWARA ELIYA DISTRICT: Galkandewatte, Talawakelle, *Gibbon & Worthington 6497* (K). KANDY DISTRICT: Royal Botanic Gardens, *Alston 184* (PDA), *Macmillan 133* (PDA). DISTRICT UNKNOWN: Lahugala tank, *Mueller-Dombois & Comanor 67072505* (PDA, US).

N o t e. The leaves of trees in the Peradeniya gardens are narrowly lanceolate. I have been unable to identify this species, which comes close to the widespread *S. leptanthum* (Wight) Niedz. but differs in its larger, more branched inflorescences.

14. Syzygium rotundifolium Arn., Nova Acta Phys. Med. Acad. Caes. Leop. Carol. Nat. Cur. 18: 335. 1836; Thw., Enum. Pl. Zeyl. 118. 1859; Alston in Trimen, Handb. Fl. Ceylon 6: 117. 1931.

Eugenia rotundifolia (non Cav.) Wight, Ill. 2: 17. 1850; Duthie in Hook. f., Fl. Br. Ind. 2: 494, 1879; Trimen, Handb. Fl. Ceylon 2: 177. 1894.

Canopy tree, –10 m tall, –1 m girth, with patchily flaky scroll-marked pale pink-brown bark, crooked twisted bole and branches, and dense rather flat crown. All parts glabrous. Twigs sharply quadrangular, slender, much branched. Lamina 10–25 × 9–16 mm, small, coriaceous, broadly obovate to orbicular, lustrous beneath, with obtuse to broadly cuneate subequal base, narrowly revolute margin and obtuse to subacuminate apex; nerves many, unequal, very slender but distinctly elevated beneath, obscure above; intramarginal nerve ± unlooped, c. 0.5 mm within margin; midrib prominent beneath and drying dark, obscurely depressed above; petiole 2–3 mm long, slender. Flowers in short densely branched terminal racemes, white or pale pink; calyx –5 mm × 4 mm, urceolate, with 4 hemispherical segments; petals small, concave, fugaceous; stamens c. 4 mm long, few, short. Fruit –10 × 8 mm, ellipsoid, with the persistent segments reflexed in a c. 3 mm diam. terminal ring, ripening green with a purplish flush.

D i s t r. Endemic; one of the commonest canopy trees in the montane forest above 2000 m.

S p e c i m e n s E x a m i n e d. BADULLA DISTRICT: Naminakuli, *s. coll. s.n.* 12.3.1907 (PDA). NUWARA ELIYA DISTRICT: Pidurutalagala, *s. coll. C.P. 1587* (PDA, K), *Ashton 2301* (PDA, US); Frotoft estate, Ramboda, *Kostermans 25097* (K); Horton Plains, *Ashton 2292* (PDA, US), *2294* (PDA, US), *2297* (PDA, US); Horton Plains, road to Ohiya, *Fosberg 50115* (K.); Hakgala nature reserve, *Ashton 2281* (PDA, US), *2285* (PDA, US), *2289* (PDA, US); *2290* (PDA, US); Totupola, *s. coll. s.n.* Sept. 1890 (PDA); Nuwara Eliya, *Mueller-Dombois & Comanor 67070937* (PDA, US), *Balakrishnan 1029* (PDA, US, K), *1196* (PDA, US, K), *Hladik 968* (PDA, US), *895* (PDA, US), *Fosberg 50115* (PDA, US), *Meijer, Dassanayake & Balakrishnan 625* (PDA, US), *van Beusekom 1500* (PDA, US), *Worthington 5460* (K); Bulu Ela arboretum, *Worthington 2918* (K). LOCALITY UNKNOWN: *Walker 200* (K).

15. Syzygium sclerophyllum Thw., Enum. Pl. Zeyl. 118. 1859; Alston in Trimen, Handb. Fl. Ceylon 6: 117. 1931.

Canopy tree –10 m tall, –1 m girth, with pale grey-brown cracked and patchily flaky bark, twisted bole and branches and dense dark shallowly hemispherical crown with upturned leaves. Twigs slender, sharply quadrangular, with very short internodes, much branched, rapidly becoming stout, yellow-brown. Lamina 15–25 × 11–20 mm, broadly elliptic to suborbicular; base obtuse to subcordate; margin subrevolute; apex obtuse or subacute; nerves many, unequal, not parallel, indistinctly elevated beneath, obscurely furrowed above; intramarginal nerve close to margin, ± obscure; midrib prominent beneath especially towards base, shallowly furrowed above; petiole 1–2 mm long, stout. Flowers white, densely clustered in short terminal cymes; calyx –4 mm long, 3 mm diam., obconical, with a prominent obscurely 4-segmented apical rim; petals c. 3 × 2 mm, elliptic, concave, fugaceous; stamens c. 3 mm long, many. Fruit –8 mm diam., globose, terminating in a distinct short c. 4 mm diam. ± unlobed crown.

D i s t r. Endemic. Locally abundant in montane forest above 2000 m in the main mountain massif.

S p e c i m e n s E x a m i n e d. NUWARA ELIYA DISTRICT: Pidurutalagala, *s. coll. C.P. 274* (PDA, K), *Ashton 2300* (PDA, US); Totupola, *Worthington 1735* (K); Nuwara Eliya, *Gardner 302* (PDA, K); Horton Plains,

Kostermans 23092A (K), *23126* (K). LOCALITY UNKNOWN: *Walker 7* (K), *s. coll. C.P. 1585* (K).

16. Syzygium oliganthum Thw., Enum. Pl. Zeyl. 118. 1859; Alston in Trimen, Handb. Fl. Ceylon 6: 116. 1931.

Eugenia oligantha Duthie in Hook. f., Fl. Br. Ind. 2: 494. 1879; Trimen, Handb. Fl. Ceylon 2: 179. 1894.

A small tree, –5 m tall, with crooked bole and dense crown of twisted branches. All parts glabrous. Twigs slender, prominently 4-ribbed, much branched, pale grey-brown. Lamina 12–25 × 7–20 mm, obovate, obtuse, base cuneate; margin narrowly subrevolute; nerves many, ascending, very slender but clearly evident and elevated beneath as also the dense tertiaries, ± obscure above; midrib slender but prominent beneath; petiole 2–4 mm long, slender. Flowers small, white, sessile, densely clustered in –5 mm long, very short, terminal or axillary cymes; calyx –3 × 3 mm, goblet-shaped, with 4 short broad subacute segments; petals –3 × 2 mm, elliptic, calyptrate; stamens –3 mm long, rather few, in a ring round the calyx cup. Fruit –7 mm diam., globose, ripening purple, with a prominent c. 3 mm diam. apical calyx rim.

D i s t r. Endemic; common along the length of the peak Sanctuary and in Ambagamuwa at 1500–2000 m.

S p e c i m e n s E x a m i n e d. RATNAPURA DISTRICT: Pinnawela, *Balakrishnan 547* (PDA, US, K), Balangoda estate jungles, *Worthington 758* (K). KANDY DISTRICT: Ambagamuwa, *C.P. 452* (PDA), *588* (K); Maskeliya side of Adam's Peak. *Worthington 2742* (K); near Gartmore estate, Maskeliya, *J.M. Silva s.n.* 29.5.25 (PDA); Moray estate, Maskeliya, *Jayasuriya & Sumithraarachchi 186* (PDA, US, K), *Balakrishnan 903* (PDA, US), *Ashton 2342* (PDA, US), *Balakrishnan, Dassanayake & Balasubrama-niam 521* (PDA, US), *Kostermans 24168, 24252, 24934* (PDA, US, K). *Davidse & Sumithraarachchi 8598* (PDA, US); Maskeliya, *s. coll. s.n.* March 1883 (PDA); Ambagamuwa, Frotoft estate, *Kostermans 25038* (K).

17. Syzygium rubicundum Wight & Arn., Prod. 330. 1834; Gamble, Fl. Pres. Madras 479. 1919; Alston in Trimen, Handb. Fl. Ceylon 6: 117. 1931.

Eugenia rubicunda Wight, Ic. Pl. Ind. Or. t. 538. 1843.
Syzygium lissophyllum Thw., Enum. Pl. Zeyl. 117. 1859.
Eugenia lissophylla Beddome, For. Man. 108. 1874; Duthie in Hook. f., Fl. Br. Ind. 2: 488. 1879; Trimen, Handb. Fl. Ceylon 2: 173. 1894.

Large tree, –40 m tall, –2 m girth, with small narrow butteresses and ribbed pale orange-brown, overall smooth, thinly oblong flaked bark. Crown olive-green, feathery, with many ascending branches. All parts glabrous. Twigs slender, sharply quadrangular, much branched, pink-brown. Young leaves rose-pink turning to olive; lamina 2.5–7 × 1.5–3 cm, narrowly elliptic, thinly coriaceous, drying dull rufous to chocolate-brown beneath; margin hardly or not revolute; base attenuate cuneate; acumen –4.5 cm long; nerves very many, very slender, distinct and slightly elevated with the reticulate tertiaries beneath, obscure above; intramarginal nerve immediately within margin; petioles 5–6 mm long, very slender, drying black. Cymes –7 cm long, slender, quadrangular, many-flowered, terminal or subterminal-axillary; flowers pale pink, small; pedicel c. 1 mm long, short; calyx –2 mm long and diam., cup-shaped, with 4 short acute segments; petals –3 × 2 mm, elliptic, concave, fugaceous; stamens –4 mm long, slender. Fruit glabrous, ripe fruit not seen.

D i s t r. Western Ghats, Ceylon. In Ceylon common in the wet zone foothills from 100–800 m and occasionally higher, in primary forest often associated with *Shorea trapezifolia*, *S. zeylanica* and *S. gardneri*.

V e r n. Pinibaru, Maha kuretiye, Karaw (S), Damba (T).

S p e c i m e n s E x a m i n e d. MATARA DISTRICT: Uluwinduwa, Morawake, *Worthington 3704* (K); KANDY DISTRICT: Deltotte, Ambaga-muwa, *s. coll C.P. 2452* (PDA, K); Dolosbage, *s. coll. s. n.* April 1882 (PDA); Tembiligala, Gampola, *Worthington 4540* (K); Imboolpitiya, Nawalapitiya lower jungle, *Worthington 376* (K); Nawalapitiya, *Worthington 382* (K); road to Laxapana power house, *Worthington 5519* (K); Attabagie, Gampola, *Worthington 2300* (K); Kitulgala-Maskeliya road, *Ashton 2335* (PDA, US). KALUTARA DISTRICT: Morapitya, Hadigalla, *Waas 1446* (K); GALLE DISTRICT: Nellowe Kande, *s. coll. s.n.* 11.3.81 (PDA). KEGALLE DIS-TRICT: Ballabela, Kelani Valley, *Worthington 2105* (K). RATNAPURA DISTRICT: Gilimale forest, *Ashton 2255* (PDA, US); Nahaveena estate, Rakwana, *Worthington 3732* (K), *3733* (K).

18. Syzygium spathulatum Thw., Enum. Pl. Zeyl. 118. 1859; Alston in Trimen, Handb. Fl. Ceylon 6: 117. 1931.

Eugenia spathulata Beddome, For. Man. 108. 1874.
Eugenia olivifolia Duthie in Hook. f. Fl. Br. Ind. 2: 495. 1879; Trimen, Handb. Fl. Ceylon 2: 178. 1894.

A small tree, –10 m tall, with compact rounded crown with many twisted branches, and rough hard deeply cracked densely narrowly flaky pink to orange-brown bark. Twigs much branched, slender, quadrangular. Lamina up-pointing, bright copper when young; 3–5 × 1–1.8 cm, obovate to oblanceo-late, thinly coriaceous, rufous to golden matt beneath, narrowly revolute, obtuse or bluntly acuminate; base narrowly attenuate-cuneate; nerves c. 6–12 pairs, ascending, set at irregular intervals and often branching or coalescing, with shorter intermediates, very slender but distinctly elevated beneath, ± obscure above; intramarginal nerve close to margin, frequently obscure; mid-rib slender, drying black beneath, narrowly depressed above; petiole 3–5 mm

long, short, slender, channelled above. Cyme –3 cm long, slender, terminal
or subterminal axillary. Flowers pale pink, –2 mm long and diam., small;
pedicel c. 2 mm long, slender; calyx cup-shaped, lobes obscure; petals c. 2
mm long and broad, small, ovate; stamens short and hardly exceeding petals.
Fruit –7 mm diam., globose, with c. 1 mm diam. shortly projecting calyx
remnant, ripening purple.

D i s t r. Endemic. Abundant in primary and more particularly secondary
forest, often remaining and apparently regenerating in grasslands after degra-
dation; at 700–1500 m in the hills bordering the drier eastern margins of the
wet zone and the intermediate zone. At Madugoda, Govindahela, Deltota,
Lagalla, Namunukula, Fort Macdonald, Maturata and Ella Plains.

S p e c i m e n s   E x a m i n e d. KANDY DISTRICT: Dungolla, near
Madugoda, *Waas 1103* (PDA, US, K); Madugoda-Mahayangana road, *Tri-
vengadum & Waas 448* (PDA, US, K); Hunnasgiriya, *Kostermans 25154* (K);
Rangala to Corbet's Gap, *Kostermans 23498* (PDA, US, K); Nugatenne,
Madugoda, *Alston 472* (PDA), *494* (PDA, K); Madugoda, *Hepper & G. de
Silva 4706* (PDA, US, K), *Worthington 4994* (K), *Ashton 2314* (PDA, US);
Pilawela, Madugoda, *Worthington 1600* (K); Rangala, Knuckles, *Ashton 2302*
(PDA, US); Corbet's Gap, Knuckles, *Ashton 2308* (PDA, US). MATALE
DISTRICT: Dikpatana, Laggala, *Jayasuriya & Bandaranaike 1829* (PDA,
US, K); Laggala, *Balakrishnan & Dassanayake 1144* (PDA, US); Dikpatana,
Rattota-Illukkumbura, *Jayasuriya 275* (PDA, US, K). NUWARA ELIYA
DISTRICT: Above Belihul Oya, Horton Plains, *Kostermans 23438* (K);
Maturata, *Alexander s.n.* July 1890 (PDA); Maturata, *s. coll. C.P. 2493*
(PDA). BADULLA DISTRICT: Palugama-Boralanda road, *Balakrishnan
1056* (PDA, US); Tonacombe estate, Namunukula, Uva, *Worthington 5415*
(K), *5428* (K); Ella plains, *s. coll. C.P. 2493* (PDA); on way to Fort Macdo-
nold, *J.M.S. s.n.* 23.5.11 (PDA). RATNAPURA DISTRICT: Govindahela
A.M.S. s.n. 31.5. 06 (PDA).

N o t e. The fruit is juicy and edible. This species is extremely difficult
to distinguish when sterile from the larger flowered *S. umbrosum*.

19. Syzygium umbrosum Thw., Enum. Pl. Zeyl. 118. 1859; Alston in Trimen,
Handb. Fl. Ceylon 6: 116. 1931.

Eugenia umbrosa (non Berg) Beddome, For. Man. 108. 1874.
Eugenia subavenis (non Berg) Duthie in Hook. f., Fl. Br. Ind. 2: 489. 1879;
Trimen, Handb. Fl. Ceylon 2: 173. 1894.

A medium sized tree with pale pink-brown smooth or shallowly flaky bark
and dense much-branched crown. All parts glabrous. Twigs slender, quadrangular, dark brown, becoming pale brown, terete. Young leaves purplish
crimson; lamina 2–4.5 × 1.2–3.2 cm, spatulate or sometimes obovate or
broadly elliptic, drying chocolate-brown; margin narrowly revolute; base

cuneate; apex narrowly retuse, obtuse, or shortly broadly acuminate; main
nerves c. 5 pairs, ± obscure beneath and, if evident, ± merging with the reticulate tertiaries, typically minutely depressed above; midrib slender but
prominent beneath; petiole 2–7 mm long, short. Flowers white with crimson
calyx (Trimen), in –7 cm long dense but slender many-flowered terminal or
axillary cymes; pedicel c. 2 mm long; calyx c. 3 mm long and diam., cup-
shaped, with 4 shallow acute segments; petals c. 3 × 2 mm, elliptic, concave;
stamens c. 4 mm long. Fruit –2 cm diam., subglobose with prominent
apical rim.

D i s t r. Endemic, common between 1000 and 2000 m in the wet zone hills
from Rakwana to Knuckles and including Namunukula.

V e r n. Vali Damba, Hin Damba (S); Naval (T).

S p e c i m e n s E x a m i n e d. NUWARA ELIYA DISTRICT: World's
end, Horton Plains, *Kostermans 23131* (PDA, US, K); Ramboda, *s. coll. C.P.
2539* (PDA, K); Hakgala Nature Reserve, *Popham & Worthington 5671* (K),
6761 (K), *3007* (K), *s. coll. s.n.* Feb. 1886 (PDA), *Ashton 2279* (PDA, US),
2284 (PDA, US); Abotsford, Dimbulla, *W. Ferguson s.n.* 23.9.85 (PDA);
Nuwara Eliya, *Meijer 44* (PDA, US); Moon Plains *Balakrishnan & Dassanayake 1132* (PDA, US). KANDY DISTRICT: Le Vallon Estate, Dotelegala,
Worthington Le Poer Power 6509 (K); Madulkelle, Knuckles, *Kostermans
25027* (K), *25037* (K); Corbet's Gap, *Worthington 5472* (K), *3581* (K),
5030 (K), *3607* (K); Nilambe, *Worthington 2806* (K). BADULLA DISTRICT:
Adisham, Haputale, *Worthington 6351* (K); Namunukula, *J.M. Silva s.n.*
12.3.07 (PDA); Ella Plains, *s. coll. C.P. 2539* (PDA, K). RATNAPURA
DISTRICT: Aigburth estate, *Worthington 2636* (K). GALLE DISTRICT:
Nilowe Kande, *s. coll. s.n.* 11.3.81 (PDA).

N o t e. Easy to confuse with *S. spathulatum*, but the nervation on the
leaf upper surface of *S. umbrosum* is usually distinctive in the herbarium,
while the dark olive-green crown of *S. spathulatum* is unmistakable in the
field. *Meijer 44* is abnormal, with leaves resembling very small *S. revolutum*.

This species produces a light timber of inferior durability.

20. Syzygium cordifolium Walp., Rep. 2: 179. 1843; Thw., Enum. Pl. Zeyl.
116. 1859; Alston in Trimen, Handb. Fl. Ceylon 6: 117. 1931.

Eugenia cordifolia Wight, Ic. Pl. Ind. Or. t. 544. 1843; Ill. 2: 16. 1850; Her-
mann, Mus. Zeyl. 24. 1717; L., Fl. Zeyl. 184. 1747; Duthie in Hook f.,
Fl. Br. Ind. 2: 491. 1879; Trimen, Handb. Fl. Ceylon 2: 176. 1894.
Calyptranthes cordifolia Moon, Cat. 39. 1824.
Eugenia androsaemoides (non DC.) Beddome, Fl. Sylv. cvii. 1874.

ssp. **cordifolium.**

Small tree, 10 m tall, 0.5 m girth, with overall smooth, patchily thinly flaky pale brown bark. All parts glabrous. Twigs stout, terete, smooth. Young leaves pale crimson, remaining so on midrib beneath; lamina (6–) 9–17 × (4–) 7–12 cm, broadly elliptic, thickly coriaceous, lustrous, drying chocolate-brown beneath, purplish above; margin prominently revolute; base cordate; apex retuse, obtuse or subacute; main nerves many (c. 14 pairs with many ± shorter intermediates), slender, ± equally raised on both surfaces; tertiary nerves densely reticulate, less distinctly elevated; intramarginal nerves ± distinctly 2-tiered, the inner c. 3–6 mm within the margin, more prominent, rather straight; midrib stout, prominent beneath, deeply channelled above; petiole 2–6 mm long, short, very stout, drying black. Cymes –8 cm long, long-branched, terminal or subterminal-axillary, stout. Flowers white, shortly pedicellate; calyx tube –6 mm long and diam., urceolate, with 4 (–5) shallowly deltoid obtuse hardly reflexed lobes; petals –6 mm × 5 mm, elliptic, concave, fugaceous; stamens –10 mm long. Fruit –2 cm diam., globose, with a distinct c. 4 mm. diam. –3 mm tall apical collar bearing the persistent reflexed calyx segments.

Distr. Endemic. Common below 2000 m in the wet zone mountains from the Knuckles to the southern slopes of the Peak Sanctuary.

Vern. Waljambu (S).

Specimens Examined. KANDY DISTRICT: Laxapana-Maskeliya road, *Kostermans 24075A* (PDA, US, K); Tumagoda, near Tamanawatta-Masenna, *Kostermans 24463* (K); Adam's Peak and Ambagamuwa, *s. coll. C.P. 350* (2622) p.p. (PDA); Devonford, Upper Dickoya, *Worthington 3237* (K); Rajsurha valley, Surakanda, *Worthington 2621* (K); Rangala, *s. coll. s.n.* Sept. 1888 (PDA); Laxapana rest house, *s. coll. s.n.* 14.5.06 (PDA); Moray estate, Maskeliya, *Ashton 2341, 2345, 2349* (PDA, US), *Kostermans 24147, 24150 A, 24225* (PDA, US, K), *Davidse & Sumithraarachchi 8700* (PDA, US); Kunadiya Parawita, *F. Lewis s.n.* Christmas 1917 (PDA, US). RATNAPURA DISTRICT: Rasagalla, above Balangoda, *Kostermans 23600* (K); Balangoda estate jungle, *Worthington 763* (K); Gilimale forest, *Ashton 2252* (PDA, US). LOCALITY UNKNOWN: *Walker s.n.* (K).

ssp. **spissum** ssp. nov.

Syzygium spissum Alston in Trimen, Handb. Fl. Ceylon 6: 117. 1931.
Myrtus androsaemoides L., Sp. Pl. 472. 1753.
Syzygium androsaemoides Walp. nec. *Eugenia and rosaemoides* DC.
Eugenia cordifolia (non Wight) Trimen, Handb. Fl. Ceylon 2: 176. 1894.

Differing as follows: Lamina ovate-lanceolate, broadly acuminate, matt beneath; main nerves frequently branching, not parallel, with less prominent intermediates; intramarginal nerve 1-tiered; cyme –12 cm long, lax; flowers smaller, calyx tube –4 mm long and diam.

D i s t r. Endemic. Rare, lowland wet zone forests; Galle, Kottawe, Pella-watte, Kalutara, Colombo.

S p e c i m e n s E x a m i n e d: KALUTARA DISTRICT: Kalutara *s. coll. C.P. 350* p.p., (PDA); Pellawatte Mukulana, *s. coll. s.n.* June 1883 (PDA). GALLE DISTRICT: Buona Vista Hill, Galle, *Meijer 267* (PDA, US); Waiting Point, Galle, *Worthington 2361* (K); Kottawe F.R. Arboretum, *Ashton 2277* (PDA, US); Kanneliya F.R., *Jayasuriya 1534* (PDA, US, K). LOCALITY UNKNOWN: *Walker 40* (K).

N o t e. The two subspecies might be considered specifically distinct were it not for the collections from both ends of the southern scarp of the Peak Sanctuary (e.g. *Worthington 763*), which share the distinctive leaf shape of ssp. *spissum* but other characters of ssp. *cordifolium*.

21. Syzygium neesianum Arn., L. Nova Acta Phys: Med. Acad. Caes. teop. Carol. Nat. Cur. 18: 335. 1836; Thw., Enum Pl. Zeyl. 117. 1843; Alston in Tri-men, Handb. Fl. Ceylon 6: 116. 1931.

Eugenia neesiana Wight, Ic. Pl. Ind. Or. t. 533. 1843; Ill. 2: 15. 1850; Duthie in Hook. f., Fl. Br. Ind. 2: 493. 1879.

Large tree, –25 m tall, –2 m girth, with pale brown shallowly flaking bark and dense oblong to irregularly hemispherical crown of pendulous branch-es. Twigs rather slender, at first ± quadrangular, becoming terete, smooth, pale brown. Lamina 5.5–10 × 1.8–5 cm, elliptic, frequently subplicate, charta-ceous or thinly coriaceous, drying lustrous dark olive-brown or chocolate-brown beneath; base obtuse or subcordate; margin shallowly subrevolute, ± undulate; apex –1 cm long slender acuminate; nerves many, with short inter-mediates and densely reticulate tertiaries, very slender but distinctly elevated beneath, more obscurely so above; intramarginal nerve ± obscurely 2-tiered, the inner c. 1–2 mm within margin, rather straight; midrib slender but promi-nent beneath, drying black; petiole 1–3 mm long, very short, slender, drying black. Cymes –8 cm long, terminal or axillary, lax, spreading; flowers white; calyx –4 × 3 mm, small, goblet-shaped, with (4–) 5 obscure segments round the lip; petals –3 × 2 mm, elliptic, concave; stamens –4 mm long. Fruit –1 cm diam., globose, woody, with ± prominent 3 mm diam. unlobed terminal collar.

D i s t r. Endemic. Common in the wet zone lowlands rain forest from Madulkelle to Morowaka, frequently remaining as a relict after felling; –1100 m.

V e r n. Panu-kera (S).

U s e s. A heavy timber used for building.

S p e c i m e n s E x a m i n e d. KALUTARA DISTRICT: Badureliya, *Cramer 4168* (PDA, US, K); Kukul Korale, June 1883, *s. coll. s.n.* p.p. (PDA, mixture with *S. assimile*); Pasdun Korale, March 1887, *s. coll. s.n.* (PDA), June

1883, *s. coll. s.n.* (PDA). MATARA DISTRICT: between Morawaka & Opata, *s. coll. C.P. 4013* (PDA). RATNAPURA DISTRICT: Illambekande, Rakwana, *Worthington 3645* (K); Kalawana-Morapitiya road, *Ashton 2334* (PDA, US); Kalawana, *Worthington 4610* (K); Morapitiya forest, *Meijer 1086* (PDA, US); Ratnapura, *s. coll. C.P. 735* (PDA, K). KANDY DISTRICT: Aratenne, Madulkelle, *Worthington 2020* (K), Andiatenne (Halgolla), Kadugannawa, *Worthington 6914* (K); Poilakanda, Kadugannawa, *Worthington 708* (K); Hantane, *s. coll. C.P. 735* (PDA, K); Ambagamuwa, *s. coll. C.P. 735* (PDA, K); Oodoowela, *Worthington 346* (K). KEGALLE DISTRICT: Pendenioya, *Worthington 5202* (K). GALLE DISTRICT: Dediyagala forest, *Hancock & Worthington 2577* (K). LOCALITY UNKNOWN: *J.S. Mackenzie s.n.* (K), *Walker s.n.* (K), *Gardner 489* (K).

N o t e. Though leaf size is variable the shape and nervation, as well as other characters, are very constant and make this a well-defined species.

22. Syzygiunn cumini Skeels, U.S.D.A. Bur. Pl. Industr. Bull. 248: 25. 1912; Alston in Trimen, Handb. Fl. Ceylon 6: 116. 1931.

Myrtus cumini L., Sp. Pl. 471. 1753.
Jambolifera pedunculata Gaertn., Fruct. 1: 178. 1788; Wight, Ic. Pl. Ind. Or. t. 620. 1843
Eugenia jambolana Lam., Enc. 3: 198. 1789; Burm., Thes. 197. 1647; Hermann, Mus. Zeyl. 185. 1747; Wight, Ic. Pl. Ind. Or. t. 535. 1843; Beddome, Fl. Sylv. t. 197. 1874; Duthie, in Hook. f., Fl. Br. Ind. 2: 499. 1879; Trimen, Handb. Fl. Ceylon 2: 179. 1894.
Calyptranthes cumini Moon, Cat. 39. 1824, nomen nudum.
Syzygium jambolanum DC., Prod. 3: 259. 1858; Thw., Enum. Pl. Zeyl. 116. 1859; id. 417. 1864.
Eugenia cumini Druce, Bot. Exch. Club Br. Isles Rep. 3: 48. 1914.

Large shrub to large canopy tree, –25 m tall, –3 m girth; bark surface pale yellow-brown, densely thinly flaky; inner bark thick, fibrous, pale brown; crown diffuse, oblong with pendant twigs and leaves. All parts glabrous. Twigs slender, terete, cream. Lamina pale yellowish green, 6.5–11 × 2.5–5 cm, elliptic to ovate-lanceolate, thinly coriaceous, minutely though distinctly punctate beneath and pitted above, drying matt pale yellow-brown; margin distinctly undulate; base cuneate, shortly decurrent; apex with –1 cm long prominent slender acumen, downcurved and twisting over when pressed; nerves very many, subequal, arising obliquely and then spreading, hair-thin though distinctly elevated beneath as also the densely reticulate tertiaries, ± obscurely depressed above; intramarginal nerve straight, c. 1 mm within margin; midrib slender, elevated beneath, shallowly channelled above; petiole 8–20 mm long, long, slender. Cymes –10 cm long, terminal or axillary but mainly ramiflorous, spreading; flower calyx –4 × 3 mm, goblet-shaped, tapering towards base, the rim orange, obscurely 4 (–5)-segmented; petals c. 4 × 3 mm, elliptic, calyptrate, fugaceous; stamens c. 4 mm long, white, filaments very slender. Fruit c. 12 (–20) × 8 (–14) mm, broadly ellipsoid, ripening purple, crowned by a c. 2 mm diam. ± prominent calyx rim.

D i s t r. India, Ceylon and eastwards to South China, Malaysia and the Pacific. Common, often gregarious as a large tree in the dry zone, in all forms of forest but especially along the margins of streams and tanks. Forming gregarious colonies as a –5 m tall shrub in the sand dunes of the north, where it plays a major part in anchoring the sand and stabilising dune ridges.

U s e s. The heavy timber is used for construction, bridges etc.

V e r n. Madan, Mahadan (S); Naval, Perunaval (T).

S p e c i m e n s E x a m i n e d. KANDY DISTRICT: Ulapane, Kandy road, *Kostermans 24623* (PDA, US, K); Hantane, *Gardner 300* (PDA, K); Pusselawa, *Ferguson s.n.* May 1878 (PDA). TRINCOMALEE DISTRICT: Trincomalee, *C.P. 3644* (PDA, K); Trincomalee-Kuchavelli, *Kostermans 24805* (PDA, US, K). AMPARAI DISTRICT: Road to Damana, *Kostermans 24377* (PDA, US, K). MATALE DISTRICT: Baligama, Galawale, *Worthington 5363* (K), *6407* (K); Dambulla, Kandalama, *Sumithraarachchi 464* (PDA, US, K). POLONNARUWA DISTRICT: Polonnaruwa-Batticaloa road at Mahaweli bridge, *Meijer & Balakrishnan 121* (PDA, US); Giritale Wewe N.W. of Polonnaruwa, *Fosberg & Ripley 51937* (PDA, US); Polonnaruwa sacred area, *Hladik 948* (PDA, US), *853* (PDA, US). HAMBANTOTA DISTRICT: Menik Ganga, Yala N.P., *Meijer 227* (PDA, US). ANURADHAPURA DISTRICT: Ritigala, *Meijer 337* (PDA, US, K), *Cramer 3034* (PDA, US); Wilpattu, *van Beusekom 1614* (PDA, US), *Hladik 820* (PDA, US); *Wirawan, Cooray & Balakrishnan 915* (PDA, US, K), *Mueller-Dombois 68091001* (PDA, US); Maradammaduwa, Wilpattu, *Ripley* 38 (PDA, US); Weerakuti Villu & Maduru Odai, Wilpattu, *Mueller-Dombois & Balakrishnan 68091210* (PDA, US, K); Kali Villu, Wilpattu, *Mueller-Dombois 68091108* (PDA, US, K); Periya Naga Villu, Wilpattu, *Cooray 69092613 R* (PDA, US, K); Panikar Villu, Wilpattu, *Davidse & Sumithraarachchi 8201* (PDA, US). PUTTALAM DISTRICT: Pallugaturai, *Wheeler 12089* (PDA, US). KURUNEGALA DISTRICT: Dunkande, *Ashton 2321* (PDA, US). JAFFNA DISTRICT: Jaffna, *Ashton 2325, 2326* (PDA, US); *s. coll. C.P. 1584* (PDA, K). VAVUNIYA DISTRICT: Vavuniya, *Kostermans 25107* (PDA, US, K). MONERAGALA DISTRICT: Lahugala Sanctuary, Kitula, *Comanor 596* (PDA, US, K). DISTRICT UNKNOWN: Eastern Province, *Vincent s.n.*; Ambale, *Senaratne 2868* (PDA).

N o t e. The tree is cultivated in India for its succulent fruit but not, apparently, in Sri Lanka where only the smaller fruited variety (var. *microcarpa* of Trimen) is common, though the shrub of northern sand-dunes has larger fruit (dimensions in brackets in the description) and obtuse or subacute leaves.

23. Syzygium makul Gaertn., Fruct. 1: 166. 1778; Alston in Trimen, Handb. Fl. Ceylon 6: 116. 1931.

Eugenia sylvestris Moon ex Wight, Ic. Pl. Ind. Or. t. 532. 1843; Ill. 2: 15. 1850; Duthie in Hook., f., Fl. Br. Ind. 2: 116. 1879; Trimen, Handb. Fl. Ceylon 2: 175. 1894.
Syzygium sylvestre Thw., Enum. Pl. Zeyl. 116. 1859.

Large tree, –30 m tall, –2.5 m girth, with ± diffuse crown. Bark surface at first pale grey-brown, smooth, becoming thinly papery flaked and dippled, pale orange-brown, with prominent lozenges of persisting old bark. Trunk freely suckering. All parts glabrous. Twigs stout, terete, pale cream-brown. Young leaf bright crimson; lamina 9–17 × 4.5–7 cm, narrowly obovate to elliptic, coriaceous, drying lustrous dark chocolate-brown beneath; margin revolute; base cuneate, shortly decurrent; apex with –1 cm long narrow downcurved acumen (twisting over on pressing); nerves many, with many intermediates, spreading, very slender, evident but hardly elevated on either surface (young trees excepted); tertiary nerves densely reticulate; intramarginal nerve very slender, c. 1 mm within margin; midrib prominent beneath, drying blackish; petiole 8–15 mm long, rather stout, drying black. Cymes –8 cm long, terminal or subterminal axillary, erect with many small white subsessile flowers; calyx –3 × 2 mm, campanulate with 4 (–5) obscure segments; petals small, concave, fugaceous; stamens c. 4 mm long. Fruit –12 mm diam., subglobose, 1–2 seeded, with small c. 3 mm diam. terminal unlobed crown, ripening purplish.

D i s t r. Endemic; common in the wet zone below 1000 m, local in the northern intermediate zone.

U s e s. The wood is used for building and plywood manufacture. The fruit is eaten by parrots.

V e r n. Alu-bo (S).

S p e c i m e n s E x a m i n e d. KANDY DISTRICT: Corbet's Gap, *Kostermans 23517* (PDA, US, K). RATNAPURA DISTRICT: Matugama-Morapitiya road *Kostermans 24970* (PDA, US, K); Morapitiya, *Kostermans 24684* (PDA, US, K), *Meijer 463* (PDA, US); Gilimale forest, *Ashton 2331* (PDA, US), *Worthington 6459* (K), *6756* (K); Orangefield estate, Rakwana, *Worthington 2146* (K), *3632* (K); Deepdene, Rakwana, *Worthington 3746* (K); Karawita Kande, *Ashton 2257* (PDA, US), *2265* (PDA, US); Ratnapura, *s. coll. C.P. 2862* (PDA, K). KURUNEGALA DISTRICT: Kurunegala, *s. coll. s.n.* Sept. 1888 (PDA), *s. coll. C.P. 2862* (PDA, K). GALLE DISTRICT: Nakiyadeniya, *Worthington 6046* (K), *5230* (K); Sinharaja via Hiniduma, *Worthington 2284* (K); Naunkitaela, Kanneliya forest, *Worthington 3677* (K); Haycock, *Worthington 2284* (K); Kanneliya forest, Worthington *6043* (K); Homadola, Udugama, *Worthington 6019* (K). COLOMBO DISTRICT:

Labugama reservoir, *Worthington 3504* (K), *3478* (K). DISTRICT UN-
KNOWN: Tambagoda, Tamanawatte-Masenna road, *Kostermans 24485* (K);
Tennahena, Hulandu Oya, *Worthington 3665* (K); s. loc. *Walker s.n.* (PDA,
K), *36* (K), *84* (K).

24. Syzygium operculatum (Roxb.) Niedz. in Pflanzenfam. 31. 7: 85. 1893;
Gamble, Fl. Pres. Madras 481. 1919; Alston in Trimen, Handb. Fl. Ceylon 6:
115. 1931.

Eugenia operculatum Roxb., Hort. Beng. 37. 1812; Fl. Ind. 2: 486. 1824, desc.;
  Wight, Ic. Pl. Ind. Or. t. 551. 1843; Duthie in Hook. f., Fl. Br. Ind. 2: 498.
  1879; Trimen, Handb. Fl. Ceylon 2: 179. 1894.
Calyptanthes caryophyllifolia Moon, Cat. 39. 1824, nomen nudum.
Syzygium nervosum DC., Prod. 3: 260. 1828.
Cleistocalyx operculatus (Roxb.) Merr. & Perry, J. Arn. Arb. 19: 246. 1938.

A large tree, –25 m tall, branching low, the branches spreading; bark
surface grey-brown, smooth, becoming flaky on trunk, milky white opales-
cent on branches. Twigs at first green, ± terete, later becoming distinct whitish. Young leaves pink, old leaves yellow-brown; lamina 6–12 × 3–5 cm,
elliptic-obovate, chartaceous, matt, with undulate hardly revoluted margin,
tapering attenuate base and –1 cm long ± slender downcurved acumen (bent
over on pressed specimens); nerves 7–15 pairs, ascending, slender but distinctly elevated beneath, narrowly depressed above as also the midrib; intramarginal nerve prominently looped, at 1–3 mm from the margin; petiole (5–) 8–11
mm long, slender. Cyme –8 cm long, –2-axillary, ramiflorous immediately
behind the leaves, lax. Flower buds –5 × 3 mm, obovoid; flowers –12 mm
diam.; calyx campanulate-calyptrate, segments obscure; petals –4 × 3 mm,
oblong; stamens –7 mm long, exceeding petals. Fruit –8 × 6 mm, ellipsoid,
purple, succulent, crowned by a c. 4 mm diam. calyx ring and persistent style
remnant.

D i s t r. S.E. Asia, India, Ceylon. Locally common in the wet and intermediate zones below 1300 m., especially in ravines and along river banks.

U s e s. The greyish-yellow wood is used for house building.

V e r n. Bata-damba, Diya-damba, Kobo-mal (S).

S p e c i m e n s E x a m i n e d. KANDY DISTRICT: Hunnasgiriya, *s. coll.*
C.P. 2801 (PDA); Peradeniya, *Kostermans 23136* (PDA, US); Andiatenne,
Kadugannawe, *Worthington 107* (K); Hantane, *Worthington 255* (K); Hewaheta, *Alston 642.* Tismada, Kadugannawa, *Worthington 1147* (K); Kellie
estate, Dolosbage, *Worthington 1184* (K); Kadugannawa, *Worthington 5977*
(K); Nilambe, *Worthington 2862* (K). BADULLA DISTRICT: Bibile-Maha-
yangana road, *Cooray 69080104 R* (PDA, US); Erabedde Arboretum,
Welimada, *Worthington 5933* (K), *6190* (K); Namunukula, *Worthington
6178* (K); Welimada-Bandarawela, *Worthington 2932* (K); Micklefield, Guru-

talawa, *Gorrie 5581* (K). GALLE DISTRICT: Udugama, *Worthington 6055* (K). MONERAGALA DISTRICT: Moneragala-Bibile road, *Ashton 3227* (PDA, US).

N o t e. *Cleistocalyx* Bl., which was resurrected by Merrill and Perry, differs from *Syzygium* only in the calyptrate calyx; I follow Schmid in not distinguishing it.

25. Syzygium gardneri Thw., Enum. Pl. Zeyl. 117. 1859; Gamble, Fl. Pres. Madras 878. 1919; Alston in Trimen, Handb. Fl. Ceylon 6: 117. 1931.
Eugenia gardneri Beddome, For. Man. 108. 1874; Duthie in Hook. f., Fl. Br. Ind. Br. 2: 174. 1879; Trimen, Handb. Fl. Ceylon 2: 174. 1894.

A medium sized tree, –20 m tall, –2 m girth, frequently suckering towards the base; with smooth pale grey or cream-brown bark and fresh-green crown. All parts glabrous. Twigs slender, terete, conspicuous pale cream. Young leaves apple-red, old leaves turning yellow; lamina 4–9.5 × 1.5–4 cm, ovate-lanceolate, chartaceous, drying dull grey-green; margin undulate, narrowly subrevolute; base cuneate; acumen –2 cm long, slender, attenuate; nerves very many, hair-slender but distinct and slightly elevated on both surfaces; tertiary nerves densely reticulate, obscure above; intramarginal nerve immediately within margin, somewhat looped; midrib slender, prominent beneath, narrowly raised above; petiole 9–13 mm long, very slender, prominent. Cymes –5 cm long, terminal or axillary, slender, much branched; flowers white, small; pedicel c. 2 mm long, short; calyx –3 mm long and diam., funnel-shaped, obscurely segmented; petals c. 3 mm long, 2 mm broad, elliptic, concave, fugaceous; stamens c. 2 mm long, very slender. Fruit –12 (–18) × 10 mm, ellipsoid-obovoid, ripening green, with shallow c. 2 mm diam. terminal ring.

D i s t r. Southern India, Ceylon. Common in the wet and intermediate zones below 1300 m, in moist places and especially on the banks of streams.
U s e s. The timber is used for building.
V e r n. Damba (S); Nir-nawal (T).
S p e c i m e n s E x a m i n e d. KANDY DISTRICT: Deltota *s. coll. C.P. 2496* (PDA, with one twig of *S. rubicundum*); Poilakande, Kadugamuwa, *Worthington 1044* (K); Attabagie, Gampola, *Worthington 2825* (K); Udawattekelle, *Meijer 87* (PDA, US); Madugoda, *Ashton 2318* (PDA, US); Kitulgala-Maskeliya road, *Ashton 2337* (PDA, US); 10 miles west of Mahayangana, *Davidse & Jayasuriya 8432* (PDA, US). RATNAPURA DISTRICT: Pettigala, Balangoda, *Worthington 3213* (K); Opanayake-Balangoda road, *Balakrishnan & Jayasuriya 881* (PDA, US); Kalawana-Morapitiya road, *Ashton 2333* (PDA, K). MATALE DISTRICT: Dambulla, *Cramer 3844* (K). KURUNEGALA DISTRICT: Badagama IBP plot, *Ashton 2319* (PDA, US). GALLE DISTRICT: Kannaliya Forest, *Ashton 2272* (PDA, US). LOCA-

LITY UNKNOWN: *Walker 90* (K), *1661* (K).

26. Syzygium micranthum Thw., Enum. Pl. Zeyl. 117. 1859; Alston in Trimen, Handb. Fl. Ceylon 6: 117. 1931.

Eugenia micrantha Beddome (non. DC., Bertol.) For. Man. 108. 1874; Duthie in Hook. f., Fl. Br. Ind. 2: 483. 1879; Trimen, Handb. Fl. Ceylon 2: 175. 1894.

A small to medium-sized tree, –10 m tall, –40 cm diam., with diffuse weeping crown and orange-brown flaky bark. Twigs terete, slender, red-brown, pendant. Lamina 4–10 × 1–2.5 cm, ovate-lanceolate, coriaceous, drying matt-grey to rufous-brown beneath, greyish purple above; margin frequently prominently revolute towards the broadly cuneate base; apex with prominent –2 cm long caudate acumen; nerves 10–13 pairs, slender but ± distinctly elevated on both surfaces as also the equally elevated reticulate tertiary nerves; intramarginal nerve distinct, c. 1 mm within margin; midrib slender, prominent beneath; petiole (5–) 7–12 mm long, slender. Cymes –5 cm long, terminal or axillary to ramiflorous, slender, pendant; flowers –2 mm diam., minute, pale green, acrid; calyx urceolate, tapering into the c. 2 mm long pedicel, segments rotate. Fruit –4 mm diam., globose, crowned with a c. 1 mm diam. calyx ring.

D i s t r. Endemic. Common between 800 and 1800 m in mid-mountain forests, on the west side of the main massifs from Knuckles to Sinharaja and also in the hills of Sabaragamuwa to the Rakwana plateau.

S p e c i m e n s E x a m i n e d. KANDY DISTRICT: Kitulgala-Maskeliya Road, Ashton *2339* (PDA, US); Moray estate, Maskeliya, *Tirvengadum & Cramer 312* (PDA, US, K), *Kostermans 24204* (PDA, US, K), *Jayasuriya & Sumithraarachchi 1573* (PDA, US, K); Wattegodde, Ambagamuwa & Gongalla, *C.P.* 1580 (PDA, K); Nawalapitya, *Worthington 916* (K); Dolosbage, *s. coll. s.n.* (PDA), *Worthington 3718* (K), *2164* (K); Devonford estate, *Worthington 3241* (K); Galbodde, *Worthington 2773* (K); Brownlow, Maskeliya, *Worthington 1911* (K); Kandy, *Wight s.n.*; Adam's Peak, *Worthington 2738* (K). RATNAPURA DISTRICT: Ellabodde Kande, *F. Lewis & J.M.S. s.n.*, 25.3.1919 (PDA). LOCALITY UNKNOWN: *Gardner 1208* (K).

N o t e. Specimens from Dolosbage and Rakwana tend to have smaller leaves; in those from Kandy and Knuckles the leaves are relatively longer, drying darker red beneath.

27. Syzygium lewisii Alston in Trimen, Handb. Fl. Ceylon 6: 117. 1931.

A small tree. All parts glabrous. Twigs pale brown, terete. Lamina 5–8 × 2.5–3.5 cm, lanceolate, coriaceous, drying chocolate-brown, with cuneate shortly decurrent base and –2 cm long prominent subcaudate acumen; main nerves many, very slender but distinctly and ± equally elevated with the reticulate tertiaries beneath, narrowly but distinctly depressed above; intramarginal nerve clearly evident, rather straight, 1–2 mm within margin; petiole 9–12 mm long, drying black or brown and rugulose. Cymes –6 cm long, erect, terminal or axillary, flowers in subsessile clusters; calyx –5 × 3 mm at anthesis, with 4 short submucronate segments; petals small, calyptrate. Fruit (young) –5 mm long and diam., ovoid, distinctly pedicellate, with c. 4 mm diam. terminal calyx ring.

D i s t r. Endemic. Rare, known only from the cited collections, the latter from skeletal soils on a rocky plateau at c. 300 m.

S p e c i m e n s E x a m i n e d. RATNAPURA DISTRICT: *F. Lewis & J.M.S. s.n.* 25.3.1919 (PDA); Udakarawita, *Balakrishnan 326* (PDA, US, K).

28. Syzygium revolutum Walp., Rep. 2: 180. 1843; Thw., Enum. Pl. Zeyl. 117. 1859; Alston in Trimen, Handb. Fl. Ceylon 6: 116. 1931.

Eugenia revoluta Wight, Ic. Pl. Ind. Or. t. 534. 1843; Ill. 2: 17. 1850; Duthie in Hook. f., Fl. Br. Ind. 2: 402. 1879; Trimen, Handb. Fl. Ceylon 2: 175. 1894.

ssp. **Revolutum**

A canopy tree, –10 m tall, –2 m girth, with greyish brown cracked, shallowly flaky and scroll-marked bark, crooked and twisted bole and branches, and diffuse rather flat crown. All parts glabrous. Twigs at first rather slender, terete, with short internodes and much branched, rapidly becoming stout; pale grey-brown. Young leaves bright apple-red; lamina 2.5–7.5 × 1.7–5.3 cm, ± broadly elliptic-obovate, thickly coriaceous, distinctly glaucous beneath (bluish in live foliage) and drying chocolate matt; margin revolute, especially at the narrowly or broadly cuneate base; base shortly decurrent; apex retuse, obtuse, subacute or shortly broadly acuminate; main nerves c. 8 pairs, arising at varying intervals, frequently branched, not parallel, with a few shorter intermediates, slender but prominent beneath; tertiary nerves densely reticulate, less prominent than nerves beneath but ± distinctly and equally raised with them and often obscurely channelled above; midrib shallowly channelled above; intramarginal nerve 1 (–2) tiered, 1–2 mm within margin; petiole 3–6 mm long, rather stout, drying black. Flowers many, pale pink, in slender but dense erect terminal or –3-axillary cymes; calyx –4 × 3 mm, with a shallow terminal cup bearing (4–) 5 shallow acute lobes and a slender basal tube; petals –3 × 2 mm, elliptic, concave, fugaceous; stamens –4 mm long, stout. Fruit –7 × 6 mm, ellipsoid, with a 3 mm diam. terminal crown; ripening purplish red.

D i s t r. Southern India, Ceylon. Common between 1600 and 2400 m on the main mountain massif from the northern slopes of Pidurutalagala to Horton Plains.

Specimens Examined. NUWARA ELIYA DISTRICT: Great Western Range, near Lindula, *Kostermans 24598* (K); Horton Plains, *Kostermans 23010* (PDA, US, K), *Worthington 1709* (K), *J.M. Silva s.n.* (PDA), *Comanor 957* (PDA, US), *Cooray 13530* (PDA, US), *Ashton 2293* (PDA, US), *2295* (PDA, US), *2298* (PDA, US); Dimbula, Abbotsford, *Ferguson s.n.* 23.9.85 (PDA); Bulu Ela Arboretum, *Worthington 2917* (K); Kandapola F.R., *Worthington 5640* (K); Pidurutalagala, *Meijer 60* (PDA, US), *65* (PDA, US). BADULLA DISTRICT: Yelumalai, Namunukula, *J.M. Silva s.n.* 12.3.07 (PDA). VARIOUS LOCALITIES: Adam's Peak & Maturata, *C.P. 2521* p.p. (PDA). LOCALITY UNKNOWN: *Walker s.n.* (K).

ssp. **cyclophyllum** stat. nov.

Eugenia cyclophylla Thw. ex Duthie in Hook. f., Fl. Br. Ind. 2: 494. 1878; Trimen, Handb. Fl. Ceylon 2: 177. 1894.
Syzygium cyclophyllum Alston in Trimen, Handb. Fl. Ceylon 6: 116. 1931.
Syzygium revolutum var. *viridis* Alston in Trimen, Handb. Fl. Ceylon 6: 116. 1931.

Differing as follows: Lamina –8.5 × 6.5 cm, broadly elliptic to suborbicular, typically lustrous beneath, becoming prominently concave with deeply revolute margin; base typically obtuse; intramarginal nerve typically 2-tiered.

Distr. Locally frequent, at similar altitudes to the type sub-species, in the mist-shrouded slopes and spurs leading down from Adam's Peak.

Specimens Examined. RATNAPURA DISTRICT: Kanadiyaparawita, *F. Lewis s.n.* Christmas 1917 (PDA); Balangoda estate, *Worthington 323* (K). KANDY DISTRICT: Base of Adam's Peak above Moray Estate, *Ashton 2350* (PDA, US), *Davidse & Sumithraarachchi 8634* (PDA, US); Adam's Peak, *s. coll. s.n.* March 1883 (PDA); Brownlow, Maskeliya, *Worthington 2751* (K); Ambagamuwa, *s. coll. C.P. 2521* p.p. (PDA). LOCALITY UNKNOWN: *s. coll. C.P. 3915* (PDA, K).

Note. A variable species. *C.P. 3915* and *s.n.*, March 1883 are examples of the very distinctive extreme form of subspecies *cyclophyllum* upon which the original description was based. Lewis' collection consists of two small twigs of this form, and a larger one in which the leaves are less markedly revolute and with broadly cuneate bases; *Worthington 2761* bears leaves which match this subspecies exactly, others which match the Ambagamuwa specimen under *C.P. 2521*—type of *S. revolutum* var. *viridis*. The identical and rather characteristic inflorescences and fruit of the two subspecies confirm beyond doubt that they are conspecific.

29. Syzygium caryophyllatum (L.) Alston in Trimen, Handb. Fl. Ceylon 6: 116. 1931.

SYZYGIUM 451

Myrtus caryophyllatus L., Sp. Pl. 472. 1753.
Eugenia corymbosa Lam., Enc. 3: 199. 1789.
Syzygium corymbosum (Lam.) DC., Prod. 3: 261. 1828.

A small tree with ascending branches and pale grey-brown smooth or minutely grid-cracked bark. Twigs rather straight, terete, rufous-brown, scurfy. Leaves frequently subopposite, up-pointing; lamina 3.5–10 × 2–5.5 cm, obovate or oblanceolate, densely punctate on both surfaces, drying dark red-brown matt beneath; base cuneate; margin narrowly or not revolute; apex obtuse or shortly subacuminate; nerves many, with many ± shorter intermediates, hair-slender but distinctly elevated beneath as also the tertiaries, ± evident but unraised above; midrib slender but prominent, drying dark brown or black beneath, narrowly channelled above; intramarginal nerve straight, c. 1 mm within margin; petiole 4–7 mm long, short, drying black. Cymes –6 cm long, dense, ascending, much branched, terminal or subterminal-axillary; flower white; calyx c. 2 mm long and diam., urceolate, small, c. 1 mm pedicellate, shallowly 4-segmented; petals –2 mm long and broad, suborbicular, calyptrate; stamens c. 4 mm long, very slender. Fruit–8 mm diam., subglobose, with prominent, c. 2 mm diam. unlobed apical collar, ripening dark purple, succulent.

D i s t r. Western Malaysia, Southern India, Ceylon. Common in secondary forest, especially on sandy soils in the wet zone lowlands and into the margins of the intermediate zone.

V e r n. Dan, Rin-dan (S).

S p e c i m e n s E x a m i n e d. GALLE DISTRICT: Hiniduma F.R., *Kostermans 24707* (PDA, US, K); Homadola, Udugama, *Worthington 6052* (K); Kottawe Arboretum, *Ashton 2676* (PDA, US). RATNAPURA DISTRICT: Kalawana-Morapitiya road, *Kostermans 24626* (PDA, US, K); Gilimale Forest, *Ashton 2260* (PDA, US); Kudawe near Weddagala, *Hoogland 11453* (PDA, US). KANDY DISTRICT: Peradeniya, *Alston s.n.* 4.11.25 (PDA), *Cooray 6904041 R* (PDA, US, K); Kandy, *Worthington 1922* (K); Atabage, *Worthington 2849* (K); Manikdiwela, Kandy-Alagalla road, *Kostermans 24040* (PDA, US). COLOMBO DISTRICT: Colombo & Negombo, *s. coll. C.P. 1583* p.p. (PDA); Negombo, *Meijer 594* (PDA, US); Pamunugama, *Comanor 1144* (PDA, US). KALUTARA DISTRICT: Ranawaka rock, Pellewatte, *Cramer 3175* (PDA, US). DISTRICT UNKNOWN: Hallawakellae forest, Welipenna road, *Balakrishnan 1169* (PDA, US); *Walker s.n.* (PDA).

N o t e. I have not seen the holotype.

30. Syzygium assimile Thw., Enum. Pl. Zeyl. 116. 1859; Alston in Trimen, Handb. Fl. Ceylon 6: 116. 1931.

Eugenia assimilis Duthie in Hook. f., Fl. Br. Ind. 2: 493. 1878; Trimen, Handb. Fl. Ceylon 2: 176. 1894.

ssp. **Assimile**

A medium sized tree with dense low crown of ascending branches, fluted bole, and red-brown roughly irregularly shallowly oblong flaky scrophulous bark. Parts glabrous but for the ± sericeous disc. Twigs rather stout, grey-brown, terete. Young leaves brilliant crimson; lamina 5–12 × 2–5 cm, elliptic-obovate to oblanceolate, coriaceous, drying ± lustrous dark chocolate-brown; margin ± prominently revolute; base cuneate or occasionally obtuse; apex shortly abruptly downcurved-acuminate, rarely obtuse; main nerves c. 12 pairs, many and with subequal intermediates, very slender, obscure and hardly raised on either surface as also the tertiaries; intramarginal nerve c. 1 mm within margin and often hidden within it; petiole 3–7 (–9) mm long, drying black. Cyme –10 cm long, rigid, many-flowered, terminal or subterminal-axillary; flowers cream; calyx –5 mm long and diam., cup-shaped, tapering to the c. 3 mm long pedicel, with 4 (–5) rotate acute segments; petals c. 3 × 2 mm, elliptic, concave, fugaceous; stamens c. 5 mm long. Fruit –15 mm diam., subglobose, ripening green, with c. 4 mm diam. apical crown.

D i s t r. S. India, Ceylon. Common throughout the wet zone hills between 800 and 2000 m, in both primary and secondary forest.

S p e c i m e n s   E x a m i n e d. KANDY DISTRICT: Elk plains near Ambawela, *Kostermans 23100* (PDA, US, K); Moray estate, Maskeliya, *Kostermans 24926* (PDA, US, K); *Ashton 2346* (PDA, US), *Balasubramaniam 895* (PDA, US); Hunnasgiriya, *s. coll. C.P. 2449* (PDA, K); Madugoda, *Ashton 2316* (PDA, US); Corbet's Gap, *Ashton 2306* (PDA, US), *Worthington 3607* (K), *Kostermans 23517* (PDA, US); Le Vallon, Galaha, *Worthington & Le Poer Power 6511* (K); Galbodde, *Worthington 6541* (K); Ramboda Pass, *Worthington 5782* (K), *2901* (K); Knuckles, *Ferguson s.n.* April 1887 (K). NUWARA ELIYA DISTRICT: Hakgala Nature Reserve, *Worthington 3009* (K); Bulu Ela arboretum, *Worthington 2916* (K); Nuwara Eliya, *Worthington 1929* (K); Naseby, Nuwara Eliya, *Worthington 5790* (K); Westward Ho. Estate, *Worthington 4048* (K); Dimbula, *Ferguson s.n.* 23.9.85 (PDA); Panathibu Kande, Uma Oya *Silva 236* (PDA); north-east of Ohiya patanas, *Ferguson s.n.* 1895 (PDA). VARIOUS DISTRICTS: Haldmilla, Reigam Korale, Deltota, *s. coll. C.P. 46* (PDA, K). DISTRICT UNKNOWN: Way to Fort Macdonald, *Silva s.n.* 25.5.11 (PDA). LOCALITY UNKNOWN: *C.P. 291* (K), *Gardner 301* (K).

U s e s. Providing a good building timber.

V e r n. Damba (S).

ssp. **acuminata** subspecies nov.

Differing as follows: Lamina elliptic-ovate; margin hardly revolute; nerves distinctly elevated beneath; petiole 10–15 mm long; cymes –6 cm long, with relatively fewer, larger flowers than the type.

D i s t r. Endemic. Local in evergreen sclerophyll forest below 800 m on the eastern margin of the wet zone, including Namunukula and Lunugala; rare in the wet zone lowlands.

S p e c i m e n s E x a m i n e d. RATNAPURA DISTRICT: Gilimale, *Worthington 6484* (K), *6458* (K); Belihul Oya, Haldemilla, *Worthington 4759* (K). KALUTARA DISTRICT: Kukul Korale, *anon. s.n.* June 1883 (PDA); BADULLA DISTRICT: Lunugala, *Worthington 6316* (K); Tonacombe, Namunukula, *Worthington 5411* (K). KANDY DISTRICT: Madugoda, *Worthington 1617* (K). LOCALITY UNKNOWN: *s. coll. C.P. 1583* (PDA, one sheet only, otherwise *S. caryophyllatum*).

N o t e. *Worthington 4759* has unusually large leaves with dull undersurface, and may represent a hybrid with another species. *C.P. 46*, Reigam Korale and *Worthington 5790* appear to be intermediate between the two subspecies; young plants of ssp. *assimile* frequently bear leaves resembling those of ssp. *acuminata*.

5. SYNCARPIA

Ten., Ind. Sem. Hort. Neap. 12. 1839.

Flaky barked trees with opposite or whorled leaves lacking prominent nervation. Flowers ± connate in dense globose, single and axillary or paniculate and terminal, capitula; calyx tube campanulate in flowers, with 4 (–5) equal short lobes; petals 4 (–5), small, patent; stamens many, with versatile latrorse anthers; ovary 2–3-locular, loculi 1-many-ovular. Fruit capsular, dehiscing loculicidally at the ovary apex. Seed linear-cuneate, with thin testa; embryo straight, cotyledons exceeding radicle.

Five species, Queensland; two planted in Sri Lanka.

KEY TO SPECIES CULTIVATED IN SRI LANKA

1 Flowers 6–10 in each head; calyx hoary...........................**1. S. glomerulifera**
1 Flowers as a rule 7 to a head; calyx glabrous............................**2. S. hillii**

1. Syncarpia glomerulifera Niedz. in Pflanzenfam. 3, 7: 88. 1893.

Metrosideros glomerulifera Smith, Trans. Linn. Soc. Lond. 3: 269. 1797.
S. laurifolia Ten., Ind. Sem. Hort. Neap. 12. 1839.

Slender tree –20 m tall with flaky bark. Innovations densely cream-hispid; twigs, peduncles and calyx sparsely shortly greyish puberulent. Twigs

c. 3 mm diam. apically, slender, terete. Leaves opposite or more usually in whorls of 4 owing to reduction of alternate internodes; lamina 3–12 × 1.5–6 cm, elliptic-lanceolate; base cuneate, subequal; apex attenuate-acuminate; nerves c. 10 pairs, slender, frequently bifurcating and with shorter intermediates, evident above, hardly elevated beneath as also the densely reticulate tertiary nerves; midrib elevated to shallowly depressed above, slender but prominent beneath; petiole 8–15 mm long. Flowers white, (5–) 7 adnate at the calyx into a capitulum; peduncles –5 cm long, opposite or –6 in a whorl, slender, subtended by leaves or by –8 × 4 mm obtuse ovate bracts; petals –8 × 4 mm, small; stamens –5 mm long, slender; style 12 mm long, slender. Fruit head –2 cm diam., depressed globose, adorned with the prominently raised 5-toothed crowns of the 6 radial and 1 terminal calyces bordering the deeply pitted receptacle apices.

D i s t r. Occasionally planted in the wet zone mountains.

V e r n. Red Turpentine (E).

S p e c i m e n s E x a m i n e d. NUWARA ELIYA DISTRICT: Abbotsford estate, *anon. s.n.*, March 1886 (PDA); Hakgala Botanic Garden, *Worthington 6759* (K), *5662* (K); Woodland near lake, Nuwara Eliya, *Meijer, Dassanayake & Balasubramaniam 605* (PDA); Le Vallon estate, *Worthington 2891* (K); Conical hill forest aboretum, *Worthington 5877* (K). BADULLA DISTRICT: Karawalla estate. Namunukula, *Worthington 5877* (K).

2. **Syncarpia hilli** Bailey, Proc. R. Soc. Queensland 1: 86. 1884.

As *S. glomerulifera* but a tall tree; lamina 10–17 × 5–10 cm, ovate-lanceolate; petiole 2–4 cm long; fruiting heads 2.5–4 cm diam.

D i s t r. Queensland. Occasionally planted in the hill country in Sri Lanka.

V e r n. Satinay.

S p e c i m e n s E x a m i n e d. NUWARA ELIYA DISTRICT: Nuwara Eliya arboretum, *Worthington 2906* (K); Conical hill above Nanu Oya arboretum, *Worthington 5880* (K).

6. ANGOPHORA

Cav., Ic. Pl. 4: 21, t. 338, 339. 1797.

Frequently glaucous and tomentose shrubs or trees. Leaves alternate or (in our species) opposite, with ± unraised slender nervation. Flowers in terminal or subterminal umbelliform cymes; calyx tube campanulate, prominently ribbed, truncate but with 5 subulate erect teeth; petals 5, distinct but ± connivent into a cap, frequently falling in one piece at anthesis. Stamens many, with versatile latrorse anthers; ovary 3–4-locular, deep-set in the calyx;

ovules many in each loculus; style slender. Fruit capsular with loculicidally
dehiscent apex; seeds 1 per cell; embryo straight, cotyledons orbicular-cordate
with the radicle ± hidden within their folded margins.

About 10 ssp., E. Australia; one cultivated in Sri Lanka.

Doubtfully distinct from *Eucalyptus* according to Johnson (Proc. Linn.
Soc. N.S.W 97. 1: 11–29. 1972).

Angophora floribunda Sweet, Hort. Brit. ed. 2: 209. 1839.
Metrosideros floribunda Smith, Trans. Linn. Soc. Lond. 3: 167. 1797.
Angophora intermedia DC., Prod. 3: 222. 1828.

Large tree with dark brown rough fibrous bark. Parts subglabrous or inflorescences sparsely villous. Twigs ± terete. Lamina 5–12 × 1–4 cm, narrowly
lanceolate to ovate-lanceolate, narrowly attenuate-acuminate; base cuneate;
midrib slender, elevated beneath, slightly elevated and with a median furrow
above; nervation ± obscure above, evident but hardly raised beneath, densely
parallel, with reticulate tertiary nerves; petiole –12 mm long, or leaf base
cordate, subsessile. Flower small, in lax terminal corymbs; calyx 5 mm
diam., –4 mm long, prominently 10-ribbed, 4-toothed; petals –3 × 4 mm, greatly exceeded by the many, 8 mm long stamens. Fruit –10 × 12 mm, bell-shaped,
retaining 4 subulate teeth round the rim.

D i s t r. Occasionally cultivated in the wet zone mountains.

S p e c i m e n s E x a m i n e d. NUWARA ELIYA DISTRICT: Coombe
wood, Talawakelle, *s. coll. s.n.*, 8.1.23 (PDA).

N o t e. The opposite leaves are very reminiscent of those of *Mesua ferrea*
(Guttiferae).

7. EUCALYPTUS

L'Her., Sert. Ang. 18. 1788; Maiden, A critical revision of the genus *Eucalyptus* vols. 1–8, Sydney, 1903–1931; Alston in Trimen, Handb. Fl. Ceylon 6:
109. 1931; Blakely, A key to the eucalypts, Canberra. 1934, revised 1955;
Pryor & Johnson, A classification of the eucalypts, Canberra. 1971; Johnson,
Proc. Linn. Soc. N.S.W. 97, 1: 11–29. 1972.

Medium to large trees, generally with twisted unbuttressed trunks and
more or less oblong crowns of twisted branches bearing frequently pendent
leaves. Bark surface either dramatically patchily white, grey, copper or brown
mottled, overall smooth and scroll-marked and exfoliating in large leathery
strips, often hanging as ribbons on branches; or flakes persistent at least on
butt, bark surface fibrous and pale on dark greyish-brown. Parts glabrous or
sometimes shortly pubescent. Leaves red when young, more or less aromatic
and pellucid-punctate, heteroblastic; juvenile and sucker leaves (in Sri Lanka)
opposite, variable but frequently rotundate and sessile or even perfoliate, fre-

quently glaucous; intermediate stage leaves larger, thicker, alternate; mature stage leaves alternate, diverse but most generally narrow and more or less falcate, usually coriaceous with prominent midrib and more or less obscure nervation, petiolate. Flowers large or small, in dense or diffuse terminal or axillary umbels or panicles, usually pedunculate; bracts fugaceous. Flower calyx variable but most frequently campanulate, sessile or shortly pedicellate, smooth or costate, truncate or with 4 minute teeth, closed apically in bud by a short or prolonged more or less leathery petaloid operculum distinguishable by and opening along a fine transverse line; operculum frequently also covered by a membranous outer operculum; stamens many, all fertile or the outer lacking anthers, free (in Sri Lanka), filaments slender and folded in bud; anthers various, latrorse or end-porous, versatile or adnate at base, usually with a distal adaxial gland. Ovary inferior, adnate to the calyx at the base or occasionally to the apex, flat to conical at apex, 2–7-celled, each cell with many ovules in 2–4 axile rows; style simple, subulate or subclavate; stigma small. Fruit a dry capsule more or less deeply sunk within the enlarged and woody calyx tube and adnate to it, the dehisced valves becoming exserted or remaining concealed.

Over 600 species; Australasia to southern Philippines. Cultivated in Sri Lanka as ornamentals, shade and timber trees in the mountains and in recent years sometimes in the lowlands.

This is a difficult genus, the species requiring experience to identify with certainty in the field. It will be seen from the key that mature tree leaves seldom provide species diagnostic characters by themselves, but minute characters of the anthers, calyx and operculum, and combinations of field characters, including those of the bark and juvenile foliate are all useful. Identification is further confounded by frequent hybridisation, even in plantations.

It has not been possible to compare the collections at Peradeniya with authentic specimens; this account is therefore based on a typewritten report, entitled Afforestation with *Eucalyptus* in Ceylon, prepared by L.D. Pryor for F.A.O. in 1964. This includes a list of all the species he definitely or tentatively identified in the field in Sri Lanka. My key is derived from that in Blakely, as are the species descriptions. Pryor and Johnson have recently suggested a new infrageneric classification of the genus based on a wide range of morphological, anatomical and other characters. They are of the view that *Angophora* should be in *Eucalyptus*; but in the absence of formal reduction by them I continue to maintain this genus as a separate entity.

KEY TO EUCALYPTUS CULTIVATED IN CEYLON

1 All filaments bearing anthers; anther versatile, opening in broad parallel auriculate lobes, usually with distal or terminal gland
  2 Anther cells distinct, broadest towards the more or less emarginate apex
    3 Filaments attached beneath the gland and in the basal half of the connective; lamina nervation very slender, almost transverse

4 Inflorescence a corymbose panicle, usually terminal
  5 Bark persistently scaly; bud operculum single...................**1. E. calophylla***
  5 Bark overall smooth, scroll-marked; operculum double
    6 Leaves lemon-scented; bud operculum obtuse; fruit as long as broad............
    ....**2. E. citriodora**
    6 Leaves not lemon-scented, bud operculum acute; fruit longer than broad........
    ....**3. E. maculata**
4 Inflorescences axillary, umbellate
  7 Fruit disc not minutely pelliculose
    8 Bark surface overall smooth, scroll-marked
      9 Buds and fruits glaucous, distinctly pedicellate; fruit pyriform, contracted at the
      orifice..**4. E. grandis**
      9 Buds and fruits not glaucous, very shortly pedicellate; fruit campanulate.........
      ....**5. E. saligna**
    8 Bark rough, fibrous, persistent
     10 Buds and fruit sessile; operculum half length of calyx tube; fruit as broad as long
     ....**6. E. botryoides**
     10 Buds and fruit pedicellate; operculum larger than calyx tube, contracted in middle;
     fruit longer than broad.......................................**7. E. robusta**
  7 Fruit disc minutely pelliculose................................**8. E. punctata***
3 Filaments tapering to a sharp point and attached near the base of the gland on the
  upper half of the connective; lamina nervation oblique, prominent
  11 Bark smooth, white
    12 Juvenile leaves prominently glaucous, orbicular, subsessile, persisting into the young
    tree; bark on butt rough.......................................**9. E. globulus**
    12 Juvenile leaves not as above; bark surface smooth throughout
     13 Fruit disc well defined, united or free from the prominently exserted valves.......
     ....**10. E. camaldulensis**
     13 Fruit disc small, band-like, valves not prominently exserted..........**11. E. alba**
  11 Bark fibrous, flaky throughout trunk or, if smooth and white, then flaky on butt and
    with long ribbon-like flakes hanging from branches
    14 Bark smooth except on butt, with long ribbon-like flakes hanging from branches;
    fruit subsessile...**12. E. viminalis**
    14 Bark flaky on trunk, smooth on branches; fruit pedicellate
     15 Buds not glaucous; fruit with small disc and shortly exserted valves............
     ....**13. E. macarthuri**
     15 Buds glaucous; fruit with well-defined convex disc and prominent valves........
     ....**14. E. nova-anglica**
2 Anther cells united distally, diverging towards the bases, overall reniform; gland terminal,
  minute
  16 Anthers cordate-reniform, dehiscing widely in semi-longitudinal almost confluent slits
  ....**15. E. deglupta**
  16 Anthers widely divergent and thus apparently dehiscing transversely across the base,
    the valves on opening appearing like the wings of a minute butterfly; trees with per-
    sistently fibrous bark
    17 Juvenile leaves strongly aromatic, smelling of peppermint when crushed
     18 Juvenile leaves narrow and willow-like, opposite for many pairs, hispid on midrib
     and internodes. Buds clavate...............................**16. E. lindleyana**
     18 Juvenile leaves broad, glabrous, opposite for up to 12 pairs. Buds urceolate-

*Species whose presence in Ceylon is tentative.

rostrate, with prominent subulate operculum.................**17. E. urceolaris***
17 Juvenile leaves not scenting of peppermint
  19 Juvenile leaves and internodes minutely hispid
    20 Leaves (especially juvenile) sweet smelling; buds pedicellate; fruit hemispherical
      to depressed-globose....................................**18. E. wilkinsoniana***
    20 Leaves not sweet smelling
      21 Buds and fruits sessile and congested into heads; juvenile leaves entire........
      ....**19. E. scabra***
      21 Buds and fruits not as above; juvenile leaves more or less denticulate
        22 Juvenile leaves narrow, willow-like; buds and fruits subsessile, fruit subglobose
        ....**20. E. sparsifolia***
        22 Juvenile leaves broad; buds and fruits pedicellate, fruits pyriform............
        ....**21. E. fastigata**
  19 Juvenile leaves and internodes glabrous, entire or sparsely denticulate only
    23 Bud operculum longer than calyx tube
      24 Mature lamina falcate-lanceolate, coriaceous.................**22. E. pilularis**
      24 Mature lamina elliptic-lanceolate, chartaceous, pale beneath......**23. E. triantha***
    23 Bud operculum small, hemispherical.........................**24. E. microcorys**
1 At least some outer filaments lacking anthers; anther adnate to filament and erect or
  oblique, without gland, truncate and opening by paired apical slits or pores. Inflorescence terminal or subterminal-axillary
  25 Bark dark, tanniniferous, deeply furrowed; leaves broadly lanceolate
    26 All outer filaments without anthers..........................**25. E. paniculata**
    26 A few outer filaments only without anthers...................**26. E. sideroxylon**
  25 Bark of trunk smooth, pale; leaves broadly lanceolate to suborbicular............
  ....**27. E. baueriana**

1. Eucalyptus calophylla R. Br.; J. Geog. Soc. 1: 20. 1831–2; Maiden, l.c. 43:
73, pl. 176; 63: pl. 257; 70: pl. 286; 73: 132; Blakely, Key ed. 2. 87, 1955.

Eucalyptus glaucophylla Hoffmg., Verz. Pfl. Nachtr. 2: 113. 1826.
Eucalyptus splachnicarpa Hook. in Bot. Mag. t. 4036. 1843.

Medium sized to large tree, with rough persistently flaky bark. Juvenile
lamina 6–7 × 5–10 cm, elliptic to lanceolate, peltate, petiolate, more or less
setose and hispid, sucker shoots usually abundant on old trees. Mature
lamina 6–18 × 2–3 cm, broadly lanceolate, glabrous, petiolate, with very
slender more or less obscure venation. Inflorescence a rather large terminal
corymb; peduncles –15 cm long, subterete; umbels 3–7-flowered. Flower
buds –15 × 10 mm, clavate, pedicellate; calyx tube 2–3 times longer than the
hemispherical operculum; anthers obovate-oblong, emarginate, cells long;
filament attached near the base of the rather large ovoid-oblong gland. Fruit
–35 × 30 mm, urceolate, woody, contracted at the orifice; disc small, oblique;
seeds black, without or with rudimentary wings.

D i s t r. Western Australia. Not known with certainty from Sri Lanka.
V e r n. Marri, Red Gum.

*Species whose presence in Ceylon is tentative.

EUCALYPTUS 459

2. Eucalyptus citriodora Hook. Mitch., Trop. Aust. 235. 1848; Maiden, l.c. 43: 88, pl. 178; 58: 433; 63: pl. 257; 74: 181, pl. 5; Blakely, l.c. ed. 2. 96.

Fairly large tree with smooth scroll-marked bark. Juvenile lamina 7–15 × 3–6 cm, oblong to lanceolate, sometimes peltate, petiolate, setose. Mature leaves petiolate; lamina 10–16 × 1–2 cm, narrowly lanceolate, glabrous, strongly lemon-scented. Inflorescence a terminal corymb; peduncles –7 mm long, terete; umbels 3–5 flowered. Flower buds –12 × 8 mm, ovoid, pedicellate; operculum hemispherical, shorter than calyx tube; anthers obovate, with long broad cells, and gland half their length. Fruit –10 × 10 mm, urceolate, contracted into a short thick neck; disc small, oblique; valves enclosed; pedicels –10 mm long, as in *F. maculata* but more slender.

D i s t r. Queensland. Planted in the hills of the intermediate zone as a shade tree and source of firewood; Pryor recommends planting there in plantation.

V e r n. Lemon-scented Spotted Gum (E).

3. Eucalyptus maculata Hook., Ic. Pl. 7: 619. 1844; Maiden, l.c. 43: 84, pl. 178, 257; 70: pl. 286; 74: 181, pl. 4; Blakely, l.c. ed. 2. 97.

Tall tree with smooth scroll-marked white, glaucous or pale pink bark. Juvenile leaves shortly petiolate. Mature leaves petiolate; lamina 10–30 × 2.5–6 cm, narrowly or broadly lanceolate; venation slender but elevated and evident, almost transverse. Inflorescence a terminal corymb; peduncles –10 mm long; umbels 3–5-flowered. Flower buds –12 × 8 mm, ovoid, acute, pedicellate; operculum hemispherical, acute, much shorter than calyx tube; anthers obovate-oblong; cells long and broad, gland dorsal or in upper half and evident from front. Fruit –18 × 14 mm, urceolate to ovoid; disc oblique; valves deeply incised.

D i s t r. Victoria, New South Wales, Queensland, in coastal ranges. Occasionally planted in the hill country tea plantations.

V e r n. Spotted Gum (E).

4. Eucalyptus grandis Hill ex Maiden, J. R. Soc. N.S.W. 52: 50. 1918; Maiden l.c. 40: 338; 75: 309; Blakely, l.c. ed. 2. 98.

Eucalyptus grandis Hill, Cat. Timb. Queensland 25. 1862, nomen; ex Maiden, For. Fl. N.S.W., 1: 79. 1903, nomen.
Eucalyptus saligna var. *pallidivalvis* Baker & Smith, Resch. Enc. 32. 1902.
Eucalyptus saligna Maiden l.c. 20: 58, pl. 99, fig. 10, 16, pl. 100, figs. 8–13, non Smith.

Large tree, –50 m tall with smooth white to pale glaucous bark. Juvenile leaves shortly petiolate; lamina 3–6 × 1–2.5 cm, oblong, lanceolate, chartaceous and undulate on drying. Intermediate leaves alternate; lamina petiolate, 12–18 × 5 –6 cm, broadly lanceolate, slightly undulate. Mature leaves petiolate;

lamina –20 × 3.5 cm, narrowly lanceolate, undulate, acuminate; venation slender but evident. Inflorescence a 3-10-flowered axillary umbel; peduncles –12 mm long, compressed. Flower buds –10 × 5 mm, pyriform, pedicellate, usually medially contracted, glaucous; operculum conical to shortly rostrate, shorter than calyx tube; anthers versatile, with long cells and large globose gland. Fruit –8 × 8 mm, pyriform, pedicellate, glaucous, thin-walled, slightly contracted at the orifice; valves 4–6, thin, usually incurved.

D i s t r. New South Wales and Queensland, moist coastal forests. Planted widely in Sri Lanka in the hill country; an important plantation species there, yielding high quality timber. Recommended for planting in the lowlands of the intermediate zone by Pryor.

V e r n. Toolur.

N o t e. Consistently misnamed *E. saligna* (q.v.) in Sri Lanka, where this species is variable and has hybridised with other species, as with *E. robusta* at Dixon's Corner (Pryor).

5. Eucalyptus saligna Smith, Trans. Linn. Soc. Lond. 3: 285. 1797; Maiden, l.c. 23: 56, pl. 99 figs. 11–15, pl. 100 figs. 1–7; 64: pl. 262; 70: pl. 287; 75: 309; Blakely, l.c. ed. 2. 99.

Eucalyptus laurberti Maiden, Proc. Linn. Soc. N.S.W. 897. 1904.

Tall columnar tree with smooth bluish exfoliating bark, sometimes persistently flaky at base. Leaves shortly petiolate; juvenile lamina 3–6 × 2–3 cm, pale green, narrowly lanceolate to ovate-lanceolate, chartaceous and undulate on drying. Mature leaves petiolate; lamina 10–20 × 1.5–3 cm, lanceolate, acuminate, venation slender. Inflorescence a 3–9-flowered axillary umbel; peduncles –12 mm long, compressed or subangular. Flower buds –9 × 5 mm, subpyriform, subsessile; operculum hemispherical to shortly rostrate, as long as calyx tube; anthers versatile, with long narrow cells and large dorsal orbicular gland. Fruit –6 × 6 mm, campanulate, truncate; disc small or obscure; valves deltoid, exserted or sometimes enclosed, usually patent.

D i s t r. New South Wales, mostly on well drained clay soils in valleys. Planted as an ornamental at Nuwara Eliya but otherwise unknown in Sri Lanka.

V e r n. Sydney Blue Gum (E).

6. Eucalyptus botryoides Smith, Trans, Linn. Soc. 3: 286. 1797; Maiden, l.c. 23: 50, pl. 98, 99; 64: pl. 262; 75: 309; Blakely, l.c. ed. 2. 100.

Eucalyptus playtpodos Cav., Ic. 4: 23, t. 341. 1798.

Dense-crowned tree –25 m tall, with persistently fibrous bark. Juvenile leaves shortly petiolate; lamina 5–8 × 3–4 cm, ovate to broadly lanceolate, chartaceous and undulate on drying, with very slender venation. Mature leaves petiolate; lamina 10–14 × 3–6 cm, dark green, broadly lanceolate, acuminate; venation very slender, more or less obscure. Inflorescence a 6–10-flowered axillary umbel; peduncles –10 mm long, 4–5 mm diam., compressed. Flower bud –12 × 6 mm, slightly angular, –2-ribbed, sessile; operculum hemispherical, obtuse or apiculate, half as long as calyx-tube. Anthers versatile, oblong, with ovate dorsal gland half length of cells. Fruit –9 × 9 mm, barrel-shaped; disc thin; valves enclosed or slightly exserted.

D i s t r. Coastal alluvium of Victoria and New South Wales. Occasionally planted in Sri Lanka.

V e r n. Bangalay.

7. Eucalyptus robusta Smith, Specimen Bot. New Holl. 39. 1793; Maiden, l.c. 23: 45, pl. 97–99; 64: pl. 263; 75: 309; Blakely, l.c. ed. 2. 100.

Medium-sized dense-crowned tree with persistently rough fibrous bark. Juvenile leaves petiolate; lamina –11 × 7 cm, broadly lanceolate to elliptic, coriaceous. Mature leaves petiolate; lamina 10–18 × 4–8 cm, broadly lanceolate, glabrous, lustrous, prominently acuminate; venation slender, almost parallel. Inflorescence an axillary to subterminal 5–10-flowered umbel; peduncle –30 mm long, compressed. Flower buds –20 × 10 mm, pyriform, rostrate, long-pedicellate; operculum rostrate, at least as long as calyx tube; anthers versatile, obovate, with large ovate dorsal gland. Fruit –15 × 12 mm, cylindrical to urceolate; disc oblique, valves usually deeply enclosed.

D i s t r. Coastal flats of Queensland and New South Wales. An important timber and charcoal species widely planted in the hill country and recommended by Pryor for plantations in the dry zone lowlands.

N o t e. Of superior timber quality but inferior form to *E. grandis* (q.v.) with which it hybridises in Sri Lanka.

V e r n. Swamp mahogany (E).

8. Eucalyptus punctata DC., Prod. 3: 217. 1828; Maiden, l.c. 23: pl. 98; 29: 194, pl. 121, 122; 64: pl. 262; 75: 309; Blakely, l.c. ed. 2. 104.

Small to medium sized tree with partly deciduous dark grey to pink flaking bark. Juvenile leaves petiolate; lamina 7–11 × 5–7 cm ovate to broadly lanceolate. Mature leaves petiolate; lamina 10–16 × 2–3 cm, dark green above, pale beneath, more or less narrowly lanceolate, venation very slender. Inflorescence an axillary 6–10-flowered umbel; peduncles to 18 mm long, compressed or quadrangular. Flower buds to 16 × 7 mm, cylindrical, obtuse, shortly pedicellate. Operculum conical to rostrate, usually much longer than calyx tube; anthers obcordate, opening in parallel slits, with large ovate dorsal gland. Fruit to 12 × 10 mm, hemispherical to campanulate, rather thick-walled; disc pelliculose, usually prominent; valves thick, broad, deltoid, pale, prominently exserted.

D i s t r. New South Wales and Queensland. Doubtfully in Sri Lanka.
V e r n. Grey Gum (E).

9. **Eucalyptus globulus** Labill., Rel. Voy. Rech. Perouse 1: 153. 1799; Maiden, l.c. 18: 249, pl. 79; 65: 218; 71: 22; Blakely, l.c. ed. 2. 161. 1955.

Eucalyptus pulverulenta Link, Enum. pl. Hort. Berol. 31. 1821.
Eucalyptus perfoliata Desf., Cat. Hort. Paris ed. 3. 408. 1829.
Eucalyptus glauca DC., Prod. 3: 221. 1828.
Eucalyptus gigantea Dehnhardt, Cat. Pl. Hort. Camald. ed. 2. 20. 1832.

Medium sized to large tree; bark smooth, bluish, scroll-marked and with flakes persisting at base in old trees. Juvenile lamina 7–16 × 4–9 cm, ovate to broadly lanceolate, cordate, sessile and often amplexicaul, prominently glaucous. Mature leaves petiolate; lamina 10–30 × 3–4 cm, dark green and lustrous, lanceolate and more or less falcate, acuminate. Flower buds usually solitary, axillary, subsessile; calyx 30 × 20 mm, turbinate, quadrangular, verrucose; operculum umbonate, verrucose, more or less shorter than calyx tube; anthers versatile, obovate, opening in broad parallel slits, with globose gland visible from front. Fruit –15 × 30 mm, depressed globose to broadly turbinate, sessile, 4-ribbed with more or less prominent shorter intermediates, verrucose; disc large, convex, smooth, sometimes extending over the thick valves.

D i s t r. Tasmania. Widely cultivated in the hill country in Sri Lanka, unimportant economically.
V e r n. Tasmanian Blue Gum (E).

10. **Eucalyptus camaldulensis** Dehnhardt, Pl. Hort. Camald. ed. 2. 20. 1832; Maiden, l.c. 33: 65, pl. 136; 64: pl. 263; 70: pl. 287; 75: 295; Blakely, l.c. ed. 2: 140.

Eucalyptus rostrata Schlecht., Linnaea 20: 655. 1847.
Eucalyptus acuminata Hook., Mitch. Trop Aust. 390. 1848.
Eucalyptus tereticornis var. *rostrata* Ewart, Handb. For. Tr. Vict. For. 301. 1925.

Small (in Sri Lanka) to rather large dense-crowned tree, typically with smooth greyish-white bark but remaining persistently fibrous in the Sri Lanka hills. Juvenile leaves petiolate; lamina 6–9 × 2.5–4 cm, narrowly to broadly lanceolate, slightly glaucous. Leaves petiolate; mature lamina uniform green, 12–22 × 0.8–1.5 cm, lanceolate, chartaceous, acuminate; nervation evident. Inflorescence a 5–10-flowered axillary umbel; peduncle –15 mm long, terete.

Flower buds –10 × 5 mm, ovoid, acute to horn-shaped, pedicellate; operculum conical to rostrate, 1½–2½ times longer than the goblet-shaped calyx tube; anthers versatile, obovate, opening in parallel slits, with small globose gland. Fruit –8 × 6 mm, hemispherical to broadly turbinate; disc domed, sharp edged; valves exserted, deltoid, acute, incurved.

D i s t r. Widespread in Australia. Widely cultivated in the hills and more recently tried as a plantation species in the dry zone.
V e r n. Murray Red Gum (E).

11. Eucalyptus alba Reinw., Fl. Ned. Indie 1101. 1826; Maiden, l.c. 25: 90, pl. 105; 65: pl. 265: 70: pl. 287; 72: 97; 75: 300; Blakely, l.c. ed. 2. 143.

Eucalyptus leucodendron Reinw. ex de Vriese, Pl. Ind. Bat. Or. 63. 1856.

Medium sized tree with smooth pink, whitish and greenish mottled scroll-marked bark. Juvenile leaves petiolate; lamina ovate to lanceolate; intermediate leaves alternate, lamina –7 × 5 cm, ovate to deltoid, petiolate, rather prominently nerved. Mature lamina 10–13 × 3–4 cm, broadly lanceolate, acuminate, chartaceous; petiole 2–3.5 cm long, long and terete. Inflorescence a 3–7-flowered axillary umbel; peduncles –20 mm long, terete or compressed. Flower buds –10 × 6 mm, clavate to ovoid; pedicels –8 mm long, prominent; operculum hemispherical, umbonate, shorter than calyx tube; anthers versatile, obovate, opening in parallel slits; gland globose. Fruit –8 × 8 mm, hemispherical to campanulate, pedicellate; disc rather thin, subtruncate; valves 4–5, broad, slightly exserted.

D i s t r. Java, Timor, New Guinea. Occasionally cultivated in Sri Lanka.
V e r n. Timor White Gum (E).

12. Eucalyptus viminalis Labill., Nov. Holl. Pl. 2: 12, t. 151. 1806; Maiden, l.c. 28: 167, pl. 117–119; 64: pl. 262; 75: 287; Blakely, l.c. ed. 2. 171. 1955.

Eucalyptus pilularis DC., Prod. 3: 218. 1828.
Eucalyptus crucivalvis F. Muell. ex Miq., Ned. Kruidk. Arch. 4: 125. 1856.
Eucalyptus saccharifera Muell. ex Miq., l.c.
Eucalyptus patentiflora F. Muell., Fragm. 2: 64. 1860.
Eucalyptus pendulosa Maiden, Proc. Linn. Soc. N.S.W. 899. 1904.

Large tree; bark overall white to cream and smooth, more flaky at base and with long ribbons persisting and hanging from branches. Leaves sessile and more or less amplexicaul. Juvenile lamina 5–10 × 1.5–3 cm, pale green, narrowly lanceolate. Intermediate leaves petiolate; lamina 8.5–27 × 4–5 cm, alternate, lanceolate, acuminate. Mature leaves petiolate; lamina 11–8 × 1.5–2 cm, pale green, lanceolate, applanate or undulate, more or less acuminate. Inflorescence a 3-flowered axillary umbel; peduncles –6 mm long, terete.

Flower buds 7 × 5 mm, ovoid to cylindroid, sessile or shortly pedicellate, operculum hemispherical to conical, usually longer than the calyx tube; anthers versatile, obovate, emarginate, opening in narrow parallel slits; gland ovate. Fruit –6 × 8 mm, sessile to shortly pedicellate, spherical to turbinate; disc usually prominent, convex or contracted upwards; valves 3–4, exserted and spreading.

D i s t r. Widespread in South Eastern Australia including Tasmania. Not apparently cultivated in Sri Lanka outside botanic gardens.

V e r n. Ribbon Gum (E).

13. Eucalyptus macarthuri Deane & Maiden, Proc. Linn, Soc. N.S.W. 24: 448.1899; Maiden, l.c. 25: 81, pl. 104; 64: pl. 262; 75: 287; Blakely, l.c. ed. 2. 170.

Eucalyptus diversifolia Woolls, Cont. Fl. Austral. 235. 1867, non Bonpl.

Spreading dark-crowned tree, –25 m tall; bark surface pale brown, rough and persistently thinly flaky on bole, deciduous and smooth on branches. Juvenile leaves sessile and more or less amplexicaul; lamina 2.5–8.5 × 1–4.5 cm, pale green, lanceolate. Mature leaves petiolate; lamina 9–13 × 1–1.5 cm, narrowly lanceolate, shortly acuminate. Inflorescence a 3–7-flowered axillary umbel; peduncles –12 cm long, terete or slightly angular. Flower buds –5 × 4 mm, ovoid, acute, pedicellate; operculum conical, as long as calyx-tube; anthers versatile, obovate, emarginate, opening widely in parallel slits, with large ovate gland. Fruit –5 × 6 mm, hemispherical to subglobose, with small disc and 3–4 exserted valves.

D i s t r. New South Wales. In Sri Lanka known only as specimen trees.

V e r n. Camden Woolly Butt (E).

14. Eucalyptus nova-anglica Deane & Maiden, Proc. Linn. Soc. N.S.W. 24: 616. 1899.

Much branched tree, –20 m tall; bark surface rough and flaky on trunk, more or less ribbony on branches, smooth on branchlets. Juvenile leaves c. 5 × 6 cm, orbicular to lanceolate, cordate, sessile, amplexicaul, prominently, glaucous. Intermediate leaves opposite or alternate, lamina 8–10 × 5 cm, lanceolate, ± cordate, subsessile, glaucous. Mature lamina 10–16 × 1–2 cm, lanceolate-acuminate, petiolate. Inflorescence a 3–6-flowered axillary umbel; peduncles –10 mm long, slender, terete. Flower bud –6 × 5 mm, ovoid to clavate, glaucous, pedicellate; operculum hemispherical to conical, as long as the calyx-tube; anthers versatile, obovoid, emarginate, opening in parallel slits, with small globose gland. Fruit –6 × 6 mm at most, hemispherical to subglobose, with a well defined convex disc and 3–4 prominent ribs.

D i s t r. New South Wales, Queensland. Occasionally cultivated in the hill country, recommended by Pryor for plantations in the dry hill patanas.
V e r n. New England Peppermint (E).

15. Eucalyptus deglupta Blume, Mus. Bot. Lugduno Batavum 1: 83. 1849; Merr., Philipp. Bur. Sci. Publ. Bot. 9: 401. 1917; Blakely, l.c. ed. 2. 231.

Eucalyptus versicolor Blume, id. 84.
Eucalyptus naudiniana F. Muell., Austral. J. Pharm. (Melb.). 537: 1886; Maiden, l.c. 12: 79, pl. 55; 61: 13.
Eucalyptus binacag Elm., Leafl. Philipp. Bot. 8: 2776. 1915.

Very large columnar diffuse-crowned tree, –60 m tall, with smooth greyish to greenish and coppery mottled bark surface. Juvenile leaves petiolate; lamina c. 5 × 4 cm, ovate to oblong-lanceolate, chartaceous, acuminate. Mature leaves petiolate; lamina 5–14 × 2–7 cm, pale olive-green, ovate-lanceolate, acuminate. Inflorescence a large terminal corymb, with 3–7-flowered compound umbels. Flower buds c. 5 × 4 mm, clavate to cylindrical, acute, pedicellate; operculum acutely conical, as long as calyx tube; anthers reniform, with a small terminal gland. Fruit c. 5 × 5 mm, ovoid-clavate to globose; disc thin; valves as long as fruit calyx, protruding.

D i s t r. Mindanao, New Britain, New Ireland. Cultivated at Peradeniya; recommended for plantations in the wet zone lowlands as a source of pulp and timber.
V e r n. Mindanao Gum (E).

16. Eucalyptus lindleyana DC., Prod. 2: 219. 1828; Blakely, l.c. ed. 2. 220. 1955.

Eucalyptus longifolia Lindl., Bot. Reg. t. 947. 1825, non Link & Otto.
Eucalyptus andreana Naudin, Rev. Hort. 346. 1890.
Eucalyptus numerosa Maiden, Proc. Linn. Soc. N.S.W. 29: 752. 1904; l.c. 6: 154, 157, pl. 29, 30; 38: 233; 61: 20; 74: pl. 6, 216.
Eucalyptus calyculata Link ex Maiden, l.c. 6: 156. 1905, nomen.
Eucalyptus diversifolia Otto ex Maiden, id. 6: l.c., non Bonpl.
Eucalyptus elata Dehn. & Giordano ex Maiden, id. 6: 157, nomen.
Eucalyptus translucens Cunn. ex Maiden id. 6: l.c.

Slender tree, sometimes reaching 45 m, with white smooth bark overall and persistently fibrous flaky butt. Juvenile leaves sessile and amplexicaul to shortly petiolate; lamina 4–7 × 0.7–1 cm, pale green, narrowly lanceolate, more or less acuminate; internodes prominently glandular. Mature leaves petiolate; lamina 10–20 × 1–1.5 cm, narrowly lanceolate, more or less acuminate; venation evident, penninerved. Inflorescence a 7–40-flowered axillary umbel;

peduncles –10 mm long, terete. Flower buds c. 5 × 4 mm, clavate, pedicellate; operculum hemispherical, much shorter than calyx tube; anthers reniform, cells papery, opening in front. Fruit –6 × 6 mm, pilular to pyriform; disc small, band-like, valves enclosed.

D i s t r. New South Wales and Victoria. Not known in Sri Lanka other than as specimen trees.

V e r n. Kayer-ro; River Peppermint.

17. Eucalyptus urceolaris Maiden & Blakely, Crit. Rev. 71: 10. 1929; Blakely, l.c. ed. 2. 227.

Eucalyptus piperita Maiden, l.c. 10: pl. 45 non Smith.

Large tree –30 m tall; bark surface persistently fibrous flaky, deeply furrowed, on trunk; branches smooth, with ribbon-like flakes persisting. Juvenile leaves sessile, sometimes subamplexicaul; lamina 3–6 × 2–3 cm, dark green above and pale beneath, lanceolate. Intermediate leaves petiolate; lamina 7–9 × 4–5 cm, alternate, broadly falcate-lanceolate, coriaceous. glaucous. Mature leaves petiolate; lamina 8–12 × 1.7–2 cm, lanceolate, more or less falcate. Inflorescence a 6–15-flowered axillary umbel, sometimes deflexed, or shortly paniculate; peduncles –12 mm long, slender, subterete. Flower buds –10 × 4 mm, cylindrical to urceolate, rostrate, pedicellate; calyx-tube urceolate to campanulate, the rim deflexed; operculum more or less prominently rostrate, much longer than calyx-tube; anthers reniform, cells adnate. Fruit –9 × 7 mm, more or less prominently urceolate; disc obscure, valves deeply enclosed.

D i s t r. New South Wales. Recorded from Sri Lanka only as specimen trees.

V e r n. Urn-fruited peppermint.

18. Eucalyptus wilkinsoniana R.T. Baker, Proc. Linn. Soc. N.S.W. 25: 678. 1900; Maiden, l.c. 8: 221, pl. 38.40; 71: 63; Blakely, l.c. ed. 2. 188.

Eucalyptus laevopinea var. *minor* R.T. Baker, Proc. Linn. Soc. N.S.W. 23: 416. 1898.
Eucalyptus pilularis Maiden, Crit. Rev. 1: pl. 4, non Smith.

Medium sized tree; bark surface red-brown, fibrous on trunk, smooth on branches. Juvenile leaves sessile or shortly petiolate; lamina 3–6 × 2–4 cm, fragrant when crushed, elliptic to broadly lanceolate; minutely velutinate. Intermediate leaves alternate; lamina shortly petiolate, 5–7 × 3–4 cm, pale green, elliptic to lanceolate-falcate, glabrous. Mature leaves petiolate; lamina 10–15 × 1.5–2.7 cm, slightly fragrant, falcate-lanceolate, acuminate. Inflorescence a 6–12 flowered axillary umbel; peduncles –15 mm long, slightly compressed. Flower buds –7×4 mm, clavate to cylindrical, pedicellate; operculum hemispherical to conical, as long as calyx tube. Anthers subversatile, reniform. Fruit –8×10 mm, depressed globose to subglobose, pedicellate to subsessile; disc usually convex, more or less prominent; valves deltoid, usually exserted.

D i s t r. Victoria and Queensland. Doubtfully recorded from Sri Lanka.
V e r n. Small-leaved stringy bark (E).

19. Eucalyptus scabra Dum-Cours., Bot. Cult. ed. 2, 7: 279, 280. 1814; Blakely, l.c. ed. 2. 199.

Eucalyptus eugenioides Sieb., Spreng. Cur. Post. 4: 195. 1827; Maiden, l.c. 8: 232, pl. 40 p.p.; 73: pl. 1.
Eucalyptus penicellata Hort. ex DC., Prod. 3: 218. 1827.
Eucalyptus undulata Tausch ex Maiden, Crit. Rev. 8: 234. 1907; nomen.

Medium sized tree –30 m tall; bark persistently fibrous overall, ± furrowed on trunk. Juvenile leaves shortly petiolate to subsessile; lamina 1.5–4 × 1–2 cm, lanceolate, undulate; midrib and margin stellate-pubescent as also the internodes. Intermediate leaves alternate; lamina petiolate, –6×3 cm, elliptic-lanceolate, ± falcate, pubescent to glabrous, applanate. Mature leaves dark green, petiolate. Inflorescence a 5–12-flowered axillary umbel; peduncles –8 mm long, compressed or subangular. Flower buds –8×4 mm, clavate, acute, shortly pedicellate; operculum conical, more or less as long as calyx tube; anthers reniform. Fruit –7×7 mm or more, hemispherical to pilular, shortly pedicellate; disc a narrow band round the broad orifice; valves small, enclosed or shortly exserted.

D i s t r. New South Wales. Doubtfully recorded from Sri Lanka.
V e r n. White stringy bark (E).

20. Eucalyptus sparsifolia Blakely, Key ed. 1. 200. 1935.
Eucalyptus eugenioides Maiden, l.c. 8: pl. 40, figs. 22a, b, non Siebr.

Small to medium sized tree –20 m tall, frequently with several trunks; crown open; bark surface fibrous, furrowed on trunk; branchlets smooth, dark green. Juvenile leaves shortly petiolate; lamina 4–9×0.6–1.5 cm, dark above, pale beneath, narrowly lanceolate-falcate, prominently scabrous, undulate, irregularly sinuate to denticulate. Intermediate leaves alternate; lamina 5–8×2 cm, dark above, pale below, lanceolate-falcate, becoming entire, acuminate; margin subrevolute, undulate; nerves more prominent below than above, evident. Mature leaves petiolate; lamina 5–12×0.8–2 cm, dark green, lustrous, more or less narrowly falcate-lanceolate, venation obscure. Inflorescence on 5–16-flowered axillary umbel. Flower buds –7×3 mm, narrowly cylindrical, shortly pedicellate; operculum conical to rostrate, slightly longer than calyx-tube; anthers reniform, small. Fruit –6 × 5 mm, subglobose; disc small, smooth, slightly raised and extending almost halfway up the small scarcely exserted valves.

D i s t r. New South Wales. Doubtfully recorded from Sri Lanka.

V e r n. Narrow-leaved stringy bark (E).

21. Eucalyptus fastigata Deane & Maiden, Proc. Linn. Soc. N.S.W. 21: 809. 1896; Maiden, l.c. 61: 1; 65: pl. 265; 70: pl. 286; 74: 206; Blakely, l.c. ed. 2. 205.

Eucalyptus regnans var. in Maiden, Crit. Rev. 7: 185, pl. 33, figs. 1b, c, 3 6–9, non F. Muell.

Tall tree, –60 m; bark fibrous stringy but for the branchlets. Juvenile leaves petiolate; lamina 3–6 × 2–4 cm, ovate-lanceolate, denticulate. Intermediate leaves alternate, petiolate; lamina 10–14 × 2.5–6 cm, lanceolate-falcate, glabrous, undulate, prominently nerved. Mature leaves petiolate; lamina 10–18 × 2–3 cm, lanceolate, undulate or applanate, chartaceous, occasionally somewhat longitudinally veined. Inflorescence a 7–12-flowered 1–2-axillary umbel; peduncles –10 mm long, slender, ± terete. Flower buds –8 × 5 mm, clavate, ovate, pedicellate; operculum conical or hemispherical, typically as long as calyx tube; anthers adnate, reniform, opening in divergent slits, with terminal gland. Fruit –7 × 7 mm, pyriform to turbinate; disc conical or domed, smooth, reddish; valves usually slightly exserted.

D i s t r. Victoria and New South Wales. Planted experimentally in the wet patanas at Pattipola.

V e r n. Cut-tail (E).

22. Eucalyptus pilularis Smith, Trans. Linn. Soc. Lond. 3: 284. 1797; Maiden, l.c. 1: 26, pl. 1, 3, 4; 55: pl. 264; 70: pl. 287; 74: 221; Blakely, l.c. ed. 2. 183.

Eucalyptus discolor Desf., Cat. Hort. Paris ed. 3, 408. 1829; Tabl. ed. 2. 198. 1832, nomen.
Eucalyptus incrassata Sieb. ex DC., Prod. 2: 217. 1828, non Labill.
Eucalyptus persicifolia DC. l.c., non Lodd.
Eucalyptus semicorticata F. Muell., J. Linn. Soc. 3: 86. 1859.
Eucalyptus fibrosa F. Muell., id. 87.

Tall columnar tree; bark surface rough on lower bole, elsewhere smooth, greenish-white. Juvenile leaves sessile and amplexicaul or shortly petiolate; lamina 3–8 × 0.6–3 cm, pale beneath, narrowly lanceolate, thinly chartaceous, with minutely denticulate puberulous margin. Mature leaves petiolate; lamina 10–12 × 2–4 cm, lustrous, lanceolate, coriaceous. Inflorescence an axillary 6–12-flowered umbel; peduncles –15 mm long, stout, quadrangular. Flower bud –10 × 6 mm, ovoid, acute, pedicellate; operculum conical to rostrate, sometimes much longer than calyx tube; anthers adnate, reniform, opening in divergent slits, with terminal gland. Fruit –12 × 12 mm, ovoid to subglobose, disc small, internally oblique; valves deeply enclosed.

D i s t r. Victoria to Queensland. Widely planted in the Sri Lanka hill country.

V e r n. Black butt (E).

23. Eucalyptus triantha Link., Enum. Plant. Hort. Berol. 2: 30. 1822; Blakely, l.c. ed. 2. 186.

Eucalyptus acmenioides Schauer in Walp., Rep. 2: 924. 1843; Maiden, l.c. 9: 263, pl. 42; 65: pl. 265; 70: pl. 287.

Large tree; bark persistently fibrous. Juvenile leaves sessile and more or less amplexicaul; lamina 5–12 × 2–4 cm, pale beneath, elliptic to lanceolate, glabrous, more or less acuminate. Mature leaves petiolate; lamina 10–18 × 2.5–3 cm, pale beneath, lanceolate, chartaceous, more or less acuminate. Inflorescence a 3–10-flowered axillary or terminal umbel; peduncle –15 mm long, angular or compressed. Flower buds –7 × 5 mm, ovate, acute, pedicellate; operculum conical to rostrate, at least as long as calyx tube; anthers adnate, reniform, opening in divergent slits, with minute terminal gland. Fruit –6 × 7 mm, globose or sometimes urceolate; disc obscure, valves enclosed.

D i s t r. New South Wales and Queensland. Doubtfully recorded from Sri Lanka.

V e r n. White mahogany (E).

24. Eucalyptus microcorys F. Muell., Fragm. 2: 50. 1860; Maiden, l.c. 9: 261, pl. 41; 54: pl. 261; 70: pl. 287; 74: 206; Blakely, l.c. ed. 2. 186.

Large stout tree –30 m, tall; bark surface persistently flaky, corrugated. Juvenile leaves pale green, sessile or shortly pedicellate; lamina 5–7 × 2–3.4 cm, elliptic or broadly lanceolate. Mature leaves petiolate; lamina 8–10 × 2–3.5 cm, lanceolate, chartaceous, acuminate. Inflorescence a 4–8-flowered axillary or terminal umbel; peduncle –20 mm long, compressed. Flower buds –7 × 5 mm, cylindrical-clavate, pedicellate; operculum hemispherical, obtuse, much shorter than calyx tube; anthers adnate, reniform, opening in divergent slits. Fruit –10 × 6 mm, pyriform to cylindric-clavate, truncate; disc obscure; valves enclosed or slightly exserted.

D i s t r. New South Wales and Queensland. Commonly planted in Sri Lanka; a recommended plantation species.

V e r n. Tallow Wood (E).

25. Eucalyptus paniculata Sm., Trans. Linn. Soc. Lond. 3: 287. 1797; Maiden, l.c. 13: 104, pl. 57; 48: 225, pl. 196, 197; 64: pl. 260; 70: pl. 287; 75: 260, pl. 9; Blakely, l.c. ed. 2. 269.

Eucalyptus nanglei R.T. Baker, Proc. R. Soc. N.S.W. 51: 418. 1917.

Large tree with dark grey hard deeply furrowed persistent bark. Juvenile leaves dark green, shortly petiolate; lamina 3–6 × 1.5–4 cm, ovate to broadly lanceolate. Intermediate leaves alternate, petiolate; lamina 7–10 × 3.5–7 cm, lanceolate. Mature leaves petiolate; lamina –13 × 3 cm, lanceolate. Inflorescence a terminal panicle; umbels 3–9-flowered; peduncles –20 mm long, subterete. Flower buds –10 × 5 mm, ovate to diamond-shaped, pedicellate; operculum acutely conical, sometimes shorter than calyx tube; outer stamens without anthers; anthers adnate, mostly oblique on filaments, subreniform to rounded-cuneate, opening in terminal slits. Fruit –10 × 10 mm, hemispherical to pyriform; disc small, valves exserted or enclosed.

D i s t r. New South Wales. Occasionally planted in the Sri Lanka hills.
V e r n. Grey Ironbark (E).

26. Eucalyptus sideroxylon A. Cunn. ex Benth., B. Fl. 3: 209. 1866; Maiden, l.c. 12: 82, pl. 55; 64: pl. 260; 74: pl. 7; 75: 250; Blakely, l.c. ed. 2. 270.

Medium sized to large tree; bark surface black, hard, deeply furrowed. Juvenile leaves shortly petiolate; lamina 4–8 × 0.5–1.5 cm, linear to broadly oblong, subglaucous. Intermediate leaves alternate, petiolate; lamina –11 × 3 cm, lanceolate, subglaucous. Inflorescences a 3–7-flowered axillary umbel; peduncles –20 mm long, subterete, deflexed. Flower buds –15 × 10 mm, acutely ovoid; pedicels elongate, slender; operculum conical, shorter than calyx tube; anthers adnate, ± oblique on filaments, cuneate-truncate, opening in terminal slits. Fruit –10 × 9 mm, ovoid or globose to goblet-shaped; disc thin and flat or internally oblique; valves deeply enclosed.

D i s t r. Victoria to Southern Queensland. Occasionally planted in the Sri Lanka hills.
V e r n. Mugga.

27. Eucalyptus baueriana Schauer in Walp., Rep. 2, Suppl. 1: 924. 1843; Maiden, l.c. 13: 120, pl. 59; 42: 62; 62: 16; 75: 267.

Medium sized to large tree with pale bluish rounded crown; bark surface grey, rough and persistent on trunk and large branches. Juvenile leaves dark green, petiolate; lamina 6–7 × 6–12 cm, orbicular to broadly lanceolate. Mature leaves with 4 cm long petioles; lamina c. 6 × 6 cm, similar but more or less glaucous, undulate. Inflorescence terminal, paniculate, or subterminal, axillary and umbellate; umbels 3–8-flowered; peduncles –12 mm long, rather robust, terete. Flower bud –10 × 5 mm, narrowly conical or clavate, sub-sessile or shortly pedicellate; operculum hemispherical to conical, usually much shorter than the calyx-tube; anthers adnate, almost truncate, obcordate to subcuneate, opening in terminal pores. Fruit –7 × 7 mm, funnel-shaped, more or less shortly pedicellate; disc obscure; valves deeply enclosed.

D i s t r. Victoria to Southern Queensland. Occasionally planted in up-country Sri Lanka.

V e r n. Blue Box (E).

8. TRISTANIA

R. Br. in Ait., Hort. Kew. ed. 2, 4: 417. 1813.

Medium sized to large trees with ribbed and frequently twisted trunks and branches, and ribbony or fibrous flaky or smooth scroll-marked bark surface as *Eucalyptus*. Twigs terete. Leaves generally spiral, obovate-oblanceolate, with slender nervation and intramarginal nerve close to margin; shortly decur-rent-petiolate. Inflorescence axillary, laxly cymose; bracts fugaceous. Flowers generally small, white or greenish; calyx tube resembling *Eucalyptus*, adnate to ovary at base, distally dilated and with 5 short lobes; petals 5, spreading; stamens many, ± united in 5 bundles opposite and ± connate to the base of the petals; filaments slender; anthers versatile, oblong, latrorse; ovary ± infer-ior, 3-locular, with filiform style and subcapitate stigma; cells with many pendulous or horizontal ovules. Fruit a small loculicidal capsule more or less imbedded in the persistent calyx at base. Fertile seeds few, recurved or pendulous, linear, ± winged; embryo straight, with plane-convex cotyledons exceeding and hiding the radicle.

About 25 species, in South-East Asia and Malaysia, New Caledonia and Tropical Australia, especially on degraded soils and open habitats in the for-mer. One species cultivated in Sri Lanka.

Tristania conferta R. Br. in Ait., Hort. Kew. ed. 2, 4: 417. 1813.

A potentially large tree –45 m tall, but not exceeding 30 m in Sri Lanka. Crown dark, hemispherical. Bark surface grey or brown, fibrous, scaly on butt, orange-brown to red-brown dappled and smooth, scroll-marked, else-where. Leaf undersurface, twigs and calyx ± grey-brown caducous pubescent. Dormant buds prominently scaly. Juvenile lamina 2.5–7 × 2–4 cm, opposite, elliptic, with decurrent base and very short petiole. Adult lamina 7–15 × 2.5–7 cm, densely spiral towards the ascending twig endings, elliptic, dark green, glossy above, matt beneath, attenuate-acuminate, tapering into the –1.5 cm long slender petiole; nerves evident beneath, ascending. Inflorescence axillary, paniculate with 3–6-flowered cymes. Calyx tube 5–10 mm long, ovoid-conical, with short obtuse peripheral lobes; petals broad, white, imbricate in bud. Stamens many, –2 cm long, white, united into 5 feathery bundles opposite the petals. Fruit a –1.5 × 1.0 cm smooth ovoid or bell-shaped 3-celled capsule; 3 valves obtuse, enclosed in the calyx; pedicels 12 mm long; seeds narrowly wedge-shaped, few to a cell.

D i s t r. New South Wales and Queensland coastal forests. Occasionally cultivated in the Sri Lanka hill country.

S p e c i m e n s E x a m i n e d. NUWARA ELIYA DISTRICT: Botanic Garden, Hakgala, *s. coll. s.n.*, 28.9.1899 (PDA), *Worthington 6763* (K); Nuwara Eliya, woodland near lake, *Meijer, Dassanayake & Balasubramaniam 604* (PDA, US). BADULLA DISTRICT: Roehampton, Haputale, *Worthington 427* (K), *5345* (K), *6709* (K).

PITTOSPORACEAE

(by Deva Duttun Tirvengadum*)

Evergreen trees or shrubs. Leaves spirally arranged, often in pseudo-whorls and crowded at the ends of the branches, simple, mostly entire, exstipulate. Flowers regular, bisexual, sometimes functionally unisexual. Sepals 5, imbricate. Petals 5, hypogynous, imbricate. Stamens 5, free or slightly connivent below, opposite to the sepals; anthers 2-celled, introrse, dehiscing lengthwise. Disc absent. Ovary superior, mostly 1-celled, with 2 parietal placentas often meeting in the middle and so falsely 2-celled; ovules few or numerous, anatropous; style simple; stigma thickened or lobed (2 to 5-lobed). Fruit a bivalved loculicidal capsule. Seeds few or many, often immersed in a viscid pulp; testa thin, smooth; endosperm horny, copious; embryo small; cotyledons small.

A family of nine small genera with about 200 species confined to the tropical and warm temperate regions of the Old World, chiefly Australia. *Pittosporum*, the only genus occurring in Ceylon, is widely distributed from West Africa (including Macaronesia), Madagascar through Asia, Malaysia and Australia to Polynesia. The Ceylon *Pittosporums* occur in the moist low country and extend to the upper montane zone.

The latest treatment of the family is that of Bakker & Van Steenis, Fl. Mal. 1(5): 345–361. 1955–58.

The family is usually divided into 2 tribes:

1. Tribe *Pittosporeae* (with capsular fruits): *Pittosporum*—in Ceylon.

2. Tribe *Billardiereae* (with non-capsular fruits)—not represented in Ceylon.

PITTOSPORUM

Banks & Soland. ex Gaertn., Fruct. 1: 286, t. 59, f. 7. 1788. Type species: *Pittosporum tenuifolium* Banks & Soland. ex Gaertn.

Erect, aromatic trees or shrubs. Leaves often crowded towards the ends of the twigs, entire (undulate towards the margin in *Pittosporum undulatum*). Inflorescence terminal (often pseudoterminal) or axillary, few or many-flowered, in umbellate or subumbellate panicles or cymes, or in corymbose

*Museum National d'Histoire Naturelle, Paris.

racemes. Flowers bisexual or sometimes unisexual, fragrant. Sepals 5, free or connate to various degrees below. Petals 5, ligulate, free or slightly connate at base or tubular. Stamens 5, erect, free, occasionally coherent with corolla tube. Pistil sessile or stipitate, 5-furrowed, generally passing into the ellipsoid ovary; ovary 1-celled with parietal placentas, sometimes falsely 2-celled by the intrusion of the placentas into the middle; ovules 2 or more on each placenta. Capsule globular, ellipsoid or ovoid, tipped by remnant of style; valves thick, woody or coriaceous, inner surface generally ribbed or pinnately striated, occasionally with resiniferous ducts. Seeds 4 or more, erect, generally compressed against each other, angular, wrinkled, reddish or blackish, coated by a resinous viscid fluid.

A widely spread and large genus with about 100 species, mostly confined to the tropical, subtropical and warm-temperate regions of both the Southern and Northern Hemispheres: South and East Asia to Korea and Japan, Malaysia, Australia, New Zealand, the Pacific (Bonin Isl., Micronesia, Melanesia, Polynesia) and Africa; three species occur in Ceylon, one of which is probably endemic, *Pittosporum ceylanicum*.

For previous studies of the taxonomy, morphology, geographical distribution and grouping of genus *Pittosporum*, see Gowda, The Genus *Pittosporum* in the Sino-Indian Region. J. Arn. Arb. 32: 265–343. 1951 and Bakker and Van Steenis, Pittosporaceae. Fl. Mal. 1 (5): 345–361. 1955–58.

KEY TO THE SPECIES

1 Young branches and inflorescences glabrous. Flowers bisexual. Ovary covered with whitish-brown tomentum. Fruit valves woody. Seeds 8. Leaves much tapering at base .... **1. P. ceylanicum**
1 Young branches and inflorescences pubescent. Flowers bisexual or sometimes unisexual. Ovary covered with brown or ferrugineous tomentum. Fruit valves thin or coriaceous. Seeds 4 or more than 10. Leaves not as about
  2 Inflorescence in umbellate cymes. Flowers always bisexual, yellowish-green. Petals not distinctly nerved. Ovary covered with brown tomentum. Fruit valves thin. Seeds 4. Petiole 0.5 to 1 cm long. Leaves coriaceous, up to 5.5 cm long. Venation pellucid.... .... **2. P. tetraspermum**
  2 Inflorescence in subumbellate compound panicles. Flowers sometimes unisexual, white or pale green. Petals 3-nerved. Ovary covered with ferrugineous tomentum. Fruit valves coriaceous. Seeds more than 10. Petiole 1 to 2 cm long. Leaves membranous, up to 13 cm long. Venation not pellucid .... **3. P. ferrugineum**

1. Pittosporum ceylanicum Wight, Ill. Ind. Bot. 1:ˈ173. 1839; Hook. f., Fl. Br. Ind. 1: 199. 1872; Trimen, Handb. Fl. Ceylon 1: 78. 1893 ("Zeylanicum"); Gowda, J. Arn. Arb. 32: 324. 1951. Type: Ceylon, March 1835, *Wight s.n.* (K).

Small tree 5 to 8 m tall. Bark warty. Stem lenticellate, greyish-white, glabrous. Young shoots, petioles and leaves glabrous, covered with tiny stipitate glands. Leaves crowded towards the ends of branches, spirally arranged, obovate-oblanceolate, up to 9 cm long, up to 2.5 cm broad, much tapering towards the base, slightly obtuse or rounded at apex, sometimes acute, margin often rather recurved, membranous, glabrous, darker above, paler beneath; venation reticulate, more distinct underneath. Petiole up to 1 cm long, glabrous. Inflorescence pseudoterminal, in long-peduncled, paniculately compound umbels, glabrous. Peduncle 4 to 6 cm long. Pedicels short, varying in length. Flower-buds oblong, 6 to 7 mm long. Flowers bisexual, yellowish-white. Sepals ovate or subacute, 2 to 3 mm long, glabrous, ciliate. Petals linear, 8 to 9 mm long, erect, spreading at ends. Filaments up to 5 mm tall; anthers oblongish, up to 1 mm long. Ovary 2 to 3 mm long, covered with whitish-brown tomentum; ovules 8; styles 4 to 5 mm tall, glabrous. Capsules subglobose, 1.5 cm long, 1.4 cm broad, subcompressed, yellowish, black when dry; valves woody, resinous, hard, with a strong mangiferous smell. Seeds 8, angular, unequal, closely packed; testa pulpy, sticky, orange-red.

D i s t r. Possibly endemic to Ceylon. The two "South Indian" specimens cited by Gowda (l.c.) lack precise locality, and, therefore, leave doubt as to their exact place of origin.

E c o l. Found in secondary submontane dwarf forests, rocky jungles or low dense forests. Flowering in April; fruiting December to January.

V e r n. Ketiya (S).

N o t e. The strong and pleasant smell of the seeds attracts insects and some fruits apparently harbour them. This explains the occurrence of unusually large swollen fruits devoid of seeds.

S p e c i m e n s E x a m i n e d. KANDY DISTRICT: Kandy, in 1819, *Moon s.n.* (BM); Madugoda, rocky jungle, *Simpson 8782* (BM, PDA); 3 miles N.E. of Madugoda, 885 m alt., low dense forest, *Jayasuriya 484* (PDA, US); 4 miles beyond Madugoda towards Mahiyangana, *Jayasuriya 373* (PDA, US), *Tirvengadum & Waas 446* (PDA, US); Kandy-Mahiyangana Road, 30/11 Culvert, *Tirvengadum & Jayasuriya 160* (G, K, L, MAU, P, PDA, US); Hunnasgiriya-Mahiyangana Road, 23/10 Culvert, *Tirvengadum & Cramer 230* (G, K, L, MAU, P, PDA, US). BADULLA DISTRICT: Jungle below Bandarawela, 21.3.1906, *Silva s.n.* (PDA); Galagama, *s. coll. C.P. 476* (BM, CAL, G, GH, K, MH, P, PDA); Haputale-Boralanda Road, 12/9 mile marker, *Tirvengadum, Cramer, Waas & Bandaranaike 582* (P, PDA, US). ANU-RADHAPURA DISTRICT: Summit of Ritigala, July 1887 *s. coll. s.n.* (PDA). LOCALITY UNKNOWN: March 1835, *Wight s.n.* (K); March 1836, *Wight s.n.* (K); *Walker 32* (G), *s. coll. s.n.* (MH).

2. Pittosporum tetraspermum Wight & Arn., Prod. 1: 154. 1834; Hook. f., Fl. Br. Ind. 1: 198. 1872; Trimen, Handb. Fl. Ceylon 1: 77. 1893; Gamble, Fl. Pres. Madras 1: 55. 1915; Gowda, J. Arn. Arb. 32: 337. 1951. Holotype: South India, *Wight 142* (K).

Shrub or small tree branching bifurcately, or in whorl at the top. Outer bark lenticellate, greyish-brown. Inner bark fibrous, moderately thick, white; exudation gummy, arange, scanty. Young branches puberulous. Young leaves and inflorescence ferrugineous hirsute. Leaves densely crowded at ends of branches, subverticillate, oval-oblong or oval-elliptic, 5.5 cm long, 2.5 cm broad, acute at base, subacute or obtuse at apex, margin entire, often revolute, coriaceous, glabrous; venation reticulate, pellucid, very distinct underneath. Petiole 0.5 to 1 cm long, slender, not grooved above. Inflorescence pseudoterminal, in umbellate cymes. Peduncle 1 to 10 mm long, or subsessile. Pedicel up to 1 cm long, puberulent. Flower-buds oblong, 8 to 10 cm long. Flowers bisexual, yellowish-green, fragrant. Sepals free, up to 1 mm long, triangular, pubescent, margin ciliate. Petals 7 to 10 mm long, linear-oblong or strap-shaped, not distinctly nerved. Filaments up to 4 mm tall, erect, included; anthers 1.5 mm long, yellowish-green, with a brown spherical patch at base. Ovary oval-oblong, up to 3 mm tall, brown-tomentose; ovules 4 per ovary; style up to 3 mm tall, glabrous. Capsule subglobose, 1 cm in diameter, tipped by withered style; valves 2, rather thin, striate inside. Seeds 4, subtrigonous, darkish red with an orange-red aril; pulp sticky, invested with a viscid exudation, strongly aromatic.

D i s t r. Widely distributed in S. India. Confined to the upper montane zone in Ceylon.

E c o l. Found along borders of montane forests, often near stream, or in disturbed forests under semi-shade. Flowering December to February.

I l l u s t r. Wight, Ic. Pl. Ind. Or. 3 (3): t. 971. 1845, Specielegium Neilgher. 1: 37, t. 43. 1846.

S p e c i m e n s E x a m i n e d. KANDY DISTRICT: Hunnasgiriya, 650 m alt., along road to Corbet's Gap, in secondary montane forest, *Tirvengadum, Cramer & Balasubramaniam 74* (K, MAU, P, PDA, US). NUWARA ELIYA DISTRICT: N'Eliya-Pundalu-Oya Rd, 1/7 Culvert, near large stream, *Jayasuriya & Cramer 763, 764* (PDA, US); Hakgala, towards summit of peak, *Tirvengadum & Cramer 58* (MAU, P, PDA, US); Horton Plains, *Tirvengadum & Cramer 99* (G, K, L, MAU, P, PDA, US), *Wight s.n.* (K). BADULLA DISTRICT: Top of Namunukula, 12.3.1907 & 3.6.1924, *Silva s.n.* (PDA); slope of Namunukula, *Tirvengadum, Cramer, Waas & Bandaranaike 588* (P, PDA, US). LOCALITY UNKNOWN: *Gardner s.n.* (K); *s. coll. C.P. 3994* (K, PDA); *Walker 99* (K); *Worthington 7093* (PDA); *s. coll. s.n.* (PDA); *s. coll. C.P. 572* (BM, CAL, G, GH, K, MH, P, PDA) & *C.P. 685* (MAU, P, PDA, US).

3. Pittosporum ferrugineum Dry. in Ait., Hort. Kew ed. 2, 2: 27, 1811; Hook. f., Fl. Br. Ind. 1: 199. 1872; Gowda, J. Arn. Arb. 32: 337. 1951; Bakker & Van Steenis, Fl. Mal. 1 (5): 355. 1955–58; Jayasuriya, Ceylon J. Sci., Bid. Sci. 12 (1): 18. 1976. Type: Based on a plant cultivated in the Royal Botanic Garden, Kew.

Tree 8 to 20 m tall, branching trifurcately. Bark warty, with prominent light brown lenticels. Young twigs, young leaves and inflorescence rusty pubescent. Leaves spirally arranged, crowded towards the ends of the twigs, narrowly obovate or oval-lanceolate, 5 to 13 cm long, 2.5 cm to 4 cm broad, acute or cuneate at base, sometimes decurrent, acuminate at tip, margin slightly revolute, membranous; upper surface olive-green or shiny, glabrous; lower surface glabrescent, except on main nerves; nerves 4 to 6 pairs; venation finely reticulate and prominent beneath. Petiole 1 to 2 cm long, distinctly grooved above. Inflorescence subterminal, in subumbellate compound panicles, densely villous-ferrugineous, arising in whorls of bracts with similar indumentum. Peduncle 1 to 3 cm long. Pedicel 0.5 to 1 cm long. Flowers bisexual or functionally unisexual, white or pale green. Calyx and corolla reflexed. Sepals free or slightly united at the base, up to 3 mm long, lanceolate, acute, sparsely villous outside and on the margin, glabrous inside. Petals oblong lanceolate, 1 cm long, sometimes coherent, easily separating, linear, acute, distinctly 3-nerved. Filaments up to 6 mm long, linear, subulate at tip, glabrous; anthers sagittiform, c. 1.5 mm long. Ovary oblong or club-shaped, up to 3 mm long, subsessile, densely ferrugineous-tomentose; style stout, up to 2 mm long. Fruits 5 to 7 per inflorescence. Capsule globose, 1 cm long, 1 cm broad, slightly flattened on the sides. Mature fruit orange, when dry turning black and warty, splitting open into 2 valves to expose the bright scarlet seeds; valves coriaceous, faintly and more or less transversely ribbed inside and varnish-like. Seeds about 16, of variable size, mucilage-coated and sticky, from signal red to chocolate-brown when dry.

D i s t r. Widespread in the Philippines, Celebes, Moluccas, East Java, Lesser Sunda Islands and Formosa. Cultivated in Kenya. In Ceylon, introduced, probably as an ornamental tree in the Peradeniya Botanic Gardens, it is now highly naturalised in the vicinity of that Garden, along the Kandy-Peradeniya Road and in the Campus of Peradeniya University.

E c o l. Introduced in Ceylon about a century ago, this tree is now commonly found on exposed knolls and among hedges in the vicinity of the Botanical Gardens, Peradeniya. Flowering: October–March. Fruiting March. The fruit is most attractive when ripe. This, in contrast with the exposed chocolate-brown dry seeds, facilitates dispersal by birds.

V e r n. Kaputu or Wal-Handun (S).

I l l u s t r. Sims, Bot. Mag. 46: t. 2075. 1819.

S p e c i m e n s E x a m i n e d. KANDY DISTRICT: Kandy, vicinity of Car Mart, *Jayasuriya 735* (PDA, US); University Campus, *Cooray 68101301* (K, PDA, US); path behind Science Block to Railway Station, *Tirvengadum & Balasubramaniam 78, 79* (G, K, L, MAU, P, PDA, US); Galaha Road, opposite Faculty of Medicine, *Jayasuriya 739* (PDA, US).

PRIMULACEAE

(by S.H. Sohmer*)

Herbs, annual or perennial, infrequently suffrutescent; leaves opposite, whorled, or basal, infrequently alternate, simple—the aquatic *Hottonia* has dissected leaves which are specialized for buoyancy; flowers usually regular, 5-merous, perfect, with a persistent calyx of 4–9 lobes and a fused, rotate salverform, or reflexed corolla of 4–9 lobes; stamens uniseriate, distinct or fused at base, as many as, and opposite, the corolla lobes, with anthers 2-celled, introrse, and longitudinally dehiscent, and with staminodia sometimes present; pistil 1, superior, unilocular, usually with 5 carpels and free-central placentation, and 1 style with capitate stigma; ovules few to many, anatropous or nearly so, with 2 integuments; fruit a capsule with 5 or 10 teeth or valves, infrequently a pyxis; seed with abundant endosperm and a small, straight embryo.

A family of approximately 28 genera and 800 species (Lawrence, Taxonomy of Vascular Plants, 1951), widely distributed but most frequent, in terms of numbers of taxa, in north temperate areas. There is but one indigenous genus in Ceylon, *Lysimachia*, with 2 species which are restricted to the hill country above an elevation of approximately 1600 m.

The indigenous species appear to prosper in the cool shade of the upland forests. Both can be abundant in places throughout the moister parts of these forests. Very few members of the family have been introduced for cultivation in Ceylon. Thwaites (1860) reported the presence of *Anagallis arvensis* L. as did Trimen (1895), Alston (1931), and Bond (1953). In addition, Trimen (1895) and Alston (1931) reported *Cyclamen persicum* Mill. as probably cultivated in Ceylon. I have not found these taxa in the field nor represented in the herbarium of the Department of Agriculture, Royal Botanic Gardens, Peradeniya. In 1926, J.M. de Silva collected specimens of *Primula obconica* Hance, and *P. malabarica* Franch. in the glass house of the Hakgala Botanic Gardens. They were obviously under cultivation there. There are presently no members of this family in Hakgala according to the director (Pers. Com., 1973). The only available evidence of cultivation or occurrence of non-indigenous members of the family is a fragment of the scape of *Primula malabarica*, and two specimens of *P. obconica*, deposited in the herbarium at

*La Crosse, Wisconsin, U.S.A.

478

Peradeniya. The family as a whole has interesting features concerning its phytochemistry and genetics. For a good summary of this information see Bentvelzen (Fl. Mal 6: 173. 1962).

LYSIMACHIA

Tourn. in L., Sp. Pl. 146. 1753; L., Gen. Pl. ed. 5: 72. 1754; Endl., Gen. Pl. II. 732. 1839; Benth. and Hook., Gen. Pl. II. 635. 1873; Pax & Knuth in Pflanzenr. 22: 256. 1905; Ray, Illinois Biol. Monogr. 24; 13. 1956.

Cerium Lour., Fl. Cochinch. 167. 1793.
Lubinia Vent., Descr. Pl. Jardin Cels. 96. 1800.
Tridynia Raf. ex Steud., Nom. ed. 2, 2: 704. 1841.
Bernadina Baudo, Ann. Sci. Nat. Bot. II, 20: 348. 1843.

Herbs, annual or perennial, creeping or upright, with sessile or petioled, opposite, alternate or whorled, entire leaves; flowers usually solitary and axillary, or in terminal or subterminal racemes or panicles, with small 5–6 parted calyces and rotate to campanulate corollas with 5–6 entire or dentate lobes; stamens 5–6, inserted on corolla tube, united at base, staminodia absent; pistil 1, with globose ovary and 1 style with capitate stigma, and few to many ovules; fruit a 5-valved capsule or irregularly dehiscent.

A genus of approximately 150 species distributed widely in temperate and subtropical areas.

KEY TO THE SPECIES

1 Plants erect, to 1.3 m high, frequently becoming somewhat suffrutescent, leaves alternate with short petioles and blades lanceolate to oblanceolate with acute bases........
....**1. L. laxa**
2 Plants relatively delicate, creeping, rooting at nodes, often covering relatively large areas of ground by branching; leaves opposite with petioles 0.2–0.6 cm and blades broadly ovate to nearly oval with truncate, subcordate, or slightly acute bases.......
....**2. L. deltoidea**

1. **Lysimachia laxa** Baudo, Ann. Sci. Nat. Bot. II, 20: 347. 1843; Bentvelzen, in Fl. Mal. 6: 180. 1962.

Lysimachia ramosa Wall. ex Duby in DC., Prod. 8: 65. 1844; Thw., Enum. Pl. Zeyl. 172. 1860; Klatt, Abh. Naturwiss. Naturwiss. Verein Hamburg 4, 4: 31, t. 17. 1866; Hooker. f., Fl. Br. Ind. 3: 503 (incl. var. *zeylanica*). 1882; Trimen, Handb. Fl. Ceylon 3: 65. 1895; Pax & Knuth in Pflanznr. 22: 271 including var. *typica* (= var. *laxa*), & var. *grandiflora* Franch. 1905; Koorders, Exkursions fl. Java 3: 35. 1912; Handel-Mazzetti, in Notes Roy. Bot. Gard. Edinburgh 16 : 75. 1928; van Steenis, Bull. Jard. Bot. Buitenz. 13: 238. 1934; Merr., J. Arn. Arb. 19: 61. 1938; Backer, Bek pt. Fl. Java (em. ed.) 8, fam. 180, p. 4. 1949; Ingram, Baileya 8: 95. 1960.

Lysimachia floribunda Zoll. & Mor., Natuur-Geneesk. Arch. Ned.—Indië 2 : 575. 1845; Walp., Ann. Bot. Syst. 1: 494. 1848.

Stems erect, considerably branched above, becoming 5-winged and thick and frequently somewhat woody below, to 1.5 m tall, glabrous; leaves decurrent, with petioles 0.1–1.2 cm long, and thin lanceolate to oblanceolate blades 3.0–15.0 cm long with entire margins, glabrous throughout and somewhat glaucous below; flowers solitary, axillary, on pedicels 1.6–4.5 cm long at anthesis, shorter than the leaves; calyx of 5 ovate, long-acuminate sepals 1.2–1.6 cm long, somewhat fused below or not at all; corolla 1.0–1.3 mm long, yellow, glabrous, of 5 broadly ovate, obtuse petals fused at base for about 1/4 of their length, and spreading at anthesis; stamens 5, inserted on the corolla tube about 1 mm above the base, with filaments 2–3 mm long and anthers the same length as filaments; pistil green, glabrous, with globose ovary 1.5–2.0 mm long at anthesis, and style about 3 mm long, and a minute, capitate stigma, ovules numerous, placentation free-central; fruit a capsule, about 8 mm long, not including persistent style, brown at maturity and dehiscing with 5 valves; seeds reddish-black, trigonous and fusiform, tuberculate, and about 1 mm long. Flowers August–September to December–January.

Distr. & Ecol. This species is often locally abundant in the shade of the upland forests above an elevation of 1600 m; finding one almost certainly means several to many others will be close at hand. It is found also in similar habitats in the Eastern Himalayas, Burma and Indonesia. The flowers are yellow and are open all day. General pollinators seem to be indicated, as various Diptera and Hymenoptera were observed visiting flowers of this species in Pidurutalagala during the late morning. Flowers August–September to December–January.

Note. Bentvelzen has shown (Fl. Malaysiana, 6: 180. 1962) that this species, which has been known under the name of *L. ramosa* Wall. ex Duby for many years, was first validly described by Baudo.

Illustr. Bond, Wild Flowers of the Ceylon Hills 131. 1953.

Specimens Examined. KANDY DISTRICT: Peradeniya Bot. Gd., *s. coll. C.P. 1896* (US). NUWARA ELIYA DISTRICT: Nuwara Eliya area, *C.F. & R.J. van Beusekom 1383* (PDA, US); Pidurutalagala, *N. Balakrishnan NBK632* (PDA, US), *L.H. Cramer 3125* (PDA), *W. Meijer 50* (PDA), *A.M. Silva* (PDA), *S.H. Sohmer, M. Jayasuriya, K. Eliezer 8420, 8421* (PDA, US); Hakgala For. Res., *S.H. Sohmer, M. Jayasuriya, K. Eliezer 8479, 8495* (PDA, US); Pattipola—Horton Plains Road, *S.H. Sohmer, M. Jayasuriya, K. Eliezer 8534, 8538* (PDA, US); Horton Plains, *N. Balakrishnan NBK404* (PDA), *NBK1032* (US), *F.R. Fosberg 53303* (US), *A.M. Silva* 4 May 1906 (PDA), *S.H. Sohmer, M. Jayasuriya, K. Eliezer 8599* (PDA, US); without further data, *N. Balakrishnan NBK 1032* (PDA). LOCALITY UNKNOWN: *Walker 148* (PDA), *s. coll. C.P. 1896* (US).

2. Lysimachia deltoidea Wight, Ill. 2: 137, t. 144. 1850; Klatt, Abh. Naturwiss. Naturwiss. Verein Hamburg 4, 4: 35, t. 19. 1866; Hook. f., Fl. Br. Ind. 3: 505. 1882; Pax & Knuth in Pflanzenr. 22: 263. 1905.

Lysimachia ferruginea Edgew. Trans. Linn. Soc. Lond. 20: 83. 1846.
Lysimachia umbrosa Gardner ex Thw., Enum. Pl. Zeyl. 172. 1860.
Lysimachia japonica Thunb. sensu Thw., l.c. 172.

Plant perennial, pubescent, with stems creeping, prostrate, well-branched, often rooting at nodes, and usually 10–20 cm long, and usually less than 1 mm wide; leaves opposite with petioles 0.2–1.9 cm long, and with blades entire, broadly ovate to oval and truncate to subcordate to slightly acute at base, subacute to mucronate at apex, 0.7–2.6 cm long and 0.6–2.9 cm wide, covered above and below with a lesser or greater amount of multicellular trichomes and brownish scabrous dots, infrequently nearly glabrous; flowers solitary and axillary with pubescent, dotted pedicels 0.7–2.0 cm long, and with lanceolate, acute, pubescent (outside) and dotted sepals 4–7 mm long and somewhat fused below, and a corolla of 5 broadly obovate, yellow, dotted, minutely crenate-dentate petals 5–7 mm long and 4–6 mm broad, fused below to form a corolla tube about 1 mm long; stamens 5, inserted on the corolla tube, filaments about 1.5 mm long and anthers about 1.5 mm long at anthesis; pistil with globose ovary about 1 mm long at anthesis, glabrous, with style about 3 mm long with capitate stigma, and with ovules relatively numerous, and free-central placentation; capsule glabrous and brown at maturity.

D i s t r. & E c o l. A variable species in terms of size and vesture and leaf shape, found in the Chekiang, Yunan and Szechuan provinces of China, the Himalayas at low elevations, and the Nilgiri Hills of Southern India as well as Ceylon. Varieties have been named according to the size and shape of the leaves, length of the petioles and nature of the investiture. The variety *cordifolia* was described by Hooker (Fl. Br. Ind. 3: 505. 1882) as having cordate or truncate leaves and being restricted to Ceylon. The individuals in Ceylon do tend to have cordate or truncate bases more frequently than in individuals from outside of Ceylon and the leaves are generally smaller in size.

Wherever found it is a taxon of moist, cool, shaded forests. In Ceylon members of the species are found above an elevation of about 1900 metres, and may be locally abundant due to vegetative spread. The species favours moist sites near streams and seepage areas in the upland forests, growing particularly well under the erect vegetation on the banks of small streams. It has also been found in the zone between wet patana and forest in association with *Ranunculus wallichianus* Wight and Arn., and *Anotis nummularia* (Arn.) Hook. f. The flowers are probably pollinated by casual insect visitors, although no vectors were observed in the field. Flowers August–September to January–February.

I l l u s t r. Bond, wild flowers of the Ceylon Hills 133. 1953.

S p e c i m e n s E x a m i n e d. KANDY DISTRICT: Peradeniya Botanic Gardens, *s. coll. C.P. 1895* (US); NUWARA ELIYA DISTRICT: Near Nuwara Eliya *s. coll. s.n.* (PDA, US); Pidurutalagala, *N. Balakrishnan NBK 629* (PDA, US); Hakgala, *A.M. Silva* 25 May 1906 (PDA); High For. Est., *A.M. Silva* 8 May 1906 (PDA); Pattipola—Horton Plains Rd., *A.M. Silva* 2 May 1906 (PDA), *S.H. Sohmer, M. Jayasuriya, K. Eliezer 8525, 8610, 8616* (PDA, US); Horton Plains, *N. Balakrishnan NBK1033* (US), *F.R. Fosberg & D. Mueller-Dombois 50030* (US), *F.R. Fosberg & M.H. Sachet 53293* (US), *F.W. Gould & R. Cooray* 13818 (US), *D. Mueller-Dombois & P.L. Comanor 67070940* (PDA, US), *J.W. Nowicke & M. Jayasuriya* 236 (US), *R.W. Read* 2009 (US), *J.M. Silva* 20 May 1911 (PDA).

PROTEACEAE

(by C.C. Townsend*)

A.L. de Juss., Gen. Pl. 78. 1789 ('Proteae'), nom. cons. Type genus: *Protea* L., Mant. alt.: 187, 328. 1771.

Trees and shrubs. Leaves alternate (spirally arranged), rarely subopposite or verticillate, simple, entire or variously toothed or dissected, or pinnate, often dimorphous, exstipulate. Inflorescences generally showy terminal, axillary or lateral heads, spikes or racemes, furnished with small caducous bracts or ebracteate, frequently geminate. Flowers hermaphrodite, rarely unisexual by abortion, actinomorphic or zygomorphic. Perianth uniseriate, tubular, straight or curved, mostly expanded near the base, the 4 perianth segments valvate and adherent for varying degrees of the development of the flower. Stamens 4, epipetalous, filaments variously connate with the tepals and sometimes obsolete; anthers bilocular, basifixed, introrse, dehiscing by longitudinal slits. Hypogynal glands 4, free and alternating with the stamens or fused into a complete or split ring, rarely absent. Ovary superior, stipitate or sessile, unilocular; ovules 1–4, orthotropous and pendulous or anatropous and ascending, with basal or parietal placentation, or numerous and biseriate; style slender, expanded at the tip, with a small terminal or lateral stigma. Fruit a follicle, drupe or nut. Seeds solitary, geminate, or numerous and biseriate, sometimes winged; endosperm absent.

A large family forming the monotypic order Proteales, with about 60 genera and over 1300 species chiefly in the warmer and drier regions of the southern hemisphere, extending northwards to Japan.

KEY TO THE GENERA

1 Leaves simple; anthers inserted at the base of the lobes of the perianth......**1. Helicia**
1 Leaves pinnate; anthers set on the expanded, concave upper part of the lobes of the perianth...**2. Grevillea**

1. HELICIA

Lour., Fl. Cochinch. 1: 83. 1790. Type species: *H. cochinchinensis* Lour., Fl.

*Royal Botanic Gardens, Kew.

483

Cochinch. 1: 83. 1790. Lit.: H. Sleumer, "A revision of the genus *Helicia* Lour." Blumea 8: 7–79. 1955.

Trees or more rarely shrubs with alternate or more rarely subopposite or verticillate, simple, entire or toothed leaves. Inflorescences of spike-like bracteate racemes, axillary on the old wood or occasionally subterminal; pedicels solitary or geminate, free or more or less connate. Perianth straight or very rarely slightly curved, slender, dilated at the base and the 4-lobed apical limb, the lobes finally becoming free and revolute. Stamens 4, inserted on the base of the perianth lobes; anthers ovoid or globose, sessile or almost so. Hypogynal glands 4, free or fused into a basal cup. Ovary sessile, biovulate, ovules anatropous; style slender and elongate, clavate at the tip with a terminal punctiform stigma. Fruit nut or drupe-like, hard or occasionally the outer layer somewhat fleshy, indehiscent or rarely tardily dehiscent along the ventral suture. Seeds globular or hemispherical, not winged.

A large genus of 87 species in S.E. Asia, Malaysia and Eastern Australia.

Helicia ceylanica Gardn. in Calc. J. Nat. Hist. 7: 453. 1847; Meisn. in DC., Prod. 14: 438. 1857, *"zeylanica"* sphalm.; Hook. f. in Fl. Br. Ind. 5: 190. 1885; Trimen, Handb. Fl. Ceylon 3: 457. 1895, *"zeylanica"* sphalm.; Sleumer in Blumea 8: 50. 1955. Type: "Banks of the Massnawatte in the Ambagamuwa District", *Gardner s.n.* (PDA, holotype).

Small tree, c. 6 m, with smooth, dark grey bark. Twigs subterete, glabrous, with greyish wrinkled cortex. Leaves oblong or oblong-obovate, 6–15 × 2.5–5 cm, rounded or broadly subacute (rarely retuse) at the apex, cuneate at the base and decurrent along the short (c. 4–6 mm) petiole, coriaceous, glabrous, midrib prominent on the lower surface but plane above, with c. 7–9 pairs of lateral nerves which branch at a little over or under half their length and gradually merge into the reticulate subsidiary venation. Racemes axillary or sited above the scars of fallen leaves, rather dense, the glabrous purple axis c. 5–8 cm long, slightly angular; peduncle 5–8 mm; pedicels slender, expanded above to a horizontal, discoid torus, purple, solitary or geminate, 3–5 mm, glabrous or sparingly pilose; bracts minute (c. 0.5–0.75 mm), glabrous or ciliate, appressed to the pedicels. Flowers pale yellow, 13–19 (–24) mm long, the narrowly ellipsoid-clavate limb 3–4 mm long, the basal swelling c. 2–3 mm long. Anthers 2 mm long. Hypogynal glands oblong-ovate, free or connate at the base, obtuse but minutely erose-denticulate at the apex. Ovary glabrous. Fruit c. 2 mm, broadly ovoid, acuminate, deep blackish-purple.

D i s t r. Endemic in moist upland forests in Central Province, alt. 605–1360 m; only two gatherings made in the present century, and probably lost in most of its old localities owing to development. Perhaps always rare and occurring only as isolated or small groups of trees.

Specimens Examined. MATALE DISTRICT: Sudugala Kande, Lagalla, Sept. 1893, *Willis s.n.* (PDA); Galagama, alt. 910 m, April 1856, *s. coll. s.n.* (PDA). KANDY DISTRICT: Rangala area, Sept. 1888, *Willis s.n.* (PDA); Knuckles, Katooloya Stretch, Streamside in jungle, 22 July 1946, *Worthington 1951* (K); Ambagamuwa, 8 Feb. 1855, *Gardner s.n.* (PDA); Navalapitiya, *Gardner s.n.* (PDA); Dolosbage, see Trimen, p. 457. BADULLA DISTRICT: Thotugalla Estate above Haputale, evergreen forest, 18 Apr. 1969, *Kostermans 23221!* (K).

2. GREVILLEA

R. Br. ex R.A. Salisbury in Knight, Cult. Proteeae 120. 1809, "Grevillia" corr. R. Br. in Trans. Linn. Soc. 10: 167. 1810, nom. cons. Type species: *G. aspleniifolia* R. Br. ex R.A. Salisbury, l.c., typ. cons.

Grevillia R. Br. ex R.A. Salisbury in Knight, l.c.
Lysanthe R.A. Salisbury in Knight, l.c. 116. 1809.
Stylurus R.A. Salisbury in Knight, l.c. 115. 1809.

Trees or shrubs with alternate, simple or pinnate leaves of very diverse form. Inflorescences of spike-like bracteate or ebracteate racemes (bracts when present minute and early-caducous), terminal and/or axillary, solitary or paniculate; pedicels solitary or 2–3 together, free. Perianth mostly recurved below the limb, sometimes straight, the segments of the limb cohering until long after the tube has split and the style become exserted. Anthers cordate-ovate, sessile at the base of the concave upper part of each segment of the limb. Hypogynal glands united into a basal annulus. Ovary stipitate, rarely sessile, biovulate, ovules anatropous; style long and slender, clavate at the tip with a punctiform stigma. Fruit a follicle, firm to lignescent, dehiscent along the adaxial suture, rarely along both sutures. Seeds flat, usually with a membranous wing.

About 170 species, almost exclusively Australian but with a very few species in Malaysia and New Caledonia.

Grevillea robusta A. Cunn. in R. Br., Prod. Fl. Nov. Holl. Suppl. 1 (Proteaceas Novas): 24. 1830; Meisn. in DC., Prod. 14: 381. 1857; Benth., Fl. Austral. 5: 459. 1870; Trimen, Handb. Fl. Ceylon 3: 457. 1895; Gamble, Fl. Pres. Madras 1243. 1925, repr. 870. 1957; Worthington, Ceylon Trees 367. 1959. Type: Brisbane River (Moreton Bay), *A. Cunningham* (K, holotype).

Medium-sized to large tree, with a tall, narrow crown, robust examples to 25–30 m, but may be smaller and more slender; bark when old dark greyish-brown, furrowed. Twigs brownish with more or less appressed whitish or rusty-brown hairs, angled or subterete. Leaves deltoid-ovate to oblong-ovate,

15–30 cm long including the 2–6 cm petiole, pinnate with mostly 5–11 pairs of opposite or subopposite pinnae, the pinnae deeply pinnatifid with entire or incised, lanceolate or linear-oblong (rarely linear) acute lobes, the lobes 1–4 cm long and (2–) 4–8 mm wide, with recurved margins; upper surface glabrous or with scattered appressed hairs and the veins obscure, lower surface densely brownish-tomentose with the midrib and primary veins running into the pinnae and lobes prominent; rhachis and petiole also brownish-tomentose. Racemes secund, many-flowered, c. 7–12 cm including the 1.5–4 cm peduncles, solitary or a few together in abbreviated panicles on short lateral branchlets on the old wood; peduncles and branchlets appressed-pilose, inflorescence axis glabrous, purplish; pedicels slender, glabrous, c. 1 cm, dilated at the apex into an oblique torus. Flowers orange to golden-brown or golden-yellow. Perianth 9–12 mm, the tube not expanded at the base, lobes narrowly spathulate, the outer c. 6 mm, the inner c. 4.5 mm. Anthers cordate-ovate, c. 1.25 mm. Disc annular, prominent, finally split. Ovary glabrous, ovoid, 1.5 mm, distinctly narrowly stipitate; style long and slender, glabrous, 1.5–2 cm, with a rhomboid-ovoid apical thickening. Fruit with the stipe curved, slightly to strongly cernuous, compressed-ovoid, c. 1.75 × 1 cm, glabrous, blackish-purple, the style hardened and persistent at the abruptly narrowed apex. Seed flat, elliptic, c. 16 × 8 mm, rounded at each end with a broad, pale wing.

D i s t r. A native of eastern Australia commonly grown in the tropics and subtropics as an ornamental tree, or in rows as wind-breaks; as such it is widely found in the hill country of Ceylon. Being a tree with a tall, narrow outline, it is also seen—though rarely—as a support for growing pepper plants.

RHIZOPHORACEAE*

(by William Macnae and F. Raymond Fosberg†)

Evergreen trees or shrubs, including mangrove species with noteworthy root formations; branching often sympodial, always in the mangrove genera; branchlets swollen at the nodes, usually pithy; leaves opposite and stipulate (except *Anisophyllea* where they are alternate and exstipulate), entire, glabrous, isomorphic (except *Anisophyllea* where they are dimorphic), corky warts often present on lower surface; nervation pinnate, or curvinerved with intramarginal veins (*Anisophyllea*); stipules conspicuous, interpetiolar, caducous leaving large interpetiolar scar; inflorescences axillary, simple or branched, usually cymose, sometimes consisting of a single flower; flowers bisexual, except *Anisophyllea* where the plants are unisexual, at the base supported by connate bracteoles; calyx of 3–16 lobes or segments above, more or less adnate to ovary below; petals free, equal in number to the calyx lobes and alternating with them, often bifid and fringed; stamens free or epipetalous, usually twice the number of petals; anthers 4-celled or multilocular, dehiscing longitudinally and inwards, except *Rhizophora* where they open through a ventral valve; disc annular and lobed or absent; ovary inferior, rarely perigynous (superior in *Cassipourea*), 2–12-celled with 2 pendulous ovules in each cell; style with simple or lobed stigma, persistent; fruit always bearing the persistent calyx, leathery, indehiscent, one-seeded; seed viviparous in mangroves; germinating in ordinary way in inland species; ennosperm fleshy or small and soon obsolete.

This is a small family, pantropical in its distribution, with a few genera, of which seven are represented in the flora of Ceylon. Several genera are principally found in coastal, brackish to saline swamp vegetation, of which they are principal components. These are commonly called mangroves and the vegetation type is called mangrove swamp (or "mangal"). The distribution of these mangrove species in Ceylon is peculiar in its discontinuity and the apparent

---

*Smithsonian Institution, Washington, D.C., U.S.A.

†The manuscript for the Rhizophoraceae was submitted in draft form, very incomplete and in a somewhat different format than is usual in botanical literature. Professor Macnae died before the treatment could be brought into final form. Fosberg largely rewrote it, inserting much additional material, and brought it into final form for use in the Flora of Ceylon. The descriptive material and taxonomic concepts are those originally included by Macnae. The literature citations, nomenclature, and keys have been somewhat rearranged and edited.

restriction of certain species to well defined regions. Mangrove trees and shrubs are restricted to sheltered shores and to the portions of those shores which lie between extreme high water and a level just below high water of neap tides. In Ceylon the tidal range is small, averaging 75 cm (30 in). This restricts the area available for colonisation by mangrove species to narrow fringes on the banks of estuaries and to areas of gently shelving lagoon shores. The high rainfall of parts of Ceylon and consequent high discharge of rivers dilutes the estuarine and lagunal waters. Hence the mangrove flora of the wet south-western coastline, comprising *Rhizophora apiculata*, *Bruguiera gymnorhiza* and *B. sexangula*, differs from that of the drier north and east where *R. mucronata*, *B. cylindrica*, and *Ceriops tagal* are conspicuous. The former group tolerates low salinities and waterlogging of the soil for long periods. The latter group is normally found in regions where salt water dominates. Although the Ma-haweli Ganga enters the sea as a deltaic system in the drier part of the island it comes from the ever wet uplands and keeps the estuarine area diluted by its sheer volume of water. It is in this region that the greatest variety of man-grove trees occurs and all "oddities" have been recorded from this area. For example both *Ceriops decandra* and *Kandelia candel* have been reported from mangrove forests in this densely forested area.

Apart from some of the more inaccessible forests of the Mahaweli-Kodi-yar delta and of some islands north of Kalpitiya all the mangrove forests of Ceylon have been exploited and over-exploited by man. Some, particularly in the south-west, have been reclaimed as coconut plantations; some have been chopped for firewood and chopped again before regeneration was com-plete. In the more populous areas then, mangrove species are present only as shrubs or pollarded trees and well grown tall trees are hard to find.

There are two tribes, the Rhizophoreae with four genera occurring in man-grove swamps and forests, and the Legnotideae comprising the inland genera. Some would separate the Anisophylleae from the Legnotideae and give them family rank.

PRACTICAL KEY TO THE GENERA AND SPECIES OF RHIZOPHORACEAE IN CEYLON

1 Plants of mangrove forests; seeds germinating in fruit while attached to tree
  2 Trees with arching prop roots; leaves mucronate...................... **Rhizophora**
    3 Leaves with short mucro; flowers in pairs on an almost sessile inflorescence in axil
      of scar of shed leaf.. **R. apiculata**
    3 Leaves with longer mucro; flowers in a cymose inflorescence in axil of a leaf not yet
      shed... **R. mucronata**
  2 Trees without arching prop roots; leaves not mucronate
    4 Trees with adpressed prop roots; with 5–6 linear-oblong calyx segments...........
    .... **Kandelia candel**
    4 Trees with buttressed base; with knee-like pneumatophores
      5 Flowers with many calyx segments................................ **Bruguiera**

6 Flowers on 2–3 flowered peduncles.................................. **B. cylindrica**
6 Flowers solitary
  7 Flowers large with 12–16 calyx segments; petals as long as or longer than calyx......
  . ...⁓..................................**B. gymnorhiza**
  7 Flowers small with 8–10 calyx segments; petals not longer than calyx.............
  ....**B. sexangula**
5 Flowers with 5–6 ovate calyx segments, on few-flowered peduncles...........**Ceriops**
  8 Petals with 3 hairs at tip; calyx reflexed in fruit........................**C. tagal**
  8 Petals fringed at apex; calyx not reflexed in fruit.....................**C. decandra**
1 Plants of inland habitats; seed not germinating in fruit attached to tree
9 Forest trees
  10 Leaves more or less identical.......................................**Carallia**
    11 Mature leaves blunt at apex.....................................**C. brachiata**
    11 Mature leaves always with a drip tip............................ **C. calycina**
  10 Leaves of two distinct sizes....................................... **Anisophyllea**
    (only one species in Ceylon)................................. **A. cinnamomoides**
9 Shrubs of dry sandy soil..**Cassipourea**
  (only one species in Ceylon)....................................... **C. ceylanica**

KEY TO THE GENERA

1 Leaves alternate, stipules none.................................... **6. Anisophyllea**
1 Leaves opposite, with interpetiolar stipules
  2 Leaves and calyx lobes leathery; fruits viviparous (seeds germinating while fruit is still
  on tree) or not
    3 Calyx lobes 4
      4 Petioles 1.5 cm or more; petals hairy within; fruit viviparous........ **1. Rhizophora**
      4 Petioles 1 cm or less; petals fimbriate margined; fruit not viviparous, crowned with
      erect sepals.. **4. Carallia**
    3 Calyx lobes 5 or more
      5 Calyx lobes more than six
        6 Flowers less than 5 mm long....................................**4. Carallia**
        6 Flowers well over 5 mm long, solitary or in 3-flowered cymes........ **2. Bruguiera**
      5 Calyx lobes 5–6
        7 Calyx lobes ovate; flowers less than 5 mm long..................... **3. Ceriops**
        7 Calyx lobes linear-oblong; flowers more than 1 cm long...............**Kandelia**
  2 Leaves and calyx lobes of ordinary texture; fruits not viviparous
    8 Calyx segments 5; ovary superior..............................._. **5. Cassipourea**
    8 Calyx segments 8; ovary inferior................................... **4. Carallia**

1. RHIZOPHORA

L., Gen. Pl. ed. 5. 202. 1754 [1753]; Ding Hou in Fl. Mal. I.5: 448. 1958 (full bibliography).

    Trees of moderate size or shrubs, with prop roots emerging from the lower stem, occasionally from the branches, tap root abortive; leaves opposite, entire, thick, often mucronate; with large interpetiolar deciduous stipules enclosing the buds; flowers in pairs on a short thick peduncle or in a shortly peduncled cyme; each bud supported by two hard, thick, fused bracts; calyx deeply divided into 4 segments, persistent, enlarging in the fruit; petals 4; stamens 8–12; ovary half-inferior, 2-celled with 2 ovules in each cell, style 1 or 5 mm long; fruit conical to ovoid, with rough surface, indehiscent; seeds 1, very rarely 2; cotyledons connate into a fleshy body continuous with, but set off from the hypocotyl, protruding when seedling is ready to fall; hypocotyl sub-cylindrical, elongate—up to 70 cm.

Two species are recorded from Ceylon.

KEY TO THE CEYLON SPECIES

1 Inflorescences stout, 2- (very rarely 4-) flowered, flowers sessile in united involucres, peduncles very short, 2 cm or usually less.......................... **1. R. apiculata**
1 Inflorescences slender, usually 4 or more flowered, peduncle several to 10 cm or more long, curved.. **2. R. mucronata**

1. Rhizophora apiculata Blume, Enum. Pl. Java 1: 91. 1827; Alston in Trimen, Handb. Fl. Ceylon 6: 107. 1931; Arulchelvam, Ceylon Forester 8: 65. 1969; Ding Hou in Fl. Mal. I.5: 452. 1958 (full bibliography).

Rhizophora candellaria DC., Prod. 3: 32. 1828; Trimen, Handb. Fl. Ceylon 2: 151. 1894.
Rhizophora conjugata sensu Arn., non L.; Thw., Enum. Pl. Zeyl. 120. 1859.

Capable of growing into a large tree with a spreading head, more usually a small tree or large shrub with prop roots descending from the branches at all levels; leaves up to 10–12 cm, lance-ovate to broadly ovate, acute at the base, tapering to an acute apex, very shortly mucronate (< 5 mm), dark green above, paler and dotted with brownish-black beneath, petiole 1–2 cm; stipules 4.5–6 cm; flowers sessile in pairs, peduncles very short, stout, from axils of fallen leaves; calyx segments oblong-ovate, acute; petals linear, flat, glabrous, creamy white, soon falling; stamens 11–12; fruit 2.5 cm, seedling up to 70 cm before dropping.

D i s t r. This species is common from the mouth of the Indus eastwards to Guam and the Solomon Islands, from Hainan and the Philippines to North Queensland.

E c o l. In estuaries and lagoons all round Ceylon, commonest where fresh water influence is strong. Flowers September, January, February, probably at all seasons.

V e r n. Kadol (S); Kandal (T).

S p e c i m e n s E x a m i n e d. WITHOUT LOCALITY: [*Thwaites*] *C.P. 1968* (PDA); *Worthington 2516* (K). PUTTALAM DISTRICT: Kalpitiya, *Macnae* in 1968 (US, PDA). COLOMBO DISTRICT: Thalahena, *Waas 720* (US); Negombo Lagoon, *Macnae* in 1968 (US, PDA); Negombo, Blue Lagoon near mouth of Dandugang Oya River, *Meijer 586* (PDA, US). GALLE DIST-

RICT: Bedduwa Lake, Bentota. *Worthington 2473* (K). TRINCOMALEE DISTRICT:Koddiar, *[Trimen]* in 1885 (PDA);Trincomalee, *Gardner C.P. 1968* (PDA); Plantain Point, Trincomalee, *Worthington 2675* (K), *2676* (K). BATTICALOA DISTRICT: Pasikudah (Kalkudah), *Worthington 6299* (K). AMPARAI DISTRICT: Kumana Lagoon, *Balakrishnan 372* (PDA, US).

2. Rhizophora mucronata Poir. in Lam., Encycl Meth. 6: 189, 1804, Thw., Enum. Pl. Zeyl. 120. 1859; Trimen, Handb. Fl. Ceylon 2: 151. 1894; Arulchelvam, Ceylon Forester 8: 65. 1969; Ding Hou in Fl. Mal. I. 5: 453. 1958 (full bibliography).

Capable of growing to a large tree with a spreading head; in Ceylon usually a many branched shrub: prop-roots descending from all levels; leaves 10–12 cm long, broadly elliptic to oval, acute at the base, bluntly acute at the apex with a long mucro up to 9 mm, glabrous, thick, bright green above, paler beneath, dotted with tiny red spots, petiole 1–1.5 cm, stout; stipules 5 cm, glabrous, soon falling; flowers 10–12 mm across on short thick pedicels, inflorescences cymose on peduncles from axils of leaves of same year; calyx segments about 1 cm, oblong-lanceolate, thick, glabrous, keeled within; petals as long as sepals, narrow, obtuse, curved, thick, induplicate, hairy within; stamens 8; style short, 1 mm (the style is 5 mm long in the closely related *R. stylosa*); fruit 4–5 cm, ovate-conical, pendulous, roughish, dark brown; seedling reaching as long as 65 cm before dropping.

D i s t r. In estuaries and lagoons under sea water dominance: it is uncommon on the west and south coasts but seen on islands north of Kalpitiya, at Negombo, and at Matara; it is common on the east coast at Batticaloa and Trincomalee. This species is common on Indo-west-Pacific shores, from South Africa to Queensland and to the Ryukyu (Yaeyama) Islands in the north and the southern Marshall Islands in the east.

V e r n. Kadol (S); Kandal (T).

S p e c i m e n s E x a m i n e d. PUTTALAM DISTRICT: Puttalam Lagoon, *Silva 44* (PDA). COLOMBO DISTRICT: Pitipane, *Waas 716* (US); Thalahena, *Waas 726* (US). KALUTARA DISTRICT: Panadura, *s. coll.* in 1881 (PDA). TRINCOMALEE DISTRICT: 79 mi. post on Trincomalee-Batticaloa road, across bay from Trincomalee, *Davidse 7563* (PDA); Cod bay, Trincomalee, *Worthington 4388* (K); Plantain Point, Trincomalee, *Worthington 2671* (K), *1013* (K); Oohooveli, Trincomalee, *Worthington 2691* (K); Trincomalee Harbor *s. coll., s.n.* (PDA). BATTICALOA DISTRICT: Batticaloa, *Macnae* in 1968 (US); 15 mi. S. of Batticaloa, *Meijer & Balakrishnan 132* (PDA, US). AMPARAI DISTRICT: Pottuvil-Panama Road, *Cooray 69073006R* (PDA, US). HAMBANTOTA DISTRICT: Ruhuna National Park, Buttuwa area, *Comanor 900* (PDA), *647* (PDA), *Wirawan 803* (PDA, US). WITHOUT LOCALITY: *[Thwaites] C.P. 1969* (PDA).

2. BRUGUIERA

Lam., Tabl. Enc. pl. 397. 1793; Ding Hou in Fl. Mal. I. 5: 457. 1958 (full bibliography).

Trees up to 40 m, often buttressed, with knee-like pneumatophores; bark smooth while young, fissured or smooth when full grown; leaves ovate-acute, entire, glabrous, black-dotted beneath, petioled, not mucronate; stipules lanceolate, glabrous, deciduous leaving a distinct scar on young branches; flowers bisexual, without bracts, articulated at the base with the pedicel, solitary or in 2–5 flowered pedunculate cymes; calyx connate with ovary below and free above, of many segments; petals bilobed, quickly shed, each embracing two stamens; stamens twice the number of petals, epipetalous, filaments unequal in length, anthers linear; ovary inferior, 2–4 celled, each with 2 ovules; style elongate, filiform; fruit included in calyx tube, usually 1-celled, 1- or 2-seeded; cotyledons connate, non-emergent; hypocotyl short, blunt, smooth or ribbed, perforating the apex of the fruit and falling with it.

Three species recorded from Ceylon.

KEY TO THE SPECIES

1 Calyx segments and petals both 8 . . . . **1. B. cylindrica**
1 Calyx segments and petals 10–16
  2 Calyx segments and petals 12–16, calyx usually red, petals ciliate toward base, flowers 3–3.5 cm long . . . . **2. B. gymnorhiza**
  2 Calyx segments and petals 10–12, never red, petals ciliate to apex, flowers 2 cm long . .
. . . . **3. B. sexangula**

1. Bruguiera cylindrica (L.) Blume, Enum. Pl. Java 1: 93. 1827, quoad basionym; Alston in Trimen, Handb. Fl. Ceylon 6: 108. 1931; Arulchelvam, Ceylon Forester 8: 69. 1969; Ding Hou in Fl. Mal. I: 5. 467. 1958 (full synonymy).

Rhizophora cylindrica L., Sp. Pl. 443. 1753.
Rhizophora caryophylloides Burm. f., Fl. Ind. 109. 1768.
Bruguiera caryophylloides Blume, Enum. Pl. Jav. 1: 93. 1827; Trimen, Handb. Fl. Ceylon 2: 154. 1894.

A bush or small tree; leaves 8–10 cm, lance-ovate, tapering to base, glabrous; stipules 2–3 cm long; cymes 2–3 flowered, in axils of upper leaves; flowers greenish; calyx smooth, of 8 segments; petals 8, erect, hairy outside, deeply bifid; stamens 16; fruit small, oblong-ovoid, smooth; seedling reaching about 12–14 cm before falling, slender, cylindrical.

D i s t r. Common on shores of lagoons between Chilaw and Puttalam lagoon and on islands of Kalpitiya, and at Trincomalee (Worthington); not seen elsewhere in Ceylon. Common from the Maldives, India and Ceylon through Indonesia and Thailand to Vietnam and New Guinea.

Specimens Examined. PUTTALAM DISTRICT: Karativu Island, Kalpitiya *s. coll.* in *1883* (PDA); Eremativu Island, N. of Kalpitiya, *Macnae* in 1968 (US); Kalpitiya, *Gardner C.P. 1969* (PDA). TRINCOMALEE DIST-RICT: Trincomalee, *Gardner C.P. 1965* (PDA); Plantain Point, Trincomalee, *Worthington 1012* (K).

2. Bruguiera gymnorhiza (L.) Savigny in Lam., Enc. 4: 696. 1798 Thw., Enum. Pl. Zeyl. 120. 1859; Trimen, Handb. Fl. Ceylon 2: 153. 1894 (incl. *B. sexangula* q.v.); Alston in Trimen, Handb. Fl. Ceylon 6: 108. 1931; Arulch-elvam, Ceylon Forester 8: 69. 1969; Ding Hou in Fl. Mal. I. 5: 461 1958 (with full synonymy).

Rhizophora gymnorhiza L., Sp. Pl. 443, 1753.

Buttressed tree up to 36 m tall; branching mostly sympodial; bark grey to almost black, roughly fissured with large lenticels on base of trunk and but-tresses; young branches with prominent scars of leaves and stipules; leaves 10–15 cm, ovate, tapering to base, acute but not mucronate, glabrous, rather thick, bright green, paler beneath; flowers large, 3–3.5 cm, solitary, drooping, peduncle 2 cm long, curved, from axils of upper leaves; calyx glabrous with 12–16 segments, usually reddish in colour; petals 12–16, brown, deeply bifid, outer margin fringed towards the base with white silky hairs, no hairs on tip of petal; fruit up to 2–3 cm, conical, hypocotyl smooth with a blunt apex, shed with fruit and calyx tube from both of which it soon separates.

D i s t r. Occasional in mangrove areas all around Ceylon except Jaffna, but never common. Distributed from southern Africa and the shores of the Red Sea to the Ryukyu (Yaeyama) Islands and to northern New South Wales, and east to the Marshall Islands.

Specimens Examined. COLOMBO DISTRICT: Negombo La-goon, *Macnae* in 1968 (US); GALLE DISTRICT: Dedduwa Lake, Bentota, *Worthington 2471* (K); Alutgama, on Bentota Estuary, *Macnae* in 1968 (PDA, US). TRINCOMALEE DISTRICT: Snug Cove (E. Point), Trincomalee, *Worthington 52* (K); Yard Cove, Trincomalee, *Worthington 1008* (K).

3. Bruguiera sexangula (Lour.) Poir. in Lam., Enc. Suppl. 4: 262. 1816; Alston in Trimen, Handb. Fl. Ceylon 6: 108. 1931; Ding Hou in Fl. Mal. I. 5: 463. 1958 (full synonymy).

Rhizophora sexangula Lour., Fl. Cochinch. 297. 1790.

Buttresseh tree up to 33 m, bark smooth, greyish, lenticels few, large, especially on buttresses; leaves 8–10 cm, ovate to elliptic-oblong, acute at both ends, pale green; stipules green or yellowish; flowers nodding, c. 2 cm long; calyx with 10–12 segments, yellowish, never red; petals yellowish-brown, densely fringed with hairs from base to apex, those towards the apex being longest, a distinct bristle in sinus between lobes.

D i s t r. It is abundant in the Negombo lagoon where it forms dense thickets of 2–3 m tall. Common in mangrove areas between Negombo and Matara, but not seen elsewhere. Common from India and Ceylon to New Guinea and Vietnam.

N o t e. This species is very similar to *B. gymnorhiza* but is more slender; included both by Thwaites and Trimen in *B. gymnorhiza* but not mentioned in Arulchelvam's survey. It occurs in soils with water of lower salinity. It prefers well-drained soils, not heavy clay.

S p e c i m e n s   E x a m i n e d. COLOMBO DISTRICT: Negombo, *s. coll. C.P. 3611* (PDA); Negombo Lagoon, *Macnae* in 1968 (PDA, US); Negombo, Blue Lagoon near mouth of Dandugam Oya River, *Meijer 584* (PDA); near Colombo, *Silva 207* (PDA); side road off A2 between Colombo and Panadura, *Comanor 993* (PDA, US, K, A, L, P, NY, HAW, MO, LE, G, BRI). GALLE DISTRICT: Dedduwa Lake, Bentota, *Worthington 2472* (K); Alutgama, on banks of Bentota Ganga, *Macnae* in 1968 (US); Galle, *Tirvengadum & Cramer 256* (US). WITHOUT LOCALITY: [*Thwaites*] *C.P. 1967* (PDA, Part); *C.P. 3611* (PDA); *C.P. 3612* (PDA).

3. CERIOPS

Arn., Ann. Mag. nat. Hist. 1: 363. 1838; Ding Hou in Fl. Mal. I. 5: 468. 1958 (full synonymy).

Small trees; stems with buttresses of adpressed stilt roots; leaves and stipules of the form typical of the family; inflorescences 2–4-flowered condensed cymes; calyx of 5 segments; petals 5, white, emarginate; stamens 10, inserted in sinuations on the disc; ovary 3-celled, each cell with 2 ovules, style simple; fruit as in *Rhizophora* with emergent cotyledonary body, radicle angular.

Two species are known in Ceylon.

KEY TO THE SPECIES

1 Calyx segments reflexed in fruit; petals not ciliate but tipped with several clavate appendages..**1. tagal**
1 Calyx segments erect in fruit; petals fringed at apex..................**2. C. decandra**

1. Ceriops tagal (Perr.) C. B. Rob., Philipp J. Sci. Bot. 3: 306. 1908; Alston in Trimen, Handb. Fl. Ceylon 6: 107. 1931; Ding Hou in Fl. Mal. I. 5: 469. 1958 (full synonymy); Arulchelvam, Ceylon Forester 8: 69. 1969.

Rhizophora tagal Perr., Mem. Soc. Linn. Paris 3: 138. 1824.

Ceriops candolleana Arn., Ann. Mag. nat. Hist. 1: 364. 1838; Thw., Enum.
Pl. Zeyl. 120. 1859; Trimen, Handb. Fl. Ceylon 2: 152. 1894.

A shrub or small tree with twigs marked by scars of leaves and stipules,
young parts glabrous; leaves 4–8 cm, ovate-oblong, tapering to base, rounded
at apex, glabrous, thick, yellowish green; flowers small; calyx segments 5;
petals white, shorter than calyx segments, emarginate; tipped with 2 or 3
minute clavate processes; fruit pendulous, less than 2 cm, rough; hypocotyl
ridged, emerging from a yellowish to reddish cotyledonary body when ripe
and ready to fall.

D i s t r. Now rather uncommon, seen only at Vallaichchennai, near
Trincomalee, at Jaffna, Mannar and Eremativu Island near Kalpitiya. It was
always found in the shelter of trees of *Avicennia marina*. This species is common from southern Mozambique to the Caroline Islands and from Taiwan to
Queensland.

V e r n. Chivukandal (T).

S p e c i m e n s E x a m i n e d. MANNAR DISTRICT: Mannar, *Macnae*
in 1968 (US). PUTTALAM DISTRICT: Eremativu Island, *Macnae* in 1968
(US); Kalpitiya, Karativu Island, [*Trimen*] in 1883 (PDA). TRINCOMALEE
DISTRICT: Trincomalee, *Macnae* in 1968 (US, PDA); Trincomalee Harbour,
[*Trimen*] in 1885 (PDA); *Gardner C.P. 1966* (PDA); Plantain Point, N. Trin-
comalee, *Worthington 2682* (K). BATTICALOA DISTRICT: Vallaichchenai,
Macnae in 1968 (US, PDA). WITHOUT LOCALITY: *Thwaites C.P. 1966*
(PDA).

2. Ceriops decandra (Griff.) Ding Hou in Fl. Mal. I. 5: 471. 1958.

Bruguiera decandra Griff., Trans. med. phys. Soc. Calcutta 8: 10. 1836.
Ceriops roxburghiana Arn., Ann. Mag. nat. Hist. 1: 364. 1838; Trimen,
Handb. Fl. Ceylon 2: 153. 1894.

Very similar to *C. tagal* in habit and foliage but differs in petals being
fringed at the apex and the calyx segments do not become reflexed in the
fruit but continue to embrace its base.

D i s t r. Trimen records that Karsten in 1890 found this species to be
abundant in the estuary of the Mahaweli Ganga at Kodiyar, but he had seen
no specimens. We have seen no specimens from Ceylon. It is common in
estuarine areas from the Bay of Bengal to Vietnam and through Indonesia to
North Queensland.

N o t e. *Kandelia kandel* has also been reported from the Kodiyar estuarine system. The record, fide Trimen, is mentioned in the Flora of British
India on the basis of a doubtful specimen in Kew. The species has not been
found west of the Sunderbans on the Ganges Delta and its occurrence in
Ceylon is doubtful.

4. CARALLIA

Roxb., Pl. Corom. 3. 8. pl. 211. 1811, nom. cons. Ding Hou in Fl. Mal. I. 5: 481. 1958 (full bibliography).

Trees, occasionally with stilt roots at the base of the stem; branches sympodial, at least in young trees; twigs solid, pithy; leaves opposite, decussate, petioled, entire; stipules, large, lanceolate; flowers in axillary cymes, these sessile or more or less peduncled, sessile or pedicelled; bracteoles 2; calyx segments 4–8; petals 4–8, cut or fimbriate; stamens 8–16, unequal, the shorter of each pair opposite the petal, inserted on a sinuous disc; ovary inferior, 5–8-celled, each cell with 2 ovules; stigma discoid or capitate; fruit fleshy, indehiscent, seed with a cylindrical curved green embryo in the axis of copious endosperm.

This genus comprises one very widespread species, viz., *C. brachiata*, and a number of species endemic to restricted localities. These latter have caused much confusion. Two species are recognised in Ceylon.

KEY TO THE SPECIES

1 Leaves mainly blunt at apex; flowers small, 3 mm long; petals with margins undulate-dentate; fruit 5 mm across...**1. C. brachiata**
1 Leaves with apices acuminate; flowers larger, 15 mm long; petals with margins incised–fimbriate; fruit 10 mm across...................................**2. C. calycina**

1. Carallia brachiata (Lour.) Merr., Philipp. J. Sci. 15: 249. 1919; Alston in Trimen, Handb. Fl. Ceyl. 6: 108. 1931; Ding Hou in Fl. Mal. I. 5: 485. 1958 pro parte (full bibliography).

Diatoma brachiata Lour., Fl. Cochinch. 296. 1790.
Carallia integerrima DC., Prod. 3: 33. 1828; Thw., Enum. Pl. Zeyl. 120. 1859; Benth., J. Linn. Soc. Bot. 3: 67. 75. 1859; Trimen, Handb. Fl. Ceylon. 2: 155. 1894.

Tree up to 50 m with erect trunk and wide-spreading crown, bark smooth in young trees, fissured in older trees, grey to dark brown; leaves up to 10 cm, on very short petioles, broadly elliptic, tapering to base, larger in young than in older trees, dark green above, paler with scattered black dots beneath; stipules large, 2 cm, enclosing terminal bud, caducous; flowers small, 3 mm, in small heads on stout branches of axillary cymes; calyx, glabrous, 8 segments; petals, small, clawed, roundish, coarsely undulate-dentate at margin; stamens twice as many as petals; style stout; fruit small, about 5 mm, berry-like, smooth, red; seed with thick orange testa, lobulate.

D i s t r. Common in moist low country, often planted. Flowers probably at all seasons, February–October. This species is widely distributed from Madagascar through Ceylon to China, and through Indonesia to Australia.

V e r n. Dawata (S).

N o t e. A gum exudes from the flower buds and glues them together. In its mode of branching and its leaves this tree shows obvious relationship with the mangroves. Some trees also develop large tufts of aerial roots from the base of the stem.

S p e c i m e n s E x a m i n e d. COLOMBO DISTRICT: Colombo, Gardner C.P. 1964 (PDA). GALLE DISTRICT: Kottawa Arboretum, Talgampola, Macnae in 1968 (US, PDA). KANDY DISTRICT: Hantana, Gardner 278 (PDA), s. coll. C.P. 1963 (PDA); Peradeniya Botanic Garden, Balakrishnan 1185 (PDA, US); Kandy, Roseneath Road, 2130 ft, Worthington 6478 (K). RATNAPURA DISTRICT: Pelmadulla Rest House, Balakrishnan & Jayasuriya 914 (PDA, US); Petiyagala, Balangoda, 2300 ft, Worthington 3218 (K); Bambarabottuwa Forest Reserve, 1100 ft, Worthington 3199 (K). BADULLA DISTRICT: Koslanda Estate, 4650 ft, Worthington 3218 (K). WITHOUT LOCALITY: Walker s.n. (PDA); Herb. R. Wight s.n. (PDA); s. coll. C.P. 1963 (PDA).

2. Carallia calycina Benth., J. Linn. Soc. Bot. 3: 75. 1859; Thw., Enum. Pl. Zeyl. 120. 1859; Trimen, Handb. Fl. Ceylon 2: 155. 1894.

A large tree with thin, rough grey bark; leaves on very short petioles, up to 10 cm, broadly ovate to oval, tapering at the base, acuminate and often drawn out into a drip tip, entire, glabrous, stiff, bright green, dotted with black beneath; flowers few, nearly 1.5 cm, on stout pedicels in scanty erect axillary cymes half as long as the leaves; bracteoles rounded, mucronate, caducous; calyx with 4 segments as long as the tube; petals 4, clawed, incised-fimbriate; stamens 8; fruit about 1 cm, pyriform, crowned with erect connivent calyx segments, red, glabrous.

D i s t r. Forests in the moist region, said to be common in the Sinharaja Forest, elsewhere uncommon. Flowers January–April, but probably sporadic. Endemic in Ceylon.

V e r n. Ubberiya (S).

N o t e. Wood red, rather heavy, hard but liable to split, medullary rays wide, giving the wood a characteristic appearance. Ding Hou combined this species with C. brachiata, but the two species occur together in the same forests where they are readily distinguishable by bark, leaves and flowers. Timber specimens are also distinct.

S p e c i m e n s E x a m i n e d. GALLE DISTRICT: Kottawa Arboretum, Talgampola, Macnae in 1968 (US, PDA); Haycock, Hiniduma, 1600 ft, Worthington 2293 (K); Homodola Estate, Udugama, 100 ft, Worthington 4116 (K); Nakiyadeniya, 250 ft, Worthington 7230 (K). RATNAPURA

DISTRICT: Ratnapura, 100 ft, *Worthington 7230* (K); Sinharaja Forest, *s. coll. C.P. 3458* (PDA); Sinharaja Forest, S.E. of Waddagala, *Meijer 900* (PDA, US). MATALE DISTRICT: Dambulla, *s. coll. C.P. 2588* (PDA). NUWARA ELIYA DISTRICT: Rambodde, *s. coll. C.P. 2588* (PDA). WITHOUT LOCALITY: *s. coll. C.P. 3458* (PDA, type); *s. coll. 2584* (PDA). DISTRICT UNKNOWN: Sumbagawa, *s. coll. C.P. 2588* (PDA).

5. CASSIPOUREA

Aubl., Hist. Pl. Guian. Fr. 1: 258. pl. 212. 1775; Alston, Kew Bull. 1925: 251. 1925.

Richaeia Thou., Nov. Gen. Madag. 1806.
Wiehea Spreng., Syst. Veg. 2: 594. 1825.
Anstrutheria Gardn., Calcutta J. nat. Hist. 6: 344–345. 1846.

Large shrubs; leaves opposite, with interpetiolar stipules; flowers axillary; calyx free, cut nearly to the base into 5 segments; petals 5, hypogynous, much cut; stamens about 30, hypogynous; ovary superior, 3-celled with 2 pendulous ovules in each cell; style long, persistent, stigma 3-lobed; fruit a fleshy capsule, 3-celled, ultimately dehiscent; seeds 4–6, with a small aril, embryo straight in the axis of the endosperm.

One species in Ceylon.

Cassipourea ceylanica (Gardn.) Alston, Kew Bull. 1925: 251. 1925; in Trimen, Handb. Fl. Ceylon 6: 108. 1931.

Anstrutheria ceylanica Gardn., Calcutta J. nat. Hist. 6: 345. t. 4. 1846; Benth., J. Linn. Soc. Bot., 3: 71, 78. 1859; Thw., Enum. Pl. Zeyl. 121. 1859.
Weihea ceylanica (Gardn.) Baill., Adansonia I. 3: 38. 1862 (as *zeylanica*); Henslow in Hook. f., Fl. Br. Ind. 2: 441. 1879; Trimen, Handb. Fl. Ceylon 2: 156. 1894.
Richiaea zeylanica O. Ktze., Rev. Gen. 1: 235. 1891.

A large shrub very much branched from the base, young parts glabrous; leaves 4–7 cm (or more) on short erect curved petioles, broadly oval, rounded at base, obtusely acuminate, entire, glabrous, shining above, bright apple green, rather paler beneath; stipules interpetiolar, small, lanceolate, acute, ciliate; flowers c. 2 cm on short, curved pedicels, solitary or rarely 2–3 in axils; buds small, globular, completely enclosed in 2 bracteoles for a long period before opening; calyx segments oblong-lanceolate, acute, densely silky outside, persistent, ultimately deflexed; petals with a long claw deeply cut into linear segments, soon falling; fruit nearly globose, tipped with a long style, dehiscent by 3 valves.

Distr. Low country principally in dry districts where it is common, rarer in moist districts but occurring near Kalutara, Galle, and Kandy. Also in southern India.

V e r n. Pana (S); Kannu (T).

N o t e. Flowers July–September, white. There is considerable variation in the shape of the leaves, those from moist parts being broadly ovate and almost membranous, those from drier parts being much narrower and coriaceous.

Bentham (1859) quotes the author as Arnott citing the same pages in the Calcutta Journal of Natural History. This must be a *lapsus calami*.

S p e c i m e n s E x a m i n e d. KALUTARA DISTRICT: 'Calutara', *Gardner C.P. 1116* (PDA). GALLE DISTRICT: *Gardner s.n.* (PDA); *s. coll. C.P. 1116* (PDA). KURUNEGALA DISTRICT: Kurunegala, *s. coll.* in 1881 (PDA). ANURADHAPURA DISTRICT: Kekirawa Road, near mile 53, *Meijer 721* (PDA, US), *724* (PDA); Summit of Ritigala, *s. coll.* in 1906 (?) (PDA); Ritigala, *Worthington 286* (K). MATALE DISTRICT: Leloya, *Jayasuriya 333* (PDA, US). KANDY DISTRICT: Peradeniya, *s. coll. C.P. 1116* (PDA). HAMBANTOTA DISTRICT: Kirinda West, *Simpson 9940* (PDA); Ruhuna National Park: Patanagala Beach, 2 m; *Mueller-Dombois 67083103* (PDA); near western boundary, *Meijer 204* (PDA); Jamburagala, *Ripley 271* (PDA); N. of Buttawa, *Mueller-Dombois 67121025* (PDA), *67121024* (PDA); Buttawa Modera, *Fosberg 50300* (PDA, US); Buttawa, *Cooray 70031910R* (PDA), *68060703R* (PDA), *68053012R* (PDA); Block I., Plot R8, *Cooray 68102102R* (PDA), *68102101R* (PDA); between Katagamuwa Tank and Situlpahuwa Ruins, *Mueller-Dombois & Comanor 67082626* (PDA); S. of Situlpahuwa, *Mueller-Dombois 68102114* (PDA). PUTTALAM DISTRICT: Wilpattu National Park, Kollankanata, *Mueller-Dombois et al. 69042737* (PDA); between Weerakuti and Maduru Odai, *Mueller-Dombois et al. 68091209* (PDA); Occapu Kallu, *Cooray 70040204R* (PDA); Manikepola Uttu, *Koyama & Herat 13423* (PDA); Puttalam, *s. coll.* in 1881 (PDA). WITHOUT LOCALITY: *s. coll. C.P. 1116* (PDA); Kaunu, *Vincent 31* (PDA).

6. ANISOPHYLLEA

R. Br. ex Sabine, Trans. hort. Soc. 5: 446. 1824; Ding Hou in Fl. Mal. I. 5: 474. 1958 (full bibliography).

Trees and shrubs; leaves alternate, usually dimorphic, without stipules; inflorescences axillary, monoecious; calyx tube adnate to ovary, of four segments; petals 4, entire; stamens 8, anthers small, abortive in females; ovary inferior, 4-celled with a solitary pendulous ovule in each cell; fruit ellipsoid, 1-seeded, floral parts persistent; seed without endosperm; embryo large, without cotyledons.

One species in Ceylon.

Anisophyllea cinnamomoides (Gardn. & Champion) Alston in Trimen, Handb. Fl. Ceylon 6: 108. 1931.

Tetracrypta cinnamomoides Gardn. and Champion in Hook. J. Bot. Kew Misc. 1: 314. 1849; 5: pl. 5 opp. 129. 1854.
Anisophyllum zeylanicum Benth. in Hook., Niger Fl. 575. 1849.
Anisophyllea zeylanica (Benth.) Hook. f. & Thw., J. Linn. Soc. Bot. 2: 86. 1858; Trimen, Handb. Fl. Ceylon 2: 157. 1894.

A tree of moderate size with dark brown bark, branches horizontal or drooping, young twigs pubescent; leaves of two kinds, the normal large and persistent, the smaller ones usually deciduous; large leaves 10–12 cm, curvi-veined on very short, broad, flattened petioles, ovate-oblong, tapering to an unequal base, obtuse or sub-acute at the apex, dark green, the smaller leaves 8–10 mm, stipuliform; flowers on short, slender, pilose pedicels, arranged in 2 or 3 very short racemes, superposed and super-axillary; calyx tube pubescent, deeply 8-furrowed; petals cuneate, deeply cut into 5 linear lacineae; fruit about 2.5 cm, fusiform.

D i s t r. Moist low country in the southwest, rather common. Flowers April–October, greenish-white. Endemic.

V e r n. Weli-penna, Weli-piyana (S).

S p e c i m e n s   E x a m i n e d. ANURADHAPURA DISTRICT: *s. coll. 2225* (PDA). MATALE DISTRICT: Matale east, 3500 ft, *Worthington 2389* (K), 2950 ft, *Worthington 2383* (K). KANDY DISTRICT: Peradeniya Estate, *s. coll.* in 1883 (PDA); Ginihathena pass, *Worthington 389* (K); Ginigathena, 1400 ft, *Worthington 2082* (K); Ambagamuwa, *s. coll. C.P. 2205* (PDA). KALUTARA DISTRICT: 'Caltura', *s. coll. C.P. 2205* (PDA). RATNA-PURA DISTRICT: Sanasgama between Pelmadulla and Ratnapura, *Macnae* in 1968 (US); Gilimale Forest Reserve, *Meijer 486* (K). NUWARA ELIYA DISTRICT: Hewahetta, *s. coll. C.P. 2205* (PDA). GALLE DISTRICT: Hay-cock, i.e., Hinidum Kande, 2167 ft, *Worthington 2279* (K).

THYMELAEACEAE

(by C.C. Townsend*)

Gilg in Pflanzenfam. 3 (6A): 216–245. 1894, nom. cons. Type genus: *Thymelaea* Mill., Gard. Dict. ed. 4 (abridged). 1754, nom. cons.

Trees or shrubs, more rarely herbs, with alternate or opposite, exstipulate, simple and entire, persistent or deciduous leaves. Flowers mostly in spikes, racemes, or dense to few-flowered often involucrate heads, rarely solitary; hermaphrodite or unisexual (dioecious), regular or slightly zygomorphic. Calyx gamosepalous, poculiform to tubular below, 4–5-lobed, the lobes imbricate, petaloid, usually spreading in flower. Petals 4–12 or absent, when present appearing as glabrous to tomentose scales alternating with stamens usually at the throat of the calyx tube. Stamens isomerous with the calyx lobes and opposite them, or twice as many with a second rank set lower in the tube and alternate with the lobes, rarely reduced to 2; anthers bilocular, introrse, dehiscing by longitudinal slits; hypogynous disc annular, poculiform or reduced to scales. Ovary superior, 1 (–2)-locular, each loculus uniovulate, the ovule pendulous and anatropous; style long and slender to practically obsolete; stigma usually solitary and capitate, occasionally divided. Fruit a drupe, nut or berry, rarely a capsule. Embryo straight, endosperm copious or more usually scanty or absent.

About 45 genera and 500 species, almost cosmopolitan in both temperate and tropical regions; especially well represented in Africa.

KEY TO THE GENERA

1 Stamens in a single rank, similar in number to the calyx lobes; fruit a 2-valved loculicidal capsule...**4. Gyrinops**
1 Stamens in two ranks, twice as many as the calyx lobes, one row emergent or exserted, the other included in the calyx tube, or all exserted; fruit indehiscent
  2 Filaments long and slender, the anthers long-exserted; flowers white.......**3. Phaleria**
  2 Anthers sessile or almost so; flowers yellow or green
    3 Petaloid appendages present at throat of calyx tube; flowers pentamerous....**2. Gnidia**
    3 Petaloid appendages absent from throat of calyx tube; flowers tetramerous..........
    ....**1. Wikstroemia**

*Royal Botanic Gardens, Kew.

1. WIKSTROEMIA

Endl., Prod. Fl. Norfolkicae 47. 1833, corr. Ench. Bot. 209. 1841, nom. cons. Type species: *W. australis* Endl., Prod. Fl. Norfolkicae 47. 1833.

Capura L., Mant. alt. 149, 225. 1771.
Wikstroemia Schrad., Gött. Gelehrte Anz. 710. 1821.
Wickstroemia Endl., Prod. Fl. Norfolkicae 47. 1833.

Evergreen or deciduous shrubs or small trees. Leaves opposite, more rarely alternate. Inflorescences of spikes or spike-like racemes, terminal on the stem and branches, paniculate. Flowers tetramerous, hermaphrodite or (not in Ceylon) dioecious. Calyx tube long-tubular, limb with the two outer lobes slightly larger than the inner. Petaloid appendages absent. Stamens 8, in two ranks, the upper emergent and the lower included. Ovary ellipsoid, cylindrical or bottle-shaped, unilocular; style distinct to almost obsolete, never long; stigma simple or lobed to double; base of ovary closely subtended by four scales, these either free or fused in pairs and thus apparently 2 only. Fruit a 1-seeded berry, fleshy and naked or more dry and included in the perianth. Seeds black, pale-ridged along one side, with a thin, semitransparent episperm; endosperm scanty or absent.

A genus of about 75 species in tropical and eastern Asia, Australia, Polynesia and Hawaii. A difficult genus taxonomically, in some regions showing considerable sexual dimorphism and complexity.

KEY TO THE SPECIES

1 Outer surface of calyx densely appressed-canescent; young twigs and leaves also considerably pilose or tomentose; hypogynal scales 4; fruit dry, included within the calyx
....**1. W. canescens**
1 Outer surface of calyx sparsely pilose only; young twigs and leaves glabrous or almost so; hypogynal scales 2; fruit fleshy, naked.............................**2. W. indica**

1. Wikstroemia canescens Meisn. in Denkschr. Königl.-Bayer. Bot. Ges. Regensburg 3: 288. 1841 et DC., Prod. 14: 547. 1857; Hook. f. in Fl. Br. Ind. 5: 195. 1886; Trimen, Handb. Fl. Ceylon 3: 458. 1895, p. max. parte. Type: Kumaon, *Wallich 1046.2* (K, lectotype).

Daphne inamoena Gardn. in Calc. J. Nat. Hist. 7: 454. 1847.
Wikstroemia inamoena (Gardn.) Meisn. in DC., Prod. 14: 547. 1857.
Wikstroemia virgata Meisn. in Denkschr. Königl.-Bayer. Bot. Ges. Regensburg 3: 289. 1841 et DC., Prod. 14: 547. 1857.

Twiggy shrub c. 1–2.25 m tall. Branchlets and twigs slender, terete, ± whitish- or yellowish-tomentose when young, glabrescent and brownish-purple when older, with pale lenticels. Leaves narrowly elliptic to elliptic or oblong, 1.8–5.5 × 0.7–1.8 cm, ± acute at the apex, cuneate below, ± appressed-pilose on both surfaces but particularly so and often tomentose along the lower surface of the midrib, mid green on the upper surface and paler or grey green below; petiole 2–3 mm, tomentose. Flower rather few and inconspicuous, greenish-yellow to yellow, frequently ± purplish-suffused on the outer surface, in lateral and terminal panicles of congested, few-flowered racemes on both stems and branches, the whole forming a leafy compound panicle; inflorescence axes densely yellowish-tomentose; peduncles to c. 1 cm, pedicels 1–2 mm, also tomentose. Calyx tube 6–8 mm, densely appressed-canescent on the outer surface, glabrous within; lobes 1.5–3 mm, oblong, obtuse to subacute, glabrous within, canescent dorsally. Anthers oblong, 1.5 mm. Ovary ellipsoid, c. 3 mm, densely furnished with yellowish appressed hairs, especially about the apex; hypogynal scales 4, linear, free; style very short, less than 0.5 mm; stigma solitary, large. Fruit included within the calyx, dry, asymmetrically ellipsoid, similarly pilose to the ovary, c. 4 mm. Seed c. 3.75 mm, asymmetrically ellipsoid-pyriform, black.

D i s t r. Also occurs from Afghanistan through the Himalayan regions to Nepal, Assam and Burma, and thence to China and Japan.

E c o l. Edges of mossy mist forests, scrub margins, streamside in "wet" patana; at higher altitudes (to c. 2300 m) in Central Province only.

S p e c i m e n s   E x a m i n e d. NUWARA ELIYA DISTRICT: Pidurutalagala, Apr. 1852, *Gardner s.n.* (PDA), (also 1973, Townsend obs.); jungle path on Horton Plains, 21 Jan. 1906, *Willis s.n.* (PDA), between Hakgala and Nuwara Eliya, 2 Mar. 1906, *Willis s.n.* (PDA), Sita Eliya, nr. Hakgala 21 March 1906, *Willis s.n.* (PDA), Horton Plains, at Ohiya Road 1½ miles from Rest House, 9 July 1967, *Mueller-Dombois & Comanor 67070939* (PDA, US); ibid., near Farr Inn, 29 Mar. 1968, *Fosberg & Mueller-Dombois 50089* (PDA, US), Moon Plains near Govt. Farm, at scrub edge above plot P. 16, 17 May 1968, *Cooray 68051732R* (PDA, US), Horton Plains, edge of forest to left and down slope from where road to Diyagama forks from road to Ohiya, 4 March 1973, *Townsend 73/159* (PDA, US); ibid., by track to North Cove c. 1 mile S.S.E. of S. shoulder of Kirigalpota, 4 Mar. 1973, *Townsend 73/161* (PDA, US).

2. **Wikstroemia indica** (L.) C.A. Mey. in Bull. Acad. Imp. Sci. Saint-Petersburg 1: 357. 1843 et Ann. Sc. Nat. (Bot.) Ser. 2 (20): 50. 1843; Meisn. in DC., Prod. 14: 543. 1857; Alston in Trimen, Handb. Fl. Ceylon 6: 249. 1931 & Kandy Fl. 12. 1938. Type: Linnean specimen 500/11 (LINN, holotype).

Daphne indica L., Sp. Pl. ed. 1. 357. 1753.
Capura purpurata L., Mant. alt. 225. 1771.
Wikstroemia viridiflora Meisn. in Denkschr. Königl.-Bayer. Bot. Ges. Regensburg 3: 286. 1841.

Wikstroemia indica var. *viridiflora* (Meisn.) Hook. f. in Fl. Br. Ind. 5: 195. 1886.
Wikstroemia canescens sensu Trimen, Handb. Fl. Ceylon 3: 458. 1895, quoad pl. Perad., non Meisn.

Small twiggy shrub, c. 0.3–1.25 m tall. Branchlets and twigs slender, terete, with scattered fine hairs when very young but soon quite glabrous, striate, blackish-purple. Leaves oblanceolate to elliptic or oblong, 1.5–6 × 0.6–2 (–2.6) cm, subcoriaceous, shining on the upper surface but duller below, glabrous or almost so, cuneate to attenuate at the base, obtuse (sometimes ± emarginate) or acute at the apex; petiole 1–2 mm, glabrous. Flowers yellow or green, in dense axillary or terminal few-flowered spikes, subsessile or shortly (to c. 3 mm) pedunculate; pedicels c. 2 mm, articulated below the middle. Calyx tube 5–9 mm, sparsely pilose on the outer surface, glabrous within; lobes 2–3 mm, oblong to ovate, obtuse, sparsely pilose dorsally, glabrous within. Anthers oblong, c. 0.75–1 mm. Ovary ellipsoid-oblong, c. 2 mm, glabrous or sparsely pilose about the style base; hypogynal scales 2, linear, acute or usually truncate or incised at the apex; style very short (less than 0.5 mm), stigma large and solitary. Fruit broadly ellipsoid to subglobose, 4–6 mm, naked, fleshy, red or green, glabrous. Seed globose-pyriform, 3.75–5.75 mm, with a short apical point, black.

D i s t r. India to China, throughout Malaysia and the Malay Islands to Australia.

E c o l. An introduced species now abundantly established on sandy roadside banks, grassland, forest margins, etc. around Kandy and Peradeniya and for some distance southwards.

S p e c i m e n s E x a m i n e d. KANDY DISTRICT: Hillcrest, Kandy, alt. 645 m, 8 Sep. 1951, *Worthington 5468*; (K), Giragama, 12 Sep. 1962, *Amaratunga 352* (PDA); Peradeniya, lower Hantane, slopes above the university and below the radio station, 6 Jan. 1970, *Fosberg 51859* (PDA, US); Anniwatte, Kandy, along roadside, 7 July 1970, *Meijer 284* (PDA, US): near Central Agricultural Experimental Station, Gannoruwa, 30 Jan. 1973, *Burtt & Townsend 29* (PDA, US); Kalugamuwa, abundant on roadside banks from here to Peradeniya, 5 Mar. 1973, *Townsend 73/166* (PDA, US); by roadside on road to Nuwara Eliya just S. of Gampola, 19 Mar. 1973, *Townsend 73/288* (PDA, US).

India to China, throughout Malaysia and the Malay Islands to Australia and Malanesia (east of Fiji) and the Philippines.

Sterile material of this species bears a striking resemblance to *Osyris lanceolata* Hochst. & Steud. ex A. DC., which is frequent on roadside banks etc. in Uva Province.

2. GNIDIA

L., Sp. Pl. ed. 1. 358. 1753; Gen. Pl. ed. 5. 168. 1754. Type species: *G. pinifolia* L., Sp. Pl. ed. 1. 356. 1753.

Lasiosiphon Fresen in Flora 21: 602. 1838.

Trees or shrubs with alternate leaves. Inflorescence dense, capitate, involucrate, terminal on the stem and branches. Flowers 4–5-merous, hermaphrodite. Calyx tube long-tubular, usually articulated and finally circumscissile above the ovary, rarely continuous. Petaloid appendages alternating with and usually much smaller than the calyx lobes, variable in form, sometimes absent, glabrous or very rarely (not in Ceylon) with a ring of hairs. Stamens 8–10, in two ranks, the upper slightly exserted and the lower included within the calyx tube; disc absent or minute and annular. Ovary sessile or stipitate, unilocular; style filiform; stigma capitate. Fruit small, dry, enclosed within the persistent calyx or calyx base; endosperm generally absent or scanty.

About 150 species in the tropics of the Old World, by far the greater number occurring in Africa.

Gnidia glauca (Fresen.) Gilg in Bot. Jahrb. Syst. 19: 265. 1894, in obs.

Lasiosiphon glaucus Fresen. in Flora 21 (2): 603. 1838.
Gnidia eriocephala Meisn. in Denkschr. Königl. Bayer. Bot. Ges. Regensburg
    3: 292. 1841; Gardn. in Calc. J. Nat. Hist. 7: 456. 1847; Thw., Enum. Pl.
    Zeyl. 250. 1861.
Lasiosiphon eriocephalus (Meisn.) Decne. in Jacquem. Voy. Ind. 4 (3), Bot.
    148. (1835–) 1844; Meisn. in DC., Prod. 14: 597. 1857; Hook. f. in Fl. Br.
    Ind. 5: 197. 1886; Trimen, Handb. Fl. Ceylon 3: 459. 1895; Gamble, Fl.
    Pres. Madras 1244. 1926, repr. 871. 1957.
Lasiosiphon eriocephalus var. *zeylanicus* Meisn. in DC., Prod. 14: 598. 1857.

A much-branched bush or occasionally a small tree, c. 1–3.3 m tall. Twigs purplish or reddish, terete, striate, rather shining, glabrous throughout or ± tomentose when young and glabrescent with age. Leaves linear-oblong to oblanceolate, oblong or occasionally broadly oblong-obovate, 3.5–10 × 1–2.8 cm, shortly acuminate to acute or more rarely (not in Ceylon) obtuse, narrowed downwards and abruptly contracted (often subauriculate) to a short (1–3 mm) petiole, quite glabrous to ± appressed-pubescent on the lower or both surfaces; venation close, fine, and oblique. Heads 2.5–4 cm in diameter, many-flowered, dense, subtended by oblong-ovate to elliptic-oblong involucral bracts c. 10–16 × 4–7 mm in length and breadth and densely whitish-tomentose on both surfaces; pedicels 2 mm, densely ± appressed-pilose. Flowers yellow, drying brown; calyx tube 8–16 mm long, glabrous within, densely long-pilose externally with the hairs patent-ascending below and appressed above, not articulated above the ovary; lobes 5, 2–3 mm, oblong, glabrous within, appressed-pilose dorsally with longer hairs centrally. Petaloid appendages varying in form from linear to oblong or lingulate, usually thickened near the tip, entire or ± toothed, glabrous. Anthers narrowly oblong, c. 1.5 mm, the upper row slightly exserted, the lower included. Ovary stipitate, ellipsoid, densely furnished with long appressed hairs; style filiform, glabrous, included, not attaining the lower row of anthers. Fruit ellipsoid, c. 4–5 × 1.5 mm, included in the calyx tube, densely long-appressed-pilose, brown. Seed lanceolate-ellipsoid, c. 3.5–4 × 1 mm, brownish-purple with a ridge along one side, striate, thinly pilose.

var. **glauca**. Type: Ethiopia, *Rueppell* (FR, holotype).

Twigs glabrous throughout, not densely pilose in the younger parts. Leaves also glabrous.

D i s t r. South and West India (Western Ghats, Nilgiri & Palni Hills); tropical Africa from Nigeria to Sudan and Ethiopia, south to Malawi, Zambia and Mozambique.

E c o l. On dry roadside banks, dry ground above rock outcrops, in open patana etc., rarely in forest, alt. c. 610–1200 m. Only recorded from the western part of Uva Province and the eastern part of Central Province, in each of which it is locally frequent.

S p e c i m e n s E x a m i n e d. MATALE DISTRICT: Galagama, *Gardner s.n.* (PDA). KANDY DISTRICT: Hantane, 1854, *Gardner s.n.* (PDA); Madugoda-Urugala road, jungle in patana, 8 Nov. 1931, *Simpson 8804* (PDA); road from Talatu-Oya to Galaha, patana, scrub, old cultivation, 31 Jan. 1932, *Simpson 9152* (PDA); Hantana patana, next ridge S. of University Circuit Bungalow, 19 Jan. 1968, *Mueller-Dombois & Cooray 68011905* (PDA, US); Corbet's Gap, near Rangala, 2 Feb. 1971, *Balasubramaniam s.n.* (PDA, US). NUWARA ELIYA DISTRICT: Matureta, Nov. 1857, *Gardner s.n.* (PDA). BADULLA DISTRICT: Meerawatte, between Welimada and Bandarawela, 7 miles S. of the former, dry patana above roadside rock, 1 Mar. 1973, *Townsend 73/140* (PDA, US).

N o t e. Having carefully examined a good deal of material of both species, I am convinced that the Indian *G. eriocephala* cannot be separated from the African *G. glauca*, which bears the earlier name. Indian material is often more abruptly and less sharply pointed in the leaf than African, but this is by no means consistent.

The exact dates of the various fascicles of Jacquemont's work are unknown, merely that publication was commenced in 1835 and completed in 1844. Happily, Decaisne's reference to Meisner in transferring *Gnidia eriocephala* to *Lasiosiphon* makes it clear that the fascicle in which this transfer was made was published later than 1841. *Lasiosiphon glaucum* Fresen. having been published in 1938, had Decaisne made no such reference, doubt could have arisen as to whether *glauca* or *eriocephala* was the correct epithet for this species. Conversely, Gardner and Meisner apparently published *Gnidia eriocephala* quite independently, taking the same epithet from a manuscript name on the same herbarium sheet (*Wallich 1051*).

var. **insularis** (Gardn.) C.C. Townsend, comb. et stat. nov. Type: (*Thwaites*) *s.n.*, Hantane, 1846 (K, lectotype).

Gnidia insularis Gardn. in Calc. J. Nat. Hist. 7: 456. 1847.
Lasiosiphon insularis (Gardn.) Meisn. in DC., Prod. 14: 598. 1857.
Lasiosiphon eriocephalus var. *zeylanicus* sensu Thw., Enum. Pl. Zeyl. 251. 1864; Trimen, Handb. Fl. Ceylon 3: 459. 1895, non Meisn.

Younger parts of twigs and lower or both surfaces of leaves more or less densely furnished with long, appressed hairs.

D i s t r. Endemic. Distr. similar to that of var. *glauca* but apparently more frequent, at least in Uva.

S p e c i m e n s E x a m i n e d. KANDY DISTRICT: Madugoda E., tall tree in jungle, 8 Nov. 1931, *Simpson 8822* (PDA), Maduldele-Panwila road, near milestone 16/12, patana, 15 Feb. 1973, *Balasubramaniam s.n.* (PDA, US). BADULLA DISTRICT: Fort Macdonald valley, patana. 11 Mar. 1906, *Willis s.n.* (PDA); between Boralande and Palugama, opposite Palavila Bungalow, milestone 4/2, occasional in open dry patana, 29 Mar. 1968, *Fosberg & Mueller-Dombois 50119* (PDA, US); Boralande-Palugama road, open space, 25 Jan. 1963, *Amaratunga 482* (PDA); c. 4 miles E. of Hakgala Botanic Garden on the road from Nuwara Eliya to Badulla, above exposed rock at roadside, 28 Feb. 1973, *Townsend 73/119* (PDA, US).

N o t e. Since Thwaites' enumeration, other authors have followed him in regarding *Gnidia insularis* Gardn. as synonymous with *Lasiosiphon eriocephalus* var. *zeylanicus* Meisn., even though Meisner himself treated *G. insularis* as a distinct species. I have now seen the type of var. *zeylanicus* [Ceylon, *Macrae s.n.*, 1829, Herb. Ledebour (LE)], and find it practically indistinguishable from the typical form of "*Lasiosiphon eriocephalus*"; hence it is in this account placed in the synonymy of var. *glauca*. Gardner designated no type in his description of *G. insularis*, merely giving the locality as: "in open jungle on the Hantane range, at an elevation of from 2000 to 3000 feet," without even mention of a collector's name. A Thwaites specimen at Kew, gathered on Hantana (the correct spelling of this range of hills) in the year previous to Gardner's description and agreeing well with it, has therefore been selected as lectotype. As Thwaites indicated, var. *glauca* and var. *insularis* run into one another; but I have studied many Indian populations of this species in the field both in the Western Ghats about Mahabaleshwar (where the plant is common) and in the Nilgiris, without finding plants with leaves to any degree persistently hairy—nor have I seen such a character in the numerous herbarium sheets of *Gnidia glauca* from Africa which I have examined. The existence of such forms in Ceylon thus seems to deserve formal taxonomic recognition.

In Uva, *G. glauca* is often associated with the composite *Microglossa zeylanica*, and very much resembles it in aspect.

3. PHALERIA

Jack, Malayan Misc. 2 (7): 59. 1822. Type species: *P. capitata* Jack, Malayan Misc. 2 (7): 59. 1822.

Drimyspermum Reinw., Syll. Pl. Ratisb. 2: 15. 1825.

Shrubs or trees with opposite leaves. Inflorescences terminal or axillary, sometimes cauliflorous, of sessile or pedunculate fascicles or umbel-like heads, peduncles when present with scattered small bracts, the inflorescence frequently involucrate with 4 or more larger bracts. Flowers pentamerous (rarely tetramerous or hexamerous), hermaphrodite, sessile, articulated at the base. Calyx tube infundibuliform or tubular, glabrous or pilose within and without; lobes spreading, ± pilose. Petaloid appendages commonly absent, rarely well-developed (not in Ceylon) or indicated by a keel. Stamens in two ranks, alternately longer and shorter, usually with well-developed exserted filaments, rarely (not in Ceylon) the dorsifixed anthers included or sessile; disk poculiform or annular, sinuate or lobed. Ovary bilocular (sometimes unilocular by abortion); style filiform; stigma capitate. Fruit a fleshy drupe, endocarp coriaceous or bony; endosperm absent.

About 20 species in tropical Southeast Asia, Micronesia, the Pacific Islands and Australia.

Phaleria capitata Jack, Malayan Misc. 2 (7): 59. 1822; Ding Hou in Fl. Mal. Ser. 1, 6 (1): 20. 1960. Type locality: "Sumatra"; holotype destroyed by fire (see Merrill, J. Arn. Arb. 33: 207. 1952.)

Drimyspermum phaleria Meisn. in DC., Prod. 14: 604. 1857 (*Drymispermum* sphalm.)
Drimyspermum cauliflorum Thw., Enum. Pl. Zeyl. 251. 1860 (*Drymispermum* sphalm.)
Phaleria cauliflora (Thw.) Beddome, For. Man. 180, t. 25 f. 5. 1873; Hook. f. in Fl. Br. Ind. 5: 199. 1886; Trimen, Handb. Fl. Ceylon 3: 459. 1895.

Shrub or small, graceful tree with elongate, ± pendulous branches, up to c. 9 m high; twigs glabrous, purplish- or reddish-brown, somewhat shining. Leaves oval-oblong to elliptic-oblong, 10.5–22 (–26) × (3.5–) 4.5–10 cm, glabrous, shining, chartaceous, narrowly acute or more commonly acuminate at the apex with the acumen c. 0.8–2 mm long, shortly or more longly cuneate at the base, nerves and secondary venation prominent on the lower surface, less so above; petiole 3–8 mm. Inflorescences terminal or in the axils of the uppermost leaf-pairs of the branches (often cauliflorous), sessile or on very short (to c. 6 mm) bracteate peduncles, capitate with c. 5–18 flowers, subtended by 4 deltoid-ovate or oblong, glabrous, c. 6–10 × 3–6 mm involucral bracts which may fall early but are commonly persistent. Flowers white; calyx tube c. 15–35 mm, narrowly tubular and gradually widening upwards in the upper quarter, glabrous within and without; lobes 4 (–5), spreading, 6–7 mm, oblong or oval-oblong, shortly puberulent on the inner surface and towards the margins and apex of the dorsal surface, or dorsally glabrous. Anthers c. 1 mm, exserted on slender white filaments c. 5–14 mm long. Ovary glabrous, narrowed above to the included or exserted style; stigma large. Drupe subglobose, c. 1–1.5 cm, apiculate at the apex, red; endocarp ± scrobiculate-netted from the interwoven fibres; seeds usually 2, smooth.

D i s t r. Malayan Islands from Java to the Moluccas; New Guinea, Philippine Islands, Caroline Islands Naturalised in the Malay Peninsula.

N o t e. Only collected once, "in moist low country below 300 m" (see Trimen), by a stream.

S p e c i m e n   E x a m i n e d. RATNAPURA DISTRICT: Pasdun Korale, nr. Hillefree (? Hellefree), May 1855, *Thwaites s.n.* (PDA).

N o t e. Recent search by at least two investigators has failed to rediscover this species.

4. GYRINOPS

Gaertn., Fruct. 2: 276, t. 140, f. 6. 1791. Type species: *G. walla* Gaertn., Fruct. 2: 276, t. 140, f. 6. 1791.

Lachnolepis Miq., Ann. Mus. Bot. Lugd.-Bat. 1: 132. 1863.
Brachythalamus Gilg, Bot. Jahrb. Syst. 28: 146. 1900.
Aquilaria sect. *Gyrinops* Hall. f., Med. Rijksherb. 44: 19, 1922.

Trees or shrubs. Leaves alternate, coriaceous, with close, fine, parallel, pinnate veins and thickened margins. Inflorescences sessile or shortly pedunculate, terminal or axillary, of fascicles or few-flowered umbel-like heads, subtended by 2-3 caducous bracts. Flowers pentamerous, hermaphrodite, the pedicels articulate at the base. Calyx tube poculiform to tubular, glabrous or pilose within, ± pilose externally; lobes spreading, pilose to tomentose. Petaloid appendages usually densely pilose, distinct and alternating with the anthers and calyx lobes or ± united to form an annulus. Stamens 5, episepalous, inserted at about the same level as the petaloid appendages; anthers basifixed, sessile or almost so; disk various or none. Ovary bilocular, stipitate or sessile; style distinct or ill-defined; stigma capitate. Fruit a 2-valved loculicidal capsule, long-stipitate. Seeds plano-convex, usually carunculate, hanging from the apex of the valves of the fruit on the filiform funicles; endosperm absent.

Eight species, all but the Ceylonese species occurring in the Malayan Islands.

Gyrinops walla Gaertn., Fruct. 2: 276, t. 140, f. 6. 1791; Meisn. in DC., Prod. 14: 602. 1857; Hook. f. in Fl. Br. Ind. 5: 199. 1886; Trimen, Handb. Fl. Ceylon 3: 460. 1895; Gamble, Fl. Pres. Madras 1244. 1925, repr. 871. 1957; Worthington, Ceylon Trees 368. 1959. Type: Ceylon, *Koenig*, Hb. Leiden *3247* (L).

Tree up to c. 15 m tall with a straight, slender trunk and a small, rounded crown; bark brownish-grey, thin, smooth, strongly fibrous. Twigs slender and wiry, rather shining and chestnut-brown when young with appressed whitish hairs, soon glabrescent and greyish. Leaves also ± densely appressed-pubescent when young, when mature glabrous or pilose along the lower surface of the midrib, oblong, entire, 3–9 × 1.2–5 cm with a short, rather abrupt, bluntish acumen up to c. 1 cm long, cuneate at the base, veins very close and fine, parallel and curving upwards slightly towards the thickened margin; petiole short, 1–6 mm. Inflorescences terminal, of few- (c. 3–5-) flowered umbel-like heads; bracts early-caducous, moderately pilose, membranous, lanceolate; pedicels c. 3–4 mm, thinly pilose. Flowers yellowish-white; calyx tube 4–10 mm, narrow, thinly appressed-pilose within and without; lobes spreading, 2 mm, oblong, increasingly pilose upwards on the dorsal surface, tomentose within. Anthers 1.5 mm, inserted at the throat and alternating with thick, lanate, petaloid appendages. Ovary c. 4–6 mm including the distinct stipe, appressed-pilose; style c. 1.5 mm. Capsule c. 2 cm, obovate, compressed, acute, reddish-brown. Seeds solitary, plano-convex, acuminate at the tip, furnished below with a narrowly triangular-subulate funicle which soon becomes slender and elongate, and a cordate-ovate caruncle; testa smooth, blackish, densely covered with short, yellowish hairs.

D i s t r. Outside Ceylon this species occurs only in the extreme southwest of India, where it appears to be very rare.

E c o l. Principally in the humid lowland forests of the southwest of the island, where it appears to be not infrequent but often encountered without flowers or fruit; also occurring in the moist forests of the Central Province. According to Trimen it ascends to 1200 m, but the highest altitude noted on a specimen is 910 m (*Meijer 498*).

U s e s. This tree well-known for its fibrous, easily stripped bark, which is employed for cordage since it is extremely tough. The wood is white and soft, and is reported as being employed in marquetry.

V e r n. Wal-aha or (Patta-) Walla (S).

Specimens Examined. KANDY DISTRICT: Hantane Hill, above Peradeniya, *Gardner 751* (PDA) (still there in 1973); Double-cut junction, Maskeliya, 2 June 1971, *Balakrishnan NBK 515, 515A* (PDA, US); Adam's Peak sanctuary, 25 July 1970 *Meijer 498* (PDA, US). KEGALLE DISTRICT: Salgala, 25 Aug. 1965, *Amaratunga 976* (PDA). COLOMBO DISTRICT: Mirigama, 7 June 1927, *Alston 675* (PDA); Hunuwala, *J.M. de Silva s.n.* (PDA); on fence bordering Royal Botanic Garden, Gampaha, 17 Aug. 1963, *Amaratunga 689* (PDA). GALLE DISTRICT: Galle, Dec. 1853, *Gardner s.n.* (PDA); Pita Kanda, 7 Feb. 1929, *J.M. de Silva s.n.* (PDA); Hiniduma Kanda (Haycock Hill), 23 Sep. 1946, *Worthington 2292* (K); ibid., 29 July 1970, *Meijer 574* (PDA, US), ibid., 14 Feb. 1973, *Townsend 73/50* (PDA, US); Nagoda Udugama, 27 Sep. 1948, *Worthington 4135* (K); Kottawa Forestry Arboretum, east of Galle, primary lowland Dipterocarp forest, 2 July 1970, *Meijer 273* (PDA, US).